A·J·R· Harvey
16/12/1970
Physics/Biology Prize
2A
Perse School for Boys
Cambridge

Certificate Physics

By the same author:

GENERAL PHYSICS

A SCHOOL PHYSICS

Part 1. Mechanics and Hydrostatics
Part 2. Sound, Heat and Light
Part 3. Electricity and Magnetism
Complete Edition

INTRODUCTORY PHYSICS (WITH R. W. TRUMP)

Certificate Physics

C. W. Kearsey, M.A.

FORMERLY SENIOR PHYSICS MASTER, KINGSWOOD SCHOOL

LONGMANS

LONGMANS, GREEN AND CO LTD
48 Grosvenor Street, London W.1
Associated companies, branches and representatives throughout the world

First Published 1965

Printed in Great Britain by
T. & A. Constable Ltd
Hopetoun Street, Edinburgh

Preface

THIS course in school physics is intended as a text-book for students at 'O' level G.C.E. and largely satisfies the requirements of the 'O' Grade of the Scottish Certificate of Education (Alternative Syllabus). The arrangement, which follows a fairly conventional sequence, is not intended as a teaching order. The chapters are sufficiently independent to permit a concentric course of study. Thus the earlier chapters on electricity can be regarded as introductory, the later ones as completing the introduction; and the Chapter on wave motion has been set in proximity to those dealing with thermal radiation, light and sound.

Recent trends in the broadening of syllabus-scope have been taken into account. The kinetic theory of matter has been introduced in the earlier chapters, and the study of wave motion extended to simple cases of diffraction and interference. The first chapters on electricity deal with electricity at rest, with direct current and with alternating current; in the later ones the production and effects of a.c. are studied in more detail, the particulate nature of matter and electricity clarified by reference to electronics and radioactivity.

The treatment follows the course of discovery by experiment and proceeds to the consideration of practical and technical applications. Many of the questions at the ends of chapters are numerical. This is inevitable in a subject which so frequently demands 'how much' or 'how big', but the questions have been designed to test physical principles rather than mere arithmetic. Other questions test the ability to apply reasoning to a problem or probe the student's comprehension in other ways. Examples are given of the use of ray diagrams in relation to problems on lenses and mirrors, and reference is made to the chief sign conventions. Worked examples involving formulae illustrate only the real-positive convention, but the corresponding ray diagrams have been drawn with the light incident from the left-hand side for ease in applying the 'new Cartesian convention'.

I am indebted to a number of industrial firms for their ready help in providing illustrative photographs or diagrams; each of these illustrations bears an acknowledgment of its source.

C. W. K.

LIST OF ABBREVIATIONS

hour	h	cubic foot	cu. ft
minute	min	mile per hour	mile/h
second	s	cycle per second	c/s
pound	lb	temperature in degrees Celsius (centigrade)	°C
gram	g		
acceleration due to gravity	g	a change of temperature on the same scale	degC
kilogram	kg		
pound force	lbf	calorie	cal
kilogram force	kgf	kilogram-calorie	kcal
foot-pound force	ft lbf	British thermal unit	Btu
foot	ft	ampere	A
inch	in.	volt	V
centimetre	cm	watt	W
cubic centimetre	c.c.	kilowatt-hour	kWh
milli-litre	ml		

atomic weight	(an average value for the natural element, natural oxygen being taken as 16)	at.wt.
atomic mass unit	($\frac{1}{16}$ of the mass of an atom of the standard oxygen isotope ^{16}O)	a.m.u.

Contents

Plates

Facing page

CHAPTER 1

Length, Mass, Time. Velocity. Acceleration

1.1. Physics and measurement. Physics deals with movement and action of forces, and with the behaviour of heat and light; with the production and transmission of sound and with the many effects which are caused by electricity. Some of these, such as heat and electricity, can effect chemical substances so as to cause a chemical change in them. So that sometimes a study of physics involves chemistry as well; and though most of the studies in this book will deal with physical changes, reference will be made to chemical changes which may occur when studying the subject.

We cannot go far in the study of physics without making measurements and this needs measuring scales, such as those of mass, and length, and time. Most scientific measurements are made in the decimal system. A suitable unit is chosen and bigger ones made ten or a hundred or a thousand times bigger, smaller ones made ten or a hundred or a thousand times smaller. The names used for the bigger and smaller units are given by adding a prefix to the name; some of these are listed below.

Mega-	1,000,000 or 10^6
Kilo-	1000 or 10^3
Centi-	1/100 or 10^{-2}
Milli-	1/1000 or 10^{-3}
Micro-	1/1,000,000 or 10^{-6}

1.2. Length. On the metric system the unit is the **metre,** the distance between two marks on a platinum-iridium bar at 0°C. A larger unit is the **kilometre** (thousand metres). Smaller units are the **centimetre** (hundredth-metre), the **millimetre** (thousandth-metre) and the **micron** or **micro-metre** (millionth-metre). In the British System of units:

1 mile = 1760 yards = 5280 feet
1 yard = 3 feet = 36 inches.

Reproductions of the standard metre are usually divided into centimetres (cm) and millimetres (mm). When using such a scale it should be held as close as possible to the length under test, and the line of sight should be perpendicular to the scale. Tenths of a scale division can be judged by eye; a **vernier attachment** gives a more accurate reading. Fig. 1.1 shows it set over a scale to record

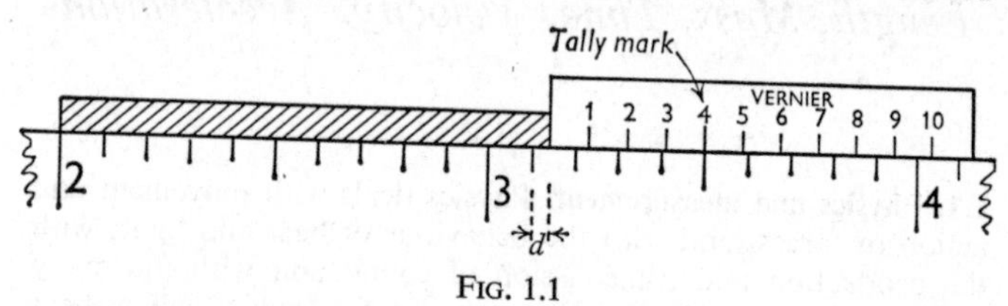

FIG. 1.1

the end reading of a rod. This vernier is made so that ten divisions of it correspond to nine scale divisions; each vernier division is shorter than a scale division by exactly one-tenth. Note that the '4' mark on the vernier tallies with one of the scale marks; looking to the left you will see that the vernier '3' fails to tally with a scale mark and is one-tenth of a scale division out; similarly the vernier '2' is two-tenths out, the '1' is three-tenths out and the zero is four-tenths out, i.e. the distance d is four-tenths of a scale division. The reading is thus 3·14 and the length of the rod $3{\cdot}14-2{\cdot}00=1{\cdot}14$. In this type of vernier the tally mark or coincidence mark indicates the next decimal place in the reading of the scale.

Fig. 1.2 shows one type of **micrometer screw gauge** used for

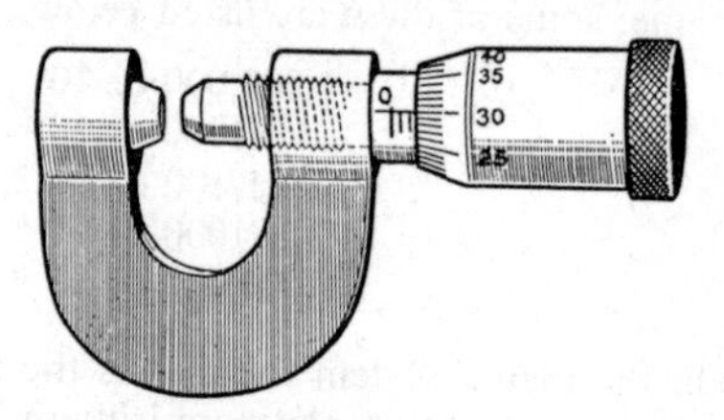

FIG. 1.2

A micrometer screw gauge reading 2·30 *mm*

measuring short distances accurately. The length of anything put between the jaws of the gauge is found by noting the number of units exposed on the scale and the number of hundredths of a division shown on the circular head (30). In this case the micrometer reads a length of 2·30 units.

1.3. Mass. The mass of a thing is a measure of the quantity of matter in it. The mass of the thing is usually found by weighing it.

The simplest form of weighing machine consists of a balanced lever with equal arms (Fig. 1.3). When two identical lumps of material (e.g. newly minted coins of the same kind, ball bearings of exactly the same size and made from the same steel) are hung from the ends of the arms they exactly balance each other. If one

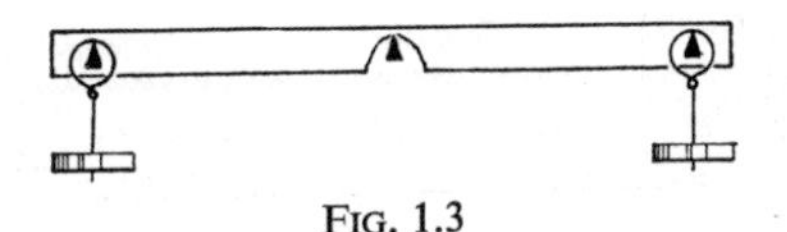

FIG. 1.3

of the lumps, say the coin, is replaced by something quite different but which still balances it, then we say that the two things have the same quantity of matter. To quantity of matter measured in this way we give the name **mass.** In this balancing method we are really balancing two forces, the weights of the objects. It is important to distinguish between the mass which we measure this way and the **weight** which helps us to do so. The heaviness of objects is due to the attraction which our planet, the earth, has for them. This heaviness is different at different places. The following table shows how **weight** varies with position, for anything which has a weight of 1000 units at sea-level in London.

London, sea-level	1000
London, 10 miles above sea-level	995
North pole, sea-level	1003
Equator, sea-level	997

It has been calculated that objects on the moon would have only 1/6th of their earth-weight; a person weighing 60 kilograms on earth would have a weight of only 10 kilogram-weight on the moon, would find it possible to jump about 10 metres high, and throw a cricket ball about 300 metres. But if he were put on a beam balance he would still balance against a standard 60-kilogram.

Material, far removed in space from other matter, would have no weight at all. Yet even in such circumstances it would be possible to show that a ball of lead has more 'stuff' or matter in it than an equal-sized ball of wood. If they were connected by a spring, pulled apart and released, each would have the same forces acting on it for the same length of time—and the lead would move the lesser distance of the two, showing its greater 'inertia' or quantity of matter. Fig. 1.4 illustrates a laboratory experiment of a similar nature; here the weight-effect of the trolleys is removed by supporting them on a level bench, and the sideways pull of the spring shows that the more loaded trolley has the greater inertia.

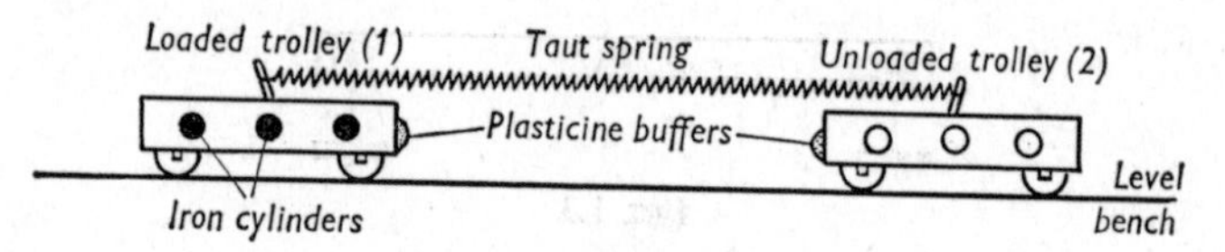

FIG. 1.4

Trolley (2) *moves faster and farther than trolley* (1) *showing that* (1) *has more inertia, or mass, than* (2)

The British Standards Institution recommended that, to distinguish between mass and weight, the latter should be shown by adding the letter f (to represent force) after the mass unit. Thus kg represents a mass of one kilogram, kgf represents a force equal to the weight of one kilogram.

The standards of mass on the metric system and on the British system are the **kilogram** and the **pound** respectively. The abbreviations for these are **kg** and **lb**. The abbreviations for the forces which the earth has on them are **kgf** for **kilogram-force** and **lbf** for **pound-force**.

Each of the mass-standards is a lump of platinum, the kilogram being the larger—a kilogram is nearly 2·2 lb. Copies for general use, made of brass, are compared with the standard from time to time. Fractions of the standard are made; a mass of one thousandth of a kilogram is called a **gram**.

1.4. Time. The time scale is not based on a decimal system. The unit is the mean solar day (the average time between successive transits of the sun across the meridian) and this unit is divided into hours, minutes and seconds.

$$1 \text{ day} = 24 \text{ hours}$$
$$1 \text{ hour} = 60 \text{ minutes} = 60 \times 60 \text{ seconds.}$$

The division of the day into its parts is done by means of clocks; most clocks work on some type of oscillating system, e.g. a swinging pendulum takes a time which is nearly independent of the extent of the swing—a fact which was first discovered by Galileo.

You can check this by setting up a simple pendulum, illustrated in Fig. 1.5. This shows a metal ball or bob hung from a length of thread which is clamped in a slit cut in a cork, so that its length can be adjusted. The length marked l is known as the length of the pendulum. A protractor set beside the pendulum can be used to measure the extent or amplitude of the swing. If the pendulum swings only two degrees each side of the vertical, the time of a complete swing (from one side to the other and back) is almost exactly the same as when it swings ten degrees each side of the vertical. You would have to make the pendulum swing thirty degrees each way for the time of swing to increase; and even then it would increase by only a $\frac{1}{2}\%$. The length of the pendulum affects the time of swing, and an approximate formula for the time of swing T in terms of the length l (in cm) is given below.

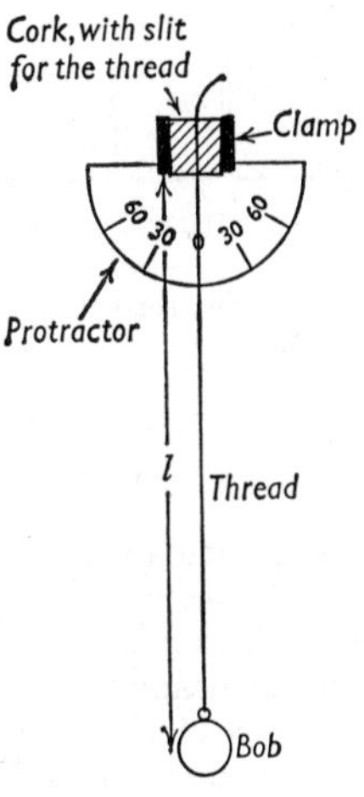

FIG. 1.5

$$T=\frac{1}{\ }\sqrt{l}$$

This formula is not exact for all places on the earth, for reasons which are given on page 11.

Special instruments are used to deal with extremely small intervals of time, such as occur in electrical discharges or in the reflection of radio waves. The second is further subdivided into the units *millisecond* (thousandth of a second) and *microsecond* (a millionth of a second); such short intervals are generally measured with a cathode ray tube. In this, as in the television tube, a beam of charged particles hits the screen and causes a spot of light. By means of electrical controls the spot of light can be made to move rapidly across the screen in, say, 100 microseconds. This gives a line of light on the screen which can be regarded as a time-base 100 microseconds long. Two electrical impulses can be applied to the tube in such a way that they each cause a notch in the line of light. If, for example, the two notches appear to be one-quarter of the length of the line apart, the impulses occurred with an interval of 25 microseconds (Fig. 1.6).

1.5. Speed. Speed is the **rate at which distance is travelled.** The measurement of speed involves the measurement of the distance gone and the time taken, then dividing the number of units of distance by the number of units of time. If a man runs 100 metres in exactly 10 seconds, his average speed is $100 \div 10 = 10$ metres per second. This does not mean that he actually had that speed all the time, for he may have been sprinting over part of the journey; to find his speed at a particular instant (*instantaneous speed*) it would be necessary to time a short section of the journey around that instant. Instantaneous speeds are often measured with a **speedometer** such as is fitted to motor-cars. Even so, the instrument itself has to be checked by the makers by driving the vehicle at a steady speed and timing a measured section of the journey.

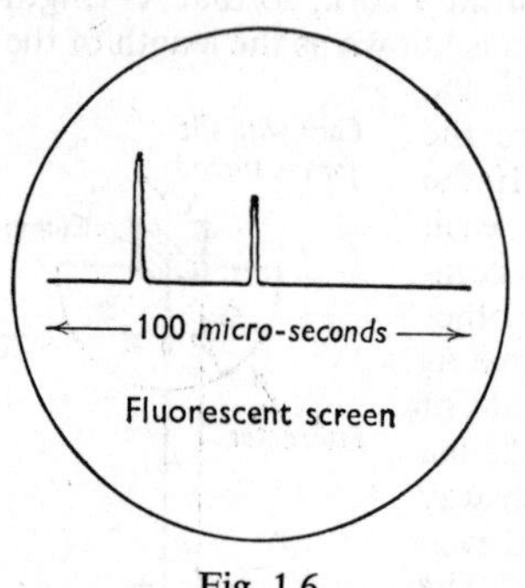

Fig. 1.6

1.6. Velocity. Many people use the terms speed and velocity as though they meant the same thing. Scientifically, velocity has a special meaning. **Velocity is speed in a given direction.** When we say that the velocity of an aircraft is 400 miles/hour north we give more information than just its speed, we give the direction of that speed as well.

The sum of two velocities does not follow the ordinary rules of arithmetic. Thus a motor-boat having a uniform speed of 4 units and moving in a stream having a speed of 3 units will get a speed of 7 units if it is moving downstream, but only 1 unit if it is moving upstream. Steered in any other direction it has a speed which is something between 7 units and 1 unit. Take, for instance, the case of driving at right angles to the stream. In one unit of time it will travel 4 units forwards and will also drift 3 units sideways. Its actual course will then be in the direction AC in Fig. 1.7, which has been drawn to scale. Measurement, or calculation, of AC shows it to be 5 units long. So the sum or *resultant* of two velocities of 4 units and 3 units at right angles is a velocity of 5 units in a new direction (the direction given by the angle BAC in Fig. 1.7). The diagram of Fig. 1.7 is known as a **vector** diagram, the name given to any

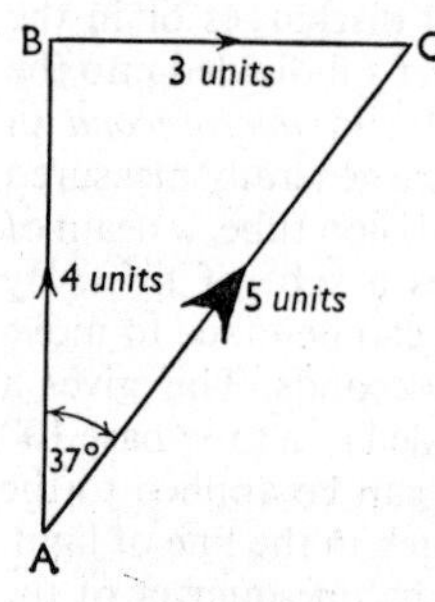

Fig. 1.7

diagram which adds or subtracts vector quantities *i.e.* those which have direction as well as magnitude.

1.7. Acceleration. A body is said to be accelerating when its velocity is changing (i.e. changing in magnitude or changing in direction). If its speed is decreasing, the body is said to be retarding; retardation can be considered as a negative acceleration. **The rate at which velocity changes** is a measure of the **acceleration.**

If a motor-car starts from rest and steadily reaches a speed of 72 km/hour in 10 seconds it is said to have an acceleration of 7·2 km/hour per second. It is not usual to state an acceleration in such a mixture of units. Since 7·2 km is 7200 metres and one hour is 3600 seconds the acceleration can be written as 2 metres/s per second. This is sometimes expressed in the form 2 metres/s^2 or as 2 metres.s^{-2}.

Acceleration due to change of speed. Fig. 1.8 shows the graph of a test-run of a car along a straight road. *OA* shows a steady

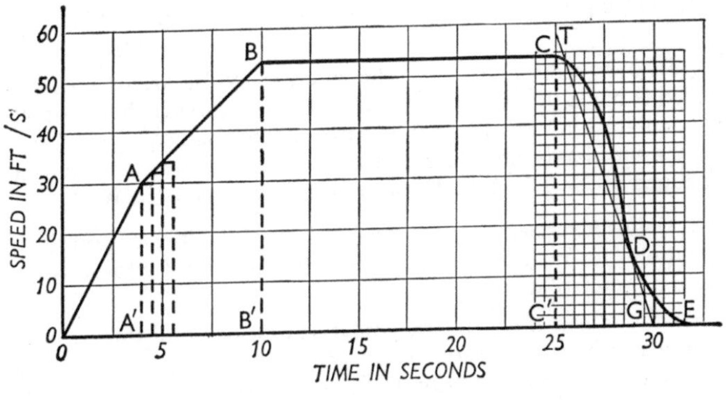

FIG. 1.8

increase in speed to 30 ft/s in 4 s, *ABC* shows a steady increase from 30 ft/s to 53 ft/s in 6 s followed by a steady maximum speed. The subsequent retardation is shown by *CDE*.

Calculations from the speed-time graph.

(a) *Acceleration.*

(i) Initial acceleration$=30$ ft/s$\div 4$ s$=7{\cdot}5$ ft/s^2.

(ii) Acceleration over $AB=(53-30)\div 6=3{\cdot}83$ ft/s^2.

(iii) Acceleration at the moment indicated by D. This is given by the slope of the curve at D, which is the slope of the tangent TG i.e. $TC'/C'G$ which is $(58-0)/(25-30)=-58/5=-11{\cdot}6$ ft/s².

(b) *Distance travelled.*

(i) Over the range BC. This range is travelled at 53 ft/s for 15 s, so the distance gone is $53\times 15=795$ ft. On the graph this is illustrated by the product of the speed BB' and the time interval $B'C'$. Since this product is represented by the area of the rectangle $BCC'B'$ we can say that the area under the line BC represents the distance gone.

(ii) Over the range AB. Here the speed is not constant. But the areas of the rectangular strips, shown in dotted lines, represent the distances gone in short intervals, assuming the journey to have been made up of a series of constant-speed jerks. The total area is thus very nearly the area $ABB'A'$. For even narrower rectangles than those shown, their total becomes even more nearly equal to $ABB'A'$.

$$\text{Distance gone}=\text{area of the trapezium } ABB'A'=\tfrac{1}{2}(30+53)\times 6 \text{ ft}$$
$$=249 \text{ ft.}$$

(iii) Over the range CDE. This is given by the area $CDEC'C$, which is made up of 5 large squares (125 small ones) plus 42 small squares—a total of 167 small squares. Each small square is 2 ft/s on the speed axis, and 0·5 s on the time axis. Its area represents a distance of $2\times 0{\cdot}5=1$ ft. Distance gone$=167\times 1=167$ ft.

1.8. Uniform acceleration in a straight line. The following formulae are useful for making calculations on the motion of bodies which have a uniform acceleration.

(i) *Speed and time.* If a body starts from rest and travels for t seconds with an acceleration of a ft/s per second it will have gained a speed of at ft/s. Therefore its final speed (v ft/s) is given by the equation

$$v=at$$

If the body had an initial speed u ft/s its final speed would have been its initial speed plus the gain in speed.

$$v=u+at \qquad . \quad . \quad . \quad . \quad (1)$$

(ii) *Distance and time.* Using the symbols of the previous paragraph, the speed-time graph is as shown in Fig. 1.9; and the distance gone s is given by the area of the trapezium $ABDO$.

$$s=\frac{u+v}{2}t \qquad . \quad . \quad . \quad . \quad (2)$$

The area is also the sum of the rectangle *ACDO* and the triangle *ABC*.

This gives $s = ut + \frac{1}{2}at^2$ . . . . (3)

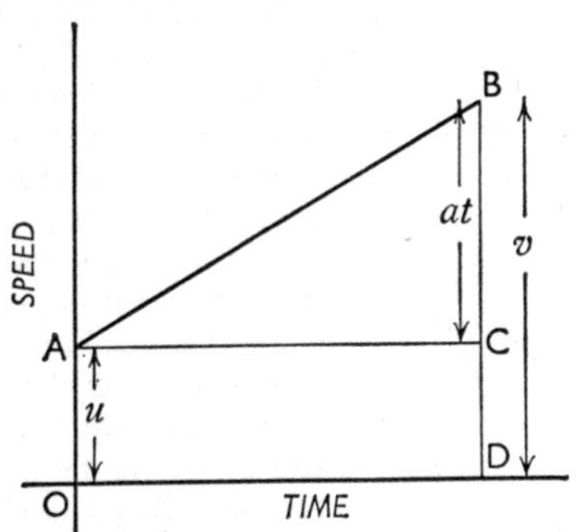

FIG. 1.9

(iii) *Speed and distance.* A formula which is useful when the time of travel is not known can be found by a re-arrangement of equations (1) and (2). Thus, from equation (1)

$$t = (v - u)/a$$

Substituting this in equation (2) gives

$$s = \frac{v^2 - u^2}{2a}$$

or

$$v^2 = u^2 + 2as$$

EXAMPLE 1. *A body falls from rest with an acceleration of* 9·8 *metres/s*^{2}. *Calculate its speed, and the distance gone, after* 1 *s.*

The speed at the end of 1 s will be 9·8 metres/s. Since it started with zero speed, the distance gone is equal to that travelled by a body moving at $\frac{1}{2} \times 9{\cdot}8 = 4{\cdot}9$ metres/s for 1 second. Therefore distance gone $= 4{\cdot}9$ metres.

EXAMPLE 2. *A car, starting from rest with an acceleration of* 3 *metres/s per second, reaches a speed of* 30 *metres/s. Calculate* (a) *the time taken,* (b) *the distance gone.*

(*a*) Let t seconds = time taken.

Then $30 = 3 \times t \quad \therefore \ t = 10$

Time taken = 10 seconds.

(*b*) Let s metres = distance gone.

Then $s = \frac{1}{2} \times 3 \times 10 \times 10 = 150$

Distance gone = 150 metres.

1.9. Acceleration due to change of direction. Acceleration is defined as **rate of change of velocity.** A change of speed is an obvious case of acceleration; but a change of direction without any change of speed is another example of an acceleration. Thus if a car is going round a circular track with a uniform speed of 10 ft/s (Fig. 1.10) it will be travelling eastwards when north of the centre, south when east of the centre; at these places it will have velocities 10 ft/s E. and 10 ft/s S. respectively. Its speed is constant but its velocity is continuously changing, not in magnitude but in direction. The change in velocity during any short interval of time can be found by a vector triangle method. Regarding OP as representing an initial velocity at A, and OQ as representing the resultant velocity at B, then the triangle method (Fig. 1.10) shows that a velocity represented by PQ must be added to the initial velocity if the car is to have the final velocity. In the actual case considered this change in velocity is given to the car by friction against the tyres; the friction acts towards the centre of the curve and is large enough to change the direction of the velocity.

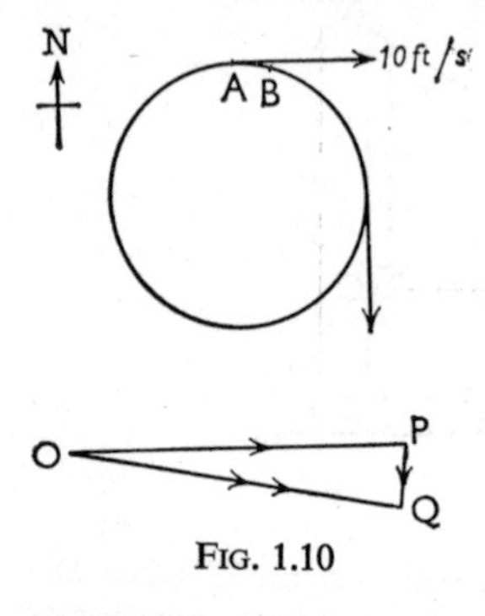

FIG. 1.10

The acceleration which results when a body moves in a curved path, even if its speed is not changing, is directed towards the centre of the curve; it is called a **centripetal** (centre-seeking) acceleration. For a body moving with uniform speed v metres/s in a circle of radius r metres the centripetal acceleration is v^2/r metres/s^2. The effect of this acceleration is very noticeable to pilots of aircraft taking sharp turns at high speed. A force is needed to give this acceleration, which in some cases may be as high as 10 g, and the pilot feels the effect of the force in his own body.

1.10. Acceleration due to gravity. Bodies which fall in a vaucum or heavy bodies which fall in air, gain speed as they fall. Light objects, such as raindrops and leaves, or wide objects such as parachutes, also begin to gain speed as they fall but air resistance soon sets a limit to their speed; each, depending on its weight and shape, finally falls at a steady speed known as the **terminal velocity.**

The free fall acceleration at the surface of the earth varies slightly from place to place. This is mainly due to the fact that the earth is not a perfect sphere, being slightly flattened at the poles; but local concentrations of dense rock can have a slight effect. An average value of the free-fall acceleration (g) is 9·80 metres/s^2 or 980 cm/s^2; this is approximately 32 ft/s^2.

Accurate values for g are usually found by timing the swing of a pendulum. The simple and approximate formula given on page 5 is derived from the more exact formula

$$T=2\pi\sqrt{\frac{l}{g}}$$

If you time the swing of a simple pendulum, as suggested on page 5, and substitute the result in this formula you will obtain a value for g.

g can also be found by timing the fall of a falling body, but over short distances the fall-time is short, and special precautions have to be taken to measure this accurately; one such method is illustrated in the following experiment.

Experiment. Measurement of g, *the acceleration due to gravity.* Make a cardboard disc to fit over a gramophone turntable, and stick a ring of plasticine or putty round its circumference. Arrange an electromagnet so that it holds a steel ball vertically above a point on the circumference of the turntable (Fig. 1.11). Then switch

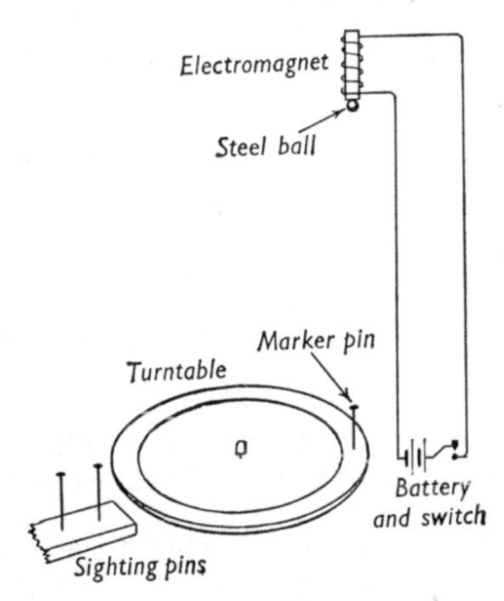

FIG. 1.11

off the current so that the ball falls into the plasticine. Remove the ball and mark the centre of the hole in the plasticine with a pin. Fix two more pins, off the turntable, to be in line with the pin which is on the turntable. Replace the ball on the electromagnet and set the turntable in rotation. Look along the line of fixed pins and when the moving pin comes in line with them switch off the electric current to release the ball. Time several revolutions of the turntable with a stop-watch, stop the turntable and measure the distance, round the circumference, between the pin and the ball. Find out what fraction of the whole circumference this is. The fall-time t is then this fraction of the time of one revolution of the turntable. Measure the distance s which the ball has fallen and calculate g from the formula $s=\frac{1}{2}gt^2$.

Repeat the experiment with different values for s and take the average of the answers obtained for g.

SUMMARY

Speed is the **rate at which distance is travelled,** the distance being measured along the actual track.

Velocity is **speed in a given direction.**

Velocity is a **vector quantity.** The resultant (or vector sum) of two vectors can be found by a triangle construction.

Acceleration is rate of change of velocity. It occurs when speed changes, or when a direction of a speed changes, as when something moves in a curved track.

Freely falling bodies have an acceleration g, which varies slightly with locality and which is about 9·8 metres/s².

Equations of motion

From rest:	Initial speed u:
$v=at$	$v=u+at$
$s=\frac{1}{2}vt=\frac{1}{2}at^2$	$s=\frac{u+v}{2}t=ut+\frac{1}{2}at^2$
$v^2=2as$	$v^2=u^2+2as$

Questions

1. Distinguish between *speed* and *velocity*. A spot of light on a vertical screen is kept moving with uniform speed along a square track, starting horizontally from the top left-hand corner. The length of each side is 300 cm and the spot goes once round the track in 5 s. Calculate (*a*) the speed of the spot, (*b*) the distance travelled in 0·65 s, (*c*) the velocity 4 s after the start.

2. A body falls from rest with an acceleration of 9·8 metres/s². What will be its speed after 4 seconds, and how far will it have travelled in this time?

3. If $g = 32$ ft/s², calculate the distances s which a body falls after time-periods t of $\frac{1}{2}$, 1, $1\frac{1}{2}$, 2 and $2\frac{1}{2}$ seconds. Plot a graph of s against t and from the graph deduce the fall-time for a 60-ft drop.

4. Explain the meanings of the terms *acceleration*, *retardation*. A car travelling at 72 km/h is brought to a stop in 4 seconds. Calculate its retardation in metres/s², and the distance travelled during the stopping process.

5. What is meant by *centripetal acceleration*? Illustrate your answer with an example.

6. A man swims at 3 ft/s across a river in which the water is flowing at 2 ft/s. If the direction of his swimming-speed is at right angles to the bank, what will be his actual velocity? What direction must he take in order to reach a point exactly opposite to his starting point?

7. A heavy body is dropped from a high cliff; give an account of the observations and the calculation you would make to obtain as accurate a value for g as possible by this method.

A stone is dropped from the top of a cliff 90 metres high. One third of the way down it strikes a ledge, bounces up 5 metres and then falls to the ground. Find the total time it takes to travel from the top of the cliff to the ground. (Assume g to be 10 metres/s² and neglect air resistance.)

8. Draw on squared paper a velocity-time graph for a body which is projected vertically upwards with an initial velocity of 25 metres/s. From the graph find the time taken for the body to reach the ground again. (Assume $g = 10$ metres/s².)

9. A car starting from rest, travels in a straight line with an acceleration of 8·0 metres/s² for 4·0 s, travels at constant speed for the next 2·0 s, and is then brought to rest with a retardation of 12·0 metres/s². Draw a speed-time graph for the motion and calculate the total distance travelled by the car.

CHAPTER 2

Force and Motion. Friction

2.1. Force. Our idea of force, any kind of push or pull, is connected with our sense of muscular effort. Thus from the effort involved in lifting things we recognise weight as a force. It is easier to say what a force does rather than to say what it is. For example, a force acting on matter may deform it, changing its size or shape; or it may set matter in motion; or, if the matter is already in motion, it will cause a change in the nature of that motion.

The fact that weight is a force gives us a simple way of defining units of force. Thus

1 g force	is the force of	1 g
1 kg force	attraction of the	1 kg
1 lb force	earth on a mass of	1 lb

Such units, called **gravitational units,** are in common use, particularly in engineering. These units are not quite exact ones, since weight varies with latitude, elevation and local variations in rock density; but the variations are very slight. For exact purposes the magnitudes of forces are defined in terms of the motion which they can produce; examples of this are given later in this chapter.

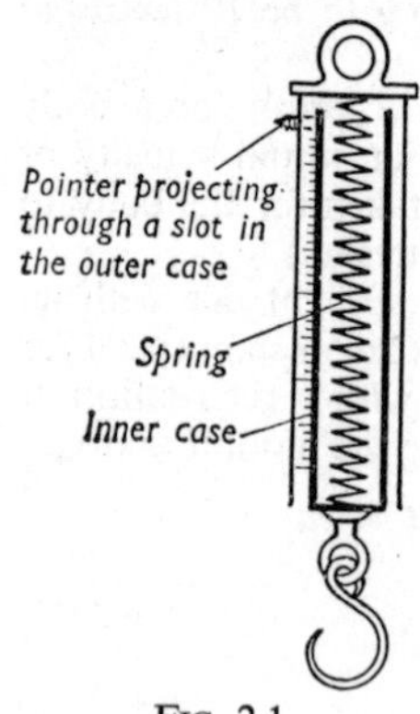

FIG. 2.1
A spring balance

Weights can be used to calibrate the springs of spring-balances (or dynamometers). The **spring-balance** (Fig. 2.1) is a simple and compact device for the measurement of force. It works on the principle that a spiral spring stretches in proportion to the force applied to stretch it. Robert Hooke (1635–1703) discovered that most solid things stretch in proportion to the force acting on them, a discovery which is known as **Hooke's law.**

Apart from their uses in weighing, spring-balances are very useful for measuring forces which act in directions other than the vertical. For example, the force required to drive a car at a definite speed can be found by towing it at this speed with a spring-balance in the tow-rope; locomotive tests are made with a spring-balance fitted to the tow-bar.

2.2. Force and motion. Galileo was one of the first to make experiments on the motion of bodies; Newton also studied the action of force on matter. His discoveries are summed up in Newton's laws of motion. The following paragraphs give an account of them.

(1) *Newton's first law. A body will remain at rest or continue with uniform speed in a straight line unless acted on by a force.*

This can be regarded as giving a definition of force, i.e. anything which will alter the position of rest or of uniform straight-line speed.

Where no force is acting, a moving object would keep its speed and direction unchanged. Thus a stone moving over the surface of a frozen lake has a nearly uniform motion. And a space-ship of the future, free from air-resistance and from the gravitational pull of the earth and sun, could attain the ideal of straight-line track and uniform speed. Its rocket engines could be used to increase or decrease its speed but it would need no power to keep up its speed.

But anything which moves in a curved path is acted on by a force; anything which moves with increasing or decreasing speed is acted on by a force. Something thrown from one person to another follows a curved path which indicates the influence of the force of gravity. A satellite in orbit shows the action of the force of gravity. If the orbit is circular the speed remains unchanged, but the direction of the speed is constantly being changed by the pull of gravity. The curved path of a vehicle rounding a bend shows the action of a force perpendicular to the curve—a force of friction in the case of a motor-car, the thrust of the rail against wheel flanges in the case of a railway train.

Since any change of velocity, whether of magnitude or of direction, is an acceleration, it follows that **force is an action which causes acceleration.** A body at rest or travelling with uniform velocity has no resultant force acting on it.

(2) *Newton's second law. When a body is acted on by a force, the rate of change of quantity of motion is proportional to the impressed force and takes place in the direction of the force.*

By 'impressed force' Newton meant the resultant force acting; for 'quantity of motion' Newton used the product (mass) × (velocity), which we now call **momentum.** For an object of constant mass the rate of change of momentum is equal to the product (mass) × (rate of change of velocity) which is the same as the product (mass) × (acceleration). The law can be expressed in symbols in the following manner.

$$F \propto m \times a$$

where F is the resultant force acting, m is the mass of the object on which it acts, and a is the resulting acceleration.

Newton derived this law from observations on pendulums and from observations on the orbits of the planets of the solar system.

Let us consider the law from the point of view of the force of weight, making the assumption that—at any one place—mass and weight are proportional. At a place where $g=9{\cdot}8$ metres/s^2 a mass of 1 kg falling freely has an acceleration of 9·8 metres/s^2, and a mass of 2 kg has the same acceleration. We can therefore draw up the following table.

Force F	$m \times a$
1 kgf	$1 \times 9{\cdot}8 = 9{\cdot}8$ units
2 kgf	$2 \times 9{\cdot}8 = 19{\cdot}6$ units
5 kgf	$5 \times 9{\cdot}8 = 49{\cdot}0$ units

This shows that twice the force gives twice the mass-acceleration product. Fig. 2.2 shows an experimental arrangement in which a total mass of 1 kg can be acted on by forces of either 0·1 kgf or 0·2 kgf. A trolley of mass 0·8 kg carrying a passenger of 0·1 kg, is, connected by a light thread to a hanger of mass 0·1 kg. The base on which the trolley runs has been tilted sufficiently to allow for friction, i.e. the trolley alone, if given a push, will run down the slope at steady speed. The resultant force on the whole system, due to gravity, is 0·1 kgf and the total mass 1·0 kg. By placing the passenger on to the hanger the force becomes 0·2 kgf and the total mass moved is the same. When the trolley and hanger are released it is found that the acceleration is 0·98 metre/s^2 in the first case and 1·96 metres/s^2 in the second—one-tenth and one-fifth of the acceleration that would have been obtained by letting the trolley and hanger fall down together freely. This, and experiments with other weights for the trolley and hanger, show that the acceleration is proportional to the resultant force acting.

It should be noted that we have assumed that the weights of objects (at any one place) are proportional to their masses; we could alternatively take Newton's statement as an axiom or assumption of behaviour, in which case the experiments show that weight is proportional to mass.

Just as the 1st law can be regarded as a definition of force, so the 2nd law can be used to define unit force. Thus unit force can be defined as the force which gives unit mass unit acceleration. Three such units are as follows:

The **dyne,** which accelerates 1 g at the rate of 1 cm/s²;
The **newton,** which accelerates 1 kg at the rate of 1 m/s²;
The **poundal,** which accelerates 1 lb at the rate of 1 ft/s².

These units are called **absolute units** because they are directly related to the units of mass, length and time and are not dependent on the earth's gravitation. From their definitions it follows that when using these units we can replace the expression $F \propto ma$ by $F=ma$, since $F=1$ when $ma=1$.

At a place where g is 9·8 metres/s²=980 cm/s²; or where g=32·2 ft/s²,

1 kgf (at that place)=9·8 newtons,
1 gf =980 dynes,
1 lbf =32·2 poundals.

EXAMPLE 1. *If, in Fig.* 2.2, *the masses of trolley, passenger and hanger are* 2·5 *kg,* 0·1 *kg and* 0·2 *kg respectively, what will be the acceleration of the system when the passenger is* (*a*) *on the trolley,* (*b*) *on the hanger?* (1 *kgf*=9·80 *newtons*).

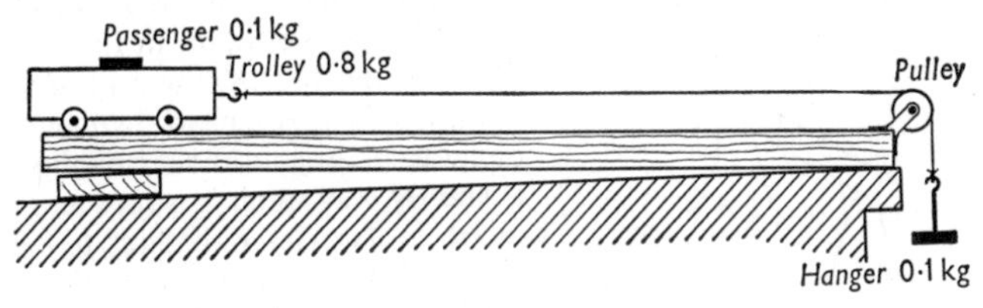

FIG. 2.2

(a) The weight of the hanger provides the force on the system.

Force=0·2 kgf=0·2 × 9·8 newtons. Total mass moved=2·8 kg.

Let a metres/s²=acceleration. Then 0·2 × 9·8=2·8 × a

whence a=0·070.

Acceleration=0·070 metre/s² or 7·0 cm/s².

(b) Here the force acting is increased from 0·2 kgf to 0·3 kgf and the total mass moved remains the same. Therefore the acceleration is increased to 3/2 of its previous value.

Acceleration=3/2 × 7·0=10·5 cm/s².

EXAMPLE 2. *Calculate the initial acceleration of a rocket launched vertically upwards from the earth's surface, the mass of the rocket being* 100 *kg and the initial propelling force being* 2600 *kgf* ($g=9{\cdot}8$ *metres/s²*).

The effective force on the rocket $=2600-100=2500$ kgf
$=2500\times 9{\cdot}8$ newtons.

Let a metres/s² be the acceleration of the rocket.

Then $2500\times 9{\cdot}8=100\times a$

whence $a=25\times 9{\cdot}8=245$

Initial acceleration $=245$ metres/s².

(3) *Newton's third law. To every action there is an equal and opposite reaction.*

By 'action' Newton meant the action of a force, and by 'reaction' the action of another force brought into play by the action of the first. Another way of expressing the law is as follows: if any body A acts on another B with a force, then B acts on A with the same force but in the opposite direction.

As both forces act at the same time, we can say that the *interactions* between A and B are equal and opposite. Thus a falling body, pulled down by the gravitational attraction of the earth, pulls the earth upwards; the movement of the earth is extremely small, because its mass is so great. The effect is more noticeable in the case of the attraction of the earth for the moon, an attraction which keeps the moon in its orbit. The reaction to this, the pull of the moon on the earth, has a slight effect on the earth's orbit; the earth follows a slightly wavy line in space as the moon in its orbit pulls first to one side and then to the other.

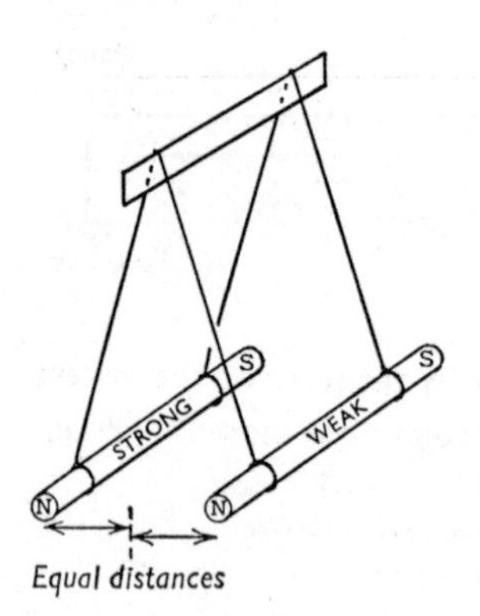

FIG. 2.3

Fig. 2.3 shows two identical steel bars, magnetised so that one is more strongly magnetised than the other. Each is hung up by equal-length threads from the same support so that they repel each other. When they come to rest it is found that each is the same distance from the centre line, showing that the weaker one repels the stronger with the same force that the stronger does the weaker. Their inter-action gives rise to equal and opposite forces. A similar inter-action, but one of attraction in this case, occurs in the taut spring illustrated in Fig. 1.4; the spring exerts equal and opposite pulls on the trolleys.

If you walk from the stern of a dinghy towards the bow, the dinghy moves backwards; you can see this happen if the bow is touching a landing stage and you walk from the stern to get ashore. Here the inter-action is the friction between your feet and the floor-boards, causing you to move forward and the dinghy backwards.

2.3. Conservation of momentum. Whenever the inter-action of two objects causes them to move, momentum is produced in each. But because the forces of inter-action are equal and opposite, and because they act for the same time, the momenta produced are equal and opposite. And because momentum is a vector quantity, equal and opposite momenta have a vector sum of zero. Momentum cannot be produced without producing, somewhere, an equal and opposite momentum. This is known as the **conservation of momentum**; if Newton's second and third laws are both true, **momentum cannot be created or destroyed.**

The experiment illustrated in Fig. 1.4 shows this, for when the two trolleys hit each other they come to a dead stop; they start with no momentum and end with no momentum and have equal and opposite momenta at all stages of their approach.

Fig. 2.4a illustrates a somewhat similar experiment, but this

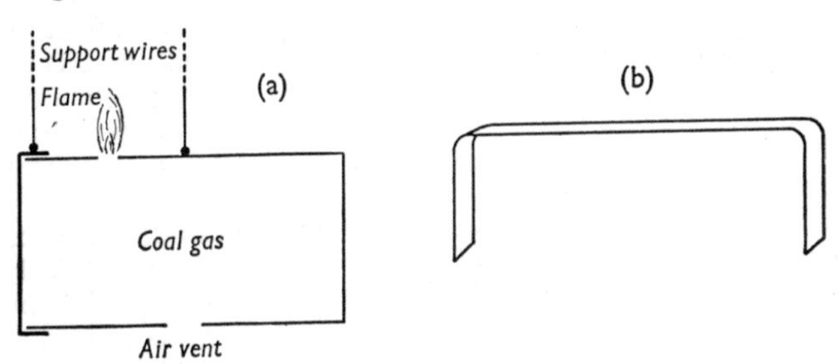

FIG. 2.4

time the inter-acting forces are explosive forces. A tin-can and lid are hung up with equal-length wires, as shown in the diagram, so that each separately can swing like a pendulum. An explosion is caused by filling the can with coal gas and lighting it at a hole in the top-side of the can; an air vent in the bottom allows air to come in to give an explosive mixture. After a few seconds the explosion occurs and the lid and can are forced apart. But the lid swings higher than the can, showing that it had the greater velocity (because the speed of a pendulum at the bottom of its swing depends on the angle of swing). But both have the same momentum (mass × velocity). For if the experiment is repeated with the strip of metal shown in Fig. 2.4b put across lid and can, there is no swinging of either lid or can after they have hit the metal strip; the explosion produces no momentum in the system as a whole.

You cannot throw a stone without producing an equal and opposite momentum; if you were standing on a frictionless surface you would slide backwards; otherwise, your momentum is transferred to the earth.

Jet propulsion gives another example of action and reaction. The fuel or the explosive drives material (usually hot gases) out of the jet and this material has momentum. The action which drives the material out of the jet gives a force of equal size, but in the opposite direction, to the container of the fuel or explosive; and gives it an equal and opposite momentum to that of the material thrust out. A rocket can therefore work in a vacuum if need be; the jet does not require any air to 'push against', since the explosive force acts on the container itself. A similar interaction occurs when a gun is fired. The force which propels the projectile also acts on the gun and causes a recoil of the gun.

2.4. Friction. When two surfaces rub against each other, there is a force acting on each of them; each force is known as a **force of friction.** This is yet another example of Newton's third law. Thus if you brush past someone, you will experience a slight drag on your movement and the person will experience a slight pull also. The amount of friction you both experience depends on the force of contact between you.

When anything is pulled over a horizontal surface the force of friction can be expressed as a fraction of the thing's weight. This fraction is known as the **coefficient of friction.** It is about 0·1 for glass moving over glass, between 0·2 and 0·5 for wood moving over wood.

Friction is much reduced by the use of wheels and rollers, and by lubrication with oil or with graphite powder. For example,

	Coefficient
Wheels on macadamised road . .	0·02–0·03
Wheels on rails at low speeds . .	0·003–0·004

But friction is not always a nuisance. Road and rail transport, even walking, would be very difficult if it were not for friction.

13. Draw a labelled diagram of a spring balance. A spring balance, intended for use up to 500 g, has no scale attached. Describe how you would use it to find the weight of a parcel which is thought to be about 300 g.

14. A man stands on a spring weighing-machine in a lift. When the lift starts to go up the machine records a weight which is greater than the man's true weight, during the journey it records the true weight, and whilst the lift is stopping it records less than the true weight. Explain these recordings.

15. A railway locomotive is fitted with arrangements to apply *sand* to the rails, *oil* to the wheel bearings. Explain the purpose of the materials printed in *italics*.

16. Explain the action of friction when a road-vehicle is turning a corner. Account for the fact that the safe speed for turning a corner is less when the surface is slippery.

17. Explain the action of friction between the tyres and the ground when a motor-car (*a*) starts from rest, (*b*) has the brakes applied when the car is in motion.

18. Give an account of the advantages and disadvantages of living in a frictionless world.

CHAPTER 3

The Structure of Matter. Some Properties of Matter

3.1. The states of matter. We recognise substances around us as being in the **solid** state, the **liquid** state and the **gaseous** state. A solid has a definite shape; it usually takes a large force to make it change its shape. A liquid has no particular shape of its own; it usually takes up the shape of the containing vessel except for the upper boundary (the surface or **meniscus**). A gas has no definite boundary; in a containing vessel it spreads throughout the vessel.

Many substances can exist in all three of these states. Thus water becomes ice if cooled sufficiently, and it changes to the gaseous state as steam when it is boiled. There must be some reason why one substance can have three such different forms. Any theory which explains the three states of matter must also explain how heat changes matter from one state to another. One such theory is the **kinetic theory** (section 3.4).

3.2. Molecules. Matter is thought to be made up of extremely small particles called **molecules.** A lump of salt can be crushed to a very fine powder, but the smallest grains of the powder still contain many millions of molecules. One such grain dissolved in a glass of water gives a saltiness in every drop of the water, which can be detected by chemical methods even if not by taste. A molecule is defined as the smallest particle of a substance which can show the properties of that substance.

Experiment. Take a crystal of potassium permanganate, about the size of a pin's head, and dissolve it in a tumbler of water. The solid is now spread out over at least 100,000 times its bulk. Now pour away all except a drop of solution at the bottom, and re-fill the tumbler. You will still have a pink solution, though the solid has been spread to 100 million times its bulk. Every drop of this faintly pink solution has some permanganate in it, about a million millionth of the original crystal.

This experiment shows that if matter is made of molecules, then the molecules must be extremely small. The largest molecules are only just visible in the most powerful microscope—the electron microscope. So some idea of their small size can be obtained from Pl. 1 which was obtained with an electron microscope. It shows such small organisms as a bacillus and a virus, both of which can cause disease in plants and animals; molecules are smaller than these.

3.3. Atoms. Heat not only changes the state of a material; it may decompose it. Thus sugar when heated forms caramel, and the caramel when heated more strongly gives carbon. Carbon is a substance which cannot be further decomposed; substances such as this are called **elements.** The molecules of substances are made up of elements, the smallest particles of which are called **atoms.** The atoms of the elements cannot be further split up by heat or by chemical action, but they can be changed to other atoms by the action of fast-moving electrical particles or by tiny uncharged particles called neutrons. Changes of this sort go on in the atomic piles which have been built in many places in the world. The new atoms formed are generally radioactive atoms, i.e. they break up, emitting electrical particles as they do so; each particular radioactive material does this at its own special rate. This property of the radioactive atoms, and many of the properties of ordinary atoms as well, suggests that the atom is largely composed of electrical particles. At one time an atom was thought to be a tiny hard round particle, a sort of miniature billiard ball. We now regard it as a core or nucleus made up of **neutrons** (uncharged particles) and **protons** (positively charged particles), surrounded by **electrons** (particles of negative electricity) which move in orbits round the nucleus (Fig. 3.1).

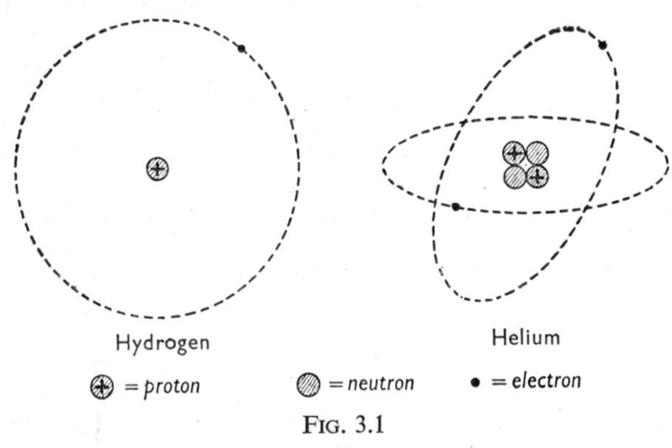

FIG. 3.1

The size of an atom is of the order of a few Angstrom units; an Angstrom unit (A.U.) is 10^{-8} cm. Even when most closely packed, as in solids, atoms are only a few A.U. apart; the electron orbits prevent a closer approach. The nucleus itself is very small indeed, about a hundred-thousandth of the size of an atom; the sizes of the nuclei are very much exaggerated in Fig. 3.1. Most of the so-called 'size' of an atom is empty space, and particles of nuclear size (such as neutrons and alpha-particles) can travel through materials for quite a distance before they hit one of the nuclei of the material.

3.4. The kinetic theory. The kinetic theory (Greek *kinema* = motion) assumes that the molecules of substances are in a state of continual motion. Passage of X-rays through solid crystalline substances shows that their molecules have a definite geometrical packing, known as a space lattice (Fig. 3.2). The molecules are kept in their

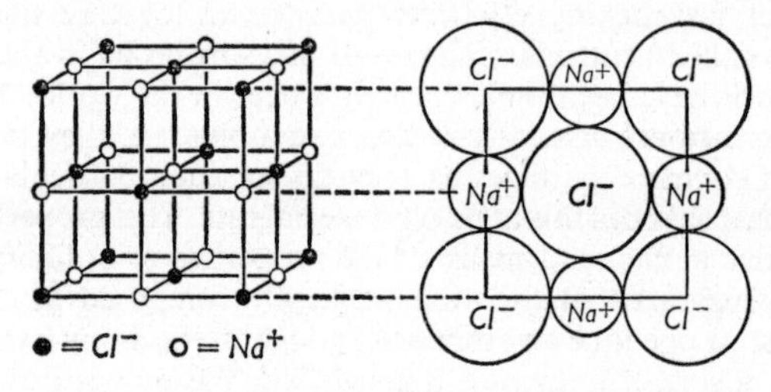

FIG. 3.2

A crystal lattice; the arrangement of atoms in a sodium chloride crystal

places by strong forces of attraction, and they can only swing to and fro about their average position. Heat increases this vibration until a stage is reached where the particles can move among each other slightly; the substance then becomes liquid and the molecules have a greater freedom of movement; shape is lost and a containing vessel is needed to hold the liquid. But there is still a considerable attraction between the molecules themselves and so the liquid has a definite surface or *meniscus*.

Further heating increases the speed at which the molecules move. The moving molecules collide with each other, and some of them move fast enough to escape from the attraction of the neighbouring molecules; in such circumstances we say that the liquid is evaporating and that what is coming from the liquid surface is a vapour. At a high enough temperature all of the liquid changes to the gaseous state. Here there is no grouping of the molecules to form a *meniscus*; the molecules move about freely in the space of the containing vessel, apart from numerous collisions with other molecules and with the walls of the containing vessel. And the bombardment of the containing vessel by the moving molecules produces a pressure on the vessel, which is characteristic of a gas.

In liquids a molecule does not move far before it hits another molecule; we say that its *mean free path* is small. In gases the mean free path is greater; it has been calculated that the mean free path of molecules in steam is about twelve times that in water.

There is no one experiment which can be said to prove the kinetic theory; the theory is based on many experiments on solids, liquids and gases. Part of this evidence is given by the effects known by the name of diffusion.

3.5. Diffusion. The Brownian movement. Common salt crystals have a density which is about twice that of water; put into water they sink. Yet their molecules can mix in with water molecules to form a solution. The concentration or density of a salt solution is the same at the top as at the bottom, no matter how long you leave the solution to stand. This is rather remarkable, for if you shake up some soil (which contains many dense particles of different sizes) with water, you can see the particles settle down when the mixture is allowed to stand—though the smallest particles may take a long time to settle. But even these small particles are not as small as molecules. The effect in the salt solution is explainable if we assume that the molecules of the salt and the water are very small indeed and also are in motion; so that the continued hitting of the salt molecules by the water from below, from sideways and from above, always keeps the salt molecules spread throughout the water.

The spreading of a salt through water can be shown by putting some crystals of a coloured salt, such as blue copper sulphate, in a glass jar and then nearly filling the jar with water. After about an hour a dense blue solution will have formed at the bottom (Fig. 3.3). A few days later the level of the blue colour will be higher up

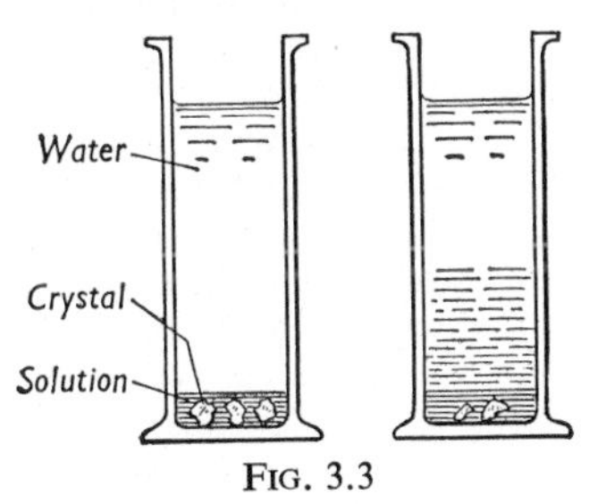

FIG. 3.3

the jar showing that the copper sulphate molecules have moved upwards. To make sure that heat effects did not help in the mixing (by convection currents, p. 28) the experiment has been repeated in a jelly; the effect still occurs.

The process which has occurred in this experiment is known by the name of **diffusion,** the mixing of substances of their own accord without any outside agent to help them mix. It can be explained if we assume that the molecules themselves are in motion.

In these diffusion experiments we see the effect of the motion of the molecules, though we do not see the molecules in motion because they are too small to see. By using particles which are larger than molecules, and which are yet very small indeed, it is possible to see under a microscope the effects of their being hit by the surrounding molecules when the particles are put into water. The particles move about in a jerky way much as a large rubber ball would do if dropped on to a crowd of people all making punching movements with their arms. The effect was first observed in 1827 by the botanist Robert Brown who noticed the effect with pollen grains suspended in water; the movement is known as the **Brownian movement.** The Brownian movement can be seen by making a mixture of Aquadag* with about fifty times its volume of distilled water. A drop of the mixture should be put on a microscope slide and examined under a microscope, illuminating the drop with a lamp to one side of the slide. The extremely small black particles of the graphite will glint in the light, so by looking at the bright specks in the field of view you will be able to watch their movement. If you see any small jerky movements they will be due to the particle being more hit on one side than on the other by movement of water molecules around the particle.

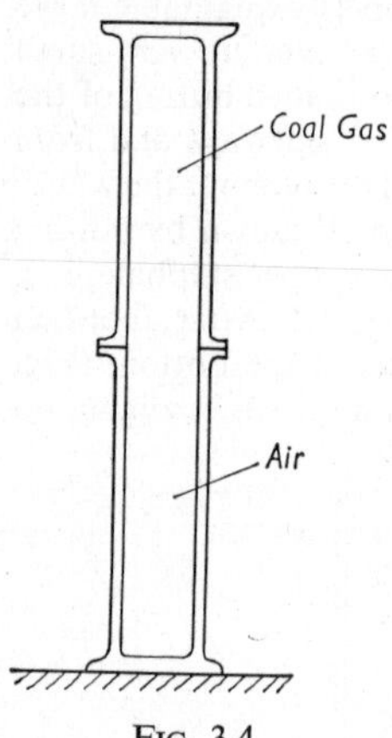

FIG. 3.4

Diffusion can also occur in gases, more rapidly than it occurs in liquids. The more rapid diffusion is evidence that the free path of molecules in gases is greater than it is in liquids. If a jar of low density gas is put mouth to mouth with a jar of high density gas, with the low

* Aquadag is the trade name of a colloidal graphite paste. It is obtainable from Acheson Colloids Ltd., London and Plymouth.

density gas at the top, the two gases become appreciably mixed in a matter of minutes. Fig. 3.4 shows an experimental arrangement using coal gas and air. After leaving the arrangement for a few minutes, the contents of both jars will light with a slight explosion or pop. This shows that the contents of the two jars have become mixed.

The actual rate of a gas-diffusion can be seen by using a coloured gas such as bromine. Bromine is a dark red liquid at ordinary temperatures, but it is volatile enough to give a red vapour which is clearly visible. Fig. 3.5*a* illustrates an experiment in which the

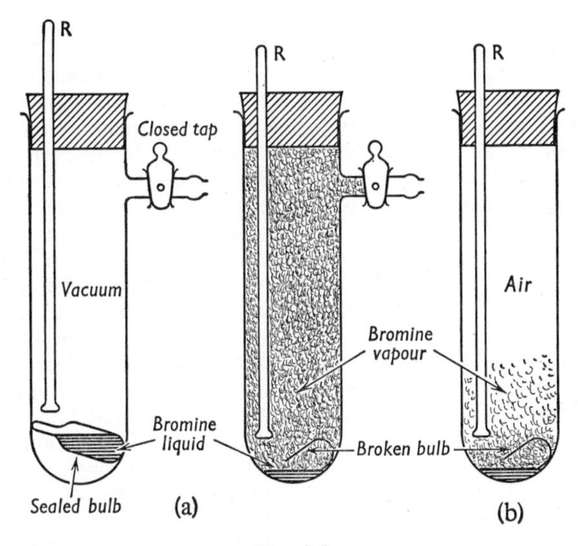

FIG. 3.5

formation of the vapour can be seen. A fragile sealed glass tube containing bromine is situated in a glass vessel which has been evacuated by a vacuum pump. When the bromine is released by breaking its container with the rod *R* the apparatus becomes immediately filled with red vapour, with some liquid bromine at the bottom. It has been calculated that the average speed of bromine molecules at room temperature is about 200 metres/s, so it is not surprising that they fly across the empty vessel almost immediately.

Many of the molecules, bouncing downwards after collisions with the walls of the vessel or with other molecules, hit the liquid bromine and re-enter it. There is a limit to the number of molecules in the vapour stage at any moment; this limit occurs when as many molecules leave the liquid per second as enter it per second.

Fig. 3.5*b* shows what has happened a short time after the bromine has been released in air instead of a vacuum. The travel of the bromine molecules is hampered by collisions with the air molecules, but as time goes on the bromine molecules diffuse into the air, and the air molecules diffuse into the bromine vapour. The rate of diffusion can be seen from the rate at which the red boundary moves upward.

3.6. Osmosis. Substances such as glass and metals, which do not allow gases and liquids to pass through them, are said to be **impervious** or **impermeable.** Porous substances such as unglazed earthenware and blotting paper are **permeable;** permeable membranes permit diffusion through them until conditions on both sides of the partition are the same. Certain materials permit the passage of some things but not of others; membranes made of such materials are called **semi-permeable membranes.** If a solution is separated from some of the pure solvent by a semi-permeable membrane which permits the passage of the solvent but not the solute, an effect called **osmosis** occurs. In the case of water solutions, osmosis occurs with such semi-permeable membranes as parchment, cellophane, pig's bladder, the enclosing membrane inside a bird's egg, the living protoplasm of plant and animal cells, copper ferrocyanide and many gelatinous silicates. Fig. 3.6 illustrates an experiment to show osmosis through cellophane. A cellophane membrane is tied tightly over the end of a glass tube and the edges of the membrane covered with some plasticine to make the joint watertight. A strong sugar solution or syrup is poured into the tube which is then filled with coloured water to act as an index in the narrow tube which is used to close the arrangement. The

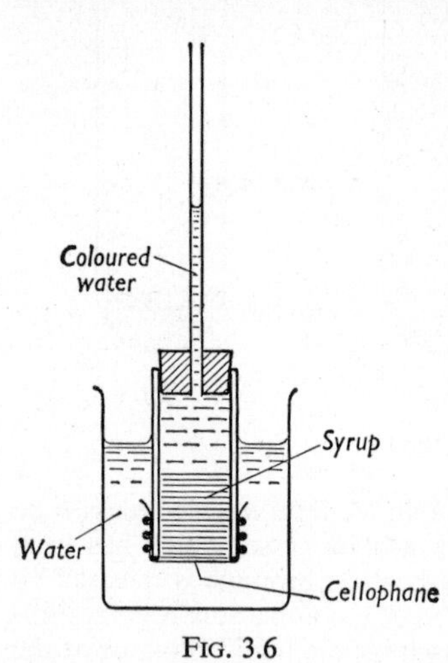

FIG. 3.6

other side of the membrane is surrounded by water. The cellophane allows the passage of water through it, but not the sugar. There is a steady rise in the index in the narrow tube showing that water is passing through the membrane to the solution. The effect is called **osmosis** (Greek *osmos* = push). The inflowing water will rise to very great heights if the apparatus does not leak and if the membrane can withstand the resulting pressure. It has been found, using a more rigid membrane, that osmosis ceases when a sufficient pressure is applied to the membrane. The pressure depends on the concentration of the solution; the applied pressure measures what is known as the **osmotic pressure** of the solution.

Plant cells have a permeable cellulose wall, lined with semi-permeable protoplasm. When plant cells are surrounded by water or weak solutions, osmosis of the water towards the cell sap keeps up a pressure inside the cell. The direction of osmosis can be reversed if cells are put in a strong solution; the resulting shrinkage of the protoplasm away from the cell wall is known as **plasmolysis.** If a strip of potato tuber is put in a strong salt solution it becomes flabby owing to plasmolysis; the original stiffness is restored by placing the flabby tissue in fresh water. The shrivelled condition of dried fruits such as sultanas and raisins is similarly altered by osmosis when they, with their sugary cell contents, are put into water. Osmosis is probably associated with the absorption of water from the soil by the root-hairs of plants; but the process is not a simple one, for the dissolved salts pass through the protoplasm as well.

3.7. Surface tension. Capillarity. The hardness and stiffness of solids suggests that there must be large forces of attraction between their molecules. The force of attraction between molecules of the same substance is known as a **force of cohesion**; it is a force which makes them cling together. The force of cohesion is less in liquids, but its effect is to be seen in the way in which small volumes of liquid tend to form rounded drops.

If a glass rod is dipped into water and withdrawn, some of the water adheres to the rod and may hang from the end in the form of a drop. This not only shows the attraction of water molecules for each other; it shows an attraction between glass molecules and water molecules. The ready clinging of water to glass can be explained in terms of the molecular theory by assuming that the attraction of glass molecules for water molecules is greater than the attraction of water molecules for each other. The attraction between molecules of different substances is known as a **force of**

adhesion. If the glass is waxed there is little or no adhesion with water; the adhesion-force of wax on water is less than the cohesion-force of the water molecules themselves. Another effect of these forces is to be seen where the surface of a liquid touches the walls of a containing vessel. For water in glass, the relatively strong force of adhesion causes the meniscus to curve upwards; for mercury in glass, the relatively strong force of cohesion causes the meniscus to curve downwards (Fig. 3.7).

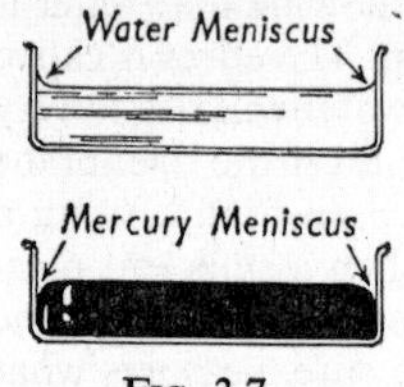

FIG. 3.7

If a drop of liquid is placed on top of a flat surface its weight will tend to make it spread. This happens readily when water is put on a *clean* glass surface; the force of adhesion assists the force of gravity. But there is less spreading for liquids which do not wet the surface they touch (Pl. 2 and Fig. 3.8). Small drops are nearly spherical; large drops, though flattened by the action of their weight, still have a noticeable height. These drops, and the hanging drop from the glass rod, behave as though the *free surface* of the water were in a *state of tension.* The force of tension which exists in the free surface of a liquid is known as **surface tension;** it tends to make the surface contract, so that drops of liquid tend to take up a rounded shape.

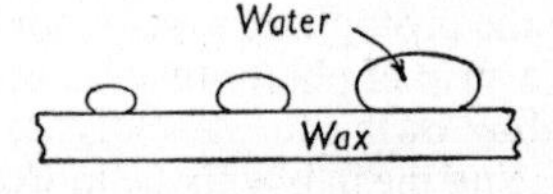

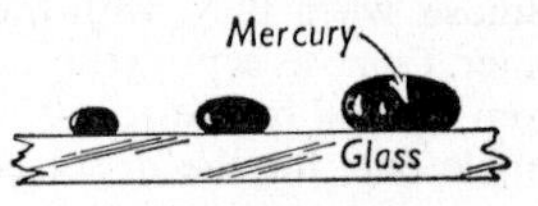

FIG. 3.8

The shape of drops of liquid on surfaces which they do not wet

You can show the surface tension in a solution of soap or other detergent using the apparatus shown in Fig. 3.9. By dipping the frame into the solution and withdrawing it a film can be formed across the frame. A light thin wire or a thin glass tube put horizontally across the frame will not move to one side or the other; but if you break the film by touching it on one side the pull of the surfaces on the other side is very evident from the rapid motion of the cross-bar.

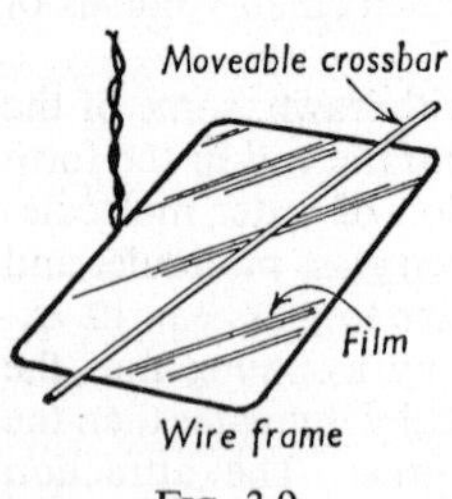

FIG. 3.9

You can also show the contractile nature of the soap films by blowing a bubble on the end of a pipe. If the bubble is left on the end of the pipe, it contracts and air is driven out of the open end; the effect can be shown by directing the air stream at the flame of a candle. In similar fashion a bulb blown on the end of a piece of glass tubing contracts when the glass bulb is re-heated in the flame; the softened glass shows the action of a tension in its surface which makes it contract.

The surface of water can hold up light objects which would otherwise sink in water. Thus a piece of flat metal foil lowered gently on to a water surface will float, held up by the forces of surface tension. If you cut the metal foil to the shape shown in Fig. 3.10 and then put a small piece of camphor in the nitch cut in

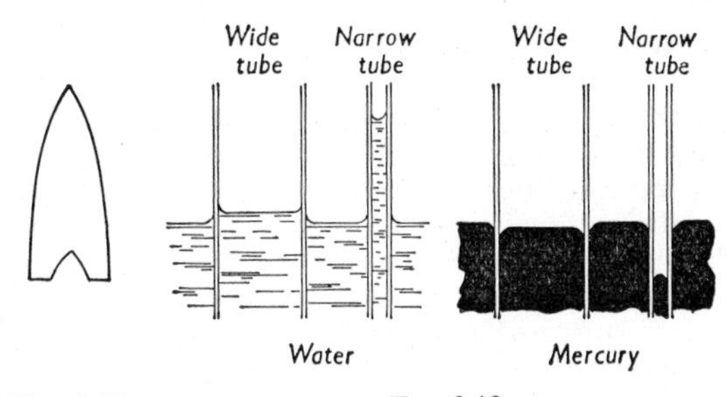

FIG. 3.10

FIG. 3.10

Capillarity effects with water and mercury in glass

the back of the boat shape, it will actually move across the water surface when put on to it. The boat appears to be driven along or pushed. Actually it is being pulled. The surface tension of a solution of camphor in water is less than that of pure water. A decrease of surface tension behind the boat results in the water surface pulling the boat forwards.

An effect connected with surface tension occurs when liquid surfaces are in contact with narrow channels. The effect is known as **capillarity.** Fig. 3.11 shows the effect of dipping glass tubes in water and in mercury. The meniscus level inside the tube is different from that outside and the effect is more marked in the narrower tubes. In the case of water (and of all liquids which wet the glass) the meniscus curves upwards so that the surface tension pulls downwards on the glass. It thus follows, from Newton's third law, that the glass pulls upward on the liquid, and so the liquid rises up the tube. In upright uniform tubes the action stops when the weight of water lifted is equal to the pull caused by surface tension. Liquids which do not wet the tube (e.g. mercury, water in greasy or waxed tubes) have their meniscus curved the other way; they pull upwards on the tube and are themselves pulled down.

There are quite a number of effects which are connected with capillarity. It is, for instance, one of the causes of the rise of water up the woody tissues of plants. The porous material of brick and mortar can cause water to rise to considerable heights by capillary action; to prevent the walls of houses from being continually damp a layer of specially waterproofed bricks ('blue bricks'), or of slate or of roofing-felt, is put in at the lower levels—this structure is known as a *damp course*. Capillary action occurs in the use of wicks in oil lamps and petrol lighters and in the absorption of liquids by blotting paper; the liquid rises through the narrow channels between the fibres.

3.8. Elasticity. Elasticity is the property of materials which makes them resist a change of volume or of shape, and recover their original condition after being deformed. A gas has elasticity, shown by the restoring pressure which occurs when its volume is reduced. Rubber has elasticity; a rubber ball will recover its shape after being compressed. Steel has an even greater elasticity for it shows a very large recovery force when deformed. On the other hand, substances such as clay, putty and plasticine are readily deformed and are therefore inelastic. The property of elasticity in solids shows that the space lattice of the molecules can be distorted, but that the molecules then exert a strong force trying to pull them back to their original positions.

Experiment. Clamp one end of a long piece of bare copper wire in a vice; about 2 metres is a suitable length, s.w.g. 26 is a suitable thickness. Grip the other end with pliers and pull on the wire. You will notice that the wire stretches slightly, and usually it regains its length on release. But if you pull harder you will find that the wire stretches several centimetres, and that it does not seem to contract when you release the pull. (Careful measurement does, in fact, show that it contracts slightly.) The wire is said to have a **permanent set,** to have been stressed beyond the **elastic limit** of the material and to have reached the **yield point.** If you pull with greater force on the wire, further yielding will take place and finally the wire will break.

The **stress** (force per unit area of cross-section) required to produce yielding or to produce breakage is known as the **yield point** in the one case, the **breaking point** in the other. These properties of materials have an important bearing on engineering.

The ties and struts of girder frameworks, the cables of suspension bridges and of elevators, all stretch or shrink under load. The yield point sets a danger limit to the loading. Structures are designed to be well within this danger limit to the loading. Steel structures usually have a safety factor of 4, which means that they will withstand four times their normal loading.

SUMMARY

Chemical **compounds** are made up of **elements** (substances which cannot be decomposed by chemical methods). A **molecule** is the smallest particle of a compound which can exist and still show the properties of that compound; similarly an **atom** is the smallest particle of an element.

The **kinetic theory** states that molecules are in a state of continual motion; they have a kinetic energy which increases with temperature. They collide with one another, and the distance travelled between collisions, or **mean free path,** is much greater for gases than for liquids. As a result, **diffusion** is more rapid in gases than in liquids.

Molecules attract each other. The forces of attraction between molecules of the same kind are known as forces of **cohesion.** Cohesion in liquids causes the surface (or meniscus) of a liquid to be in a state of tension, known as **surface tension.** Surface tension pulls on objects with which the surface is in contact, and it tends to make the surface contract.

Attractions between molecules of different kinds are known as forces of **adhesion;** it is these forces which make one substance adhere to another. Strong adhesion between a solid and a liquid makes the liquid wet the solid, makes the liquid meniscus curve upwards and is the cause of **capillarity.**

Elasticity is the property of materials which causes them to recover their original condition after being deformed.

Questions

1. Distinguish between the three states of matter. Give some examples of the way in which properties of the three states of matter are explained by the molecular theory.

2. What is meant by a *molecule* of a substance, an *atom* of an element? Describe any one simple experiment or observation which suggests that the molecules of a substance are extremely small.

3. Describe an experiment to illustrate *diffusion* in gases, and

another experiment to illustrate diffusion in a liquid. Give an explanation of each experiment in terms of the kinetic theory.

4. Particles of a solid, submerged in a liquid of exactly the same density, are observed with a microscope. A particle about the size of a pin's head appears motionless, but a particle which is so small that it is only just visible in the microscope is seen to move in a jerky manner. Account for these observations in terms of the kinetic theory.

5. Measure the distance marked 1μ (1 micro-metre or micron) in Pl. 1. Measure the length of the bacillus shown in Pl. 1. Hence deduce the true length of the bacillus. Assuming that the picture-size of the virus is $\frac{1}{2}$ mm, deduce the real size of a virus.

6. Some bromine (a red liquid having a red vapour) is suddenly put at the bottom of a sealed flask. Use the ideas of the kinetic theory to forecast the molecular movements which should occur when (*a*) the flask contained nothing else in it at all, (*b*) the flask contained air at atmospheric pressure.

At what stages in such an experiment would you expect to observe (i) evaporation, (ii) diffusion?

Account for the fact that the final pressure in (*b*) is greater than atmospheric.

7. Assuming that the average speed (in metres/s) of a molecule, of molecular weight M, at a temperature t°C is given by the square root of $25 \times 10^3(t+273) \div M$, calculate the average speed of bromine and oxygen molecules at temperatures of (*a*) 27°C, (*b*) 327°C.

(Molecular weights: oxygen = 32, bromine = 160).

8. A stoppered bottle is half-full of water and has air above the water. Some liquid bromine is introduced at the bottom of the bottle; after a day or two the water is coloured red, and after that the air appears red. Describe the molecular movements which cause these effects.

9. Distinguish between *impermeable*, *permeable* and *semi-permeable* membranes or partitions. Give one example of each. Describe how you would use one of these membranes to demonstrate *osmosis*; what, if anything, would have happened if you had used one of the other membranes in conducting the experiment?

10. Two porous pots P and Q are each half-full of a sugar solution. Each stands, separately, in a vessel of water so that the water and the sugar solutions are at the same level. The pores of P are sealed with a semi-permeable membrane. Describe and explain the changes which take place in these two arrangements, and state whether the changes would occur after a matter of minutes, hours or days.

11. Explain what is meant by the surface tension of a liquid. Describe two simple experiments which show effects due to surface tension.

12. Explain: (*a*) a sugar cube, held with one corner just touching the surface of water, quickly becomes wet throughout the cube, (*b*) a glass bulb on the end of a glass tube begins to contract when the bulb is heated to a temperature at which glass softens.

13. Describe the difference in the behaviour of water when a few drops of it are put on a horizontal glass plate (*a*) when the glass is clean, (*b*) when the glass is greasy. Give an explanation of the difference in behaviour.

14. Describe two simple experiments which show that soap films have a force in them which tends to make them contract.

15. Give an account of the action of capillary tubes of different bore when dipped into (*a*) water, (*b*) mercury.

16. Two solutions of different substances have the same density. How would you find out which of them has the greater surface tension?

17. What is meant by the terms *elasticity*, *elastic limit*, *yield point*, *safety factor*? The yield point of copper is approximately 12 kgf/sq. mm. How would you check this experimentally, given a long copper wire whose area of cross-section is 0·25 sq. mm?

CHAPTER 4

The Density of Matter

4.1. Mass, volume and density. A 250-c.c. beaker full of mercury weighs nearly $3\frac{1}{2}$ kg. If you lift it up you are likely to exclaim at its heaviness. Yet there is nothing remarkably heavy about anything weighing $3\frac{1}{2}$ kg; what you find surprising in the case of mercury is to find $3\frac{1}{2}$ kg packed in so small a space. To get the same mass of water you would need to have $3\frac{1}{2}$ litres of it; the same mass of balsa wood would occupy about 70 times as much space as the mercury. We express this by saying that mercury is **denser** than water, water denser than balsa wood. Matter seems to be more concentrated in mercury than in water. This is due partly to the fact that mercury molecules have more mass than those of water, partly to the fact that mercury molecules are closer together. To this concentration of matter, or concentration of mass, we give the name **density,** i.e. the density of mercury is greater than the density of water.

Density is measured by the number of units of mass contained in one unit of volume. So that if 3 cu. metres of cork weigh 750 kg the density of cork can be stated to be $750 \div 3$ or 250 kg per cu. metre. The simple division sum gives the numerical value of the density; the units are named from the mass and volume units in which the measurements were made. This can be expressed in the form of an equation

$$d=\frac{m}{v}$$

where d represents the number of units of density,
m represents the number of units of mass,
v represents the number of units of volume.

In using the equation, care must be taken that the units on the left-hand side correspond with those on the right.

The unit of density on the British system of units is lb/cu. ft, on the metric system it can be either the g/c.c. or the kg/cu. metre. The density of water at 4°C, for example, is 62·4 lb/cu. ft, 1·000 g/c.c., 1000 kg/cu. metre. But there are other units; thus gas densities are commonly measured in g/litre. A litre is defined as the volume of a kilogram of water at 4°C. It was originally intended that the litre be exactly 1000 c.c., but a careful test showed it to be 1000·027 c.c. Burettes and other graduated vessels are now usually marked in *millilitres* (ml) or *mils* instead of c.c.; but for most practical purposes the difference between 1 ml and 1 c.c. is insignificant.

4.2. Determination of density; volume measurement. The determination of density involves the determination of a mass and a volume. The mass can be found by weighing; the method of finding the volume depends on whether the substance is solid, liquid or gaseous.

Solids. If a solid is of regular shape (e.g. a rectangular block, a cylinder, a sphere) the volume can be found by calculation from its dimensions. For example, a glass rod 12·0 cm long and 0·70 cm in diameter was found to weigh 11·55 g.

Calculation. Taking π as 22/7

$$\text{the volume} = \frac{22}{7} \times \frac{1}{4} \times \frac{7}{10} \times \frac{7}{10} \times 12$$

$$\text{Density} = 11{\cdot}55 \div 4{\cdot}62 = 2{\cdot}50 \text{ g/c.c.}$$

If the solid is of irregular shape the volume can be found by a displacement method. If the solid is small enough to slip into a narrow measuring cylinder, its volume can be found as illustrated in Fig. 4.1*a*. The first reading represents the water level before

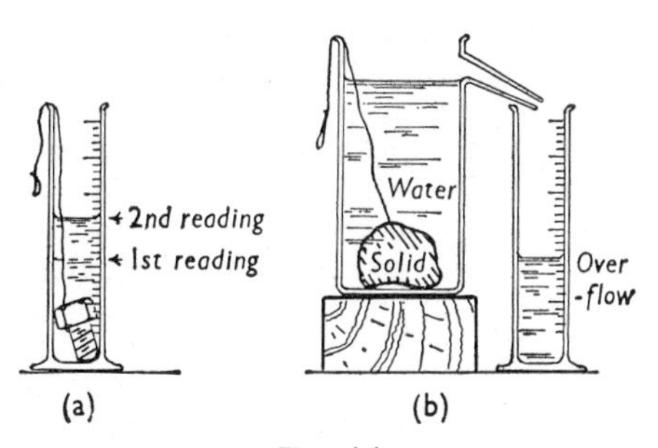

FIG. 4.1

introducing the solid, the second reading shows the level after that. The difference of the two readings gives the volume of the solid. If the solid is too big to go into a measuring cylinder, an overflow-can method may be used; this is illustrated in Fig. 4.1*b*. The can is first filled with water to overflowing and is then allowed to drain;

after that the solid is introduced and the overflow caught in the measuring cylinder gives a measure of the volume of the solid.

The displaced water can be found more accurately by weighing it, as in the volumenometer method illustrated in Fig. 4.2. The

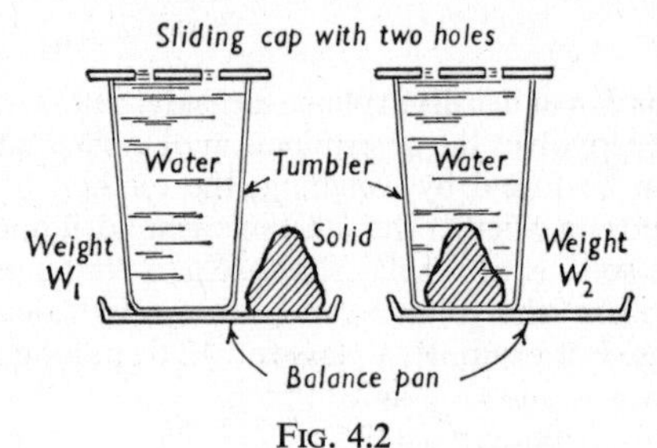

FIG. 4.2

A simple volumenometer

diagram shows a small tumbler fitted with a perspex lid into which two holes have been drilled. The volumenometer, full of water, is first weighed with the solid outside the volumenometer and is then weighed again with the solid inside the volumenometer. The difference gives $(w_1 - w_2)$, the weight of water displaced by the solid. But since 1 gram of water occupies 1 c.c., the volume of the solid is $(w_1 - w_2)$ c.c.

Another example of displacement found by weighing is given on page 109.

Liquids. The liquid under test is transferred to a weighed beaker from an instrument such as a pipette, a burette or a measuring cylinder. It is important that the instrument should be clean and grease-free to prevent drops of liquid clinging to its sides; in the case of the burette and the measuring cylinder the volume transferred is found from the difference of two scale readings, i.e. not all the available liquid is run out. A graduated flask or a graduated density bottle (Fig. 4.3) can be used to find the density of a liquid. The vessel is weighed empty and then filled with liquid to some definite mark—the top

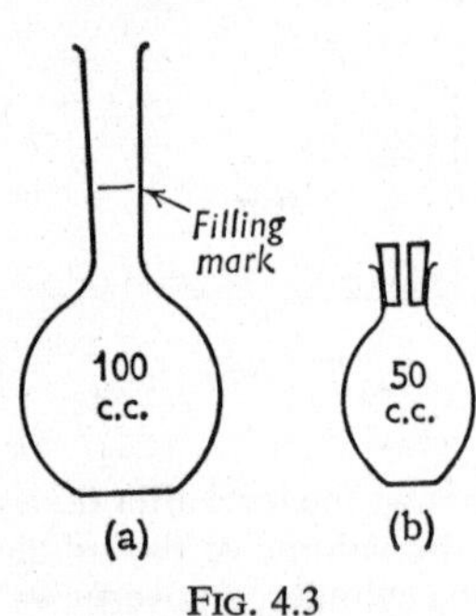

FIG. 4.3

(*a*) *A measuring flask*
(*b*) *A density bottle*

of the capillary tube of the stopper in the case of the density bottle. The difference of the two weighings thus gives the mass of a definite volume of liquid, and so the mass of 1 c.c. can be calculated.

The **common hydrometer** (Fig. 4.4) gives direct readings of density on the scale which is marked on its stem. The instrument is floated in the liquid and the corresponding density is read from the position of the meniscus on the scale. The more accurate types are 6–12 in long and so need an appreciable depth of liquid to float them. Where a compact instrument is of more importance than accuracy of reading, the hydrometer can be made smaller; Fig. 4.5 shows a type which is used to test the acid density of an accumulator. On pressing the bulb air is driven out of the container and on releasing the bulb a sample of acid is drawn up into the container to float the hydrometer. From the reading obtained it is possible to estimate the extent to which the accumulator is charged.

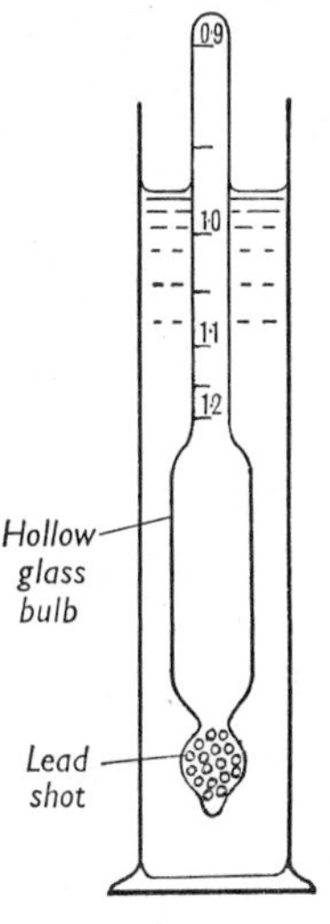

FIG. 4.4
A common, or constant-weight, hydrometer

Other methods for finding the density of a liquid are given in Chapter 12.

Gases. Gases completely occupy their containing vessel, and the volume of the vessel can be found by filling it with water from a graduated vessel. A round-bottom flask fitted with a tube and tap is generally used; it is weighed full of the gas under test, the gas is then removed by means of an exhaust pump and the flask and its fittings are reweighed to find the decrease in weight. (A round-bottom flask is used because it can withstand the large forces due to external air pressure.)

The density of air can be found without the help of an exhaust pump by using the arrangement shown in Fig. 4.6. Air is first driven out by boiling some water in the flask, the clip is then closed and the whole arrangement weighed after it has been allowed to cool. The clip is opened to let air in and the flask with the air in it is reweighed. The volume of the air space in the flask is found by pouring water into the flask from a large measuring cylinder until the flask is full of water. In an actual test 450 c.c. of air were found to have a mass of 0·54 g. So that 1 c.c. of air has a mass of $0{\cdot}54 \div 450 = 0{\cdot}0012$ g. The temperature of the air was 17°C, so the density of the given sample of air at that temperature was 0·0012 g/c.c. (This is a value for *damp* air under the conditions of the experiment.)

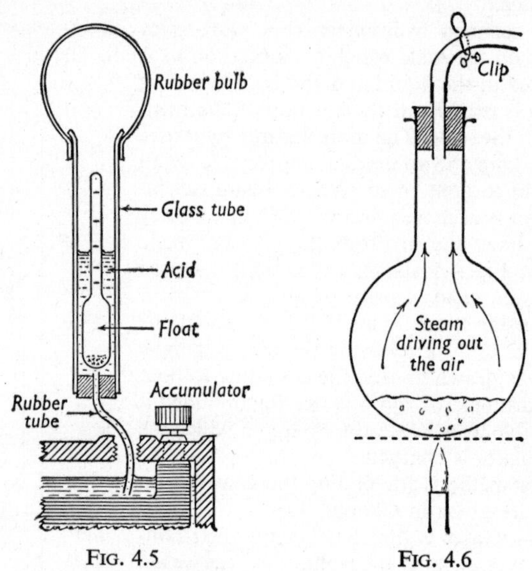

FIG. 4.5

Testing the acid density in a lead accumulator

FIG. 4.6

4.3. Relative density. The number given for the density of a substance depends on the units. The number for water is 1·000, 1000 or 62·4 depending on whether the units are g/c.c., kg/cu. metre, or lb/cu. ft. The corresponding numbers for zinc are 7·1, 7100 and 433, numbers which show that zinc is 7·1 times as dense as water or 7·1 times as heavy as an equal volume of water. This fact is expressed in the phrase 'the relative density of zinc is 7·1'. **Relative density (r.d.),** also known by the name **specific gravity (sp.gr.),** is defined by the ratio

$$\frac{\textbf{Density of the substance}}{\textbf{Density of water}}$$

which has no units. This ratio is also equal to

$$\frac{\textbf{Weight of a substance}}{\textbf{Weight of an equal volume of water}}$$

This idea of comparing weights is useful in problems dealing with units such as kilograms, tons.

EXAMPLE 1. *Calculate the weight of liquid displaced when a block of sulphur, of sp.gr. (relative density)* 2·00, *is submerged in* (a) *water,* (b) *petrol sp.gr.* 0·7. (*Wt. of block* = 3·0 *kgf.*)

The block will displace, or push aside an equal volume of water; since the block weighs twice as much as an equal volume of water, the weight of water displaced will be 3·0 ÷ 2 = 1·5 kgf.

The corresponding volume of petrol weighs only 0·7 of the weight of the water so the weight of petrol displaced = 0·7 × 1·5 = 1·05 kgf.

EXAMPLE 2. *Calculate the mass, in kg, of a cubic metre of air. The sp.gr. of air is* 0·00129.

Since 1 c.c. of water weighs 1 g.
1 c.c. of air will weigh 0·00129 g.
but 1 cu. metre = 100 × 100 × 100 = 10^6 c.c.
so 1 cu. metre of air weighs 0·00129 × 10^6 g.

This is 1290 g or 1·290 kg.

In the last problem the density of air was given relative to that of water. The relative densities of gases are often calculated relative to hydrogen gas at the same temperature and pressure. The results are known as **vapour densities,** of which the following table gives some examples:

Hydrogen	1	Carbon dioxide	22·0
Helium	2·0	Sulphur dioxide	32·0
Neon	10·1	Chlorine	35·5
Nitrogen	14·0	Ammonia	8·5
Oxygen	16·0	Hydrogen chloride	18·25

Avogadro (1776–1856) assumed that equal volumes of gases at the same temperature and pressure contain equal numbers of molecules. If so, the above vapour densities give the relative masses of the molecules of substances—assuming that all the molecules of any one substance have the same mass. Atomic research has shown that this last assumption is not correct. Thus ordinary neon gas contains molecules whose masses relative to that of the hydrogen molecule are 10·0, 10·5 and 11·0. Since there are two atoms in each hydrogen molecule it follows that neon contains a mixture of molecules whose masses are 20·0, 21·0 and 22·0 times that of a hydrogen *atom*.

Table of Densities
(in g/c.c.)

Metals

Magnesium	1·74	Silver	10·5
Aluminium	2·70	Lead	11·3
Zinc	7·10	Mercury	13·6
Tin	7·30	Gold	19·3
Iron	7·50–7·90	Platinum	21·4
Brass	8·10–8·50	Osmium	22·5
Copper	8·90		

Common Solids

Wood (oak)	0·6 –0·8	Cork	0·22–0·26
Wood (box)	0·85–1·1	Ice	0·92
Rubber	1·15–1·7	Marble	2·70

Liquids

Water	1·00	Saturated salt solution	1·20
Petrol	0·68–0·72	Saturated hypo solution	1·33
Methylated spirit	0·82	Carbon tetrachloride	1·60

Gases
(at standard temperature and pressure)

Air	0·001293	Hydrogen	0·000090

SUMMARY

Density is the concentration of mass in relation to the space which it occupies; it is measured by the **mass per unit volume.** Two of the units in which it is expressed are g/c.c. and kg/litre.

$$d=\frac{m}{v}$$

where d, m and v, represent density, mass and volume respectively.

Relative density (r.d.) or specific gravity (sp.gr.) is the density of a substance relative to the density of water

or
$$\frac{\text{Weight of a substance}}{\text{Weight of an equal volume of water}}$$

This is a ratio and has no units.

The **vapour density of a gas** is given by the ratio

$$\frac{\text{Density of the gas}}{\text{Density of hydrogen at the same temperature and pressure}}$$

The result gives the average mass of the molecules of the gas compared with the mass of a hydrogen molecule.

Questions

1. Calculate (*a*) the density of a metal, 5·1 c.c. of which weigh 42·33 g, (*b*) the volume of a piece of cork weighing 10·3 g and having a density of 0·25 g/c.c., (*c*) the mass of 150 c.c. of benzene, density 0·88 g/c.c., (*d*) the volume of mercury, density 13·6 g/c.c., which weighs 1 kilogram.

2. Calculate the density of copper given that 21·0 c.c. of it have a mass of 186·9 g. What will be the mass of 80 c.c. of the copper?

3. Distinguish between *density* and *specific gravity* (*relative density*). Express the densities of benzene and hydrogen in kg/cu. metre. (Sp.gr. of benzene = 0·88; of hydrogen = 0·000090.)

4. A 56-lb weight, made of metal of sp.gr. 7·0, is lowered into a vessel which is full of water. Calculate the weight of water which will have overflowed from the vessel when the weight is completely submerged.

5. Calculate the mass of a square sheet of glass 0·250 cm thick, the length of each side being 0·500 metre. Name any one instrument you would use to find the thickness of such a sheet accurately. (Density of glass = 2·60 g/c.c.)

6. 25·0 g of salt (sp.gr. = 2·20) are dissolved in 100 g of water. Calculate the density of the solution, assuming that the volume of the solution is equal to the sum of the volumes of the salt and the water.

7. Describe how you would find the density of ice given a supply of alcohol, a liquid in which ice sinks. (*Hint.* If a solid remains poised in a liquid, i.e. neither floats nor sinks, the density of the liquid is equal to that of the solid.)

8. A hollow glass stopper weighs 7·5 g and has an external volume of 7·0 c.c. Calculate the volume of the hollow space in the stopper. (Density of the glass = 2·50 g/c.c.)

Describe any one way of measuring the external volume of the stopper experimentally.

9. An empty density bottle weighs 22·43 g. When full of salt solution it weighs 79·01 g, and when full of water it weighs 73·85 g. Calculate the sp.gr. (relative density) of the salt solution. Explain why it is necessary, in conducting an experiment of this type, to wash out the bottle before filling it with water.

10. A thread of mercury, at 10°C, is 15·45 cm long and weighs 10·16 g. Calculate the area of cross-section of the thread. (Density of mercury at 10°C = 13·6 g/c.c.)

11. 1·00 c.c. of lead, of sp.gr. 11·4, and 21·00 c.c. of wood, of sp.gr. 0·50, are tied together. State, giving your reason, whether the bundle will float or sink in water.

CHAPTER 5

Moments. Balances. Stability

5.1. The turning effect of a force. Forces are often used to set up a rotation or turning movement. The turning of a door-handle or the opening of the door itself are examples of this. The force you apply to the pedals of a bicycle has a turning effect; so, too, the force applied in the use of a screwdriver or a spanner. It is a matter of common experience that the wider the handle of a screwdriver, or the greater the length of a spanner, the greater is the **leverage** or turning effect. To measure this turning effect, which depends on force and distance, we might have to add together the force and the distance, or multiply them together, or try some other formula. Experiments show that it is the product of force and distance which measures the turning effect of a force; this product is known as the **moment of the force.** It is defined in the following manner.

The moment of a force about a point is equal to the product of the magnitude of the force and the perpendicular distance between the line of action of the force and the point.

Fig. 5.1 shows a simple experimental arrangement for showing

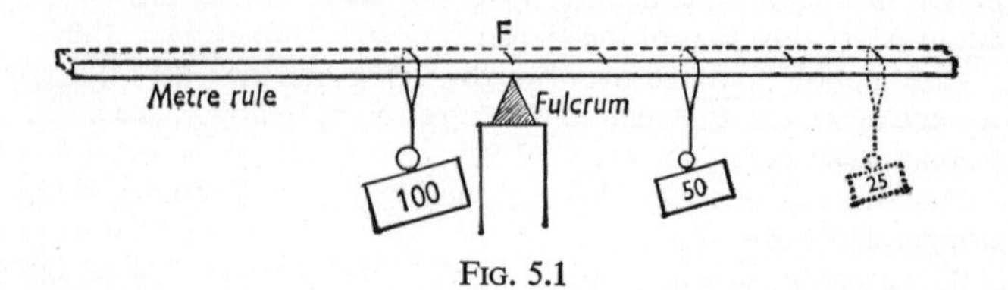

FIG. 5.1

the moment of a force. A metre rule is first balanced on a pivot or fulcrum, and a 100-g weight is hung on the left-hand side at a distance of 10 cm from F. The turning effect of this weight can be counter-balanced by a 50-g weight hung 20 cm from F on the right-hand side, by hanging a 25-g weight 40 cm from F, and by a 40-g weight hung 25 cm from F. The product of the force and distance on the right-hand side is always the same, 1000 units in fact. Since these different forces all counter-balance the turning effect of the force of the other side, the number 1000 can be taken as a measure of this turning effect; this is also borne out by the fact that the product of force and distance on the left-hand side is also given by $100 \times 10 = 1000$.

Note that in this experiment the forces on each side of the pivot have turning effects which are clockwise on one side and anti-clockwise on the other. The experiment therefore shows that, when the lever is balanced, the clockwise moment about the pivot is equal to the anti-clockwise moment about the pivot. This is a particular case of a more general **principle of moments** which is given on page 49.

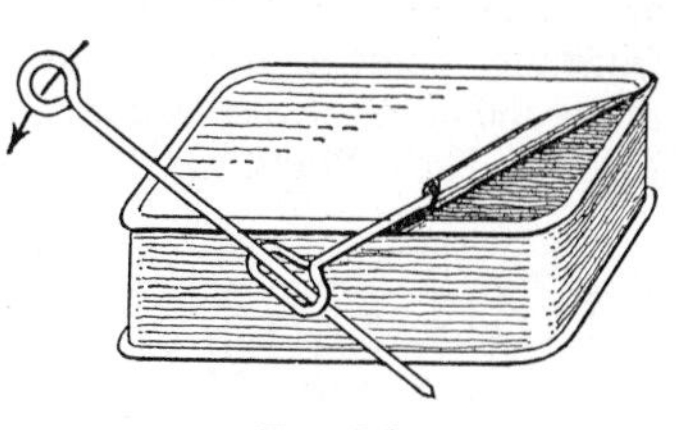

FIG. 5.2
Lengthening a lever

The moment of any force can be made larger by increasing the perpendicular distance of its line of action from the pivot. When a spanner is used to turn a nut, or a hammer to extract a nail, it is more effective to hold the tool at the far end. To open a sardine tin easily, you can use a long skewer to increase the moment of your force (Fig. 5.2). To obtain the best leverage the force must be suitably inclined as well as suitably placed (Fig. 5.3*a*). When your bicycle crank is sloping, the moment of your force will be reduced, as in Fig. 5.3*b*, unless you push at right angles to the pedal (Fig. 5.3*c*).

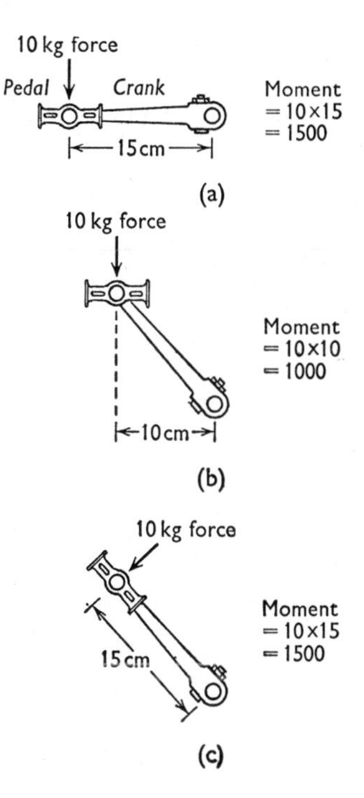

FIG. 5.3

5.2. Centre of gravity. The weight of a body is due to the attraction of the earth for its molecules. The weight is thus due to a set of parallel forces, such as are illustrated in Fig. 5·4, and is equal to the sum or *resultant* of these forces. For a rigid body there is one point at which the weight appears to act, or seems to be concentrated, no matter what the position of the body may be. This point is known as the **centre of gravity (c.g.).** When a body is freely suspended from any point in it the body hangs with its centre of gravity under the point of suspension. Consider the uniform rod shown in Fig. 5.5. The resultant of the parallel forces acting on its molecules

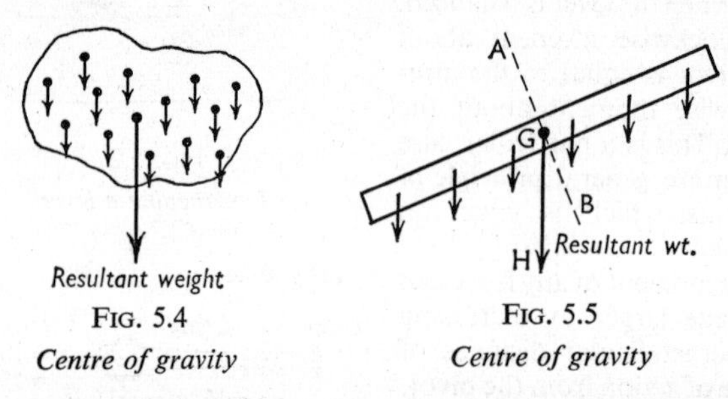

FIG. 5.4
Centre of gravity

FIG. 5.5
Centre of gravity

is in the direction GH. If the rod had been set horizontally the resultant would have acted along AGB. The two directions intersect at G which is therefore the centre of gravity of the rod.

The intersection of the lines of action of an object's weight can be used to determine the c.g. of the object experimentally. Thus Fig. 5.6 shows a sheet of cardboard freely pivoted on a horizontal pin. From the pin, and in front of the cardboard, hangs a plumb-line to show the direction of the earth's pull. The direction of this line can be marked on the card; then by repeating the experiment with other holes in the card, such as B and C, the intersection of the lines obtained on the card will give the c.g. of the card, G in the diagram.

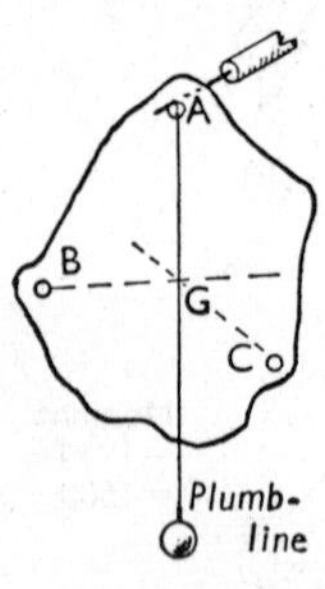

FIG. 5.6

The centre of gravity of a body is not always within the material of the body; it is sometimes outside it. If you use the method of Fig. 5.6 with an L-shaped piece of card you will find that the lines you draw on the card would meet, if produced, at a point outside the card.

The position of the c.g. of a body is a factor of great importance in connection with the stability of a body (see p. 52).

5.3. Principle of moments. Reference was made on page 47 to the fact that in a balanced object the clockwise and anti-clockwise moments about the pivot are equal. The statement is true for other points besides the pivot, and the following is a statement of the **principle of moments.**

If a body is in equilibrium under the action of forces which lie in one plane, then the sum of the clockwise moments is equal to the sum of the anti-clockwise moments about any point in that plane.

You can check this principle by reference to Fig. 5.7 which shows a spring-balance supporting a uniform bar, weighing 1 kg,

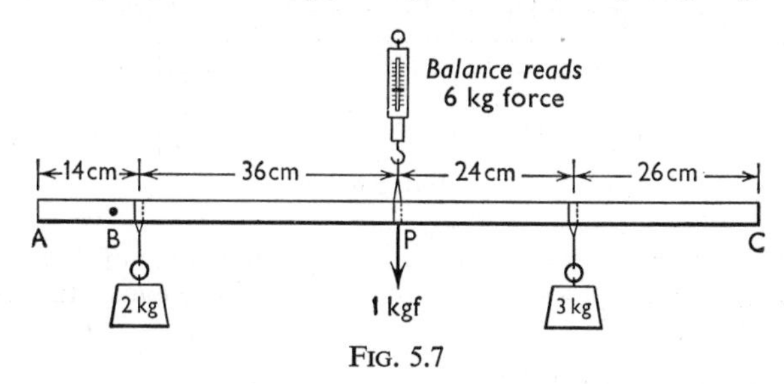

FIG. 5.7

at its centre of gravity. Weights of 3 kg and 2 kg have been hung, counterpoised from the bar. The spring-balance reads 6 kgf, the downward force on the spring due to the weights $(1+3+2)$ kgf; it is also the upward force of the spring on the loaded bar. Note that the anti-clockwise moment about P is $2\times36=72$ units, and that the clockwise moment about P is also 72 units (3×24). An inspection of the diagram will show that the total clockwise moments are equal to the total anti-clockwise moments about any point in the plane of the diagram if all the forces acting on the bar are considered. Take the point C for example.

Anti-clockwise moments $=(3\times26)+(1\times50)+(2\times86)=300$
Clockwise moments $= 6\times50 = 300$

Check for yourself the clockwise and anti-clockwise moments about the points B (40 cm from the pivot) and A (at the end of the bar).

EXAMPLE. *A uniform beam, of weight* 50 *kgf, is supported at its ends and carries a load of* 300 *kgf in the position shown in Fig.* 5.8. *What thrusts will the supports have to bear?*

The downthrusts on the supports will be accompanied by upthrusts on the beam (Newton's third law). Let these upthrusts be

X kgf and Y kgf. Then by taking moments about the point A the value of Y can be calculated, since the moment of X about A is zero.

$$\text{Clockwise moments} = \text{anti-clockwise moments}$$
$$(300 \times 3) + (50 \times 4) = Y \times 8$$
whence
$$Y = 137{\cdot}5$$

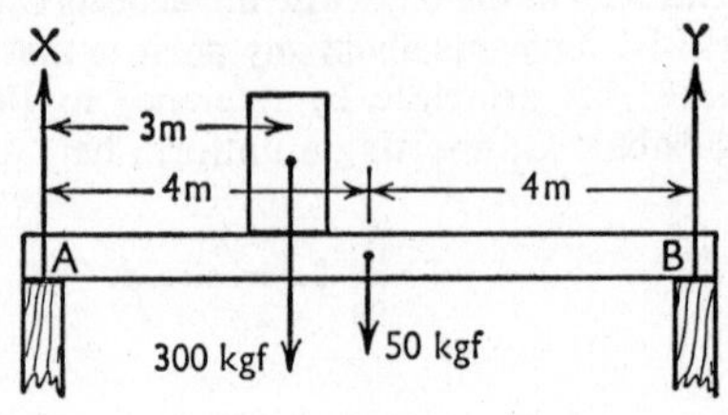

FIG. 5.8

Similarly, by taking moments about B, the value of X can be found. Alternatively, since the total upward force equals the total downward force,

$$X + Y = 350$$
$$X = 350 - Y$$
$$= 350 - 137{\cdot}5$$
$$= 212{\cdot}5$$

5.4. The beam balance. A metre rule balanced on a knife edge or fulcrum can be used as a simple balance. The centre of gravity of the ruler is first found. The object under test and the standard weight are then hung from the beam and the weights removed to such positions that the ruler still balances at its centre of gravity (Fig. 5.9).

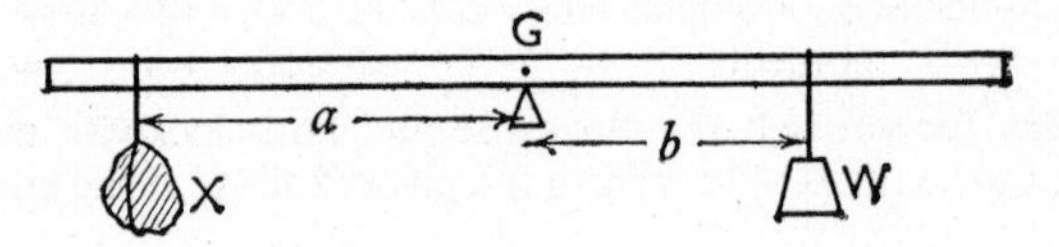

FIG. 5.9

Taking moments about F.

$$X \times a = W \times b$$

$$X = W \times \frac{b}{a}$$

This simple ruler-balance is top heavy because the centre of gravity of the beam is above the point of support. Fig. 5.10 shows a typical balance beam used in accurate balances. The c.g. of the beam is below the central knife-edge k_1; screw D is used to control the position of the c.g. and so alter the sensitiveness of the balance.

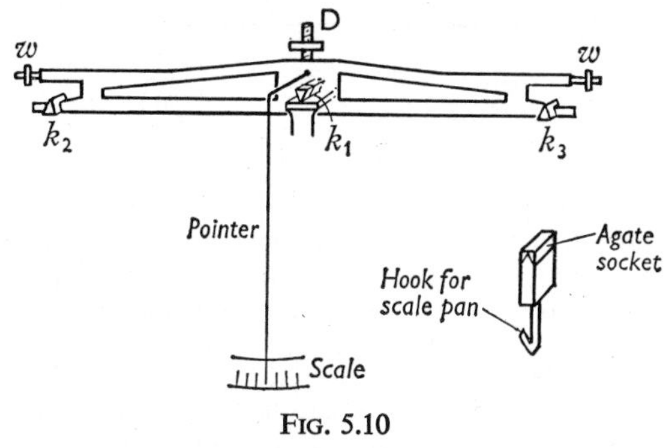

FIG. 5.10
A balance beam

The central knife-edge is made of agate, a hard stone, and it rests on agate supports; the agate knife-edges k_2 and k_3 support the scale-pans. Small screws w at the ends of the beam enable the operator to trim the balance.

The side knife-edges are set in the beam so that they shall be equal distances from the centre. This can be checked by weighing an object in the left-hand pan and then weighing it in the right-hand pan. The two weights should prove equal. If there is a noticeable difference the balance has not been properly made. But even with a faulty balance it is possible to find the correct weight either by the **double weighing method** or by the **counter-poise method.**

Double weighing. This consists of weighing separately in each pan as already indicated. Let the balance arms be a and b in length and the true weight of the body be W. Then from Fig. 5.11

$$Wa = W_1 b \quad \ldots \ldots \quad (1)$$

on reversal $$W_2 a = Wb \quad \ldots \ldots \quad (2)$$

(1) ÷ (2) gives $$\frac{W}{W_2} = \frac{W_1}{W}$$

$$W^2 = W_1 W_2 \text{ or } W = \sqrt{W_1 W_2}$$

$\sqrt{W_1 W_2}$ is known as the *geometric mean* of the two weighings.

Counterpoise method. The object in one pan is counterpoised with sand (or with weights) in the other. The object is removed and weights are put in its place until the balance is again counterpoised. These weights give the true weighing of the object.

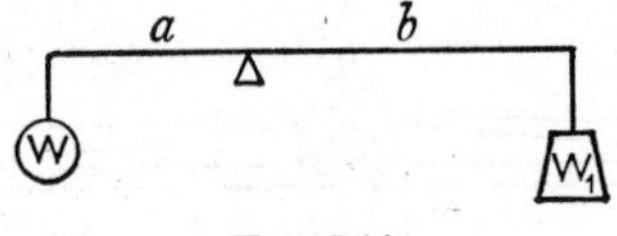

FIG. 5.11

5.5. Stability. A body which is not easily toppled over by the action of a force is said to have a good stability. Heavy objects are clearly more stable than are light ones of the same size and shape. The reason for this is shown in Fig. 5.12(*a*), which shows a block of wood, originally standing on a rough surface, tilted by the action of a horizontal force *F*. The centre of gravity G has been slightly raised in consequence. When *F* is removed, the moment of the weight *W* about A returns the block to its original position. The untilted

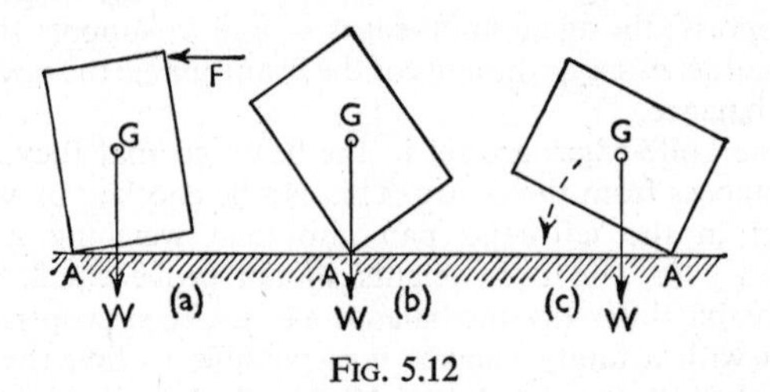

FIG. 5.12

block is said to be in **stable equilibrium.** Stage (*b*) shows the block balanced with G vertically above A. It is now said to be in **unstable equilibrium,** for the slightest further tilt causes the moment of the weight to turn it over, as shown in (*c*).

When a body is in stable equilibrium, a slight tilt or a slight displacement raises its centre of gravity; when a body is in unstable equilibrium, a slight displacement lowers its c.g. On the other hand, when a car is pushed along a level path or an ordinary door is opened, there is no change in the height of the c.g., and car and door will remain in their new positions. They are in **neutral equilibrium.** Fig. 5.13 shows a ball in various stages of equilibrium.

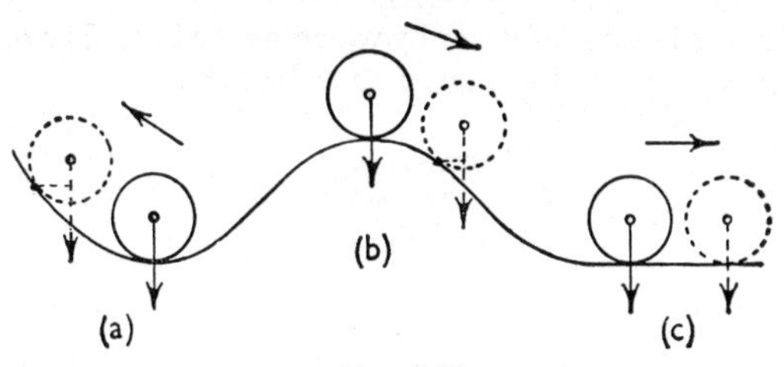

FIG. 5.13

Types of equilibrium: (a) stable, (b) unstable, (c) neutral. In each position the ball is in equilibrium, but the effect of small displacement is different in the three cases

In Fig. 5.14, showing a table lamp with centre of gravity G, the angle BAG is called the **safe angle of tilt.** This angle may be increased and the lamp made more stable by lowering G (by insert-

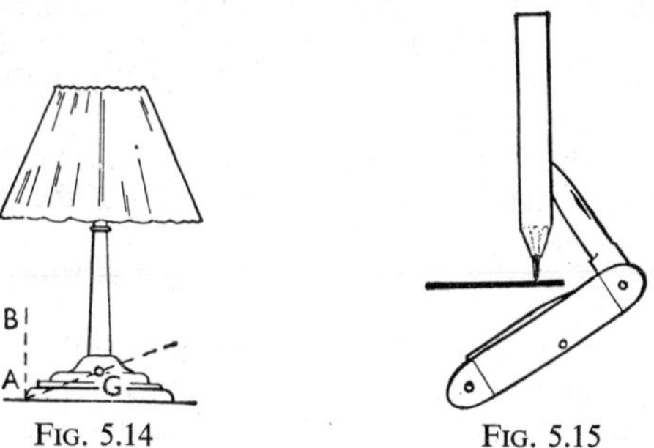

FIG. 5.14

FIG. 5.15

A pencil, with a penknife attached, balances on its point

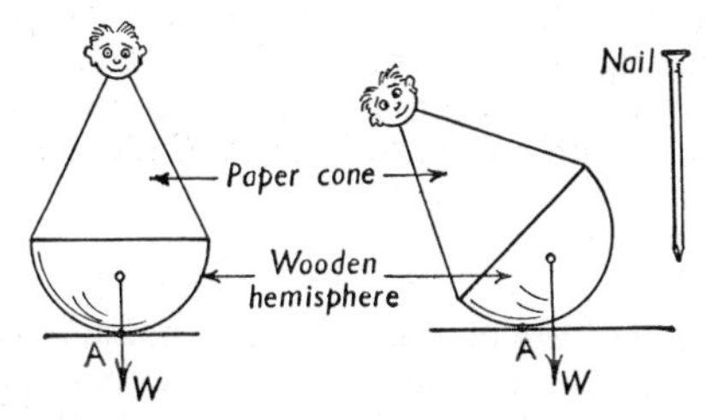

FIG. 5.16

However far this toy figure is tilted, it returns to the vertical. If a nail is pushed through the head, the centre of gravity is raised and the figure can be tilted to rest on its side

ing lead in the bottom of it), or by widening the base. The influence of the c.g. is illustrated in Figs. 5.15, 5.16, 5.17.

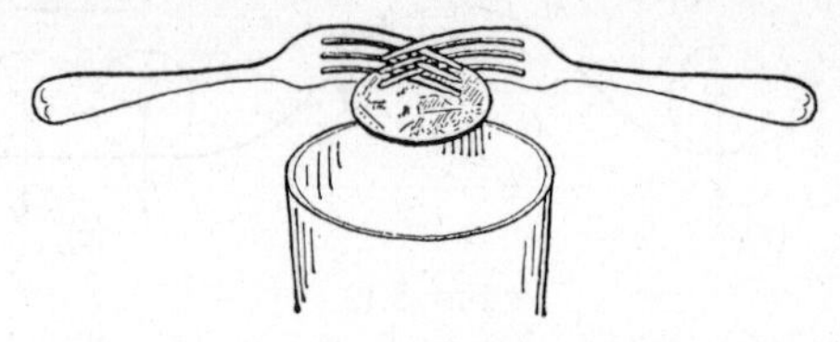

FIG. 5.17
Two table forks, interlocked on a penny, balance on the rim of a tumbler

SUMMARY

The **moment** of a force about a point is its 'turning effect' or leverage about that point; it is measured by the product of the magnitude of the force and the perpendicular distance between the point and the line of action of the force.

For a system of forces in equilibrium, **the total clockwise moments and the total anti-clockwise moments of the forces about any point are equal.**

The **centre of gravity** of a body is the point at which its weight appears to act.

The equilibrium of a body is said to be stable if the body returns to its initial position of equilibrium after being displaced; tilting a body away from a position of stable equilibrium is accompanied by a rise in the c.g. of the body.

The degree of stability of a body at rest can be expressed in terms of its **safe angle of tilt;** when the safe angle of tilt is exceeded, a vertical line through the c.g. lies outside the base.

The tendency of a vehicle to overturn when turning a corner is least for vehicles with a large 'safe angle of tilt', i.e. low c.g. and wide track.

Questions

1. Define the *moment* of a force about a point. A vertical pillar AB, 6 ft high, has a horizontal force of 20 lbf applied to the top of it, A. Calculate the moment of the force about B, (*a*) in lbf-ft units, (*b*) in lbf-in. units. Calculate (*c*) the moment of the force about B if the force is applied at an angle of 45° to the vertical instead of horizontally.

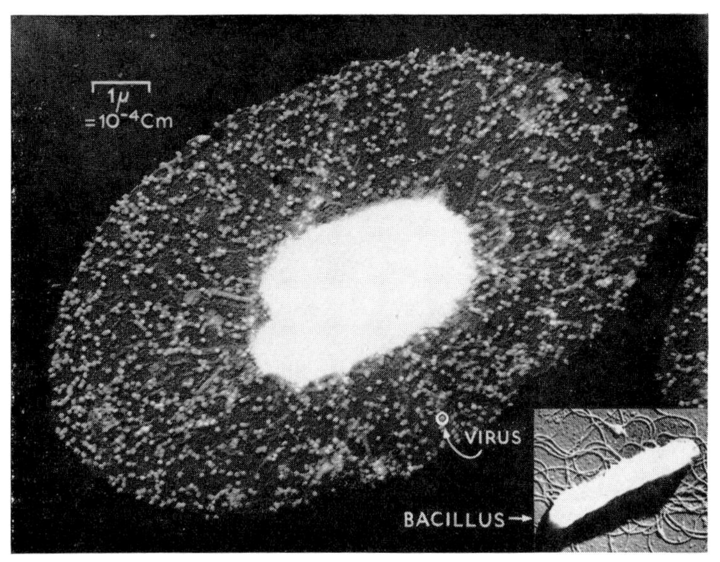

1. *Electron micrograph of a red blood corpuscle from a chick; the cell is infected with influenza virus. A bacillus is inset for comparison of size.* [p. 25]

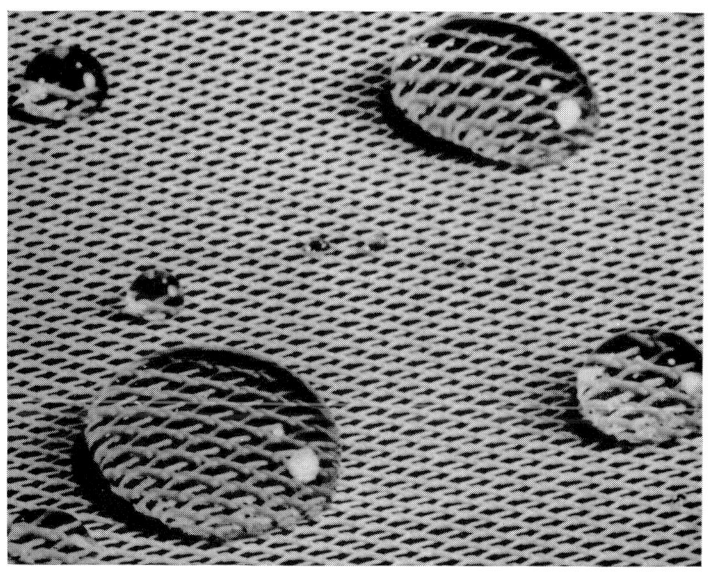

2. *The shape of drops of liquid on surfaces which they do not wet.* [p. 32]

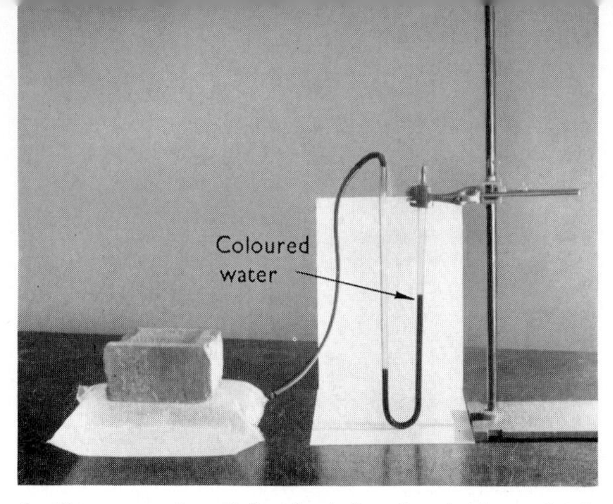

3. *Air pressure, in an inflated polythene bag, holds up a brick.* [p. 83]

4. *Hydraulic car-lift in operation. This is a centre-post lift capable of dealing with loads up to 3 tons. A pipe, below the floor, leads air at 150 lb/sq. in. from a compressed-air tank to the surface of oil in the underground cylinder which houses the ram. This pressure, transmitted by the oil to the base of the ram, gives a large upward thrust on the ram.* [p. 83]

2. Two spheres A and B, of weight 1 kgf and 2 kgf respectively, are attached to a light rod, one at each end. The centres of the spheres are 90 cm apart. Show that the arrangement will balance at a point which is 30 cm from B.

3. Estimate the moment of the forces required for each of the following operations: (*a*) screwing a screw into soft wood, (*b*) opening a water-tap which is rather stiff, (*c*) turning the steering wheel of a car. In each case show on a diagram your estimate of the dimensions of the arrangement and of the forces required.

4. A measuring cylinder is more stable if a lead ring is fitted round it near the base. Explain this. Refer in your answer to (*a*) the force required to knock it over, (*b*) the safe angle of tilt.

5. What is meant by stating that a body is in *stable equilibrium*? State, giving reasons, whether you consider the following to be examples of stable equilibrium: (*a*) a weight hanging from a cord, (*b*) a balanced see-saw, (*c*) a truck at rest on level rails, (*d*) the magnet of a compass.

6. What is meant by the *centre of gravity* of a body? What advantage, if any, is to be obtained by designing each of the following so that it has a low centre of gravity? (*a*) A motor-car. (*b*) A coal bucket. (*c*) A flagpole. Give reasons for your answers.

7. A string is used to hold up a metre rule, balanced horizontally with weights of 20 g and 140 g hanging from the 30-cm and 90-cm marks respectively. The rule weighs 100 g. Find the point at which the supporting spring is attached to the rule; calculate the tension in the spring.

8. A uniform bar 3 metres long, of weight 60 kgf, is held horizontally by two parallel cords, one attached to each end of the bar. Either cord will break under a force of 250 kgf. How far from the centre of the bar can a load of 300 kgf be hung without breaking a cord?

9. A square paving stone, of weight 50 kgf, lies flat on level ground. Calculate the least force required to begin to lift up one edge of the stone, the other edge still resting on the ground. Explain the fact that even less force is required to continue tilting the stone, provided that the force is applied in a suitable direction.

10. State the *principle of moments*. Describe how you would verify the principle experimentally.

A uniform metre rule, of weight 120 gf, has a 72-g weight hung from the 20-cm mark and a 6-g weight hung from the 90-cm mark. The rule is placed horizontally across a knife-edge at the 40-cm mark. Draw a labelled diagram of the arrangement, and deduce the direction in which the rule will tilt. Find the vertical force, applied at the 100-cm mark, which will hold the rule horizontal.

11. A trunk of weight 180 lbf is slung from a horizontal pole carried on the shoulders of two porters who are 6 ft apart. If the sling is 2 ft from the rear man, how much of the load is supported by each man? (Neglect the weight of the pole.)

CHAPTER 6

Resultants and Components. Parallelogram and Triangle of Forces

6.1. Resultant force. If two or more forces act on a body, the single force which would have the same effect on the body is known as the **resultant** of the forces.

The resultant cannot be found by the ordinary rules of arithmetic. This is because forces have direction as well as magnitude. They are vector quantities (see p. 7), and the rules for finding their resultant are the same as for finding a resultant velocity, which is also a vector quantity. A simple illustration of the effect of two inclined forces is given when a hanging weight is pulled sideways. Fig. 6.1 shows the effect produced in such a way that the forces involved can be measured. It shows a horizontal force of

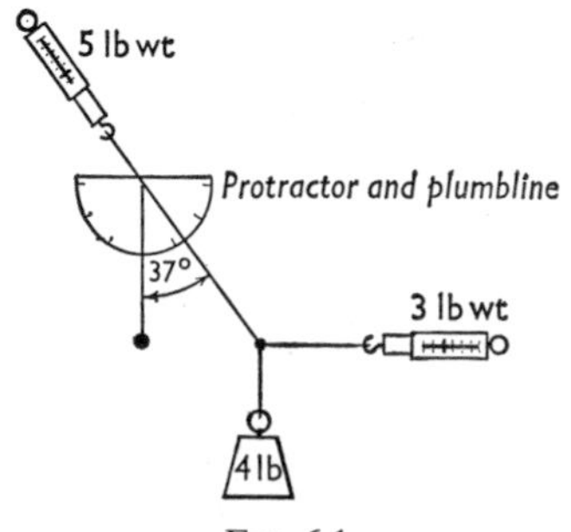

FIG. 6.1

3 lb wt recorded by the lower spring balance, and a vertical force of 4 lb wt due to the hanging load, producing a resultant effect which pulls the cord into a direction which lies between the vertical and the horizontal; and the upper spring balance shows that the effective pull on the cord is 5 lb wt In this case the resultant is a force of 5 lb wt acting in a direction which makes an angle of 37° with the vertical, as is shown by the protractor. This, and other experiments on forces, proves that the resultant force can be

found from a vector diagram using either the **parallelogram method** or the **triangle method.**

6.2. The parallelogram of forces. The parallelogram of forces is illustrated in Fig. 6.2 and can be expressed in words in the following manner.

If two forces P and Q, acting so that their lines of action pass through a point O, are represented in magnitude and direction by lines OA and OB then the diagonal OC of the parallelogram OACB represents the magnitude and direction, and also the line of action, of the resultant force (R).

Fig. 6.3 shows the method applied to the two pulls of the hanging weight example.

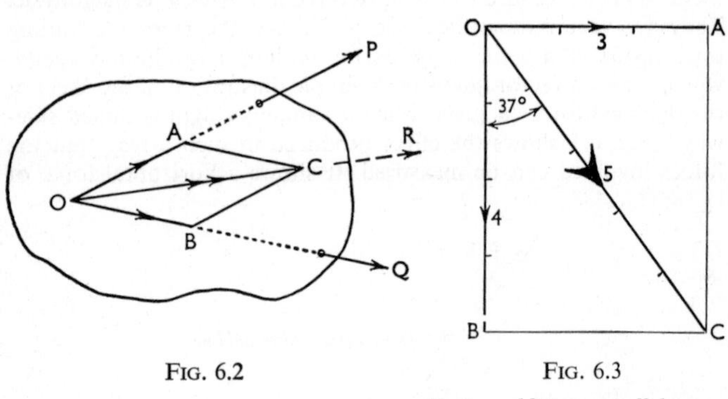

FIG. 6.2

FIG. 6.3

Vector addition, parallelogram method

6.3. Resultant by the triangle method. Suppose that a body is acted on by two forces P and Q as in Fig. 6.4. From point O draw a line OA to represent the direction of one of the forces (of P in Fig. 6.4) and make the length OA proportional to the magnitude of the force. From A draw a line AB on the same proportion-scale to represent the direction and the magnitude of the other force (the force Q in Fig. 6.4). Then the line OB represents in direction and in magnitude the resultant force R. Note that in this diagram the line AB represents the force Q but that it does not show its true line of action; it shows only how large the force is and what its direction is. Fig. 6.5 shows the triangle method used for the two pulls of the hanging weight example.

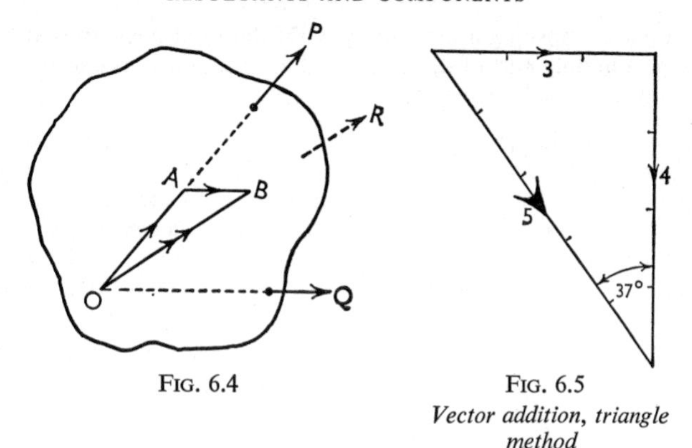

FIG. 6.4

FIG. 6.5
Vector addition, triangle method

6.4. Equilibrant. When a set of forces acts on a body so that there is a resultant force, a single force can be found which will neutralise the effects of these forces. This force is known as the **equilibrant,** because it is in equilibrium with the other forces. From this it follows that the equilibrant of a set of forces is equal and opposite to the resultant of the set of forces.

6.5. Components. Just as two forces can be replaced by a single force, the resultant, so any force can be replaced (either in actual fact, or for the purposes of purely theoretical argument) by two forces. The two are known as **components** of the original force. Although components can, if desired, be chosen in any two directions, it is often convenient to determine the components of a force in two directions at right angles; such components are known as **rectangular components** or **resolved parts.** They can be found by a vector diagram, and this has been done in Fig. 6.6. for the case

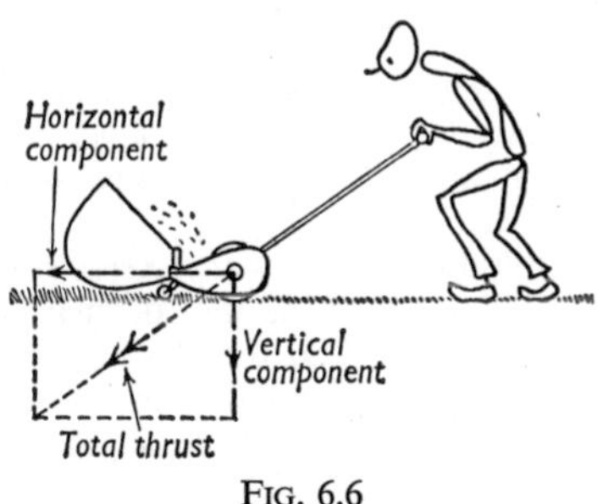

FIG. 6.6

of a person pushing a lawn mower. Of the total push exerted by the person only part of it, the horizontal component, is effective in driving the machine forwards.

6.6. The equilibrium of forces. Two forces can be in equilibrium only when they are equal in magnitude, opposite in direction, and when they have the same line of action. Thus if they are situated as shown in Fig .6.7(*b*) forming what is known as a **couple,** they will have a turning effect on the body and will set it in rotation. A couple has no resultant and cannot be balanced by a single force.

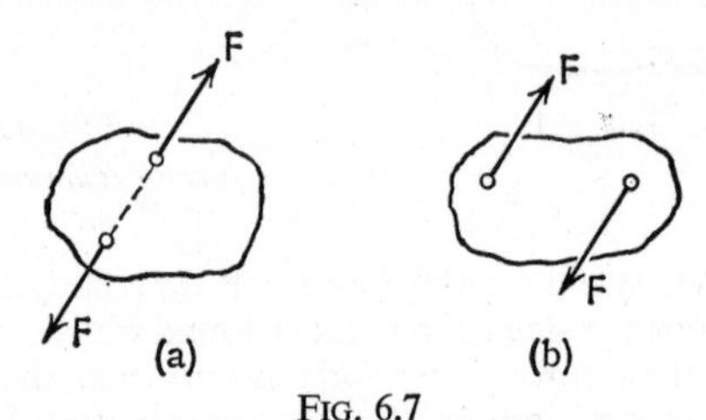

FIG. 6.7

(*a*) *Two forces in equilibrium.* (*b*) *Two forces, constituting a* couple, *not in equilibrium*

If three forces, whose lines of action are not parallel, are in equilibrium, then their lines of action must lie in one plane and must also meet at a point. Furthermore, three such forces in equilibrium can be represented in magnitude and direction by the sides of a triangle taken in order. This follows from the triangle method for the sum of vectors, and from the fact that any one of the three forces can be regarded as the equilibrant of the other two. The phrase 'taken in order' means that the arrows, indicating the directions of the forces, must follow each other round in the same direction—clockwise or anti-clockwise.

EXAMPLE 1. *A loaded sledge, of weight* 150 *kgf, is held on a smooth slope by a force which is parallel to the slope. Find* (a) *the force required,* (b) *the force which the slope exerts on the sledge. Angle of slope* = 20°.

Fig. 6.8*a* shows the three forces which keep the sledge in equilibrium. The force N is known as the 'normal reaction' of the ground. It acts at right angles to the slope because the slope is smooth, and it acts through the point of intersection of the other two forces. Fig. 6.8*b* shows the triangle of forces; the following instructions tell you how to draw it.

Draw the line AB to represent the force of 150 kgf, e.g. make it 150 mm long. Draw AN and BF parallel to the forces N and F respectively. They intersect at C, and ABC is the required force triangle. Measure the lengths of BC and AC, i.e. 51 mm and 141 mm respectively.

Then $F = 51$ kgf and $N = 141$ kgf.

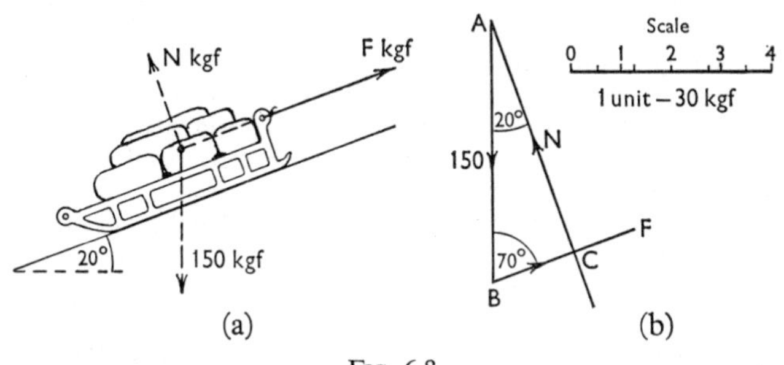

FIG. 6.8

SUMMARY

The **resultant** of two or more forces is the single force which has the same effect as the forces.

A force is a vector quantity and the resultant of a system of forces is their vector sum. Vector addition can be performed by a triangle or by a parallelogram method.

A system of forces which has no resultant is said to be in **equilibrium.** If a system of forces is not in equilibrium and if a single force added to the system produces equilibrium, then that force is called their **equilibrant;** it is equal and opposite to their resultant.

Questions

Note. If you use a scale diagram in any of the following problems, make the diagram as large as the paper will allow, at the same time choosing a scale which will be easy to interpret. On the diagram make a record of the scale, showing the relation between force and length of line. Squared paper is very suitable for these diagrams.

1. What is meant by the *resultant* of two forces? Find the magnitude and direction of the resultant of forces of 5 kgf and 12 kgf acting at right angles. In what circumstances would the resultant of these two forces be just over 7 kgf?

2. State the theorem known as the parallelogram of forces. Find the magnitude and direction of the resultant of two forces acting at an angle of 135°, the forces being 4·0 lbf and 3·5 lbf. Describe an experimental method of checking your result.

3. Forces of 3 units, 4 units and 5 units, whose lines of action meet at a point, are directed eastwards, northwards and westwards respectively. Find their resultant.

4. What is meant by the *equilibrant* of two forces? Find the equilibrant of a force of 4 kgf acting northwards and a force of 5 kgf acting in a direction 60° east of north.

5. What is meant by the *components* of a force? Illustrate your answer by a diagram. A taut wire under a tension of 25 kgf makes an angle of 60° with the horizontal. Find the vertical and horizontal components of the tension in the wire.

6. A light string passes horizontally from a fixed point Q, over a pulley P to a freely hanging known weight W. Explain how you could find the weight of a body (less than W) by hanging the body on the string between P and Q. What do you consider to be the greatest weight which you could measure with this arrangement?

7. A light cord hangs loosely, its ends tied to pegs which are on the same horizontal line. When a weight is hung from the mid-point of the cord, the cord becomes taut. Explain this, and show that the tension in the cord is much greater than the suspended weight if there is not much sag in the cord.

8. The mid-point of a piece of catapult rubber is pulled so that the two parts of the rubber make an angle of 70° with each other. If the force of the pull is 5 kgf and acts mid-way between the two parts of the rubber, what is the tension in each part of the rubber?

9. A boat is towed, from the bank, at a steady speed along a straight canal. If the tow-rope makes an angle of 15° with the bank and its pull on the boat is 120 lbf, what are the components of this pull in directions along and perpendicular to the canal? Suggest the causes which are preventing (*a*) acceleration of the boat, (*b*) drift of the boat towards the bank.

10. A weight, hanging on cord, is pulled so as to make the cord have an angle of 30° from the vertical. Do you consider that more pull is required if the direction of pull is at right angles to the final position of the cord, rather than horizontal? Give your reasoning, and show how you would check your answer (*a*) by experiment, (*b*) by a calculation or a scale diagram.

CHAPTER 7

Work. Energy. Power

7.1. Work. The term work has, in scientific language, a special meaning. It is used in connection with the action and the movement of a force; the work that a force does is measured by the **product of the force and the distance which the force moves in its own direction.** Thus if a load is dragged a horizontal distance of 5 metres by a steady horizontal force of 3 kgf the work done is $3 \times 5 = 15$ units; if it is dragged 15 metres by the same force the work done by the force is $3 \times 15 = 45$ units.

Note that work is measured in terms of **force** and **distance,** not in terms of force and time. You do work when you stretch a spring; but no work is done in keeping it stretched, even though you may become tired in doing so. Note too that the measurement is made in terms of the distance moved **in the direction of the force.** So that the work done in lifting weights is measured in terms of the **vertical distance** which the weight has been lifted. Suppose that you lift a heavy suitcase vertically from the floor and put it on a table; you do a certain amount of work. You may, however, prefer to stand back from the table and swing the suitcase in an arc up to the table top. Though the case will have moved through a greater distance, you will still have done the same amount of work, because it is the vertical distance which counts in the calculation of work done against the downward force of weight.

7.2. Units of work. The gravitational units of work are based on the lifting of weight. Thus a **foot-pound** is the work done when a 1-lb weight is lifted vertically 1 ft, starting from rest and ending at rest. Similarly a **metre-kilogram** (m-kgf) is the work done in lifting 1 kg vertically 1 metre.

EXAMPLE 1. *Calculate the work done in the following instances:* (a) *A* 14-*lb weight is lifted, vertically,* 3 *ft,* (b) a 14-*lb weight is dragged* 3 *ft across a level bench against a friction force of* 4 *lbf,* (c) *a* 14-*lb weight is dragged* 5 *yd up a smooth slope of* 1 *in* 20.

(*a*) Work done against gravity $= 14 \times 3 = 42$ foot-pounds.

(*b*) Work done against gravity = 0.
Work done against friction = 4 × 3 = 12 foot-pounds.
Total = 12 foot-pounds.

(*c*) The weight will have risen a vertical height of 15/20 = 0·75 ft. Thus the work done against gravity = 14 × 0·75 = 10·5 foot-pounds. (No work will have been done against friction as it is a smooth slope.)

The word foot-pound is really a shortened version of foot-poundweight. Because the force of a poundweight (lbf) varies slightly with position on the earth's surface, the foot-pound (ft lbf) is a slightly variable unit. The variation is so slight that it scarcely matters in large-scale calculations such as occur in engineering. A precise standard of work, commonly used in laboratory measurements and in electrical engineering, is the joule.

A **joule** is equal to the work done by a force of one newton (see p. 17) moving a distance of one metre in its own direction. For this reason a joule is often referred to as a **metre-newton.** A newton is nearly 100 gf, so if you lift 100 g through a height of 1 metre you will have done approximately one joule of work. This is very nearly equivalent to $\frac{3}{4}$ foot-pound.

7.3. Energy. Energy is defined as the **capacity for doing work.** Anything which can do work is said to possess energy, and the work which it can do is a measure of the energy which it possesses. If you lift a load of 20 kgf through a height of 2 metres you will have done 40 m-kgf units of work (or 40 × 9·8 = 392 joules, at a place where $g = 9{\cdot}8$ metre/s²). This is therefore a measure of the muscular energy which you have put into the job. It is also a measure of the extra energy of the weight because of its raised position; suitably geared to a machine it could do 40 m-kgf or 392 joules of work in falling back to its original position.

Energy exists in many different forms, and examples are given in the following paragraphs.

Potential energy. Potential energy is stored energy. A raised weight and a wound-up spring have potential energy; both can be made to do work by releasing the stored energy. Large amounts of potential energy are available at waterfalls, and in many parts of the world the energy of natural or artificial waterfalls has been used for hydro-electric power (the generation of electrical power from water-power). At the Niagara Falls a drop of 160 ft is used to provide nearly half a million horse-power. At hydro-electric stations the water is led through pipes, called *penstocks*, to the turbines which drive the generators (Fig. 7.1).

The energy from chemical reactions, such as occur in explosives or in rocket propulsion, is another example of stored or potential energy.

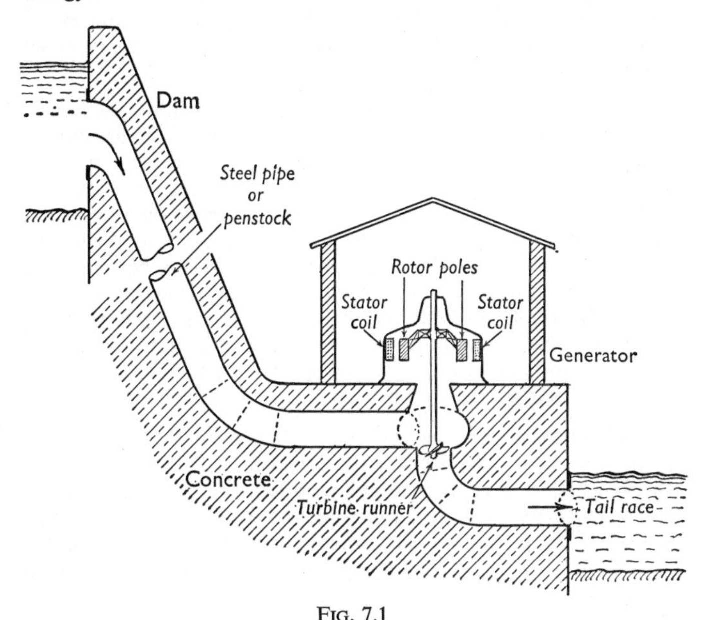

FIG. 7.1

Hydro-electric station. Generation of electrical power from water power

Kinetic energy. The kinetic energy of a body is the energy it possesses because of its motion; it is measured by the work done in bringing the body to rest. One example of this is a moving hammer head which, in driving a nail into wood, does work against the resistance of the wood. A rotating fly-wheel has kinetic energy; thus in a motor-cycle engine, the fly-wheel does work in driving the machine and in working the strokes of the engine between one explosion stroke and the next.

Heat energy. The hot gases from the explosion in a petrol engine and the hot steam in a steam engine do work on the machines which they drive. The exhaust gases are not as hot as the exploded mixture. Some heat is lost in warming up the cylinder and in other heat losses; but some of the available heat has been converted to an equivalent amount of work. Heat is therefore regarded as a form of energy; the available energy from hot bodies comes from the kinetic energy of their molecules.

Electrical energy. The energy of an electric current is evident in the heat which it gives when it flows through a wire, and in the work which is done when an electric motor is driven from an electrical supply.

7.4. Energy from the sun. The energy of the sun's radiation is enormous, and nearly all our sources of energy can be attributed, directly or indirectly, to the sun. Heat from the sun provides energy which evaporates water on the earth, and the upward currents of warm damp air give rise to clouds. These have considerable potential energy, and some of it—in the form of high-level water supplies—is used by man for hydro-electric schemes. Light from the sun is necessary for plant growth, supplying the necessary energy for photosynthesis, the process in green plants whereby substances such as starch, sugar and wood are synthesised from carbon dioxide and water. The energy absorbed in photosynthesis is used by man in the food he eats and in the fuel he burns.

7.5. The conservation of energy. One of the most notable discoveries of the nineteenth century was the **principle of the conservation of energy** which states that energy cannot be created or destroyed, but may change its form. A simple illustration of this occurs in the swinging of a pendulum. The potential energy of the bob, due to its height, is continually changing as the level of the bob changes; so too is the kinetic energy due to its motion, which is greatest at the bottom of the swing. It is found that at all stages of the swing the sum of the potential and kinetic energies is constant. The same applies to a freely falling body, which loses potential energy as it falls but gains an equal amount of kinetic energy. But when it hits something and comes to rest the energy is seemingly lost. What actually happens is that heat is produced, and the kinetic energy of molecular motion is increased. When an electrical generator is used to light lamps, the work done in turning the generator is converted to electrical energy which is then transformed into heat energy and light energy.

Like many another theory or principle, that of the conservation of energy has had to be altered since it was first put forward. The changes which take place in atomic piles give an enormous output of energy. This energy can be traced to the disappearance of the mass of some of the matter which makes up the pile. Mass can be converted into energy, and matter itself must be regarded as one of the forms of energy. Conversely, energy itself has mass. Particles moving at speeds approaching that of light (3×10^{10} cm/s or 3×10^{8} m/s) have more inertia than they have when at rest, i.e. a greater force is required to give them the same acceleration; they have more mass because of the mass-equivalent of their kinetic energy.

Einstein derived an equation for the mass m of an energy E. If c=speed of light in space

$$m=\frac{E}{c^2} \quad . \quad . \quad . \quad . \quad . \quad (1)$$

whence $$E=mc^2 \quad . \quad . \quad . \quad . \quad . \quad (2)$$

From equation (1) it follows that the mass of a quantity of energy is small, because c is so large. Equation (2) shows that if matter is converted to other forms of energy, then large amounts of energy are obtainable from small masses—9×10^{20} ergs from 1 g, 9×10^{16} joules from 1 kg.

7.6. Units of energy. Energy can be measured in the same units as work. **Potential energy, kinetic energy** and **electrical energy** are commonly expressed in these units. Heat energy is usually measured in calories or in British thermal units (Btu); knowing the mechanical equivalent of heat, examples of which are given below, the work available from a quantity of heat can be calculated. Thus:

1 cal. of heat converted to work can do 4·185 joules of work.

1 Btu of heat converted to work can do 778 foot-pounds of work.

Similarly there is an energy-equivalent of mass, viz. 1 g of mass is equivalent to 9×10^{20} ergs or 9×10^{13} joules.

Calculation of kinetic energy. The kinetic energy of a body moving with a speed v can be calculated, either from the work which must be done to give it this speed or from the work done in stopping it.

It is equal to $\frac{1}{2}mv^2$ absolute units, where m=the mass of the body.

Consider a force to act on a mass, which is initially at rest, moved as shown in Fig. 7.2. Let the resulting acceleration be a; suppose the mass to move a distance s and gain a speed v. Then $v^2=2as$.

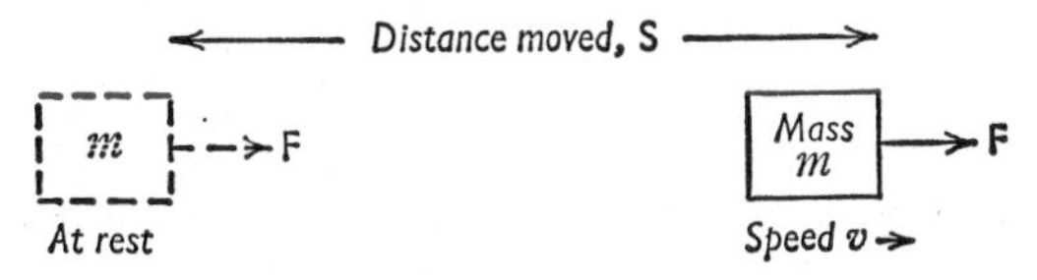

FIG. 7.2

$\therefore$ Work done $= Fs = mas$

$$= \frac{mv^2}{2}$$

$$\therefore \text{Kinetic energy} = \frac{mv^2}{2}$$

Since the formula $F = ma$ only applies when F represents the number of absolute units of force (poundals, dynes, newtons) it follows that the energy is also in absolute units (ft-poundals, ergs, joules).

In using this relationship it is therefore advisable to use one of the three main systems of units: f.p.s., c.g.s., m.k.s.

EXAMPLE 2. *Calculate the kinetic energy of* (a) *a mass of* 2 *kg moving with a speed of* 6 *metres/s,* (b) *the molecules, moving at* 300 *metres/s, in* 4·00 *g of mercury vapour.*

(a) Kinetic energy $= \frac{2 \times 3 \times 3}{2} = 9$ metre-newtons or joules

(b) On the m.k.s. system, $4{\cdot}00 \text{ g} = 4{\cdot}00 \times 10^{-3}$ kg

$$\therefore \text{Kinetic energy} = \frac{4{\cdot}00 \times 10^{-3} \times 9 \times 10^4}{2}$$

$$= 180 \text{ joules}$$

On the c.g.s. system, $300 \text{ m/s} = 3 \times 10^4$ cm/s

$$\therefore \text{Kinetic energy} = \frac{4{\cdot}00 \times 9 \times 10^8}{2}$$

$$= 1{\cdot}80 \times 10^9 \text{ ergs}$$

7,7. Power. Power is defined as the **rate of doing work** or rate of expenditure of energy. Power is therefore expressed in such units as foot-pounds/s, joules/s. Neither of these is a very rapid rate of working; larger units have been chosen which are multiples of them.

1 joule/s = 1 watt
1000 watts = 1 kilowatt (kW)
550 ft lbf/s = 1 horse-power (hp)

The term **horse-power** came into use in the earlier half of the nineteenth century when steam engines were beginning to replace horses for driving the pumps in mines, and when it was naturally important to 'rate' the performance of a given engine. James Watt tested some horses by making them work a machine for pulling a weight up a shaft. He estimated that each did 22,000 foot-pounds per min; he added the rather large proportion of 50% for work done against friction and so estimated

$$1 \text{ hp} = 33{,}000 \text{ foot-pounds/min}$$

(The **metric hp,** defined as 75 metre-kgf/s, is very nearly the same as the British hp; it is actually 0·984 British hp.)

$$1 \text{ hp} = 746 \text{ watts, or approximately } \tfrac{3}{4} \text{ kilowatt.}$$

The power-input to electrical machines is found from the voltage across their terminals and the current flowing. The volt is defined in such a way that the product of the voltage across the terminals and the current in amperes gives the power supplied in watts.

When power is supplied to a machine, the rate at which the machine does work is never as great as the input of power. Some power is lost in the transmission, generally as the result of friction. The ratio

$$\text{Output of power} \div \text{Input of power}$$

is known as the mechanical efficiency (ϵ) of the machine. The ratio ϵ is always less than 1, i.e. less than 100%; 100% efficiency is an ideal which cannot be obtained in practice. If an engine is driven at the rate of 10 hp and itself does work at the rate of 7 hp then its efficiency is 0·7 or 70%.

EXAMPLE 3. *Estimation of the horse-power developed by a person running up a flight of steps.*

The following results were obtained by timing, with a stop-watch, the ascent of a flight of steps by a boy of weight 142 lbf.

27 steps, each of vertical height 8 in
Total rise = 18 ft
Time taken = 4·1 s
Weight lifted = 142 lbf

$$\text{hp} = \frac{142 \times 18}{4{\cdot}1 \times 550} = 1{\cdot}1$$

EXAMPLE 4. *To estimate the horse-power developed by a cyclist.*

The cyclist is towed, by a runner, or another cyclist, at a steady rate along a level stretch of road, with a spring balance in the tow-rope near the handle-bars. The rider notes the average balance reading (which gives the towing force, mainly used to overcome air-resistance). Another observer times the journey of the cycle over a measured distance to find the average speed.

Towing force = 4·0 kgf

Distance travelled = 50 metres

Time taken = 14·2 s

$$\text{Rate of working} = \frac{4 \times 50}{14{\cdot}2} \text{ metre kgf/s}$$

$$= \frac{4 \times 50}{14{\cdot}2 \times 75} \text{ metric hp}$$

$$= 0{\cdot}187 \text{ metric hp}$$

SUMMARY

Work = Force × distance moved in the direction of the force.

Energy is the capacity for doing work. It is commonly measured in the same units as work. Other units, such as heat units, can be expressed in terms of their work equivalent, e.g. 1 Btu is equivalent to 778 ft-lbf, 1 calorie is equivalent to 4·185 joules.

Energy can exist in different forms. As far as is known at present, energy cannot be created or destroyed.

Kinetic energy, energy which a body possesses because of its motion.

$$\text{Kinetic energy} = \tfrac{1}{2}mv^2 \text{ absolute units}$$

Power is the rate of doing work.

1 hp = 33,000 ft-lbf/min. = 550 ft-lbf/s

(The metric hp, defined as 75 metre-kgf/s, is very nearly the same as the British hp; it is actually 0·984 British hp.)

1 watt = 1 joule/s   1 kilowatt = 1000 watts.

The **mechanical efficiency** of a machine is defined as the ratio

$$\frac{\text{Output of work}}{\text{Input of work}}$$

This is also equal to

$$\frac{\text{Output of power}}{\text{Input of power}}$$

Questions

(Take g, where necessary, as 32 ft/s² or as 9·8 metres/s².)

1. Define the terms *work* and *energy*. A body of weight 7 kgf hangs on a cord with its centre of gravity 2 metres below the point of support. It is set swinging so that the cord swings through a total angle of 120°. Find the energy required to set it swinging.

2. Calculate the work done in each of the following examples. (*a*) A 7-lb weight is lifted, vertically, 4 ft. (*b*) A 7-lb weight is dragged 4 ft across a level bench, the friction force opposing the motion being 2 lbf. (*c*) A 7-lb weight is dragged 30 ft up a smooth slope of 1 in 15.

3. Distinguish between *potential energy* and *kinetic energy*. Give one example of each.

A 10-kg weight is supported 25 metres above the ground. What is its potential energy? If the weight is allowed to fall freely, what will be, at the moment when it is 15 metres above the ground, (*a*) its potential energy, (*b*) its speed, (*c*) its kinetic energy?

4. What is meant by the principle of the *conservation of energy*? The energy of waterfalls is primarily due to the sun. Justify this statement, giving an account of the energy changes involved.

5. If it requires 1400 foot-pounds of work to operate a machine in order that it may lift a mass of 112 lb through a vertical distance of 10 ft, what is the efficiency of the machine?

6. Calculate the work needed to lift a load of 60 kgf through a vertical distance of 2·5 metres using a machine which has an efficiency of 75%.

7. Define the term *horse-power*. Convert to horse-power (*a*) 110 foot-pounds/s, (*b*) 132,000 foot-pounds/min.

8. Express the following in *metric horse-power* (75 metre-kgf/s). (*a*) 100 kg lifted 25 cm in 4·0 s, (*b*) 150 g lifted 300 cm in 0·20 s, (*c*) 300 litres of water lifted 10·0 metres in 2·50 s, (*d*) 750 watts.

9. Calculate the kinetic energy of (*a*) a cyclist, of mass 65 kg, travelling at 8 m/s, (*b*) a car of mass 800 kg travelling at 30 m/s, (*c*) a bullet of mass 2 g travelling at 500 m/s, (*d*) a truck of mass 9000 kg travelling at 40 cm/s.

Calculate the forces required to stop the motions of (*b*) and (*d*) in a distance of 10 metres.

10. Calculate the kinetic energy of the molecules in 1 g of a gas when the speed of the molecules is (*a*) 400 m/s, (*b*) 600 m/s.

11. Calculate, in kilowatts, the rate at which energy is produced in an atomic pile which converts 1 milligram of mass into energy in 100 s.

12. A uniform cylinder, 0·800 m long and 0·300 m in diameter, lies on a horizontal floor; its weight is 250 kgf. One end is slowly raised until the cylinder stands vertically. Calculate (*a*) the least vertical force required to begin the lifting, (*b*) the *gain* in potential energy of the cylinder.

Write brief notes on the changes in energy which occur when a vertical cylinder is tilted and then released so that it rocks to and fro.

CHAPTER 8

Simple Machines

8.1. Terms used in connection with machines

Effort. The force applied to operate the machine.

Load. The resistance which the machine overcomes. This is often a weight to be lifted, but is sometimes a frictional force as, for example, when things have to be towed.

Mechanical advantage (or force ratio) (m.a.). This is defined as the ratio

$$\frac{\textbf{Load (L)}}{\textbf{Effort (E)}}$$

It is found by experimental test on the machine and is usually quoted for a particular load. In any machine which is affected by friction or by the weight of the moving parts the mechanical advantage increases with increasing load—but it never exceeds the velocity ratio of the machine.

Velocity ratio (v.r.). This is the ratio

$$\frac{\textbf{Distance moved by the effort (e)}}{\textbf{Corresponding distance moved by the load (l)}}$$

This indicates the gearing of the machine. It is a feature of the design of the machine and is unaffected by friction or the weight of the moving parts.

Mechanical efficiency (ϵ). No machine will do more work than the work which is done to operate it. Work done against friction or in raising the weight of the moving parts results in a loss of mechanical energy. When the input and output of work are more nearly equal, the greater is the efficiency of the machine. The efficiency is defined as the ratio

$$\frac{\text{Work done by the machine}}{\text{Work done on the machine}} \text{ or } \frac{\text{Output of work}}{\text{Input of work}}$$

The efficiency is expressed as a fraction, as a decimal, or as a percentage. Thus an efficiency of $\frac{3}{4}$, or 0·75, is an efficiency of 75%. From the definition of work:

$$\epsilon = \frac{L \times l}{E \times e} = \frac{L}{E} \div \frac{e}{l} = \text{m.a.} \div \text{v.r.}$$

and since ϵ cannot be greater than 1, the m.a. cannot be greater than the v.r., and will be equal to it only in a perfect machine. The v.r. of a machine therefore gives some clue to the force-ratio; in an ideal machine the two will be equal, but in general the force-ratio will be the smaller.

8.2. Pulley systems. When a taut cord goes over a frictionless pulley, the cord has the same tension on each side of the pulley. When the parts of the cord on each side of the pulley are parallel, their tensions give a double force on the pulley. For example, the pull in the rigging of small boats is sometimes increased by the method shown in Fig. 8.1, where the pulley receives nearly twice the force of the effort. Fig. 8.2 shows the same idea used for haulage, the pull on the boat being (in the absence of friction) twice the pull of the effort.

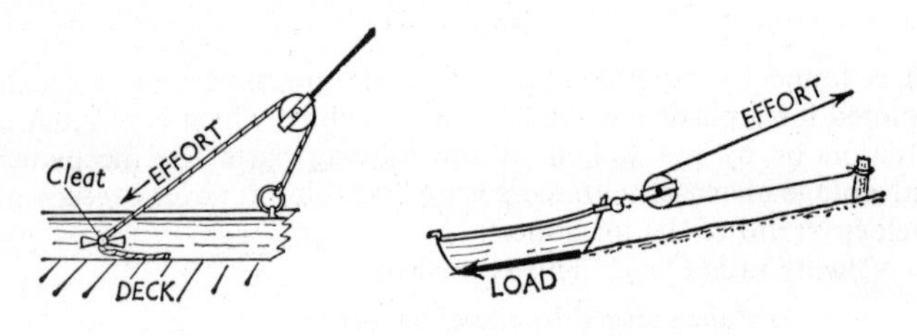

FIG. 8.1
Boat rigging

FIG. 8.2
Single pulley with a V.R. of 2

The extra pull to be had by passing a rope round a pulley is used in pulley hoists, one type of which is shown in Fig. 8.3 (*a*) and (*b*). The upper double pulley block is stationary, while the lower double pulley block is attached to the load. The rope is fastened to the underside of the top block and passes round the four pulleys as shown, so that the effort is applied fourfold. Thus in a weightless, frictionless system the mechanical advantage would be 4; in practice, it works out to be less than 4, because of friction and the weight of the bottom block. But the velocity ratio, which is not affected by such matters, is always 4. If the load is lifted 1 unit, the effort has to haul in 1 unit of rope from each of the 4 sections between the pulleys, so the movement of the effort is 4 units.

8.3. Windlass or wheel and axle. Fig. 8.4 illustrates an experimental test on this type of machine. A 3-kg weight hanging from the axle was found to require weights (on the effort side) of 750 g or 0·75 kg to pull up the load at a steady speed. So the mechanical advantage was $3{\cdot}0 \div 0{\cdot}75 = 4$. The velocity ratio of the machine is equal to $D \div d$, the ratio of the diameters of the wheel and axle respectively. Thus if the machine was turned round once, the load would rise

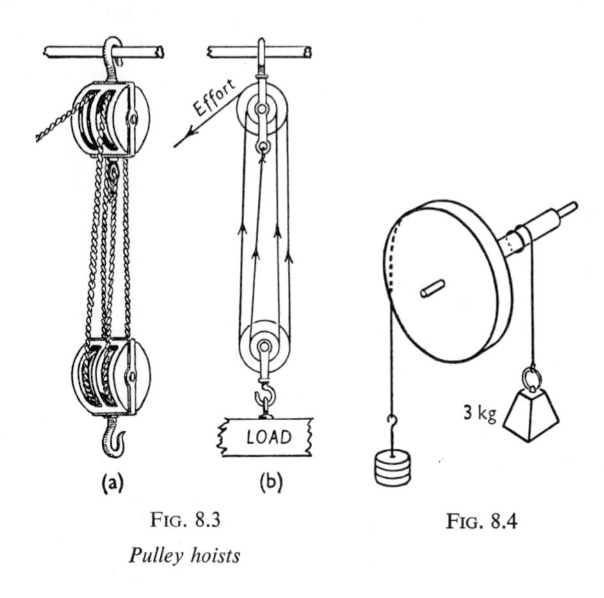

FIG. 8.3
Pulley hoists

FIG. 8.4

πd, the circumference of the axle, and the effort would move πD, the circumference of the wheel; and $\pi D \div \pi d = D \div d$. In this particular machine the ratio was 5. So the efficiency of the machine was $4 \div 5 = 0{\cdot}8$ or 80%.

8.4. Levers. Levers are among the most efficient of simple machines. They are commonly pivoted at or near their centre of gravity so that little energy is wasted in moving the weight of the lever itself, and the friction at the pivot is usually small in comparison with the load. The forces involved in the action of levers can usually be calculated by application of the principle of moments. Levers are generally classified according to the position of the fulcrum or pivot in relation to the positions of the load and effort. Illustrations are given in Fig. 8.5.

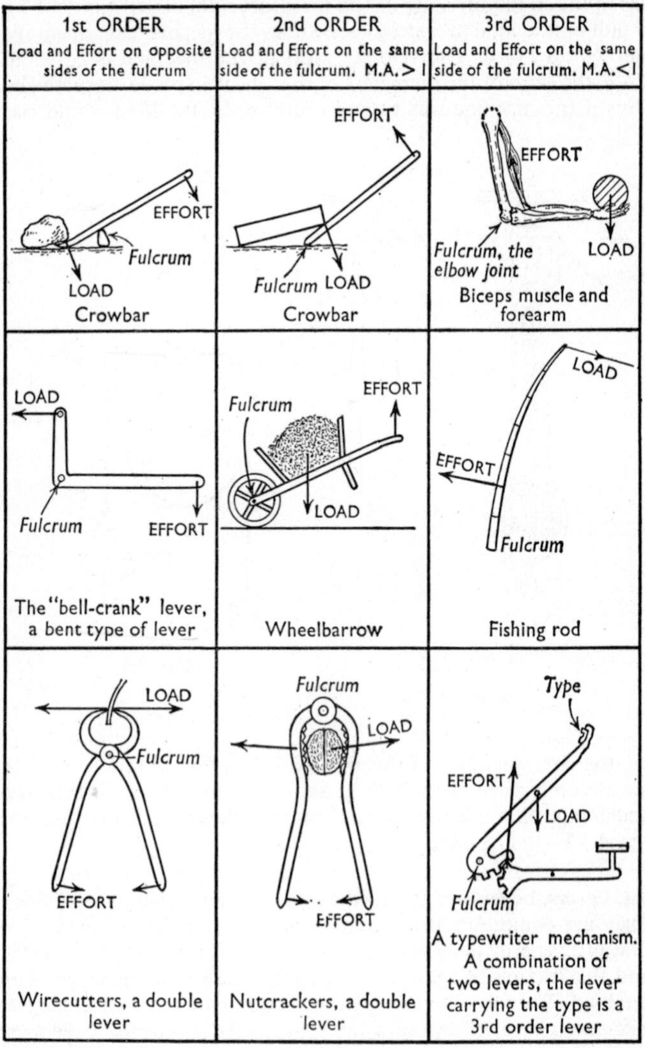

1st ORDER Load and Effort on opposite sides of the fulcrum	2nd ORDER Load and Effort on the same side of the fulcrum. M.A. > 1	3rd ORDER Load and Effort on the same side of the fulcrum. M.A. < 1
EFFORT Fulcrum LOAD Crowbar	EFFORT Fulcrum LOAD Crowbar	EFFORT Fulcrum, the elbow joint LOAD Biceps muscle and forearm
LOAD Fulcrum EFFORT The "bell-crank" lever, a bent type of lever	EFFORT Fulcrum LOAD Wheelbarrow	LOAD EFFORT Fulcrum Fishing rod
LOAD Fulcrum EFFORT Wirecutters, a double lever	Fulcrum LOAD EFFORT Nutcrackers, a double lever	Type EFFORT LOAD Fulcrum A typewriter mechanism. A combination of two levers, the lever carrying the type is a 3rd order lever

FIG. 8.5
Types of lever mechanism

SUMMARY

A machine enables work to be done more easily or more quickly; but it does not do more work than is used to operate it.

Mechanical advantage, a force ratio, is defined as Load ÷ Effort. It is found by doing an experimental test on the machine.

Velocity ratio, a ratio of the speed at which the effort moves to the speed at which the load moves, is usually defined as

$$\frac{\textbf{Distance moved by the effort}}{\textbf{Distance moved by or against the load}}$$

Velocity ratio is determined by the way in which the machine is designed; it is unaffected by friction or the weight of the moving parts.

Efficiency, or **mechanical efficiency,** is defined as

$$\frac{\textbf{Work done by the machine}}{\textbf{Work done on the machine}} \text{ or } \frac{\textbf{Output of work}}{\textbf{Input of work}}$$

and can be proved to be equal to the ratio

$$\frac{\text{Mechanical Advantage}}{\text{Velocity Ratio}}$$

Loss of efficiency is due to work done against friction or work done in raising the weight of parts of the machine.

Questions

1. What is meant by the terms *load* and *effort* as applied to machines? Illustrate your answer by reference to (*a*) a pulley hoist, (*b*) a bicycle, (*c*) a boat driven by a hand-operated paddle-wheel, (*d*) a nutcracker.

2. Define the terms *mechanical advantage* and *velocity ratio*. How, if at all, would you expect the magnitudes of these ratios to alter as a result of oiling a machine? Give reasons for your answers.

3. Define the term *efficiency* as applied to machines. Explain the fact that the efficiency of a pulley hoist is less than unity. Calculate the efficiency of a machine if 7000 foot-pounds of work has to be done to make it lift 2240 lb through a vertical distance of 2 ft.

4. Calculate the work done by a person in lifting a weight of 5·60 kgf through a vertical height of 1·20 metres, (*a*) without the aid of a machine, (*b*) using a machine which has an efficiency of 70%.

5. A pulley hoist with a velocity ratio 4, and a mechanical advantage 3, is used to raise a load of 120 lbf through a vertical

distance of 20 ft. Calculate (*a*) the effort required, (*b*) the distance moved by the effort, (*c*) the work done by the effort, (*d*) the work done by the machine, (*e*) the efficiency of the machine.

6. A machine is operated by a 100-kg weight which falls 10·0 metres and lifts a load of 500 kgf. Calculate (*a*) the loss of potential energy of the driving weight, (*b*) the greatest vertical height through which the load can be raised.

7. A simple weighing machine is made of a uniform bar 100 cm long, of weight 5·0 kgf, and pivoted at a frictionless pivot 2·00 cm from one end. Find the weight that must be suspended at the end of the long arm so as to balance a load of 365 kg suspended at the end of the short arm.

8. Calculate the work which must be done to operate a pulley hoist, which is 80% efficient, to lift a load of 120 lb through a vertical distance of 20 ft.

9. In order to raise a load of 400 kgf through a distance of 4 metres with a certain machine it is found necessary to apply an effort of 100 kgf through a distance of 20 metres. Calculate (*a*) the mechanical advantage, (*b*) the efficiency.

10. Describe, with the aid of diagrams, three examples of the use of levers in common life. Choose examples in which at least one has a mechanical advantage which is less than unity.

CHAPTER 9

Pressure

9.1. Force spread over an area. Some of the effects of force depend on the area over which the force acts. This is particularly so in the penetration or in the cutting or deforming of materials. When you push a drawing-pin into a board, the penetration is due to the small area of the pin-point; the fact that your thumb is not harmed is due to the larger area of the pin-head. The cutting ability of a knife depends on the sharpness of its edge; the sharper the edge, the smaller is the area of cross-section and the greater is the penetration due to the applied force. Sometimes we wish to avoid penetration, and then the area over which the force acts is increased; for example in ski-ing, the sportsman spreads his weight over runners with ten times the area of his walking-boots and so does not sink at all deeply into the snow.

The distribution of a force over an area is known as a **stress;** if the force is a push-force or **thrust** the stress it causes is called a **pressure,** and the pressure is measured by the **thrust acting per unit area.** Dividing the number of units of thrust by the number of units of area gives a measure of the pressure exerted. This is expressed by the following equation

$$\textbf{Pressure} = \frac{\textbf{Thrust}}{\textbf{Area}}$$

Some of the units in which pressure can be measured are therefore lb wt. per sq. in. (lbf/sq. in.), kg wt. per sq. cm (kgf/sq. cm), dynes per sq. cm, newtons per sq. metre.

EXAMPLE 1. *A rectangular glass block* 12 *cm* × 6 *cm* × 2 *cm weighs* 360 *g. Calculate the greatest pressure which it can exert when resting on a horizontal surface.*

The greatest pressure will occur when it is resting on the face with the smallest area, i.e. the 6 × 2 face of area 12 sq. cm.

$$\text{Pressure} = 360 \div 12 = 30 \text{ gf/sq. cm}$$

EXAMPLE 2. *Over what area must a force of* 10 *kgf act in order to produce a pressure of* 50 *kgf/sq. cm?*

If A sq. cm. is the area

$$50=\frac{10}{A}$$

$$50A=10$$

whence

$$A=\frac{10}{50}=0{\cdot}2$$

Hence the required area is 0·2 sq. cm

EXAMPLE 3. *Air at a pressure of* 3 *lbf/sq. in is applied to push a piston which has an area of* 1 *sq. ft. Calculate the thrust on the piston.*

Let T lbf be the thrust; then since there are 144 sq. in to the sq. ft.

$$3=\frac{T}{144} \text{ whence } T=432$$

So that the thrust is 432 lbf.

9.2. Pressure in fluids. Fluids, because of their weight, can exert a pressure. Although air has quite a small density, the pressure of the air around us is about 15 lbf/sq. in or 1 kgf/sq. cm. At very great ocean depths pressure is very large indeed, about 1 ton force per sq. in at the depth of 1 mile. As might be expected, liquid pressure increases regularly with depth. It is found that fluid pressure is the same in all directions at a given depth, acting perpendicularly to any surface which the fluid touches. You can detect the upwards and sideways pressures of mercury when you push your finger into it; and if you put your hand into a plastic bag and then push the bag into a bowl of water the side pressures of the water are felt as they push the bag against your hand. Fig. 9.1 shows a can of water, with equal-sized holes in it, being used to illustrate some of the features of fluid pressure. The directions of the water jets show that the water pressure is at right angles to the surface of the vessel; the relative speeds of the jets show that there is an increase of pressure with depth.

Fig. 9.2 shows a liquid of density d g/c.c. in a vertical cylindrical vessel filled to a height h cm. If the area of the base is A sq. cm, the volume of the liquid is hA c.c.

Downthrust = weight of liquid = hAd gf
Pressure of liquid (p) = $hAd \div A$ gf/sq. cm
= hd gf/sq. cm

$$\mathbf{p = h \times d}$$

Pressure = Vertical height × density

(If the height is measured in ft and the density in lb/cu. ft, pressure is given in lbf/sq. ft.)

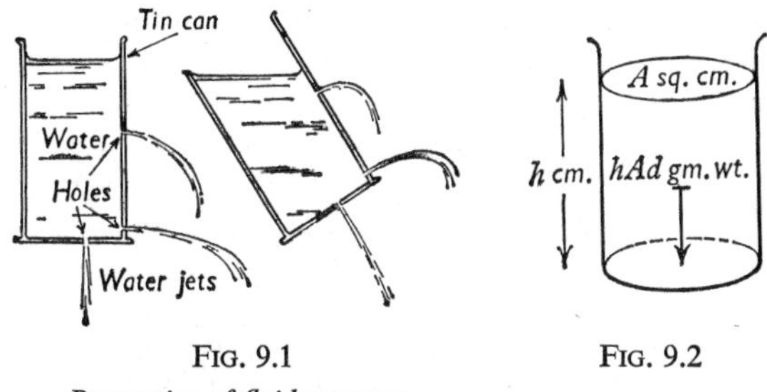

FIG. 9.1

Properties of fluid pressure shown by water-jets

FIG. 9.2

This formula has been derived by considering a vessel with vertical sides, so that there is no downthrust or upthrust from the sides of the vessel to consider. But fluid pressure is quite independent of the shape and cross-section of the containing vessel. The fact can be tested experimentally by means of the apparatus shown in Fig. 9.3. A bottle with the bottom removed is arranged with its mouth downward, and a rubber membrane is tied securely across the mouth; a cork and glass tube fit into the neck of the bottle. Water is poured to a convenient level X into the tube, and a pointer is used to indicate the level to which the membrane is depressed. Then the cork and tube are removed. It is found that the membrane rises, although there is the same weight of water above it. If water is now poured into the bottle to reach the level X it is found that the membrane is depressed to the same position as before.

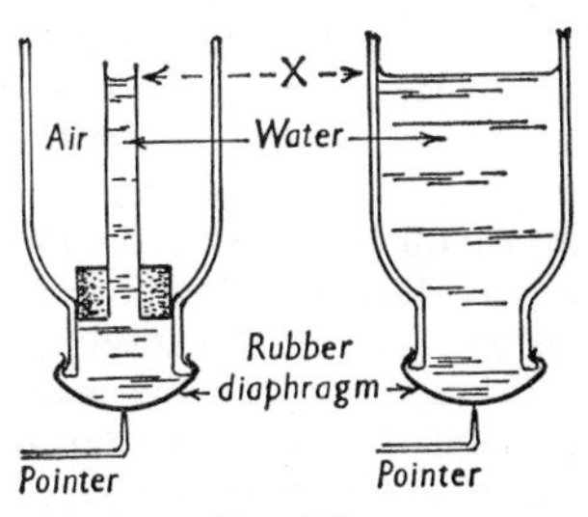

FIG. 9.3

Equal pressures from different weights of liquid

9.3. Transmission of pressure. If you push something with a stick or a rod as a connecting link, the stick or rod transmits the applied force; but if you apply a thrust to a fluid, using a piston to develop the pressure, it is the **pressure** and not the original thrust which is transmitted. Hence large thrusts can be produced from small ones by applying the resulting pressure to a piston which has a large area.

This effect can be demonstrated by linking together a bicycle pump and a car pump as shown in Fig. 9.4. In this case it is the air in the system which transmits the pressure produced by the

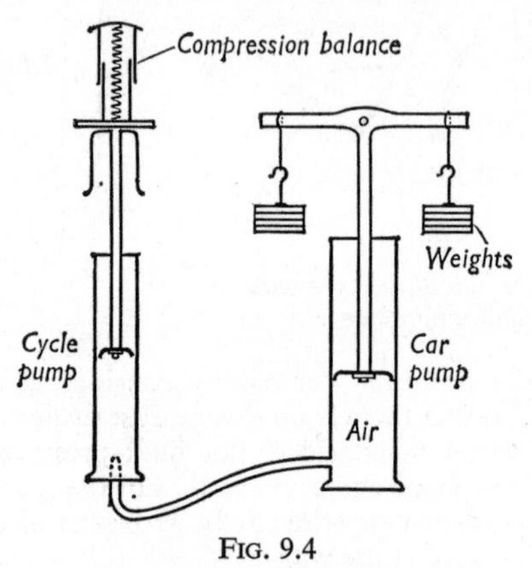

FIG. 9.4

A small thrust on a small piston gives a large thrust on a large piston owing to transmissibility of pressure

thrust on the bicycle pump handle. This thrust is measured by means of a spring compression-balance, and the force on the larger piston is counter-balanced by weights.

In an actual test the reading of the compression balance was 1·15 kgf. The internal diameter of the cycle pump was 2·00 cm so the area of cross-section was $\pi(1{\cdot}00)^2 = 3{\cdot}14$ sq. cm, and the resulting pressure $1{\cdot}15 \div 3{\cdot}14 = 0{\cdot}366$ kgf/sq. cm. The internal diameter of the car pump was 4·50 cm, giving an area of $\pi(2{\cdot}25)^2 = 15{\cdot}8$ sq. cm. Theoretically the thrust on the piston should be $0{\cdot}366 \times 15{\cdot}8 = 5{\cdot}8$ kgf. In fact a weight of 5·7 kgf was just lifted by the arrangement.

By sealing a rubber tube into a paper or plastic bag and blowing into the tube, it is possible to raise quite heavy weights, e.g. a brick (Pl. 3). The small pressure which is acting can be shown by connecting a U-tube containing water to the rubber tube after the bag has been blown up with the brick on it.

In an actual test, the difference of levels in the U-tube was 13·4 cm, and as the density of water is 1·00 g/c.c. the pressure required to hold up this column of water is $13{\cdot}4 \times 1{\cdot}00 = 13{\cdot}4$ gf/sq. cm.

The brick weighed 3300 g and its surface area was 244 sq. cm, so the pressure required to hold it up is, theoretically, $3300 \div 244 = 1{\cdot}35$ gf/sq. cm.

If the brick is placed with one of its smaller surfaces in contact with the bag, the larger pressure required is shown by the rise of water-level in the U-tube.

The production of large thrusts from small pressures is applied in all sorts of **pneumatic machinery** (worked by compressed air) and **hydraulic machinery** (worked by water or oil pressure). Fig. 9.5 shows a section through a hand-operated car jack of the hydraulic type. When the lever is pushed to the right, the small pump-piston

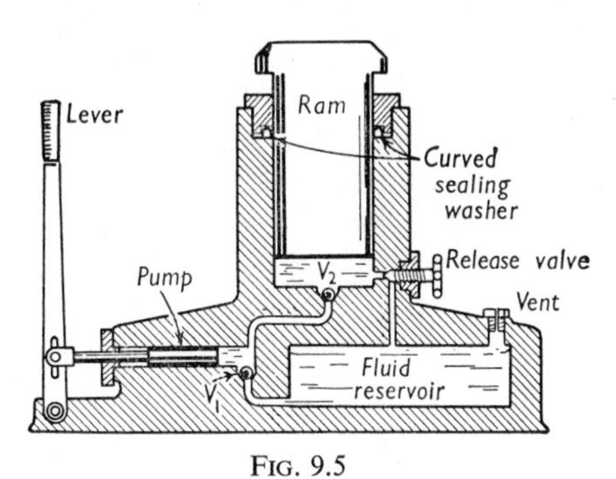

FIG. 9.5

Hydraulic jack

presses oil through the valve V_2; the pressure acting on the larger base of the ram gives a large upward thrust. On the return stroke of the piston the valve V_2 shuts, and more oil is drawn through V_1 to the pump chamber. After a load has been lifted, the ram can be returned to its starting point by opening the release valve so that the liquid can flow back to the reservoir.

Many garages have car lifts (Pl. 4) for raising a car above floor level, to get at the under-parts of the car. These lifts work by oil pressure applied to a cylindrical piston; usually an electric motor is used to work the pump which applies pressure to the oil.

Fig. 9.6 illustrates the hydraulic brake system on a car. The retractable undercarriage of an aircraft is also operated by thrusts from an oil-pressure system.

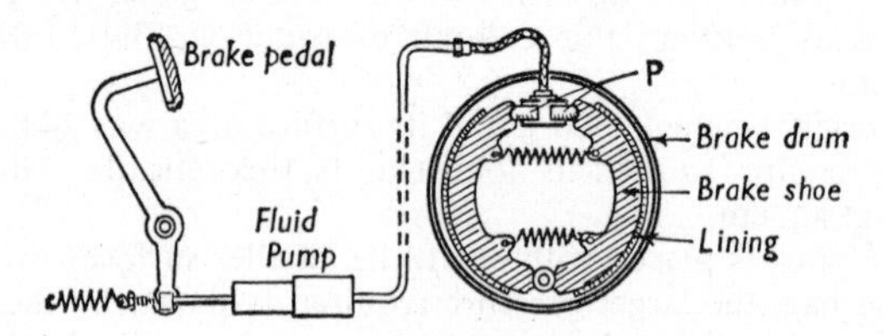

FIG. 9.6

Hydraulic brake. The pistons, marked P, push against the hinged brake shoes and so push them against the outer brake drum

9.4. Comparison of densities using balanced columns of liquid. Fig. 9.7 shows some of the ways in which balanced liquid pressures can be used to compare the densities of liquids. Fig. 9.7 (*a*) shows a U-

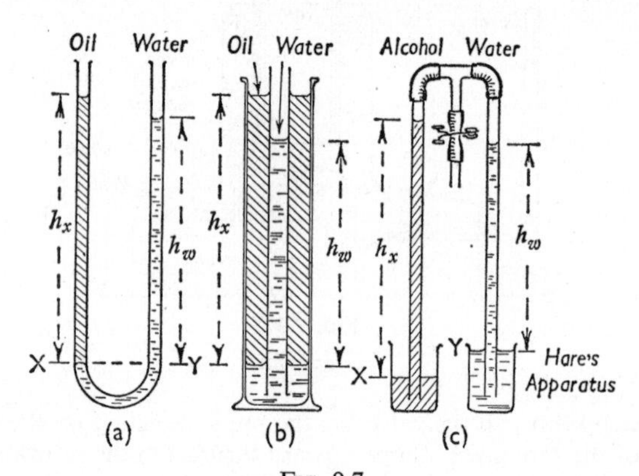

FIG. 9.7

Balanced columns of liquid

tube, originally about half-full of water, in which a light oil (e.g. paraffin) has been poured. The pressures of the columns marked h_x and h_w balance each other. In Fig. 9.7 (*b*), oil has been poured into a glass vessel which initially contained a little water with a glass tube dipping in it. The pressure of the oil presses water up the glass tube, and again the columns h_x and h_w balance each other.

In each case, pressure of liquid at X = pressure of water at Y,

$$\text{i.e. } h_x d_x = h_w d_w$$

where d_x, d_w are densities of liquid and water respectively

$$\text{so } \frac{d_x}{d_w} = \frac{h_w}{h_x}$$

Relative density (or sp.gr.) of liquid =

$$\frac{\text{Height of water column}}{\text{Height of liquid column}}$$

These methods of comparing densities are suitable only for liquids which do not mix. An apparatus which is suitable for all liquids is Hare's apparatus, shown in Fig. 9.7 (*c*). The liquids are sucked up from separate vessels; the low-pressure air at the top acts as a link or buffer, transmitting its pressure equally to the two columns. So it is the columns h_x and h_w which balance each other, and the relative density of the liquid is h_w/h_x.

The tubes need not be of uniform bore because the arrangement is a pressure-balance and not a weight-balance. The method is an accurate one since the columns can be made quite long and therefore measured to a high degree of accuracy. The tubes are usually not less than 5 mm in diameter to reduce the effects of surface tension (see p. 31), and although the two limbs of the apparatus can have different bores it is usual, for convenience, to have them of the same bore.

9.5. Pressure gauges. One of the simplest types of pressure gauge is a U-tube containing a liquid and fitted with a scale to measure the difference of levels when pressure is applied to one limb (Fig. 9.8). This type of gauge is called a *manometer*. Readings with it are usually recorded in centimetres, metres, inches or feet of the liquid it contains. For example, the average pressure of the household gas main is 13-15 cm of water, a person's lung pressure (exerted by blowing) is about 5-7 cm of mercury. Pressure recordings of this type can be converted to units such as gf/sq. cm or kgf/sq. cm by the use of the formula: Pressure = Height × Density. The mercury barometer is a special type of manometer in which the pressure to be measured, atmospheric pressure, is applied in such a way as to push up a column of mercury.

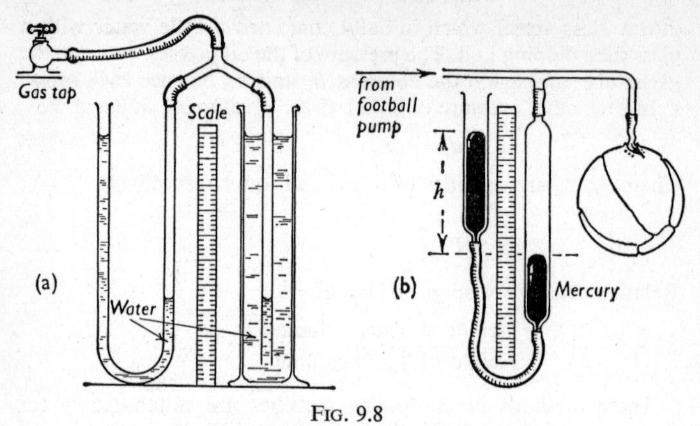

FIG. 9.8

Manometers, gauges for measuring pressure

There are several types of direct-reading pressure gauge. One of them, the Bourdon gauge (Fig. 9.9), consists of a phosphor-bronze tube shaped like a question-mark. Pressure applied within it makes the tube curve outwards much as a glove straightens out when you blow into it. The tip of the tube is linked to a ratchet and cog-wheel which works a pointer moving over a scale.

Open-tube manometers and most types of Bourdon gauge register what are known as 'excess pressures', i.e. a reading of

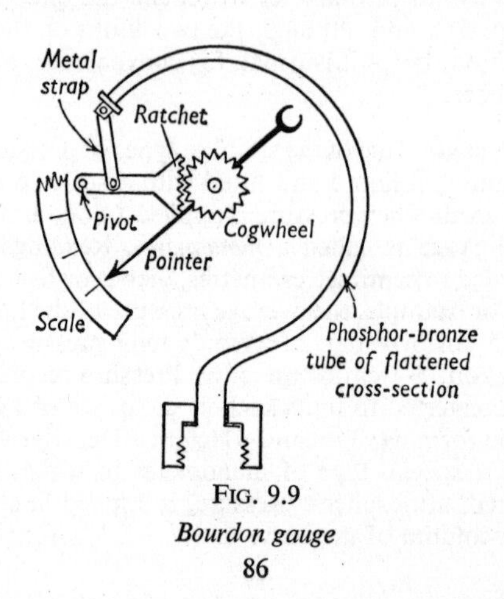

FIG. 9.9

Bourdon gauge

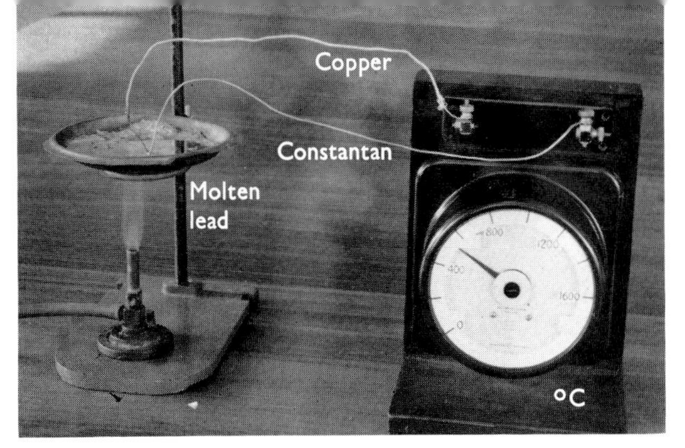

5. *A copper-constantan thermocouple with the junction in molten lead. The galvanometer has been calibrated to read in °C, and it shows the temperature to be 550°C. (The melting point of lead is 327°C.) This particular thermocouple will not work over the full range shown on the meter because the junction itself melts at about 1200°C; for higher temperatures a platinum platinum-rhodium thermocouple is used.* [p. 116]

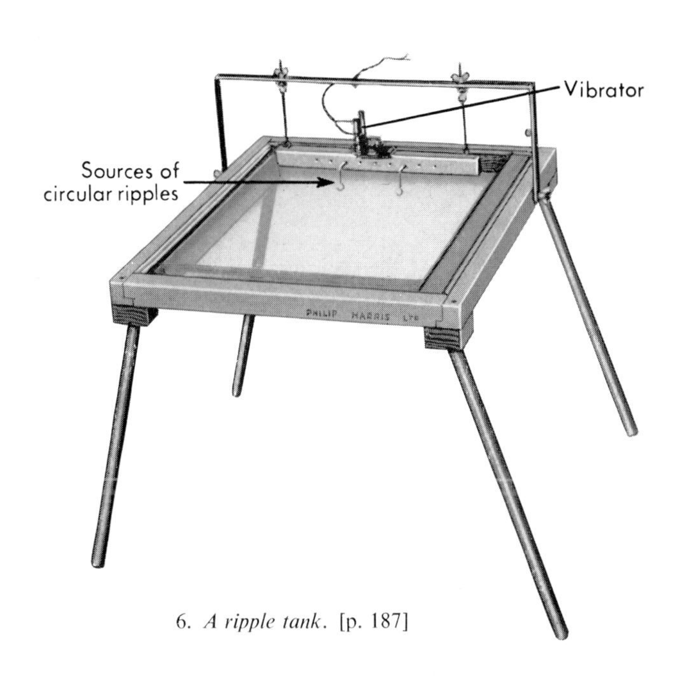

6. *A ripple tank.* [p. 187]

7. *Reflection of a sound pulse from a plane surface.* [p. 198]

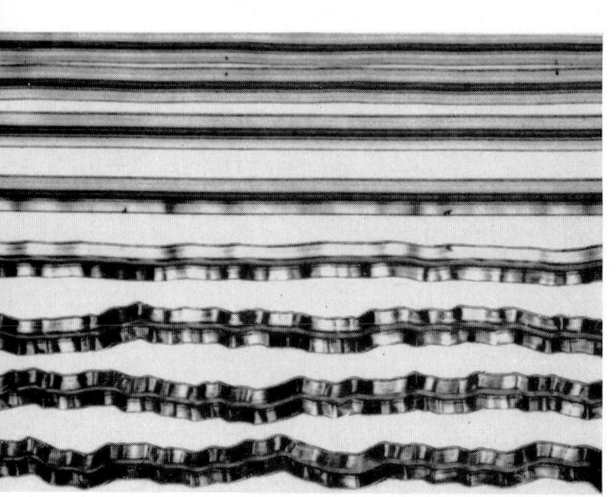

8. *Grooves on a long-play gramophone record, magnified 56 times. The mid-line of each track shows the wave-form, the width of the track shows the amplitude. The uniform grooves occur when there is no input signal.* [p. 215]

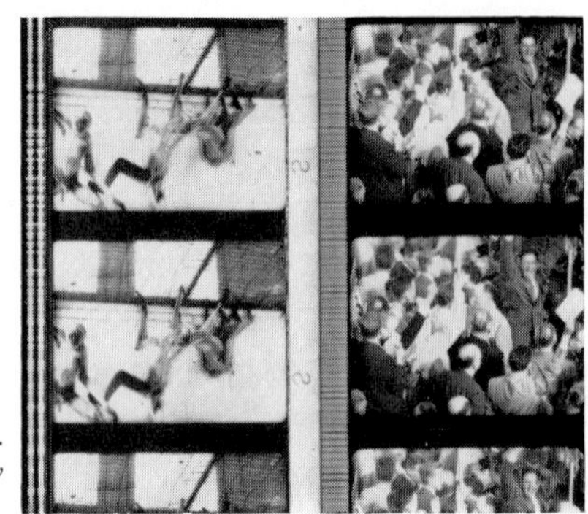

9. *Portions of film sound-track showing variable area and variable density sound recording.* [p. 215]

20 units represents a pressure of 20 units greater than the surrounding atmospheric pressure.

9.6. Fluids in motion. When pressure is applied to drive a fluid along a horizontal pipe there is usually a continuous decrease of pressure in the direction of the flow; energy associated with the pressure is used to overcome fluid friction. The effect is more noticeable with viscous fluids and in narrow pipes.

An interesting effect occurs when there is a constriction in the pipe; the pressure falls in the constriction and rises again beyond it. The effect is illustrated in Fig. 9.10. The speed of flow must clearly

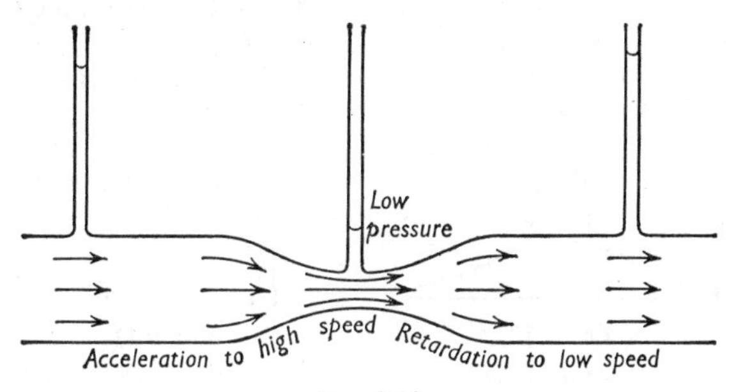

FIG. 9.10

Changes in pressure associated with changes in the speed of flow

be greater in the narrow part, for water is almost incompressible. Some of the potential energy of the pressure is used to give the water the extra kinetic energy and so there is a decrease of pressure; this state of affairs is reversed as the water speed falls on entering a wider section of the pipe.

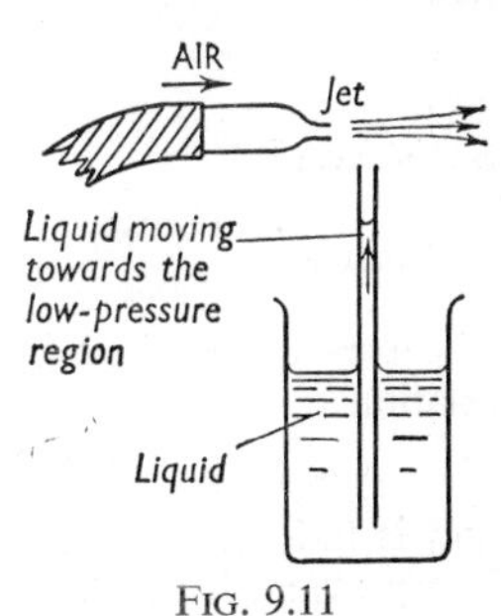

FIG. 9.11

Low pressure around a jet

The low pressure in tapering jets of a liquid or of a gas has been applied to devices for producing sprays, as in scent sprays, disinfectant sprays and paint sprays. A simple arrangement is illustrated in Fig. 9.11, which shows a jet of air being blown across the top of a tube which dips into a liquid. The low pressure around the air jet causes atmospheric pressure to drive liquid up the tube; the issuing liquid is blown into a spray as it mixes with the jet. A similar action causes an intake of air at the air-hole of a bunsen burner (Fig. 9.12). The **filter pump** produces a moderately good vacuum with the aid of a water jet. The arrangement is shown in Fig. 9.13. There is a low-pressure region round the water jet, and air flowing towards it is carried with the jet into the cup-shaped tube below; here it mingles with the issuing water stream.

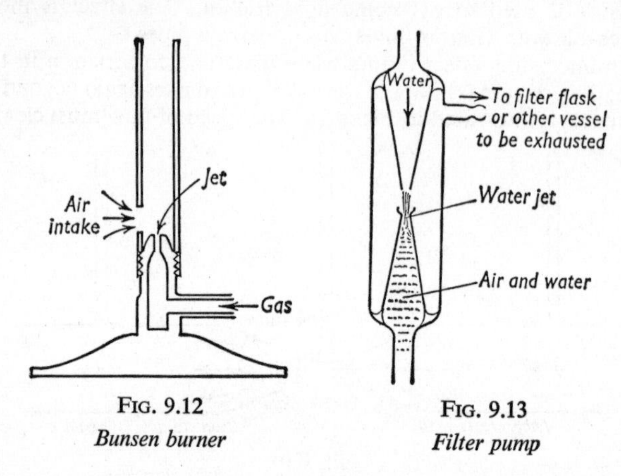

FIG. 9.12
Bunsen burner

FIG. 9.13
Filter pump

When an aerofoil is driven through the air, the air streams over it (Fig. 9.14). The shape of the aerofoil affects the lines of air flow so that a pressure increase occurs below it and a decrease of pressure above. This gives the resultant lift which makes flight possible.

SUMMARY

$$\textbf{Pressure} = \frac{\textbf{Thrust}}{\textbf{Area}} \qquad \textbf{Thrust} = \textbf{Pressure} \times \textbf{Area}$$

The pressure exerted by a fluid column at rest is given by the relation

$$\textbf{Pressure} = \textbf{Vertical height} \times \textbf{density}$$

and is independent of the cross-section of the containing vessel. The pressure is constant at all points on the same horizontal level within the fluid, and it **acts in all directions**; where a fluid is in contact with the surface of a solid the thrust on any part of the solid surface is **perpendicular to the surface.**

A **fluid** which is confined and put under pressure **can transmit** the **pressure in all directions.** The fact has been applied to the design of hydraulic and pneumatic machinery.

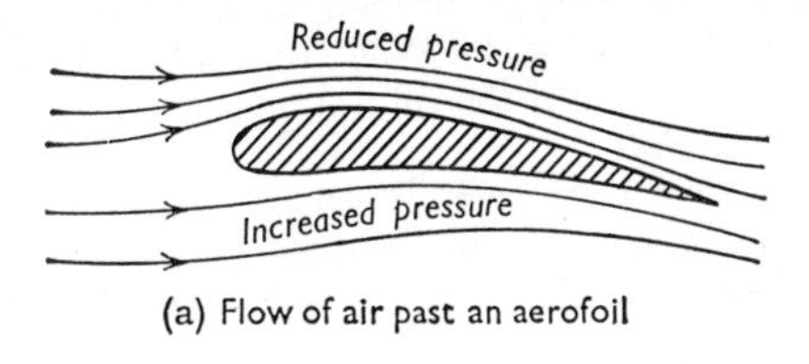

(a) Flow of air past an aerofoil

(b) Arrows show the forces on an aerofoil due to increase of pressure below and decrease of pressure above it

FIG. 9.14

Action of a moving aerofoil

Questions

1. Distinguish between the terms *thrust* and *pressure*. A cube of side 3 cm, made of material of density 7 g/c.c., rests with one face on a horizontal surface. Calculate (*a*) the thrust on the surface, (*b*) the pressure, under the cube, on the surface.

2. Over what area must a thrust of 4·4 lbf act in order to produce a pressure of (*a*) 100 lbf/sq. in, (*b*) 8·0 kgf/sq. cm, (*c*) 10 gf/sq. cm? (1 kg = 2·20 lb.)

3. A person pushes a drawing-pin into wood by pressing with the thumb, exerting a steady force of 1·50 kgf. Calculate (*a*) the pressure at the point of the pin, (*b*) the pressure on the person's thumb. (Areas of pin-point and pin-head are 1/300 and 3·0 sq. cm respectively.)

4. A vertical test-tube is pushed, open end downwards, to the bottom of a tall tank filled with water. Explain the rise of water into the tube.

5. Planking laid on a very muddy ground will take the weight of several men without sinking down as much as any one of them would do when stepping on the bare mud. Explain this.

6. Calculate the greatest and least pressures which a rectangular block of metal 18·0 cm × 5·0 cm × 6·0 cm, of weight 5·40 kgf, can exert when resting on a horizontal surface.

7. A motor-car has a weight of 1800 lbf, and the pressure in each of the four tyres is 30 lbf/sq. in. What area of each tyre must be in contact with the ground if the total weight is equally distributed over the four wheels?

8. In one of his experiments, Pascal sealed a long vertical tube into the top of a large barrel full of water. On pouring a small jugful of water into the tube, the barrel burst. Give an explanation of this.

9. What is a *manometer*? Draw a diagram to show how you would use a water manometer to measure the pressure of gas at a gas-tap. Describe the effect of gradually tilting the manometer while it is in use.

10. A water manometer connected to a gas main reads 12·5 cm. Calculate (*a*) the pressure of the gas, in excess of atmospheric pressure, (*b*) the reading of a brine manometer attached to the main if the density of the brine is 1·20 g/c.c.

11. A person's lung pressure, as recorded by a mercury manometer, is 9·0 cm of mercury. Express this pressure in (*a*) gf/sq. cm, (*b*) kgf/sq. metre.

What is the maximum weight which the person could 'blow up' using a vertical cylinder fitted with a piston of diameter 28·0 cm? (Density of mercury = 13·6 g/c.c. Take π as 22/7.)

12. Draw a labelled diagram of Hare's apparatus ready for a determination of the sp.gr. (relative density) of a salt solution. Show clearly the distances you would measure and prove a formula for the calculation of the result.

13. Draw a diagram to show the structure of some form of hydraulic machine such as a hydraulic press or hydraulic jack. Explain the production of pressure in the fluid and explain how it is that this pressure gives rise to a very large thrust.

14. Draw a labelled diagram of a filter pump and explain the fact that it can be used as an exhaust pump.

15. Draw a labelled section diagram to show the structure of a bunsen burner. Explain the action of its jet when it is used with the air-hole open.

16. A person, of weight 72·0 kgf, sits on a light square platform of side 30 cm. The platform rests on a large inflated balloon. Calculate (*a*) the pressure, in excess of atmospheric, of the air in the balloon, (*b*) the difference of levels of a brine manometer connected to the air in the balloon. (Density of brine = 1·20 g/c.c.)

CHAPTER 10

Atmospheric Pressure. Barometers. Pumps

10.1. The pressure of the atmosphere. We live at the bottom of a deep layer of air; deep enough, in spite of its low density, to produce a pressure which varies between 0·95 and 1·10 kgf/sq. cm. Yet we scarcely notice it, partly because the pressure acts in all directions (pushing us up as well as down) and partly because the tissues of the body have fluids in them which are at approximately the same pressure. The effects of atmospheric pressure only become noticeable when air is removed from a vessel. The screen of a cathode-ray tube, such as is used in television, has a vacuum inside, and the thrust on a 50-cm tube with an area of 2500 sq. cm, is approximately 2500 kgf. Such tubes are made of quite thick glass to stand up to this large thrust. Electric discharge lamps, which contain gas at very low pressure, and the vacuum-type radio valves are made cylindrical to give the necessary strength.

10.2. Barometers. The first mercury barometer was devised by Torricelli and set up by his pupil Viviani in Italy in 1644. It was suspected that the air-pressure is large, so a dense liquid was chosen for the means of measuring it. The following is an account of how a simple barometer can be set up. A strong glass tube, about 1 metre long and sealed at one end is filled with clean dry mercury. The tube is tapped from time to time during the filling to dislodge any air bubbles. When the tube is nearly full a finger is placed over the open end and a bubble of air is allowed to run up and down the tube to collect any remaining air bubbles. The tube is then completely filled by the addition of more mercury, closed with the finger and inverted in a bowl of mercury. When the finger is removed, mercury flows out from the tube into the bowl, leaving a column about 76 cm high in the tube, with an empty space or vacuum above it. A vacuum formed in this way is still called a *Torricellian vacuum* in honour of its discoverer. By means of a ruler the difference of the two mercury levels can be measured—the distance H in Fig. 10.1. This is the atmospheric pressure, at that time, in centimetres of mercury.

If the tube of a simple mercury barometer is tilted the mercury appears to flow up the tube, but if the vertical distance between the levels is measured it is found that this is still unchanged. And if the tube is suddenly tilted, then the mercury hits the end of the tube with a sharp metallic click, showing the complete absence of air in the space above the mercury. By carefully lifting the tube it is possible to lift it completely clear of the mercury in the bowl without any falling out of the tube; if a little mercury is then dislodged, by tapping the tube, the remaining mercury does not fall out but is driven with considerable force to the top of the tube—clearly showing the upward pressure of the atmosphere on the mercury column.

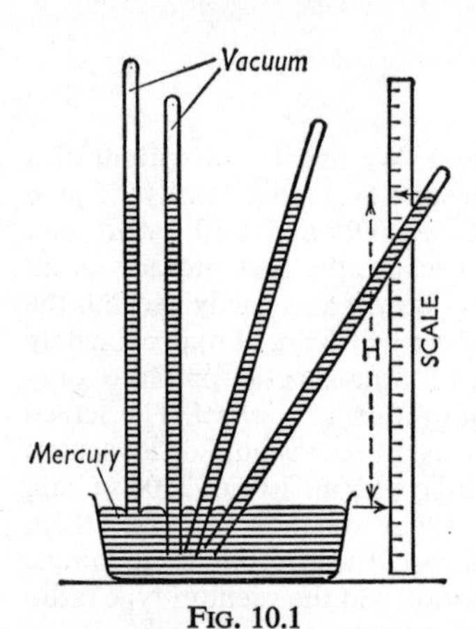

FIG. 10.1
Torricellian or simple cistern barometer

Travelling upwards into the atmosphere gives a reduction in pressure, for there is then less air above you as you travel. The first experimental test of this was done by Pascal in France. A mercury barometer carried up the Puy-de-Dôme showed a fall in the mercury level of nearly 8 cm; a barometer at the foot of the hill showed little change. Air has only about a twelve-thousandth of the density of mercury, so that one has to travel upwards about 12,000 cm or 120 metres for the barometer to fall by 1 cm. A barometer can thus be used for estimating height; when so used it is called an **altimeter** and its scale is then usually marked in feet or in metres. The altimeter of an aircraft is really a barometer, but it is the aneroid type which is used, since a mercury barometer would be too large and cumbersome.

The **aneroid barometer** (Fig. 10.2) is of quite a different type and contains no liquid (Greek *a*, without; *neros*, liquid). It is more compact than mercury barometers; it is portable, can be used in any position, and some types have been designed as small as a watch. The essential feature of this barometer is a circular metal box, exhausted of air and corrugated to give the necessary strength; a U-shaped spring keeps it from collapsing and a metal rod attached to the spring moves in and out as the surface of the box moves under the variations of air pressure. These small move-

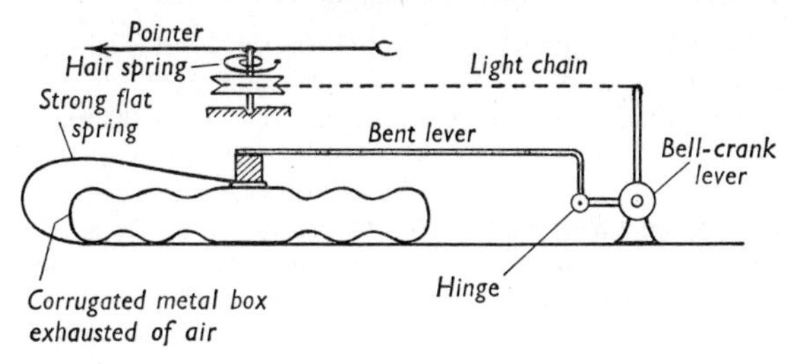

FIG. 10.2
Aneroid barometer

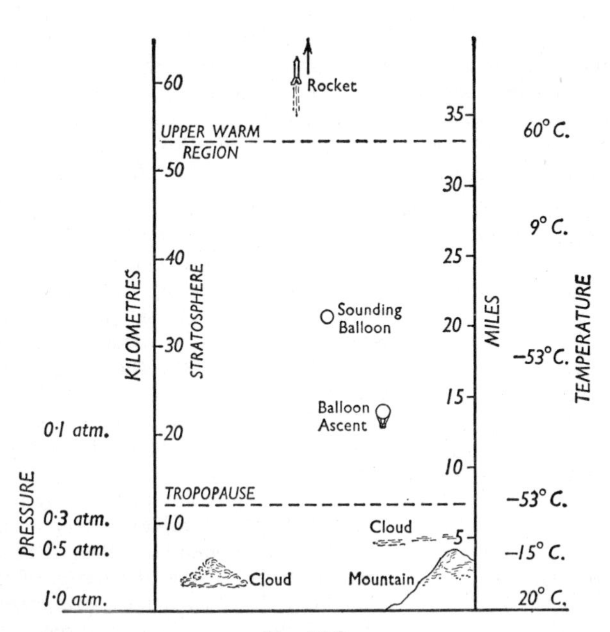

FIG. 10.3
The upper atmosphere

ments are magnified by a system of levers which then move a small pulley fitted with a pointer and a hair spring.

10.3. The extent of the atmosphere. From sea-level a climb of 120 metres results in a fall in the barometric height of 1 cm. The fall becomes gradually less as you ascend, until at 8000 metres the pressure is 25 cm of mercury. Much information about the upper atmosphere has been obtained from balloons and rockets. These can be equipped with small radio transmitters which send a continuous record of atmospheric pressure, temperature and moisture-content back to the earth. Evidence from meteors ('shooting stars') shows that the atmosphere extends to at least 160 kilometres. Meteors are small bodies in space, cold and dark until they become white hot through entering the earth's atmosphere at colossal speed; by taking photographs of them from different points, their height has been estimated and found to be approximately 160 km. The general features of the atmosphere are illustrated in Fig. 10.3. It is found that temperature falls evenly to $-53°C$ at a height of about 12 km in temperature latitudes, after which the temperature remains almost constant to a height of about 30 km. At very great heights the temperature is higher than at the earth's surface. The region in which the temperature falls steadily is known as the **troposphere**, and the region above this is the **stratosphere.**

10.4. Pumps. A simple form of pump is the *syringe*, used for medical purposes or for garden spraying; it consists of a barrel with a narrow or a perforated nozzle, and a solid piston (Fig. 10.4). When the nozzle is placed in a liquid and the piston is withdrawn, a partial vacuum is formed below the piston, and the atmospheric pressure drives liquid up into the barrel. Atmospheric pressure acts in a similar way when you fill a pipette, or when you drink through a drinking straw.

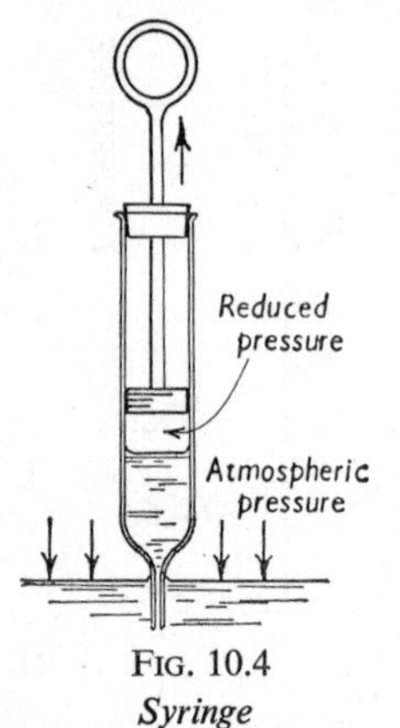

FIG. 10.4
Syringe

The **lift pump** is similar to the syringe, but it contains two valves to keep up the flow of liquid; one of the valves (the foot valve) is at the foot of the barrel of the pump, and the other is in the piston (Fig. 10.5). Both valves open upwards only. Raising the piston reduces the air pressure below it, and so the atmospheric pressure closes the piston-valve; it also drives the water up the pipe and through the foot valve. On the downstroke the foot-valve closes, and air (in later strokes, water) is driven through the piston-valve. Water above the piston is lifted up and out through the spout, while atmospheric pressure drives more water up the pipe through the foot-valve. Since atmospheric pressure is approximately equivalent to that of a 10-metre water-column, the piston must not be higher than this above the water level, and in practice it is usually arranged to be not more than 7 metres above the water level. For deeper wells the pump barrel is lengthened as shown in Fig. 10.6.

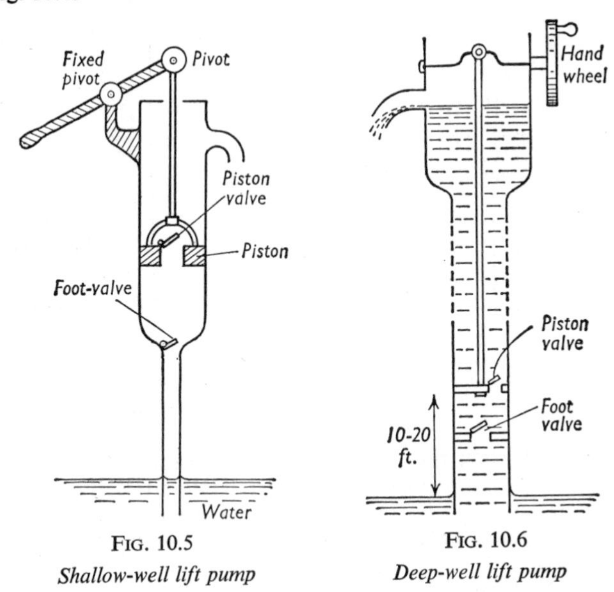

FIG. 10.5
Shallow-well lift pump

FIG. 10.6
Deep-well lift pump

The **force pump** is used for driving water to great heights. It consists of a barrel with a foot-valve opening upwards, a solid piston, and an exit pipe containing the other valve which opens outwards from the barrel. The pipe is below the piston. The action can be deduced from Fig. 10.7; note that the delivery stroke is downwards. To obtain a more even flow of water an air-dome can be fitted to the delivery pipe, the compressed air in it maintaining the flow during the upstroke. The height to which water can be forced depends only upon the force available to move the piston. Another way of securing a more even flow is to use a **plunger pump**

(Fig. 10.8). This is a kind of lift-pump in which water is delivered on the downstroke because the plunger displaces water as it enters the barrel; the **stirrup-pump** is a pump of this type.

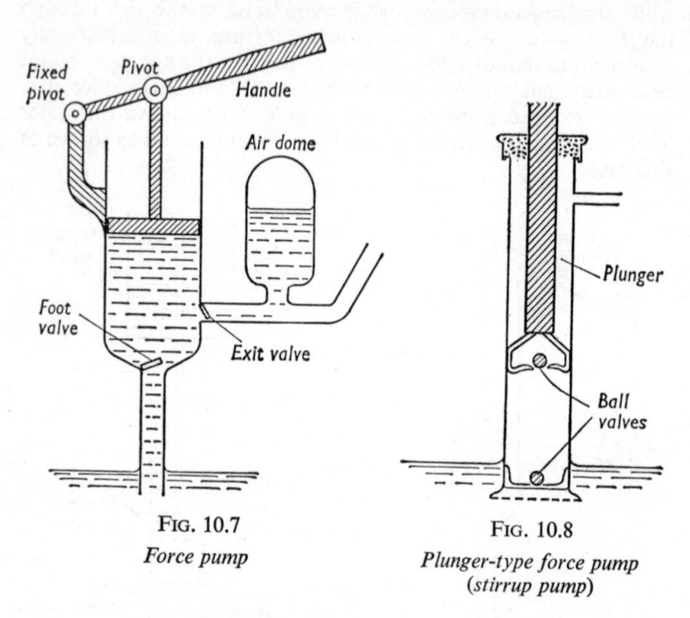

FIG. 10.7
Force pump

FIG. 10.8
Plunger-type force pump (stirrup pump)

The connecting rods of force pumps are made thicker than those of lift-pumps because most of the effort is on the downstroke, which makes the rod more liable to bend. In lift-pumps the rods are mainly in a state of tension, and so they do not need to be so thick.

10.5. The siphon. An inverted U-tube may be used to empty a vessel, such as an aquarium tank, when the vessel is not provided with a tap. You can test the action of a siphon in the following manner.

Fill a vessel with water. Fill a long rubber tube with water, either by immersing it all in the water or by sucking the air from it. Clip one end (C) of the tube, and take that end out of the water and down, so that C is lower than the level A in the vessel (Fig. 10.9). On opening the clip you will find that water will flow out of C, but only whilst C is below the level of A; also, the lower C is below this surface, the faster will the water flow from C.

The following is one way of explaining the siphon effect. When the clip is closed, the water in the pipe is stationary, so the pressure at A′ is equal to that at A, i.e. atmospheric pressure. But the downward pressure at C is greater than this by h cm of water, since it is h cm lower down in the water column; therefore when the clip is opened the water can force its way out to the atmosphere.

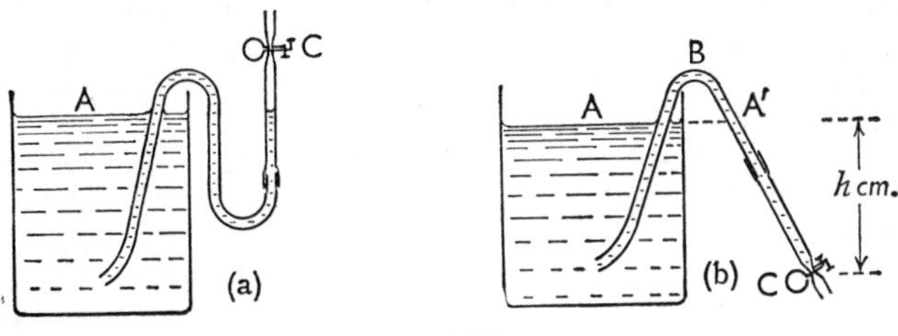

FIG. 10.9
A siphon

SUMMARY

The atmosphere exerts a pressure which is about 15 lbf/sq. in. or 1·0 kgf/sq. cm at sea-level. The corresponding columns of water and mercury which give this pressure are approximately 34 ft (11 metres) and 30 in. (76 cm) respectively.

A **barometer** is an instrument for measuring atmospheric pressure; in a mercury barometer the pressure of a column of mercury is balanced against the atmospheric pressure.

The atmosphere extends to a height of at least 100 miles (160 km); the pressure and the density decrease with height; most of the atmospheric changes which affect the weather occur in the **troposphere** which has an average height of 7 miles (11 km).

Questions

1. Give a brief description of an experiment which shows that the atmosphere exerts a pressure.

2. Calculate the thrust, due to atmospheric pressure, on the top surface of a rectangular table 3 ft × 2 ft if the atmospheric pressure is 15 lbf/sq. in. Explain the fact that the total effect of atmospheric pressure does not put much strain on a table.

3. Conical glass vessels which have a vacuum inside, such as filter flasks and television tubes, have thick walls, whereas the walls of electric lamps are relatively thin. Explain this.

4. Give two examples of effects which are started by a suction action. To what extent are the effects due to atmospheric pressure?

5. Explain the fact that there is a limit to the height through which water can be raised by a lift pump. Suggest any one factor which might limit the height to which water could be driven by a force pump.

6. A distillation flask is partly filled with water and then corked. The side tube is connected to a vertical glass tube 100 cm long, the end of which dips under water. If the water in the flask is kept boiling for a few minutes and then cooled, water flows up the vertical tube and fills the flask. Explain this.

Describe and explain what would happen if the experiment were repeated with the vertical tube dipping under mercury instead of under water.

7. Describe how you would siphon water from a tank which is about one-third full. How would you expect the rate of flow of the water to be affected by (*a*) the area of cross-section of the siphon, (*b*) the length of the siphon? Give reasons for your answers.

8. Water from a pond is to be pumped to a tank which is 50 ft above the level of the pond. Draw a diagram of a pump which is suitable for the purpose, and explain the action of the pump.

How will the diameter of the pump barrel affect (*a*) the volume of water delivered in each stroke, (*b*) the force required to operate the pump?

9. One face of the box of an aneroid barometer has an effective area of 20 sq. cm. By how much will the thrust exerted on it by the atmosphere change when the mercury barometer falls by 1 cm? State the units in which your answer is given. (Density of mercury $= 13{\cdot}6$ g/c.c.)

10. Calculate the barometric height in a water barometer at a place where a mercury barometer reads 75·0 cm; give your answer in metres. What, apart from its large size, are the disadvantages of a water barometer? (Relative density of mercury $= 13{\cdot}6$; assume that water vapour exerts a pressure of 2·0 cm of mercury.)

11. Describe how you would construct a simple mercury barometer and use it to measure the pressure of the atmosphere. Why is mercury a suitable liquid to use in a barometer?

What would be the effect, if any, on the barometer reading if the tube (*a*) was narrower at the top than at the bottom, (*b*) was not quite vertical? Give reasons for your answers.

CHAPTER 11

Boyle's Law. Air Pumps

11.1. The compression of air. Air is fairly easily compressible. But it resists being compressed, exerting a force on whatever is compressing it. You can detect this effect if you put your finger over the end of a cycle-pump and push in the handle; the volume of the enclosed air becomes smaller, and you have to push harder as you reduce the volume. This resistance is due to the increased pressure of the gas when it is confined in a smaller space. Robert Boyle referred to this property of the air as 'the spring of the air' and he conducted experiments to find out how the pressure and volume were related. He discovered that the pressure and volume of a definite mass of air are inversely proportional if the temperature of the sample remains constant, i.e. doubling the pressure gives half the volume, halving the pressure gives twice the volume, one-third the pressure gives three times the volume and so on. Experiments conducted, since Boyle's time, with other gases show that the statement is true for any gas, a fact which is expressed in the statement known as **Boyle's law:**

The volume of a fixed mass of any gas is inversely proportional to its pressure, the temperature of the gas being constant.

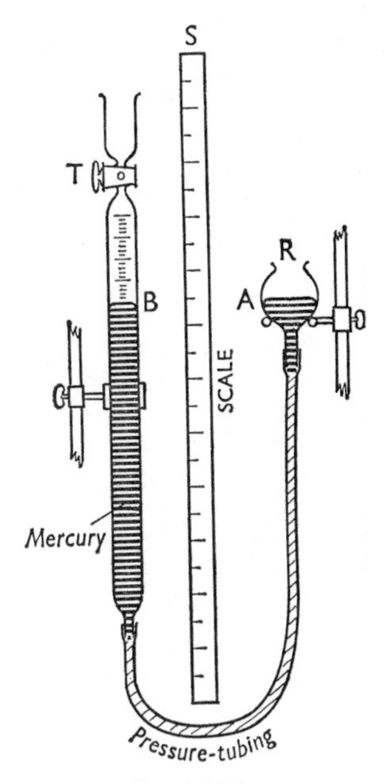

FIG. 11.1

11.2. Verification of Boyle's law. Fig. 11.1 shows one of the forms of apparatus which can be used to test the law. If air is to be tested it is admitted to the graduated tube by opening the tap T; the mercury reservoir R, which is connected to the tube by thick-walled rubber tubing, is adjusted so that the tube is about half-full of air. The tap is then closed and the volume of air observed on the graduations of the tube. Though the mercury surfaces are at the same level, this does not mean that there is no pressure. The pressure of the enclosed gas is in fact atmospheric, so it is necessary to take a reading of a barometer. The pressure of the gas can now be increased by raising R or decreased by lowering R. The vertical difference in mercury levels can be found by taking readings on the scale S, and this difference is either added to or subtracted from the atmospheric pressure, depending on whether the level A is above or below B. The corresponding volume of the gas is observed for each pressure reading taken.

The following is a set of observations taken with this apparatus; the volumes were adjusted to be simple whole numbers to simplify the calculations.

The average value of the product $P \times V$ is 1500 and none of the individual values differs from this by more than 12, i.e. less than 1%; this sort of difference is what one might expect from personal errors of measurement with this apparatus.

Volume V (c.c)	Atm. pressure (cm Hg)	Scale Readings		$A-B$ (cm)	Total pressure P (cm Hg)	$P \times V$
		A (cm)	B (cm)			
20·0	75·0	—	—	0	75·0	1500
16·0	75·0	78·0	50·0	+28·0	93·0	1488
10·0	75·0	130·5	55·0	+75·5	150·5	1505
30·0	75·0	20·0	45·0	−25·0	50·0	1500
40·0	75·0	0·0	37·3	−37·3	37·7	1508

If a gas having a volume V_1 at a pressure P_1 is altered (at constant temperature) to have a volume V_2 at a pressure P_2, then

$$P_1V_1=P_2V_2$$

This mode of expression of Boyle's law is useful in solving pressure-volume problems on gases at constant temperature.

EXAMPLE 1. *A closed rubber balloon contains* 400 *c.c. of air at a pressure of* 1·2 *kgf/sq. cm. Calculate the pressure of the air in the balloon when its volume is* (a) *reduced by* 80 *c.c.,* (b) *increased by* 80 *c.c. Assume the temperature to remain constant.*

(*a*) $P_1=1{\cdot}2,\ V_1=400,\ V_2=320.$

$$1{\cdot}2\times 400=P_2\times 320$$
$$\therefore P_2=1{\cdot}5$$

New pressure $=1{\cdot}5$ kgf/sq. cm.

(*b*) $P_1=1{\cdot}2,\ V_1=400,\ V_2=480.$

$$1{\cdot}2\times 400=P_2\times 480$$
$$P_2=1{\cdot}0$$

New pressure $=1{\cdot}0$ kgf/sq. cm.

EXAMPLE 2. *A bubble of air, trapped* 16 *cm below the top surface of a mercury barometer, becomes dislodged and rises into the vacuum. As a result the reading of the barometer falls from* 75·0 *cm to* 74·0 *cm and the space at the top of the barometer has a volume of* 4·0 *c.c. Calculate the volume which the bubble occupied before it became dislodged.*

The arrival of the air at the top pushed the mercury column downwards $75{\cdot}0-74{\cdot}0=1{\cdot}0$ cm. Therefore the pressure of the air at the top $=1{\cdot}0$ cm Hg. Initially its pressure was 16 cm Hg.

$$P_1=16,\ V_1=?,\ P_2=1{\cdot}0,\ V_2=4{\cdot}0$$
$$16\times V_1=1{\cdot}0\times 4{\cdot}0$$
$$V_1=0{\cdot}25$$

Initial volume of the bubble $=0{\cdot}25$ c.c.

EXAMPLE 3. *A motor tyre tested with a tyre gauge shows a reading of* 1·20 *kgf/sq. cm (in excess of atmospheric pressure). A pump with a stroke of* 35 *cm is used to pump air into it. How far will the piston move before the tyre valve opens? (Assume that Boyle's law is applicable to the air in the pump and take atmospheric pressure to be* 0·90 *kgf/sq. cm.)*

The valve will not open until the pressure in the pump is at least $(1{\cdot}20+0{\cdot}90)$ kgf/sq. cm. The initial pressure of the air in the pump is 0·90 kgf/sq. cm. If d cm is the length of air space in the pump when the pressure is 2·10 kg/sq. cm, then taking lengths as representing volumes, we have

$$35\times 0{\cdot}90=d\times 2{\cdot}10$$

whence $d=15$

The piston will therefore have to move at least $35-15=20$ cm for the valve to open.

11.3. Exhaust pumps. The simple type of vacuum pump invented by Guericke and illustrated in Fig. 11.2 (*a*) is similar in its action to the lift pump (p. 95). One defect of Guericke's pump was the large force needed to lift the piston as the vessel became exhausted, since atmospheric pressure exerts a kilogram force on each sq. cm of the piston. This difficulty was overcome by the engineer Smeaton who closed the top of the barrel and introduced a third valve in that place (Fig. 11.2(*b*)). As the piston rose, the air above it was compressed until it could lift this upper valve and escape. The piston then descended for the extraction of more air, leaving a low pressure above it, which eased the next lift-stroke.

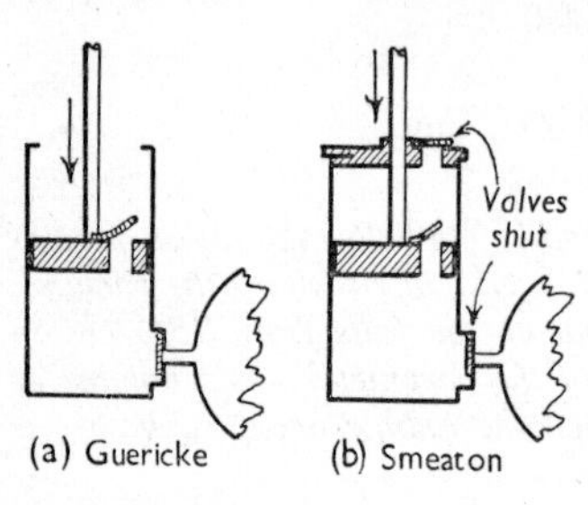

FIG. 11.2
Types of vacuum pump

The theory of pumps of this type can be considered by applying Boyle's law to the successive expansions which take place. If the vessel is initially at 1 atm pressure and the volumes of vessel and pump barrel are V and B respectively, each expansion stroke causes the volume to increase from V to $(V+B)$ thus making the pressure $V/(V+B)$ of what it was before. If $V=2B$ the fraction $V/(V+B)$ is $\frac{2}{3}$ and the pressure after successive strokes becomes

$$1;\ \tfrac{2}{3};\ \tfrac{2}{3}\times\tfrac{2}{3}=\tfrac{4}{9};\ \tfrac{4}{9}\times\tfrac{2}{3}=\tfrac{8}{27};\ \tfrac{8}{27}\times\tfrac{2}{3}=\tfrac{16}{81}$$

and if $V=B$ so that the fraction is $\frac{1}{2}$, the pressures are

$$1;\ \tfrac{1}{2};\ \tfrac{1}{2}\times\tfrac{1}{2}=\tfrac{1}{4};\ \tfrac{1}{4}\times\tfrac{1}{2}=\tfrac{1}{8};\ \tfrac{1}{8}\times\tfrac{1}{2}=\tfrac{1}{16}$$

These figures show

(i) that the larger the volume of the pump barrel the more rapid is the decrease of pressure,

(ii) that the first few strokes cause a greater decrease of pressure than do subsequent ones,

(iii) that the pump can never completely exhaust the vessel.

The *filter pump* has been described on page 88.

Nowadays, most vacuum work is done with *rotary pumps.* The pump barrel is cylindrical, as it is in the plunger pumps. The axis of the cylinder is horizontal and it lies in a small tank of oil with a pipe leading out, from near the top, to the vessel to be exhausted;

this is the intake pipe in Fig. 11.3. The air is collected and driven out by a rotating blade. To make the ends of the blade keep contact with the sides of the cylinder the blade is built in two parts with a compression spring between them; the blades and spring lie in an off-centre rotor which is driven from a shaft passing through the side of the tank. Stage (*a*) in Fig. 11.3 shows some of the gas, A, flowing down the intake as the rotor turns. In stage (*b*), part of A

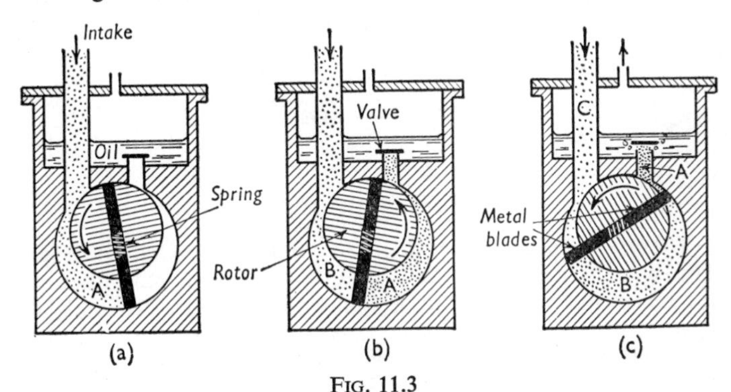

FIG. 11.3
Action of a rotary exhaust pump

has been trapped and compressed; more gas, B, flows down the intake. In stage (*c*), A is being driven through the valve, B is being compressed, and more gas, C, flows down the intake.

These pumps are generally driven by an electric motor and they can quickly reduce the pressure to as low as a hundredth of a millimetre of mercury.

11.4. Compression pumps. The bicycle pump and football pump are similar types of compression pumps, and you should unscrew them and examine the parts. The piston of a cycle or car pump is a cup-shaped washer, greased and somewhat flexible, concave towards the outlet (Fig. 11.4). The forward stroke causes an increase

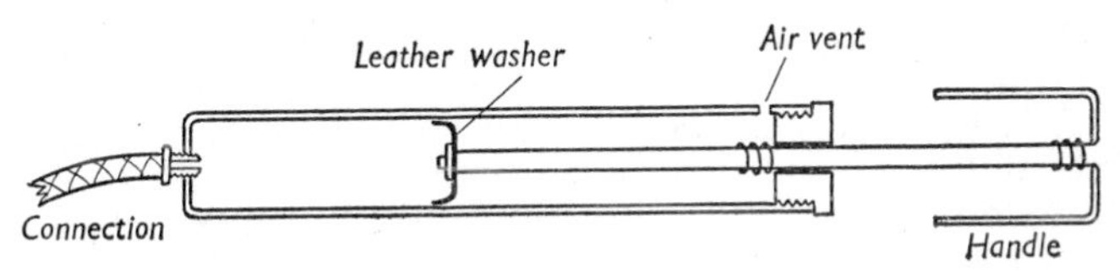

FIG. 11.4
Bicycle pump

of pressure as the volume is decreased, and this forces the washer against the sides of the barrel, thus making it airtight. When the pump pressure becomes more than the tyre pressure, the valve opens and air is forced into the tyre. On the return stroke, air in front of the piston is reduced in pressure, and air at atmospheric pressure behind the piston forces its way forward between the sides of the washer and the barrel.

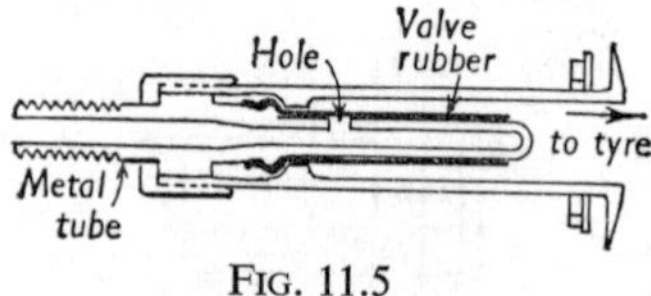

FIG. 11.5

One type of tyre valve

The tyre-valve acts as the outlet valve of the pump. One type (Fig. 11.5) consists of a narrow metal tube, threaded at one end, closed at the other, and provided with a small hole at the side. The hole is covered by a thin rubber sleeve open at both ends. On the compression stroke the air at the hole lifts the rubber and passes into the tyre, while on the outward stroke (or when the tyre is fully inflated) the air in the tyre presses the rubber sleeve against the hole and closes the valve.

The football pump, which is similar in construction and action to the bicycle pump, has a ball valve in the nozzle to prevent the return of air from the football to the pump.

SUMMARY

Boyle's law states: **The volume of a fixed mass of gas is inversely proportional to its pressure, the temperature of the gas being constant.**

$$P \propto \frac{1}{V} \text{ or } P = k.\frac{1}{V};\ PV = \text{const. or } P_1V_1 = P_2V_2$$

At constant temperature, the density of a gas is proportional to its pressure.

An exhaust pump decreases the pressure by the same fraction at each stroke; it does not cause the same difference of pressure at each stroke and cannot completely exhaust a vessel. On the other hand a compression pump applied to a container of fixed volume causes equal increases of pressure for each stroke, provided that the pressure is not high enough to liquefy the gas.

Questions

1. State Boyle's law. A sample of air has a volume of 10·0 c.c. when under a pressure of 20 lbf/sq. in. Calculate the pressures corresponding to volumes of 5·0, 10·0, 25·0, 40·0 and 50·0 c.c. if there is no leak of air into or out of the sample and if the temperature remains constant.

Plot a graph of pressure against volume. Use the graph to find the volume when the pressure is (*a*) 50 lbf/sq. in., (*b*) 16 lbf/sq. in.

2. A gas has a volume of 700 c.c. under a pressure of 24 atmospheres. Calculate the change in the pressure of this gas when its volume is (*a*) reduced by 100 c.c., (*b*) increased by 100 c.c. (Assume that the change is due only to pressure and not to temperature or leak or addition of gas.)

3. A vertical cylinder, sealed at the base and closed at the top by a light frictionless plunger, contains 120 litres of air at atmospheric pressure (1·05 kgf/sq. cm). Calculate the change in the volume of the air when a weight of 315 kgf is put on the plunger, the temperature of the air remaining constant. (Area of the plunger = 900 sq. cm.)

4. What volume of air, initially at atmospheric pressure, is required to inflate a flat tyre, of capacity 28 cu. in. when inflated, to a pressure of 33 lbf/sq. in. in excess of atmospheric? (Atmospheric pressure = 15 lbf/sq. in.)

5. The density of oxygen at 15°C and atmospheric pressure is 1·36 g/litre. What is the density of oxygen at 15°C and under a pressure of (*a*) 10 atmospheres, (*b*) 100 atmospheres?

A cylinder of compressed oxygen has an internal volume of 4 litres; the temperature is 15°C and the pressure of the gas 200 atmospheres. Calculate the mass of oxygen contained in the cylinder.

6. If a small bubble of air enters the space at the top of a mercury barometer, the barometric reading falls. Explain this. Calculate the fall in the barometric reading due to the admission of 0·10 c.c. of air at atmospheric pressure, the volume of the space above the mercury after the admission being 20·0 c.c. (Atmospheric pressure = 760 mm of mercury.)

7. A vessel containing 500 c.c. of air at 10·45 kgf/sq. cm is put in connection with an evacuated vessel of capacity 5000 c.c. Calculate the resulting pressure.

8. Draw a diagram to show the structure of a simple exhaust pump of the barrel-and-piston type. Explain the action of the pump.

If the effective capacity of the barrel of such a pump is 500 c.c. and it is used to exhaust a vessel of capacity 300 c.c., what will be the pressure (*a*) after one stroke, (*b*) after three strokes? (Initial pressure = 16 lbf/sq. in.)

9. If the gas pressure in the mains is 4 in. greater than atmospheric (which is 34 ft of water), what volume would 51 cu. ft passing through the gas-meter occupy if it were collected at atmospheric pressure?

10. Describe a bicycle pump and explain its action in pumping up a bicycle tyre. Explain the fact that at each successive stroke the piston completes more of its stroke before air begins to enter the tyre.

11. A test-tube contains 50·0 c.c. of air at atmospheric pressure (76 cm. of mercury) and at room temperature. It is put, with its open end downwards, into a beaker of mercury; 2·50 c.c. of mercury enter the tube. Calculate (*a*) the pressure of the air in the test-tube, (*b*) the distance of the mercury meniscus inside the test-tube below that in the beaker.

12. A horizontal capillary tube, sealed at one end, has a 20-cm length of air enclosed in it by a column of mercury 19·0 cm long. What will be the distance occupied by the enclosed air if the tube is placed vertically (*a*) closed end downwards, (*b*) closed end upwards? (Atmospheric pressure=76·0 cmHg.)

13. The pressure of a gas at a given temperature is proportional to its density.

Show that this statement accords with Boyle's law and that the statement can be explained in terms of the kinetic theory. Show that the statement cannot be precisely true if the molecules are so closely packed that the forces of attraction between them are not negligible.

CHAPTER 12

The Principle of Archimedes. Flotation

12.1 The principle of Archimedes. Archimedes' principle deals with the upward force or upthrust which acts on things which are immersed (partly or completely) in a fluid. The effect is due to the increase of fluid pressure with depth. Anything immersed in a fluid experiences thrusts which are perpendicular to its surface. These are illustrated (Fig. 12.1) for a potato hanging in water. It is found that, no matter what the size or shape of an object may be, the resultant of all these thrust-forces is always vertically upwards. There is no resultant sideways force; in the case of the hanging

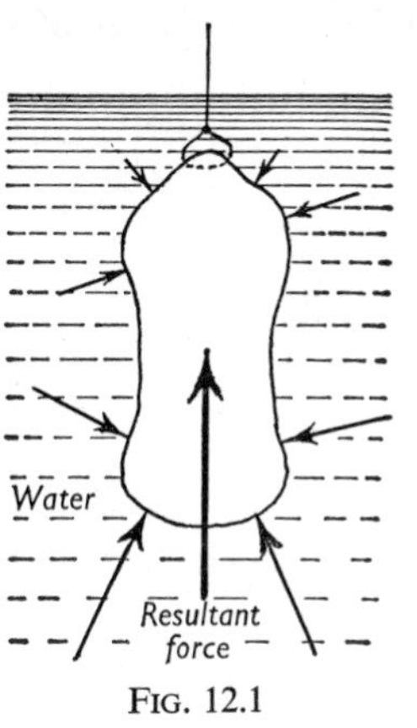

FIG. 12.1

Resultant upthrust due to fluid pressure

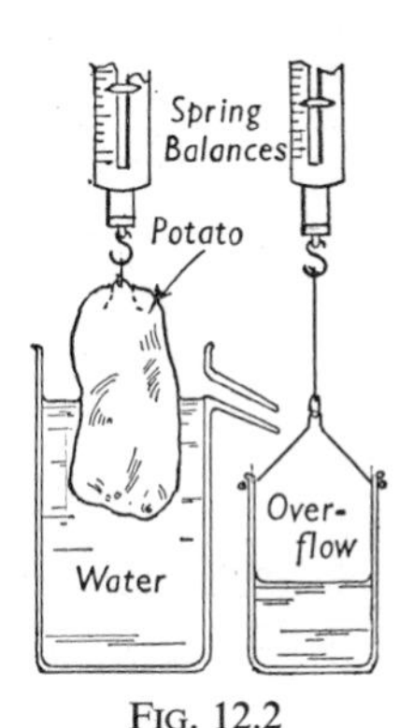

FIG. 12.2

Upthrust equals weight of displaced liquid

potato any sideways force would have caused the supporting string to hang away from the vertical. The magnitude of the upthrust is given by Archimedes' principle which states:

Any body completely or partially immersed in a fluid experiences an upthrust which is equal to the weight of fluid which the body has displaced.

Fig. 12.2 shows an experimental method of checking the principle. It shows a potato hanging from a spring balance. The weight of the potato is noted and it is then lowered to various depths in an overflow can filled to the spout with water. The displaced water overflows into a small can hanging from another spring balance, which weighs the overflow. A record is made of the decrease in the reading of the left-hand balance and the increase in the right-hand one. The figures show that at all stages of immersion the upthrust is equal (within the limits of experimental error) to the weight of water displaced, and that once the potato has been fully submerged, any further lowering has no effect on the apparent weight.

If the experiment is repeated with other liquids in the container, it is still found that the upthrust of the liquid equals the weight of liquid displaced. By doing the experiment with other substances hanging from the balance it can be shown that the upthrust does not depend on the weight of the hanging object.

The upthrust on an object is always accompanied by an equal downthrust on the containing vessel. Using the arrangement shown in Fig. 12.3, for example, it is found that the beaker of water

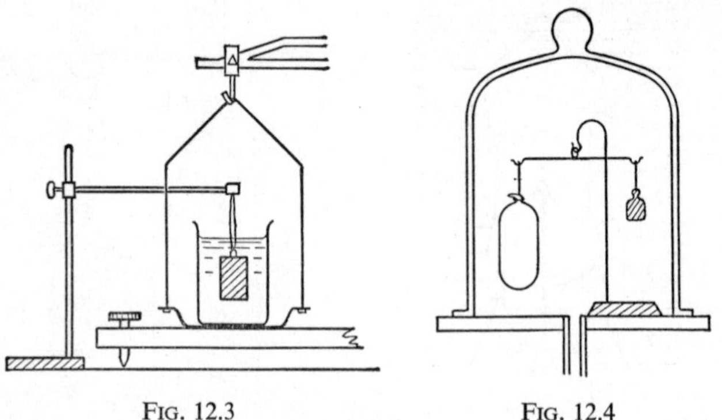

FIG. 12.3
Downthrust on a vessel of liquid

FIG. 12.4

weighs more when the solid is hung in it and that the increase is equal to the weight of water displaced. This is another illustration of Newton's third law—action and reaction are equal and opposite.

Archimedes' principle applies to all fluids, to gases as well as to liquids. The atmosphere exerts an upthrust on bodies, equal to the weight of air which they displace. This is not a large force when the bodies are small, but it is of prime importance in giving lift to a balloon; and it has to be taken into account when accurate weighings are required in scientific measurements. Fig. 12.4 shows an apparatus which illustrates the effect. A sealed glass bulb is counterpoised on a small beam balanced by a piece of lead, and the arrangement stands under a bell-jar connected to a vacuum pump. As the air in the bell-jar is removed, the balance is no longer counterpoised. The loss of air-upthrust causes it to tilt, the glass bulb moving downwards.

12.2. Archimedes' principle applied to find volume, density and specific gravity.

Volume. The volume of an irregular body which sinks in water, and which does not dissolve in water, can be found by weighing it in air and then in water as illustrated in Fig. 12.5. Thus, suppose

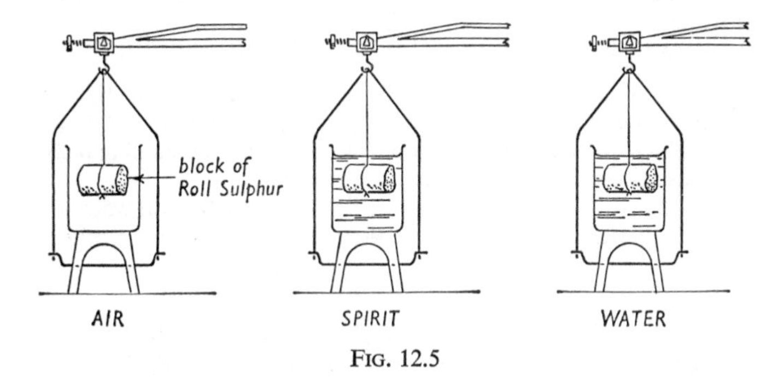

FIG. 12.5

that an iron bolt weighs 75·10 g in air and 65·10 g when completely immersed in water. The difference, 10·00 g, is due to 10·00 g of water displaced. Since 1 g of water occupies 1 c.c., the volume of the bolt is 10·00 c.c.

Density. (Mass per unit volume.) Once the volume has been found by weighings in air and in water, the density can be calculated. Thus in the case of the iron bolt referred to above, the density of the iron is 75·10 ÷ 10·00 = 7·51 g/c.c.

Specific gravity. (Wt. of substance ÷ Wt. of an equal volume of water.) By hanging a solid from the beam of an accurate balance and weighing it first in air, and then submerged in a liquid and then submerged in water, we can calculate the specific gravity of both the liquid and the solid from one set of observations. Fig. 12.5 illustrates a set of weighings in which the relative densities of wood spirit and a lump of roll sulphur are being found. The sulphur is hung by means of a very fine thread so that the volume of liquid displaced by the thread is negligible; before transferring the sulphur to the beaker of water the lump has to be washed free from any wood spirit which may have been clinging to it. It is also important to make sure that there are no air bubbles on the lump and that the lump does not touch the side of the beaker.

Specimen results. The sulphur alone weighs . . . . 39·8 g
Submerged in water it weighs . . . . . . 19·8 g
So the water it displaces weighs . . 39·8 − 19·8 = 20·0 g
Relative density of sulphur = 39·8 ÷ 20·0 = 1·99
The sulphur alone weighs . . . . . . 39·8 g
Submerged in spirit it weighs . . . . . . 23·8 g
So the spirit it displaces weighs 39·8 − 23·8 = 16·0 g.
But the sulphur displaces the same volume of spirit as it does of water.
Relative density of wood spirit = 16·0 ÷ 20·0 = 0·80.

12.3. Flotation. Hydrometers. A floating body is held up by the weight of the fluid which it has displaced. This fact about all floating bodies is referred to as the **principle of flotation: a floating body displaces its own weight of fluid.**

Fig. 12.6 shows cubes of different materials floating on water or mercury. Note that some of the solids sink in further than others

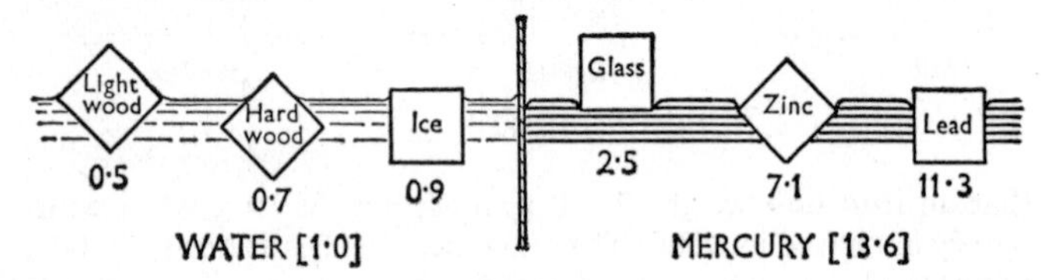

FIG. 12.6

in order to displace their own weight of liquid. The fraction submerged is equal to the ratio of the density of the solid to the density of liquid. Thus if v is the volume of the submerged part of the solid and V the whole volume of the solid, d and D being the densities of solid and liquid respectively,

Weight of floating body = Upthrust

= Weight of liquid displaced

$$V \times d = v \times D$$

whence

$$\frac{v}{V} = \frac{d}{D}$$

But v/V is the fraction submerged and d/D is the relative density of the solid compared with the liquid, i.e.

Fraction submerged = Density ratio

The tube shown in Fig. 12.7 can be used as a simple hydrometer, to find the density of the liquid from the depth to which the hydrometer sinks in water and in the liquid. The tube is loaded with lead shot until it floats about three-quarters under water, and the immersed length is measured. The tube is then floated in another liquid, and the new immersed length measured. It follows from the law of flotation that

$$\text{Sp.gr. of liquid} = \frac{\text{Immersed length of tube in water}}{\text{Immersed length of tube in liquid}}$$

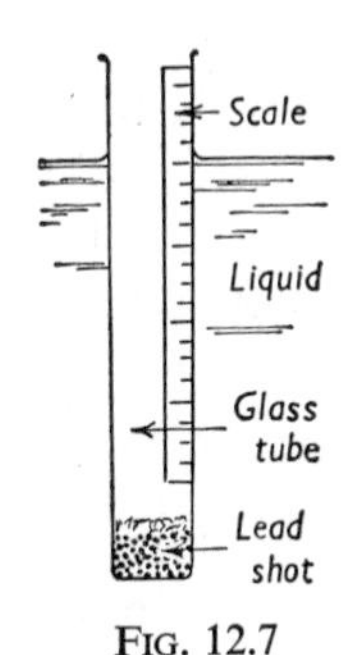

FIG. 12.7

A simple hydrometer

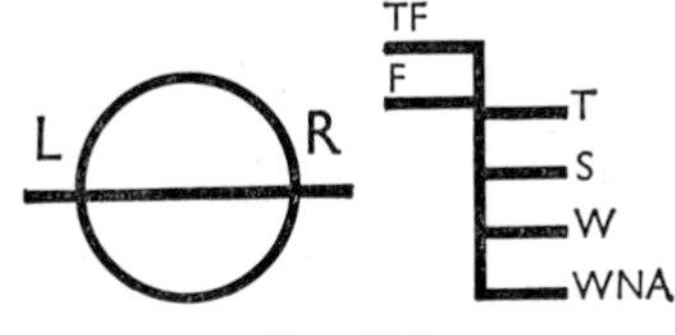

FIG. 12.8

Plimsoll lines: permissible water lines for laden ships. The sea-water lines are L.R. (the Lloyd's Register mark); T, tropical: S, summer; W, winter: WNA, winter in North Atlantic. The F line is for fresh-water loading: TF, tropical fresh-water

12.4. Ships. Balloons. The flotation of ships is another example of a supporting upthrust due to water displacement. The shape of the hull is designed to give a displacement great enough to support the ship, engines, crew and cargo. When a ship is loaded with extra cargo, it moves down until it displaces sea water equal to its new weight. But there must be a certain minimum height of deck above the water-line for safety. This 'minimum freeboard' depends on the type of vessel and its trade-routes. In 1876, largely as a result of the activities of Samuel Plimsoll, a definite load-line was made compulsory; the line is known as the Plimsoll Mark (Fig. 12.8).

Balloons filled with a gas of low density will rise in air, just as a block of wood will rise when released under water. In both cases the upward force is due to the weight of displaced fluid—the surrounding air in the case of the balloon. In a hydrogen balloon it is not really the hydrogen which does the lifting, for even hydrogen has weight. Actually the lift comes from the displacement which occurs as the balloon is blown up. Air at 15°C and at atmospheric pressure has a density of 1·29 kg/cu. metre, so a spherical balloon of diameter 7 metres, volume approximately 180 cu. metres, would experience an upthrust of $180 \times 1{\cdot}29 = 232$ kgf; the hydrogen required for filling it would weigh a fourteenth of this, about 17 kgf. Fig. 12.9 illustrates the effective lifts of equal-sized blloons filled with different gases.

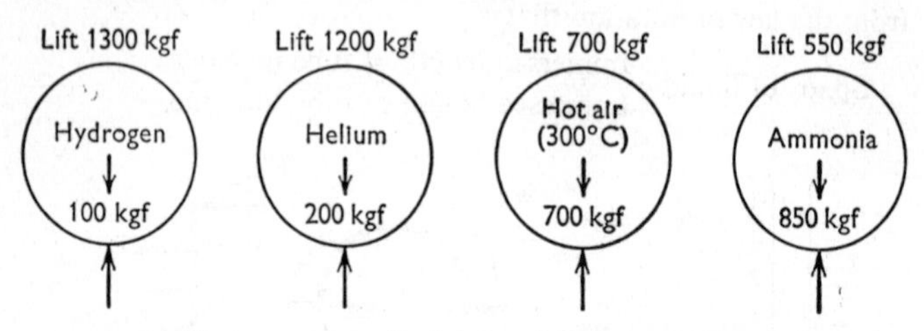

FIG. 12.9

Resultant lifts of different balloons

SUMMARY

When a body is completely or partially immersed in a fluid (any liquid or gas) **it experiences an upthrust which is equal to the weight of fluid which the body has displaced.**

The upthrust acts vertically through the centre of gravity of the displaced fluid.

When a body floats it displaces a weight of fluid equal to its own weight.

Solids which normally sink in a liquid can be shaped to give a displacement large enough to support their weight and make them float.

Air displacement provides the force which drives a balloon upwards.

Questions

1. Three cubes, one of wood, one of aluminium, and one of zinc are the same size, the length of each side being 4·00 cm. They weigh 40·0 g, 172 g and 454 g respectively. Calculate the apparent weight of each of the metal cubes when immersed in water, and the

force required to submerge the wooden cube in a liquid of density 0·80 c.c.

2. Explain the following. (*a*) A large stone lifted out of water appears to become heavier as it is withdrawn. (*b*) Iron floats on mercury but sinks in water. (*c*) It is possible for an iron dish to float on water.

In the case of (*c*) explain the conditions under which the dish may either float or sink.

3. A hollow 2-gallon drum has an external volume of 2¼ gallons and weighs 3 lb. Calculate the force required to submerge it in water. (1 gallon of water weighs 10 lb.)

4. A wood raft, of surface dimensions 2·00 metres × 1·00 metre, floats on water with 15·0 cm showing above the water line. What length of it will show above the water line if a person weighing 60·0 kg steps on to the centre of the raft? (1 cu. metre of water weighs 1000 kg.)

5. A glass globe on one pan of a beam balance is counterpoised with lead shot, the whole arrangement being in air. State and explain the direction of tilt of the beam if the arrangement is subsequently situated in a vacuum.

6. A ball of volume 120 c.c. floats, half submerged, on a liquid of density 1·60 c.c. What is the weight of the ball?

7. A solid body weighs 8·00 kgf in air and 2·50 kgf when completely immersed in water. Calculate the specific gravity (relative density) of the substance.

8. A block of stone of mass 132 kg hangs from a cord and is completely immersed in water. Calculate the tension in the cord. (The specific gravity or relative density of the stone is 3.0.)

9. Account for the fact that a partially inflated balloon, released at sea-level, becomes fully inflated at high altitudes.

10. Which of the following substances will float in salt solution of sp.gr. 1·2 and which will sink in petrol of sp.gr. 0·7? Pitch (sp.gr. 1·1), cork (sp.gr. 0·25), aluminium (sp.gr. 2·7), box-wood (sp.gr. 0·9).

Describe how you would determine experimentally, by a flotation method, the density of pitch. Assume that only a small piece of pitch is available.

11. A rod of wood, 15 cm long and 1 sq. cm cross-section, has a plug of lead within it so that it will float upright. It floats in water with 12 cm submerged. What is the weight of this simple hydrometer? Draw a section diagram of the hydrometer, half-size. On the diagram mark the density values which correspond to the following lengths submerged: 15, 12, 10, 9, 8 and 6 cm.

12. A cylinder of rubber, hanging from a thread, is lowered into a measuring cylinder containing water and the rubber becomes just submerged. The reading of the water level changed from 30·0 c.c. to 50·5 c.c. Draw sketches to show the positions of the rubber and the water levels before and after immersion. Explain the fact that the tension in the thread becomes less and the pressure on the base of the measuring cylinder greater due to the immersion of the rubber. By how much does the tension change? If the area of cross-section of the measuring cylinder is 5·00 sq. cm, by how much does the pressure on its base change?

13. Make a diagram such as Fig. 12.9 for balloons containing hydrogen, hot air, cold air. Find the lifting forces when they are in an atmosphere of carbon dioxide, which is 22 times as dense as the hydrogen.

CHAPTER 13

Thermometers. Temperature Scales

13.1. Thermometers. Thermometers are instruments used to measure the **temperature** or relative hotness of things. There are many different kinds of thermometer, the commonest being the liquid-in-glass type, containing mercury or coloured alcohol. These make use of the expansion of liquids when heated, and because the expansion is not very great the liquid is put in a bulb which is joined to a capillary tube. When a thermometer has been made, a scale must be given to it, with a suitable zero mark, and a suitable size for the temperature units or **degrees.** The size of a degree is settled by choosing two fixed points, temperatures which are the same the world over, and dividing the interval between them into equal parts or degrees. The chosen **fixed points** are the temperature of pure melting ice, and the temperature of steam from water boiling at normal pressure (76 cm Hg). On the **centigrade** or **Celsius** scale the interval is divided into **100** equal parts, and on the **Fahrenheit** scale into **180** equal parts; thus the Fahrenheit degree is about half the size of the centigrade one. The centigrade **lower fixed point** ('ice-point') has been called zero, so the **upper fixed point** is 100°C. This zero is not the lowest temperature attainable. Fahrenheit chose a lower zero, the temperature of a mixture of ice and salt. Because this zero is 32 Fahrenheit degrees below the lower fixed point, the melting point of ice is 32°F and the normal boiling point of water $32+180=212$°F. Since Fahrenheit's time much lower temperatures have been reached. The temperature of solid carbon dioxide ('dry ice' or Drikold) is −80°C, and of liquid air −182°C. Lord Kelvin (1824–1907) showed that theoretically there is a lower limit to temperature, a temperature at which bodies have no heat left in them, and at which all motion of the molecules ceases. This, to the nearest whole number, is −273°C. On the Kelvin Absolute scale this is treated as zero and is known as the **absolute zero;** on this scale the melting point of ice is 273° and the normal boiling point of water 373°. Readings on the constant volume gas thermometer (p. 116) agree very closely with the Kelvin absolute scale.

Of the liquids used in thermometers, alcohol has the merits of cheapness and a fairly large expansion in comparison with other liquids. Its low boiling point (78°C) restricts its use in the higher ranges, but its low freezing point (–114°C) makes it useful for low temperatures. The corresponding mercury range is 357°C to –40°C; the upper limit is raised to 400°C by having nitrogen in the tube. The relatively small expansion of mercury means that the stem has a much finer bore. Mercury has the advantage of being readily obtainable in the pure state and also of not wetting the glass container. In relation to the scale of the standard gas thermometer the expansion of mercury in glass is very nearly uniform.

A quick-acting thermometer with a wide temperature range is the **thermocouple.** This consists of two different kinds of wire, with one end of each joined together. If the other ends are connected to a sensitive galvanometer and the junction is heated, a small voltage is produced and registered by the instrument. These thermocouples have many uses in industry; for instance, the recording galvanometer (with temperature scale) can be set up in an office some distance from the furnace in which the thermocouple is placed. Pl. 5 shows a copper-constantan thermocouple being used to take the temperature of a bath of molten lead.

Thermocouple and other types of thermometer can be calibrated at the ice and steam points. At other temperatures they are usually checked against the readings of a standard thermometer such as the **constant-volume gas thermometer.** A simple form of this is shown in Fig. 13.1. It consists of a bulb containing gas (generally hydrogen

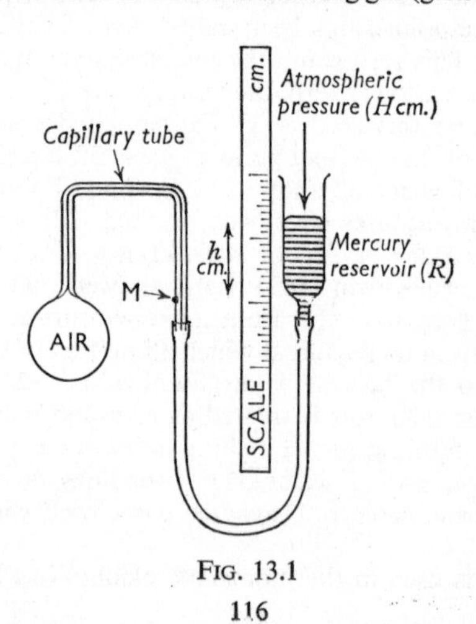

FIG. 13.1

or nitrogen, but air can be used) connected by a capillary tube to a mercury manometer. The mercury reservoir R is always adjusted to bring the mercury to the fixed mark M, and the pressure of the gas is then equal to the barometric height plus the vertical column h. Observations are taken of the pressure of the gas at the ice-point (p_0), at the steam-point (p_{100}) and at the required temperature (p_t). One-hundredth of ($p_{100}-p_0$) represents 1 degC; this is usually of the order of 3 mm Hg. This number divided into the increase (p_t-p_0) gives the required temperature t, in °C.

13.2. Checking the fixed points. Importance of standard conditions. Thermometers bought from the manufacturer rarely have a guarantee that their readings are correct. For accurate work their readings should be checked, or else they should be sent to a testing laboratory (such as the National Physical Laboratory). A check of the steam and ice points is a fairly simple matter and is well within the range of a school laboratory.

The upper fixed point, or steam point, can be checked by passing a current of steam round the thermometer as shown in Fig. 13.2*b*.

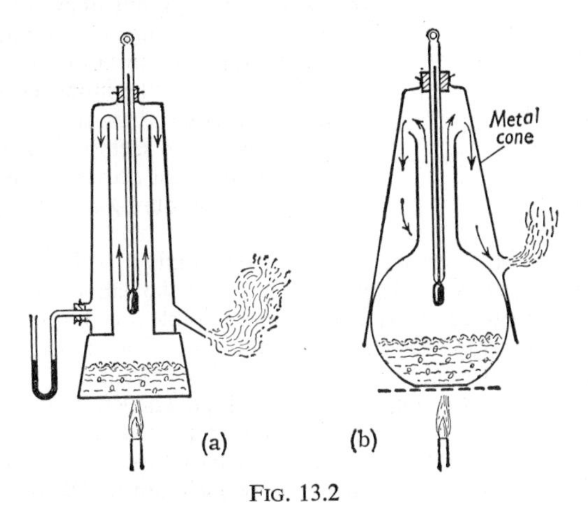

FIG. 13.2

Readings of the thermometer are taken over a period of two to three minutes to check that the reading is steady. If in this experiment the thermometer does not read exactly 100°C it may not necessarily be faulty. The atmospheric pressure may not be exactly 76 cm of mercury. A barometer reading should be taken and a correction applied. A change of 2·7 cm in the barometer means a corresponding change of 1 degC in the boiling point (roughly 1 degC per inch). It is important to have the whole of the mercury column heated by the steam, and to check that the pressure of the steam in the apparatus is atmospheric. Manufacturers test the upper fixed point with a **hypsometer**—which is a tall instrument (Fig. 13.2*a*).

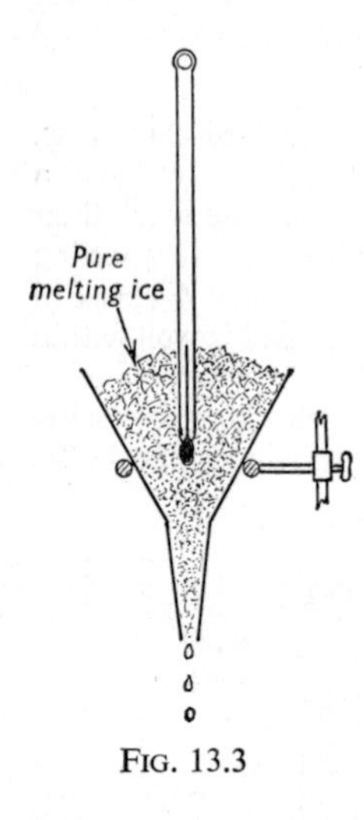

FIG. 13.3

The lower fixed point can be checked by putting the thermometer in a funnel of crushed ice as shown in Fig. 13.3. The level of the mercury on the scale is observed when conditions have become steady. No correction need be made for atmospheric pressure; a change of 1 cm in the barometer changes the melting point of ice by only 0·0001 degC.

13.3. Factors which affect the fixed points. Dissolved substances affect the boiling point and freezing point of water. Thus if you dissolve anything in water and take the temperature of the boiling solution, you will find that the thermometer reads a higher temperature than the true fixed point. But the steam itself is at its normal temperature; it is not necessary therefore to have absolutely pure water in a hypsometer.

If you put some crushed ice in a can and mix it well with a small quantity of common salt, you will find that the temperature of the mixture is a degree or two below the ice-point. It is thus important to use pure melting ice in checking the lower fixed point.

The effect of pressure on the upper fixed point can be shown using the apparatus illustrated in Fig. 13.4. The left-hand diagram illustrates steam being produced under a pressure higher than atmospheric, by forcing the steam to pass through a column of mercury before it can escape; in such circumstances the steam temperature is above the normal. If the clip is closed and the mercury vessel and the source of heat removed, the water still goes on boiling. Even if the water is cooled below 100°C, the water will boil again if cold water is poured over the sides of the flask. The cooling condenses some of the steam and so causes a very low pressure in the flask (as can be seen from the collapse of the rubber tubing near the clip). The water boils at a lower temperature when under reduced pressure. (A round-bottomed flask is used for this experiment to withstand the pressure of the surrounding atmosphere.)

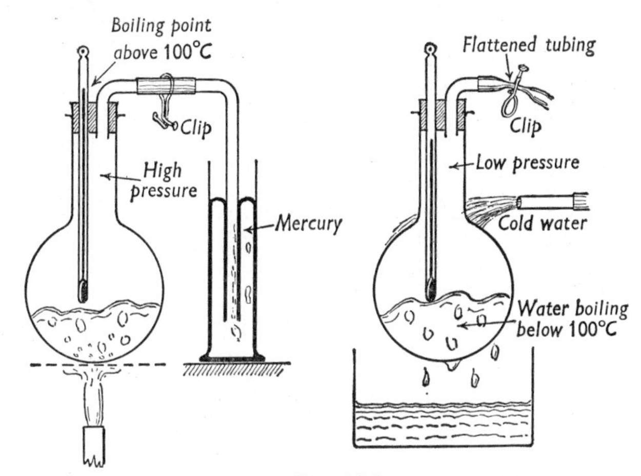

FIG. 13.4

Effect of pressure on boiling point

13.4. Centigrade and Fahrenheit scales. Because the Fahrenheit degree (degF) is smaller than the centigrade degree (degC) there will be more of them in a given temperature range. The actual relation is

$$\frac{\text{No. of degF in any given interval}}{\text{No. of degC in the same interval}} = \frac{9}{5}$$

This formula, together with a knowledge of the ice-point values on the two scales can be used to convert temperatures from one scale to the other. Suppose that f°F $= c$°C. Then, as is shown in Fig. 13.5, $(f-32)$ degF $= c$ degC

$$\therefore \frac{f-32}{c} = \frac{9}{5}$$

If either f or c in this formula is known, then the other can be calculated.

The conversion can also be solved graphically, and Fig. 13.6 shows a graph ranging from −40°C (which is also −40°F) to 100°C.

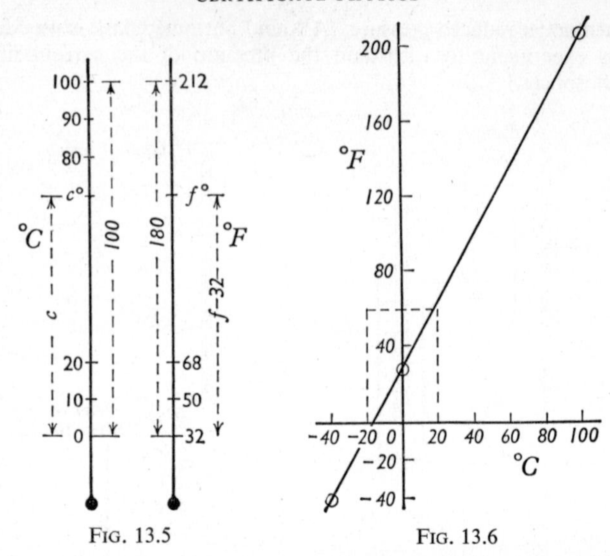

FIG. 13.5 FIG. 13.6

13.5. Maximum and minimum thermometers. Most thermometers designed to register maximum and minimum temperatures are fitted with an index which is moved by the meniscus of the liquid. Fig. 13.7 illustrates two such thermometers designed by Rutherford. The alcohol thermometer registers minimum temperatures,

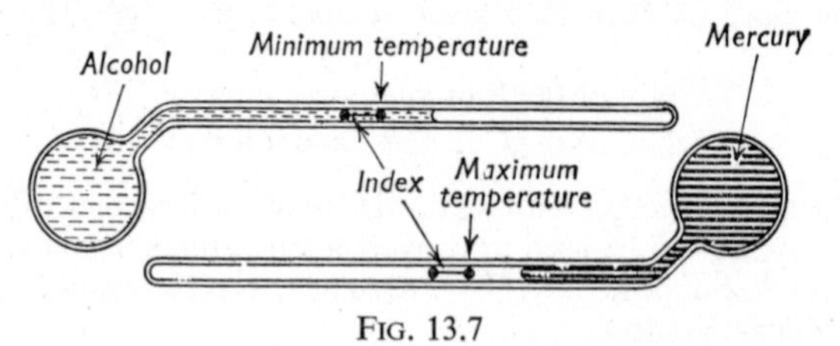

FIG. 13.7

Rutherford's thermometers for maximum and minimum temperatures

since its concave meniscus pulls the index to the lowest temperature reached; the convex meniscus of the mercury thermometer pushes the index to the highest temperature reached. After a reading has been taken, the index, commonly made of coloured glass, is shaken back to the meniscus line or, if the index is made of steel, is pulled back to the position with a magnet. A combined form of maximum and minimum thermometer is shown in Fig. 13.8. **It is an alcohol thermometer fitted with a mercury piston,** and each end of the mercury column moves an index, pushing one index forward during the expansion and the other back during the contraction. The tube is bent into a U-shape to make the arrangement more compact. The space above the mercury column is partly filled with alcohol; air and alcohol vapour in the rest of the space provide a pressure which keeps the liquid columns intact.

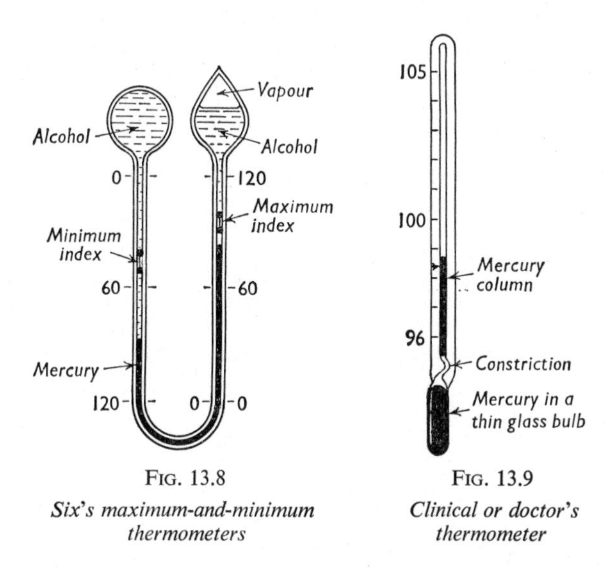

FIG. 13.8
Six's maximum-and-minimum thermometers

FIG. 13.9
Clinical or doctor's thermometer

The **clinical** or doctor's thermometer (Fig. 13.9) is a special form of thermometer usually graduated in degrees F. It is designed to record temperatures only a few degrees above and below the normal body temperature (98·4°F or 36·9°C); its stem is short and is graduated over the range 95–105°F or 35–40°C. The main feature of the instrument is a kink or constriction in the tube near the bulb. The mercury in expanding forces its way through the constriction to reach the maximum position. When the thermometer is removed from position (the mouth or the armpit usually), the mercury cools, contracts and breaks at the constriction, leaving a column of mercury in the capillary. To re-set the thermometer, the isolated mercury column is shaken back towards the bulb. The bulb is small and its walls are thin, so that the thermometer is quick-acting and reaches its final temperature after 30 to 60 seconds; because the volume of mercury used is small, the capillary tube has to be very fine, and the front of the stem is shaped as a cylindrical glass lens to magnify the thin column.

SUMMARY

Temperature scales are based on two fixed points; the **ice point,** temperature of pure melting ice, and the **steam point,** temperature of steam from water boiling under standard atmospheric pressure. The interval between the two points is known as the **fundamental interval.** This is divided into 100 parts or degrees on the Celsius or centigrade scale, into 180 degrees on the Fahrenheit scale; hence

$$5 \text{ degC} = 9 \text{degF}$$

The ice-point is zero on the C scale and 32 on the F scale; hence

$$\frac{f-32}{c-0} = \frac{9}{5}$$

The **constant-volume gas thermometer** can be used over a large temperature range. It is also used as a standard thermometer, against which the readings of others can be checked.

Absolute zero, the zero of the Kelvin Absolute scale, is −273·2°C.

Questions

1. Construct a copy of Fig. 13.6 on graph paper. From it discover the Fahrenheit temperatures corresponding to 50°C, 30°C, 15°C and the centigrade temperatures corresponding to 100°F, 50°F, 15°F. Check your observations by calculation.

2. A temperature of '27 degrees of frost' is a temperature which is 27 Fahrenheit degrees below the melting point of ice. Calculate this temperature (*a*) in °C (*b*) in °F.

3. Draw labelled diagrams of the apparatus you would use to check the lower and the upper fixed points on a mercury thermometer. Why is it necessary to read the barometer when checking the upper fixed point?

4. Express 17°C on the Absolute scale and 1000° Absolute on (*a*) the C scale, (*b*) the F scale. Assume that Absolute zero is at −273°C.

5. An ungraduated mercury thermometer attached to a millimetre scale reads 22·8 mm in ice and 242·4 mm in steam at standard pressure. What will it read when the temperature is 22°F?

6. If the distance between the upper and lower fixed points on a thermometer is 14·4 cm, what is the distance between degree-marks when the scale is (*a*) a centigrade one, (*b*) a Fahrenheit one? Calculate the temperature (in °C and °F) corresponding to a mark M which is 5·4 cm above the lower fixed point.

7. At 10°C an uncalibrated thermometer reads 15 units, and at 80°C it reads 50 units. Find graphically or otherwise, the reading on the uncalibrated thermometer at the upper and lower fixed points.

8. Draw a labelled diagram to show the structure and the scale of a clinical thermometer. What features make it quick-acting, sensitive, and short?

9. Give two reasons why water is less suitable than alcohol for use in thermometers. In what respect is mercury more suitable than alcohol for use in thermometers?

10. The lengths of a degree interval on two mercury thermometers, one having a centigrade scale and the other a Fahrenheit scale, are 2·0 mm and 1·0 mm respectively. Calculate (*a*) the distance between the upper and lower fixed points of each thermometer, (*b*) the distance between the lower fixed point and the −15 mark on the Fahrenheit thermometer.

11. A thermometer with a stem of uniform bore reads 102 on the scale when at the upper fixed point (100°C) and −0·5 on the scale when at the lower fixed point (0°C). Calculate the temperature which this thermometer would record when the true temperature is (*a*) 50°C, (*b*) −10°C.

12. What type of thermometer would you use to take the temperature in each of the following instances? Give a reason for each answer. (*a*) Boiling oil, (*b*) the water at the bottom of a deep lake, (*c*) a live rabbit, (*d*) the interior of a glowing coke fire, (*e*) an oven used for baking.

13. Describe an experiment which shows that the boiling point of water is raised by an increase of pressure.

CHAPTER 14

Expansion

14.1. Expansion of solids. A piece of apparatus which shows that a metal expands both in length and in cross-section is illustrated in Fig. 14.1. The rod just fits the length-gap and the hole in the gauge when both are cold. The rod, held in a wooden handle, is heated in a flame; it then fits neither the gap nor the hole until the rod is cooled again. If the hole-end of the gauge is heated, the cold rod fits in the hole more freely. It seems as though the hole has expanded. What has happened is that the metal of the gauge has expanded outwards in all directions leaving a bigger hole; another way of explaining the effect is to consider that the ring of metal which frames the hole has expanded and increased its circumference.

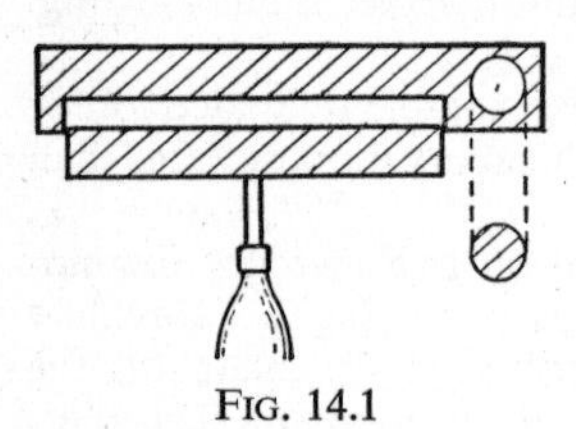

FIG. 14.1
Rod-and-gauge apparatus

The expansion of solids can be measured using the apparatus shown in Fig. 15.1. It turns out to be very small, a matter of millionths of the original length for each degree rise. Thus zinc expands 26 millionths of its length for each Centigrade degree rise, steel only 11 millionths. A bar of steel one million millimetres long (1000 metres) would expand 11 mm if heated 1 deg C, 1100 mm if heated 100 degC.

Although the expansion is so small, many substances will exert very large forces if their expansion is confined. It depends on how compressible they are. Thus you could heat a corked tube of air without blowing the cork out, though the pressure on the cork would undoubtedly increase. You could stop the expansion of a rubber ball, heated in your hands, merely by squeezing it. But you could not stop the expansion of a steel ball, small though the expansion would be; something far greater than hand pressure would be needed for this. Uneven heating can cause brittle materials to crack (see p. 127). For example, if a piece of roll sulphur is held over quite a small flame, pieces of the sulphur fly off in all directions owing to the expansion of the top layers away from the bottom layers of the material.

Damage can occur if allowances are not made for expansion˙ Thus the metal parts of fire-grates and stoves are made to have a loose fit, with gaps between them and the surrounding parts. Overhead telephone wires are never drawn perfectly taut, for a drop in temperature might produce enough tension to snap them. Steam pipes are sometimes looped to allow for expansion, and the ring supports which hold the pipes in place are made as split rings for the same reason. Motor-car pistons are made slightly smaller than the cylinders in which they move, piston rings being fitted to make the system gas-tight; these too are split-rings with a gap to allow for expansion when the engine becomes hot. The roadway of large bridges may have as much as two or three feet allowance for expansion, the ends of the bridge moving over large rollers which allow freedom of movement. Even brickwork, which does not expand as much as metals do, has its expansion allowed for in high-temperature furnaces such as blast furnaces.

On the other hand, use can be made of the large forces which accompany expansion or contraction. The steel tyre of the driving wheel of a locomotive is forced on hot; it is then quickly cooled, and it shrinks and grips the wheel tightly. In a similar manner the tubes of which the barrels of big guns are made are 'shrunk on', and the stresses set up in the tubes give them the additional strength to withstand the force of the explosion. In some instances, shrinking-on is done by an initial cooling. A pulley can be made to grip its driving shaft by first cooling the shaft—originally slightly larger than the hole in the pulley—with solid carbon dioxide or liquid air. The pulley is forced on to the shaft and then the system allowed to warm up.

Two strips of metal, bolted or welded together, curl when heated or cooled if their expansions are different; the longer piece of metal is on the outside of the curve. The effect can be shown with iron and brass, but is even more marked if brass and invar steel are used. **Invar** is a steel alloy containing 36% of nickel and it expands only very slightly when heated. Strips of brass and invar, known as *bimetal*, have a number of important applications. They are made by welding bars of the two metals together and then rolling the compound bar into strips. A coil of narrow bimetal strip curls and uncurls with change of temperature and has been used to work a pointer-type thermometer (Fig. 14.2). Bimetal is also used in thermostat switches and in fire alarms, the bending of the strip being used either to break or to make a contact in an electrical circuit (Fig. 14.3). Electric ovens, electric irons and electric water heaters are generally fitted with a **thermostat,** which automatically switches off the supply when the hot parts reach a definite temperature. The principle is the same as in Fig. 14.3 but the brass side of the strip faces the contacts.

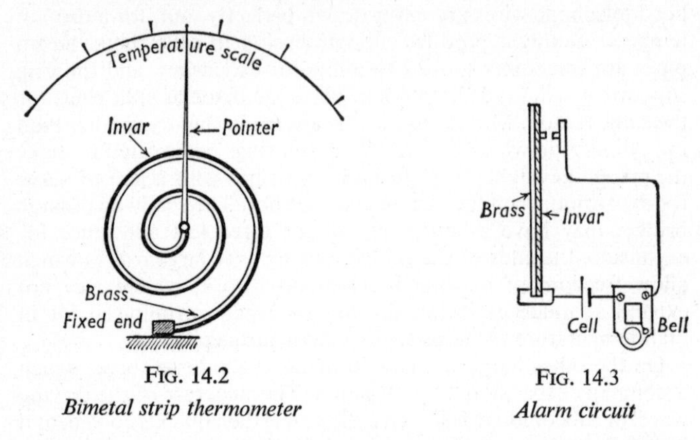

FIG. 14.2

Bimetal strip thermometer

FIG. 14.3

Alarm circuit

The different expansion of metals has also been used to compensate clocks and watches for the effects of temperature change. The time-keeping properties of a pendulum clock depend partly on the length of the pendulum. An increase in the length causes a slower rate of swing and the clock loses. Fig. 14.4 shows two types

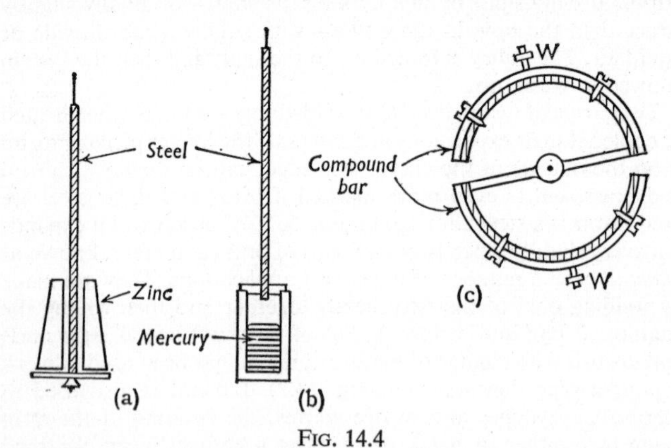

FIG. 14.4

Compensation for expansion in clock pendulums and in the balance of a watch of compensated pendulum. In (*a*), the type used for Big Ben, expansion of the steel rod lowers the bob, while the upward expansion of the zinc tube, which has about twice the expansion of the steel, raises the bob enough to keep the centre of gravity of the system unchanged. In (*b*) the compensation is brought about by a rise in the level of the mercury.

The time-control of a watch consists of a steel hair-spring and a balanced wheel. When the temperature rises, the metal spring becomes less elastic and the spokes of the balance wheel expand. Both these effects, of which the first is the more important, tend to make the watch slow down. The wheel is compensated by making the rim in two sections carried by two spokes. Each section is a curved compound-bar of steel and brass, with the brass on the outside. The expansion of the spokes carries the rim outwards, but the inward curling of the compound-bar sections compensates not only for this but for the weakening of the hair-spring. Fig. 14.4*c* shows a two-spoked wheel. The discovery of alloys having very small expansion has made compensation necessary only in the most accurate of timepieces.

A solid which expands only very slightly when heated is **silica.** (Sand is an impure form of silica.) Vessels made of pure silica look like glass, while the less pure forms are milky white. One of the trade names for the material is 'Vitreosil'. If boiling water is poured into an ordinary thick glass tumbler, the vessel will break. The inside of the tumbler expands, but the outside remains cold and does not expand at the same time. The resulting force breaks the tumbler. Vitreosil has such a very small expansion that a vessel made of it suffers little force with sudden change of temperature; it may actually be made red-hot and then put into cold water without damage. Pyrex glass is another commercial heat-resistant glass. Vitreosil and Pyrex glass are used for making kitchen-ware and laboratory vessels.

14.2. Expansion of liquids. The expansion of liquids is more noticeable than the expansion of solids. Different liquids expand different amounts, as can be shown experimentally by filling two flasks, of equal size, with each of the liquids under test. The flasks are fitted with identical glass tubes to show up the expansions which occur on heating (Fig. 14.5). The heating is done by a water bath which is kept well stirred. When a reasonable expansion has occurred, heating is stopped, stirring is continued until the levels are again stationary, and the new levels are marked. A comparison of the rises in level of the liquids gives a comparison of their expansions.

In this experiment there is a slight expansion of the glass container; the sides of the vessel expand outwards, just as the sides of the hole expand outwards in the experiment on page 124. The effect can be shown by using sudden heating instead of slow heating. Either of the flasks of cold liquid is taken, and the position of the liquid level is marked. The flask is then plunged quickly into hot water. There is a sudden drop in the liquid level, followed by a considerably greater steady rise. The sudden drop shows that the glass vessel has expanded outwards, the steady rise shows that the expansion of the liquid is greater than that of the glass.

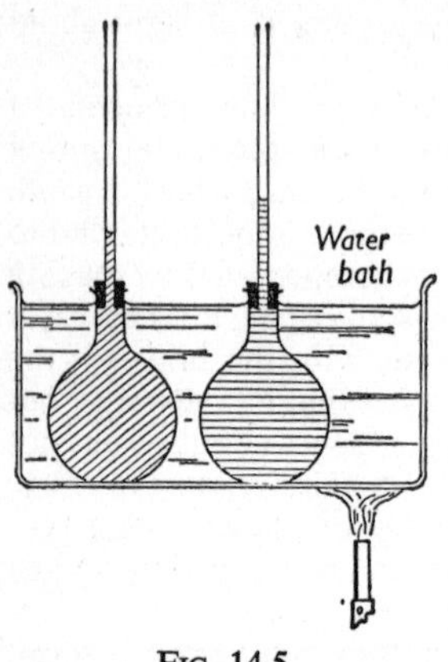

FIG. 14.5

The volume expansion (called 'cubical expansion') of liquids is round about a thousandth of their original volume for each centigrade degree rise in temperature; some values are given in the table on page 139. Liquid expansion is put to use in thermometers and also in some thermostatic devices, one of which is illustrated in Fig. 14.6.

The expansion of water is peculiar. It is not uniform, the expansion between 30°C and 50°C being double that between 10°C and 30°C. The use of a thermometer in conjunction with the flask-and-tube apparatus of Fig. 14.5 will readily show this. If water is cooled below 10°C, there is a small contraction until the temperature reaches 4°C; between 4°C and 0°C a small expansion occurs. Over this range the changes are so small that the expansion of the glass vessel may hide the effect. The difficulty can be overcome by using a silica vessel; or by putting into the glass vessel one-seventh of its volume of mercury, when the expansion of the mercury compensates for the expansion of the glass. If a given mass of water at room temperature is cooled to 4°C its decreasing volume results in an increase in density; below that temperature the density becomes less. Water thus has a **maximum density at 4°C.** This peculiarity has an important bearing on pond life, the temperature of the lower levels of ponds and lakes hardly ever falling below 4°C however cold the surface weather may be. A similar effect is to be noticed even above ground if a bucket of water is left outdoors in frosty weather; ice forms on the surface of the water and becomes appreciably thick before ice forms at the sides or at the bottom of the bucket. The sinking of the relatively warm water (4°C) delays any freezing there.

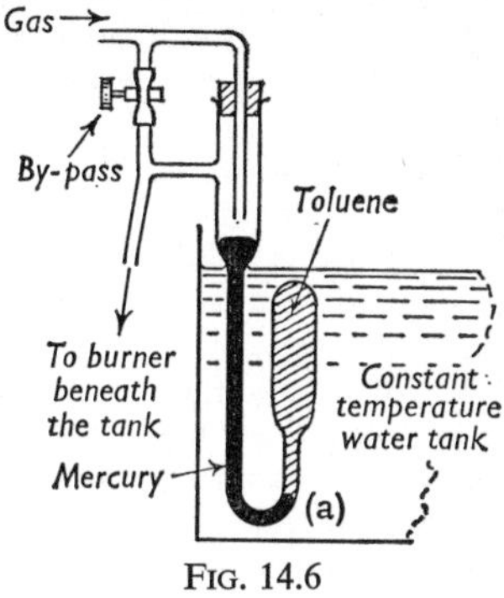

FIG. 14.6

A thermostat. As the water tank becomes heated by the burner beneath it, the toluene expands. The mercury column moves upwards; at the required temperature it closes the main gas-supply pipe. Enough gas then goes through the by-pass tube to keep the burner-flame just alight. If the tank should fall below the required temperature, contraction of the toluene re-opens the supply pipe

14.3. Expansion of gases. If the volume expansion of lead is taken as 1 unit, that for water averages about 10 units; for gases it is about 100 units. A remarkable feature of gas-expansion is that equal volumes of different gases expand the same amount when heated through an equal rise of temperature. For each centigrade degree rise in temperature gases expand 1/273 of the volume which they would occupy at 0°C —provided that the pressure remains constant. This general behaviour of gases was first discovered by Charles in 1787; the previous statement is one way of stating Charles's law (p. 137).

SUMMARY

Solids expand in all directions when heated. The amount of expansion is different for different solids; it is extremely small for silica and certain nickel-steel alloys. Vessels such as flasks and beakers expand outwards when heated, so their internal capacity is increased.

Liquids increase in volume when heated; in general, the effect is greater than in the case of solids. The expansion of water is abnormal; over the range 0°C to 4°C water contracts with rise of temperature, and the expansion above this range is not uniform.

Questions

1. Describe a simple experiment which shows that a metal bar expands both in length and in cross-section when heated.

2. How would you show that alcohol expands more than mercury when equal volumes of these liquids are heated through the same range of temperature?

3. How would you show that the expansion of water over the range 30–50°C is greater than over the range 10–30°C?

4. Describe and explain what happens when (*a*) a bottle is filled with boiling water, tightly corked, and allowed to cool, (*b*) a bottle is filled with cold water, tightly corked, and heated to 90°C.

5. A mercury thermometer, with a bulb which is not very thin, is suddenly immersed in hot water. The mercury level shows a slight fall, followed by a large rise. Explain these observations.

6. An expanding substance, if confined, usually exerts a very large force. To what extent is this statement true for (*a*) gases, (*b*) metals? A mercury-in-glass thermometer, heated above its normal range, was found broken as a result. Explain this, and suggest a likely place for the breakage to take place.

7. A mercury thermometer, used to take the temperature of an oil bath by putting the bulb just below the oil surface, reads 90·0°C. When the whole thermometer is put under the oil, the thermometer reads 91·0°C. State how, if at all, the following might have affected the rise in the reading:

(i) The pressure in liquids increases with depth.
(ii) A thermometer does not give a true reading unless all of the liquid in it is at the same temperature.
(iii) Glass tubes have a bigger cross-section when heated.

8. Describe the structure of bimetal strip. Give one practical application of it, illustrating your answer with a diagram.

9. Give examples, one in each case, of the practical application of the expansion of (*a*) a liquid, (*b*) a metal.

10. State how, if at all, a rise in the temperature of a copper washer affects (*a*) its internal diameter, (*b*) its volume, (*c*) its weight, (*d*) its density.

11. Draw a labelled diagram of a device which would switch on a light, or ring a bell, if the temperature in a greenhouse fell below a certain value.

12. Draw a labelled diagram of a heating device and thermostat which could be used to keep a tank of water warm and at a steady temperature.

13. A glass tube is fitted with an aluminium ring which just grips it in hot weather. Explain the fact that the tube is liable to crack in cold weather.

14. Water at the bottom of a pond, frozen at the surface, is

rarely colder than 4°C and is not likely to be warmer than this. Give an explanation of these facts. What type of thermometer would you choose for finding the temperature of water at the bottom of a frozen pond? Give a reason for your choice.

15. An air thermometer is made from a capillary tube, open at one end and having a bulb at the other end; the index is a short thread of mercury in the capillary tube. Explain the fact that this thermometer is more sensitive to temperature changes than if it were filled with alcohol. When the ice-point of this thermometer is regularly tested, it is found that the position of the index varies from day to day. Explain this. State, giving your reason, whether this would also occur if the open end of the capillary were sealed.

CHAPTER 15

Coefficients of Expansion. The Gas Laws

15.1. Coefficients of expansion. Many substances expand uniformly when heated, i.e. the expansion of a given specimen is the same for each degree rise in temperature, whether from 0° to 1° or from $t°$ to $(t+1)°$. The expansion depends on the initial size of the specimen; so that it is convenient to calculate the expansion of it per degree in comparison with its original size (the original size being determined at some definite temperature, usually 0°C). Values obtained in this way are called **coefficients of expansion.** Tables giving some of these coefficients are given at the end of the chapter.

Definitions. The coefficient of $\left\{\begin{matrix}\text{linear}\\\text{superficial}\\\text{cubical}\end{matrix}\right\}$ expansion of a substance is the fraction of its $\left\{\begin{matrix}\text{length}\\\text{area}\\\text{volume}\end{matrix}\right\}$, at 0°C, which the substance expands for a rise of one degree.

Thus if the coefficient of linear expansion of a metal is 0·000018 per degC this metal expands 0·000018 of its length, at 0°C, for each degC rise, i.e.

0·000018 of a foot	if it was a foot long	at 0°C
0·000018 of a mile	if it was a mile long	at 0°C
0·000018 of 6·28 cm	if it was 6·28 cm	at 0°C

Such coefficients are usually expressed per degC; if expressed per degF the corresponding number will be 5/9 of that per degC, i.e. the metal referred to above has a coefficient of 0·000010 per degF.

If a substance has a length l_o at 0°C and its coefficient of linear expansion is α, then it will expand α of l (or $\alpha \times l_o$) when heated to 1°C. When heated to t°C it will expand t times as much.

Hence

$$\textbf{Expansion} = \boldsymbol{l_o \times \alpha \times t} \quad . \quad . \quad . \quad . \quad (1)$$

The length of a solid at room temperature differs from its length at 0°C by only about 1 part in 5000. Therefore the following approximation is often used in calculating expansions when the length at 0°C is not known.

$$\textbf{Expansion} = l \times \alpha \times \textbf{temp. change} \quad . \quad (2)$$

where l = the original length at any temperature not far from 0°C.

Similarly, for volume expansion,

Expansion in vol.
= Original vol. × cubical coefft. × temp. change . . (3)

This approximation is adequate for most calculations on liquids.

Equation (3) may be used for gases only by substituting 'volume at 0°C' for 'original volume'; the coefficient for gases is so large that the volume at, say, room temperature is quite different from the volume at 0°C.

EXAMPLE 1. 5·60 *litres of benzene at* 0°*C rise in temperature to* 20°*C. Calculate the new volume.* (*Coefficient of expansion of benzene* = 0·00125 *per degC.*)

Expansion = 5·60 × 0·00125 × 20 litres
= 0·140 litre
New volume = 5·60 + 0·140 litres
= 5·74 litres

EXAMPLE 2. *Calculate the length of a zinc rod,* 95·00 *cm long at* 15°*C, when cooled to* −25°*C.* (*Coefficient of linear expansion of zinc* = 0·0000260 *per degC.*)

Although the length of the rod at 0°C is not given, it will make very little difference to the calculation if this length is taken as 95·00 cm.

Contraction = 95 × 0·000026 × 40 cm
= 0·0988 cm
New length = 95·00 − 0·0988
= 94·90(1) cm

EXAMPLE 3. *The distance between two points, measured with a brass scale at* 20°*C is* 83·70 *cm. Calculate the distance between the two points if the brass scale reads correctly when at* 0°*C.* (*Coefficient of linear expansion of brass* = 0·0000187 *per degC.*)

At 20°C each 'cm' of the brass scale will be more than a true centimetre owing to expansion.

Increase of each 'cm' = 1 × 0·0000187 × 20 cm
= 0·000374 cm
Each 'cm' on the scale will be 1 + 0·000374 cm
83·70 'cm' lengths = 83·70 + 0·000374 × 83·70 cm
= 83·70 + 0·031 cm
= 83·73(1) cm

EXAMPLE 4. *56·00 c.c. of sulphur dioxide at 20·0°C, heated to 100·0°C at constant pressure, occupy a volume of 72·00 c.c. Calculate the coefficient of expansion of sulphur dioxide.*

The volume of the gas at 0°C can be found from simple proportion. There is an expansion of 16·00 c.c. for a rise in temperature of 80·0 degC. Therefore there will be a contraction of 4·00 c.c. if the temperature falls from 20·0°C to 0°C, and the volume at 0°C will be 56·00 − 4·00 = 52·00 c.c.

If γ is the required coefficient,

$$16{\cdot}00 = 52{\cdot}00 \times \gamma \times 80{\cdot}0$$

whence $$\gamma = 0{\cdot}00384$$

Coefficient of expansion of sulphur dioxide = 0·00384 per deg C.

15.2. Finding the coefficient of linear expansion of a solid. The material is generally chosen in the form of a rod, a tube or a wire, and is steam-heated with one end of the material kept fixed; the expansion is so small that it has either to be magnified by a lever or by an optical system, or measured by an accurate gauge (e.g. a micrometer gauge or a travelling microscope).

A method using a screw-gauge is illustrated in Fig. 15.1. A tube

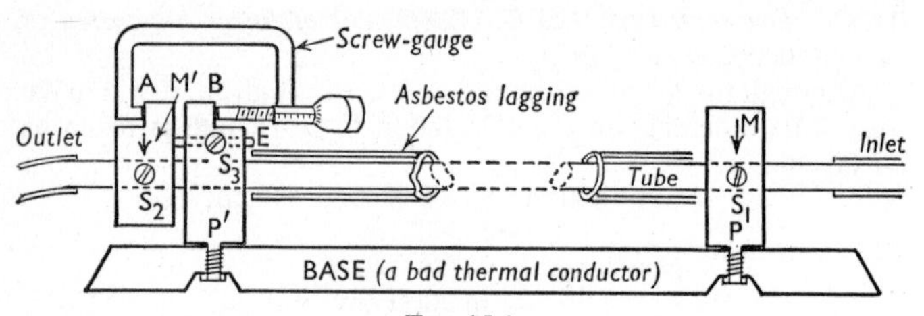

FIG. 15.1

of the substance passes through holes in two pillars P and P′, and is firmly clamped in one of them (P) by a screw (S_1). Another screw (S_2) clamps a metal boss to the tube, and the distance AB is measured with the screw-gauge while cold water, at an observed temperature, is flowing through the tube. To keep the metal boss firmly in position while AB is being measured, the screw S_3 is used to fix an extension (E) of the boss. S_3 is then loosened, steam is passed through the tube and another measurement is made of the distance AB; S_3 is again screwed on to E while making this measurement.

The difference of the two gauge readings gives the expansion (e), the difference between the steam-temperature and the initial temperature gives the temperature rise (t), and an initial measurement of the distance MM′(l) with a ruler gives the length of the part of the tube whose expansion has been studied.

Then $e = l\alpha t$, from which α can be calculated.

Specimen results for copper.

Barometric height = 73·2 cm ∴ Steam temp. = 99·0°C
Initial temp. = 16·0°C ∴ Rise in temp. = 83·0 degC
Gauge readings: (i) 14·10 mm, (ii) 15·15 mm
Expansion = 1·05 mm = 0·105 cm
Length MM′ = 75·7 cm

$$\therefore \text{Coefficient of linear expansion of copper} = \frac{0{\cdot}105}{83 \times 75{\cdot}7}$$

$$= 0{\cdot}0000168 \text{ per degC.}$$

15.3. Superficial and cubical expansion. The coefficients of superficial and cubical expansion of a *solid* can be calculated from the linear coefficient. If α, β and γ are the coefficients of linear, superficial and cubical expansion respectively, then for isotropic solids (those which expand equally in all directions)

$$\beta \simeq 2\alpha; \quad \gamma \simeq 3\alpha$$

Consider a cube of side 1 metre. Then each face will have an area of 1 sq. metre and the cube will have a volume of 1 cu. metre. If the cube is heated one degree then the sides of the cube will each be $(1+\alpha)$ metres. Each face will now have an area of $(1+\alpha)^2$ or $1+2\alpha+\alpha^2$ sq. metres, and the volume of the cube will be $(1+\alpha)^3$ or $1+3\alpha+\alpha^3$ cu. metres.

∴ Increase in each unit of area per degree $(\beta) = 2\alpha + \alpha^2$,

Increase in each unit of volume per degree $(\gamma) = 3\alpha + 3\alpha^2 + \alpha^3$

α is so small that α^2 and α^3 are relatively negligible.

$$\beta \simeq 2\alpha \qquad \gamma \simeq 3\alpha$$

15.4. Expansion of liquids. Since a liquid takes the shape of its containing vessel, we are concerned only with the coefficient of cubical expansion. There are two such coefficients, the absolute or **real coefficient** (γ) and the **apparent coefficient** (γ'), depending on whether the expansion of the containing vessel has been allowed for or not. The difference between these coefficients is approximately equal to the coefficient of cubical expansion of the containing vessel.

15.5. Expansion of gases. Fig. 15.2 shows two forms of apparatus by means of which the coefficient of expansion of a gas at constant pressure can be found. In (*a*) the thermometer serves two purposes;

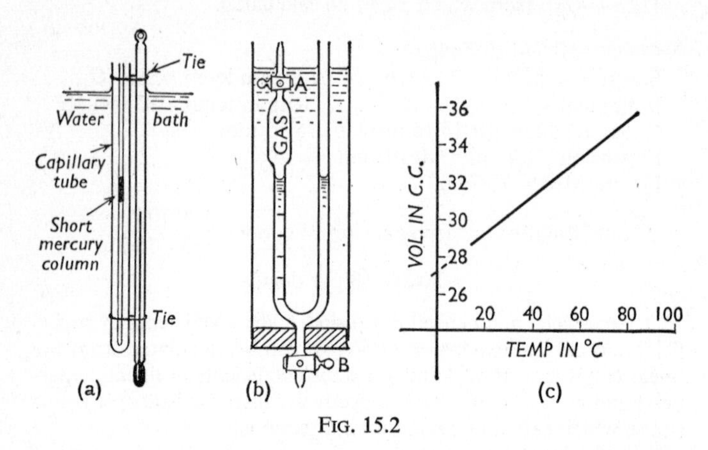

FIG. 15.2

it is used to take the temperature of the water-bath during the heating, and the graduation marks are also used as a scale to measure the length of the gas-column enclosed in the capillary tube (this length is proportional to the volume of the gas if the tube is of uniform bore). The tube is open to the atmosphere, so the pressure in the apparatus is likely to remain constant during the course of the experiment.

In (*b*) the apparatus has volume graduations on it and contains concentrated sulphuric acid to enclose and to dry the gas. The tap A can be used to admit the particular kind of gas to be tested; the tap B is used to run acid out from the apparatus as the water is heated—steam or electric heating is used. The acid levels must be on the same horizontal line whenever a reading of volume is taken, in order to maintain constant pressure in the gas.

For calculation of the coefficient it is necessary to know the volume at 0°C. To obtain this the volume-temperature observations are plotted graphically as shown in Fig. 15.2*a*. If v_{80} and v_0 are the volumes, read from the graph, at 80°C and 0°C respectively, then the coefficient of expansion is

$$\frac{v_{80}-v_0}{v_0}\div 80=\frac{v_{80}-v_0}{80v_0}$$

15.6. The gas laws. Substances in the gaseous state are classified as *gases* or *vapours* according to whether they are above or below their *critical temperature.* Below the critical temperature a gaseous material can be liquefied by applying pressure; above the critical temperature no amount of pressure will liquefy the material, which is then a true gas. At room temperature, carbon dioxide (critical temperature = 31°C) and sulphur dioxide (critical temperature = 157°C) are really vapours, and so the gas laws apply only approximately to these substances at room temperature. Hydrogen (critical temperature = −240°C), on the other hand, is a true gas.

For gaseous substances which are well above their critical temperature the coefficient of expansion at constant pressure is 1/273 per degC.

The expansion of gases was first investigated by Charles in 1787. His results are expressed as Charles's law which states: The volume of a fixed mass of gas at constant pressure changes by 1/273 of its volume at 0°C for each degC change in temperature.

The graphs of Fig. 15.3 illustrate the contraction of samples of

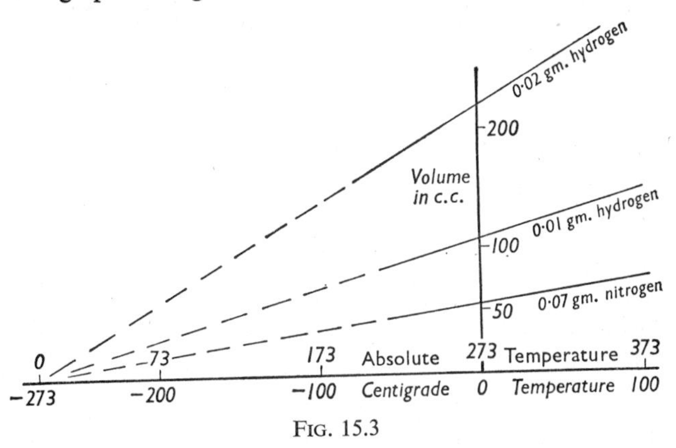

FIG. 15.3

Contraction of gases cooled at constant pressure

gas when cooled. The slope of the lines is such that they all point to zero volume at −273°C. This is the absolute zero of the Kelvin or Absolute scale of temperature; on this scale the temperatures of the ice and steam points are 273° and 373° respectively.

Charles's law can therefore be expressed in the following form:

The volume, v, of a fixed mass of a (permanent) gas at constant pressure is directly proportional to its Absolute temperature, T.

Absolute temperature = centigrade temperature + 273

The gas laws of Boyle (see p. 99) and Charles can be summarised by the equation

$$\frac{pv}{T} = \text{a constant}$$

This equation is known as the **gas equation;** it applies even when there is a change in all the three variables—pressure, volume and temperature. It is useful for the conversion of volumes of gas, found under experimental conditions, to the corresponding volumes under standard conditions, e.g. standard temperature 0°C, standard pressure 76 cm of mercury—conditions which are usually given the abbreviations s.t.p. or n.t.p.

EXAMPLE. 34·20 *ml of dry oxygen are collected at a temperature of 24°C and at a pressure of 77 cm of mercury. What will be the volume of the oxygen at s.t.p.?*

Since the value of pv/T must be the same in both cases:

$$\frac{76v}{273+0} = \frac{77 \times 34{\cdot}20}{273+24}$$

$$\therefore\ v = 34{\cdot}20 \times \frac{77}{76} \times \frac{273}{279} = 31{\cdot}85 \text{ ml}$$

SUMMARY

A coefficient of expansion of a substance is the **fraction** of its $\begin{pmatrix}\text{volume}\\ \text{area}\\ \text{length}\end{pmatrix}$ (at 0°C) which the substance expands for a rise in temperature of **one degree.**

The coefficient of cubical expansion of a solid is approximately 3 times its coefficient of linear expansion.

Expansion = Original size × rise in temp. × coefficient.

The coefficient of cubical expansion of the permanent gases is approximately 1/273 per degC. From this it follows that the **volume of a gas is proportional to its Absolute temperature.** i.e. to (C temperature + 273).

The gas laws can be expressed by the **gas equation**

$$\frac{pv}{T} = \text{constant}$$

Coefficients of Linear Expansion		Coefficients of Cubical Expansion	
Substance	Coeff. (per degC)	Substance	Coeff. (per degC)
Lead . . .	0·0000291	Air . . .	0·00367
Zinc . . .	0·0000260	Carbon monoxide	0·00367
Aluminium . .	0·0000233	Hydrogen . .	0·00366
Copper . . .	0·0000167	Carbon dioxide .	0·00371
Steel . . .	0·0000110	CCl_4 . . .	0·00125
Platinum . .	0·0000088	Ethyl alcohol .	0·00110
Soda glass . .	0·0000085	Paraffin oil . .	0·00090
Pyrex . . .	0·0000030	Glycerin . .	0·00053
Concrete . .	0·0000012	Water (20–40°C) .	0·00030
Invar . . .	0·0000009	Water (10–20°C) .	0·00015
Fused silica . .	0·0000005	Mercury . .	0·00018

Questions

(Unless otherwise stated, use as data the coefficients given in the above tables.)

1. What is meant by the statements: (*a*) the coefficient of linear expansion of tin is 0·000020 per degC, (*b*) the coefficient of cubical expansion of brass is 0·000056 per degC?

2. Calculate the expansion, resulting from a rise of 1 degC, of a bar of steel of length (*a*) 1 ft, (*b*) 1 mile, (*c*) 1 kilometre, (*d*) 500 cm. Give your answers to (*a*) in ft and in inches, to (*b*) in miles and in ft, to (*c*) in kilometres and in cm, to (*d*) in cm.

3. Calculate the expansions of the following. The units required in each answer are given in square brackets: (*a*) 50 cm of lead heated through 100 degC [cm], (*b*) 20 metres of aluminium heated from 20°C to 100°C [cm], (*c*) 1000 c.c. of zinc heated from 20°C to 70°C [c.c.], (*d*) 1 cu. metre of paraffin oil heated from 0°C to 100°C [c.c.], (*e*) 10 litres of air heated at constant pressure from 0°C to 80°C [ml], (*f*) 1000 gallons of petrol, initially ice-cold, coefficient of cubical expansion 0·00100 per degC, heated to 67°F [gallons].

4. A rod of metal, one metre long at 0°C, expands 1·57 mm when heated to 98°C. Calculate its coefficient of linear expansion.

5. 100·0 ml of a liquid at 0°C, seem to be 102·0 ml when heated to 80°C in a glass vessel. Calculate (*a*) the coefficient of apparent expansion and (*b*) the coefficient of real expansion of the liquid. (Coefficient of *linear* expansion of the glass = 0·0000087 per degC.)

6. A surveyor's steel chain is exactly 66 ft long at 15°C. What will be its length at −10°C, and what will be the error in measuring, at this temperature, a distance of 500 ft? (Coefficient of linear expansion of steel = 0·000012 per degC.)

7. A square metal plate, each side 100 cm long at 0°C, has a circular hole of diameter 40 cm in the middle of it. At what temperature will the sides be 101 cm long, and what will then be the diameter of the hole? (Coefficient of linear expansion of the metal = 0·0000125 per degC.)

8. Calculate the rise in temperature needed to cause 1 metre of each of the following metals, initially at 0°C, to expand by 1·00 mm (i) lead, (ii) copper, (iii) platinum.

9. Calculate the lengths of each of the following metals, initially at 0°C, which will expand 2·00 mm when heated to 100°C (i) zinc, (ii) steel, (iii) invar.

10. A steel rod is 100 cm long at 0°C. What must be the length, at 0°C, of an aluminium rod if the difference between its length and that of the steel rod is not to vary with temperature?

11. A vapour has a volume of 43·5 ml at 20·0°C. When heated, at constant pressure, to 100·0°C it has a volume of 55·5 ml. Calculate (*a*) the volume which the vapour would have at 0°C, assuming that it contracts uniformly, (*b*) the coefficient of expansion of the vapour. (Do not assume that Charles's law applies to vapours.)

12. A gas has a volume of 35·6 ml at 25·5°C and at 740 mm Hg pressure. Reduce this volume to s.t.p.

13. A litre of gas at 0°C and 1 atmosphere pressure is suddenly compressed to one-quarter of its volume, and its temperature rises to 273°C. Calculate the resulting pressure of the gas.

14. How would you determine the coefficient of expansion of air at constant pressure?

7·25 ml of a gas at a temperature of 15·0°C occupy 9·00 ml when heated to 85·0°C at constant pressure. Calculate the coefficient of expansion of the gas.

15. The density of air at 0°C and a pressure of 760 mm Hg is 1·29 g/litre. What mass of air will a flask, of volume 4 litres, contain at a temperature of 37°C and a pressure of 95 mm Hg?

16. Calculate (*a*) the density of air at 327°C under a pressure of 1 atmosphere, (*b*) the mass of 1 cu. metre of air at this temperature and pressure. (Density of air at s.t.p. = 1·29 g/litre.)

CHAPTER 16

Heat Units. Specific Heat

16.1. Heat units. A heat unit is defined as the amount of heat required to change the temperature of a definite mass of water by 1 degree. Two units on the metric system are the **calorie** and the **kilogram-calorie;** on the British system the **British thermal unit (Btu)** and the **therm** are often used.

A calorie	**is the amount of heat required to raise the temperature of**	**1 g**	**of water**	**1 degC**
A Calorie (kg cal)		**1 kg**		**1 degC**
A British thermal unit		**1 lb**		**1 degF**
A therm		**100,000 lb**		**1 degF**

The calorie, or g-degC unit, is a small unit but is much used in laboratory work. The Calorie, a kg-degC unit, is 1000 times as big and is sometimes known as the *large calorie*; this is the unit referred to when the heat value of foods is quoted. The British thermal unit (Btu), a lb-degF unit, is a unit much used by engineers, while the therm is a unit on which the Gas Boards base their scale of charges for the gas they supply—the gas being measured by the meter in cubic feet but charged for by calculation of the amount of heat obtainable by burning it.

16.2. Instruments used for measuring quantities of heat are called **calorimeters.** Calorimeters of special design are made for measuring the heat available from fuels and foodstuffs. The heat given out by completely burning unit mass of a fuel or foodstuff is known as its **calorific value.** Even a foodstuff is a fuel of a sort; for though some of the food we eat is used in building up the body, a large proportion of it is oxidised by chemical changes in the body. This provides the energy for muscular movement and—in the case of warm-blooded animals—the heat for keeping the body warm. So that a knowledge of calorific values has some bearing on the relative merits of different kinds of food.

The following table gives the calorific values of some fuels and foodstuffs:

SOLID AND LIQUID FUELS (Btu per lb)	
Coal and coke	12,000 to 14,000
Petrol, 'Calor' gas, Paraffin	20,000
Alcohol	11,600

GAS FUEL (Btu per cu. ft)	
Coal gas	about 480

FOODS (kg cal. per lb)	
Most fats and oils	9,000
Bacon	3,000
Beefsteak	1,100
Codfish	300
Walnut	3,300
Sugar	1,860
Oats	1,720
Bread	1,200

Types of calorimeter which can be used to find the calorific values of solid fuels and foodstuffs are illustrated in Figs. 16.1, 16.2. The heat from the reaction is used to heat a measured

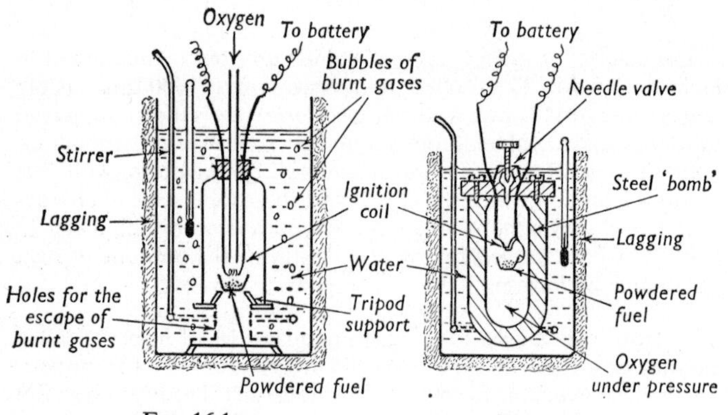

FIG. 16.1

Darling's fuel calorimeter. The fuel is burnt in a stream of oxygen

FIG. 16.2

Bomb calorimeter. The fuel is burnt in a strong vessel containing oxygen under pressure

quantity of water; from the resulting temperature-rise the heat generated can be calculated Thus if 1200 gm of water are raised from 10°C to 25°C the heat supplied to the water is 1200 (25 – 10) = 18,000 cal = 18 kilogram calories.

Allowance has to be made for the fact that (i) the parts of the apparatus take in some of the heat, (ii) some of the heat is lost to the surroundings. (i) is allowed for by finding the *thermal capacity* of the calorimeter structure, i.e. the heat required to raise the temperature of it by 1 degree. This is found either by a separate experiment or, if the specific heat of the material is known, by calculation. (ii) can be largely prevented by surrounding the calorimeter with a bad conductor of heat such as felt or cotton wool.

16.3. Thermal capacity. Specific heat. If hot water is added to cold water in a containing vessel, there is an exchange of heat between the two quantities of water and some of the heat is also absorbed by the containing vessel. The heat absorbed by the containing vessel can be calculated in the manner shown in the following example.

EXAMPLE. 300 *g of water at* 26·0°*C added to* 200 *g of water at* 5·0°*C gave a mixture whose temperature was* 17·0°C.

Calculation

Heat lost by hot water $= 300 \times (26 - 17) = 2700$ cal
Heat gained by cold water $= 200 \times (17 - 5) = 2400$ cal

The two values differ by 300 cal, showing that not all of the heat was gained by the cold water. Some may have been lost to the surroundings, some was definitely required to warm the can which contained the water.

Suppose that in this example the can weighed 125 g and was made of aluminium. Then it took 300 cal to heat the can $17-5 = 12$ degC, or $300 \div 12 = 25$ cal to heat the can through 1 degC. The can is therefore said to have a **thermal capacity** of 25 cal/degC, the thermal capacity of an object being defined as the amount of heat required to change the temperature of the object 1 degree. Thermal capacities are measured in such units as cal/degC, Btu/degF.

Knowing the thermal capacity of the whole can, it is possible to work out the heat required to change the temperature of 1 g of the material by 1 degC. For the aluminium in this can it is $25 \div 125 = 0{\cdot}20$ cal/g degC, which is known as the **specific heat** of the material.

The **specific heat** of a substance is defined as **the amount of heat required to change the temperature of unit mass of the substance by 1 degree.**

The heat gained or lost when a mass m, of specific heat s, changes in temperature by θ degrees is $ms\theta$.

Thus

Heat needed to change 1 unit of mass by 1 degree $=$ s units
Heat needed to change m units of mass by 1 degree $=$ ms units
Heat needed to change m units of mass by θ degrees $= ms\theta$ units

s is usually given units such as cal/g degC, Btu/lb degF, but it is sometimes quoted merely as a number. A table of specific heats is given on page 145. Note that they are nearly all less than 1, i.e. water has a relatively high specific heat. This has an important bearing on climate. The sea rises in temperature less rapidly than the land, which has a smaller average specific heat; conversely, land masses cool more rapidly than the sea. Places near the sea do not experience such extremes of temperature as do inland places. You may have noticed at the sea-side that dry rock and dry sand, heated by the sun, are warmer than the water in shallow pools. The effect is partly due to the lower specific heat of rock and sand.

The use of water in heating-pipes and hot-water bottles is largely a matter of convenience, but it is also true that the high specific heat of water makes it more suitable than other liquids for the purpose.

Specific heats of solids are usually found by mixing warm water and cold solid, or by mixing the hot solid with cold water. The latter method is more usual, because there is then a larger change in temperature of the solid. Examples of each are given in the following experiments.

Experiment 1. *Specific heat by a 'method of mixtures'*. A 'tin' can (i.e. a tin-plated iron can) was partly filled with lumps of iron and was found to weigh 555 g. It was left to attain room temperature, 15·0°C; 100 ml (100 g) of water at 30·0°C was added, swilled round, and the final temperature was 24·0°C.

Calculation

Heat lost by the water $= 100 \times (30 - 24) = 600$ cal
$\therefore$ The iron took 600 cal to heat it $(24 - 15) = 9$ degC
$\therefore$ Thermal capacity of the iron $= 600 \div 9 = 66{\cdot}6$ cal/degC
But the mass of the iron $= 555$ g
Specific heat of iron $= 66{\cdot}6 \div 555 = 0{\cdot}12$ cal/g degC

Experiment 2. *Specific heat: mixing hot solid and cold water.* A lump of the solid is weighed and heated to the steam point by some form of steam heater. The solid is quickly transferred to a weighed calorimeter into which a definite volume of cold water has been put from a measuring cylinder. Before this the temperature of the calorimeter and contents is taken; afterwards the mixture is well stirred and the final temperature found.

It is a good plan to start with the cold water below room temperature. In the early stages of the experiment the cold water gains heat from the room, which partly corrects for loss of heat to the room later.

Specimen results

Weighings		*Temperatures*	
Calorimeter (iron) . .	100 g	. . . . .	12·5°C
Water (790 ml) . .	790 g	. . . . .	12·5°C
Aluminium block . .	500 g	. . . . .	100·0°C
		Mixture . .	23·0°C

Thermal capacities			
Calorimeter (sp.ht. 0·1).	10	Rise in temp. .	10·5 degC
Water	790	Fall of temp. .	77·0 degC
Total	800		

Calculation. Let s = sp.ht. of aluminium

Heat gained $= 800 \times 10{\cdot}5 = 8400$ cal

Heat lost $= 500 \times 77 \times s$ cal

$\therefore\ 500 \times 77 \times s = 8400$

whence $s = 0{\cdot}22$

Specific heat of aluminium = 0·22 cal/g degC.

The specific heat of a liquid can also be found by the method of mixtures, by adding to the liquid in a calorimeter a hot solid of known mass and specific heat.

Table of Specific Heats

Substance	Sp.ht.	Substance	Sp.ht.
Aluminium	0·22	Water	1·00
Steel	0·11	Ethyl alcohol . .	0·61
Tin	0·056	Glycerin . . .	0·58
Copper	0·093	Paraffin oil . . .	0·51
Brass	0·091	Saturated brine . .	0·79
Mercury	0·033		
Lead	0·031	Gases at constant volume	
Ice	0·50		
Marble	0·22	Hydrogen	2·45
Sand	0·20	Helium	0·75
Glass	0·16	Air	0·17

SUMMARY

A **calorie** is the amount of heat required to change the temperature of 1 g of water by 1 degC and is known as a g-degC unit.

The **British thermal unit** (Btu) is a lb-degF unit. A therm is 100,000 Btu.

The **thermal capacity** of a body is the amount of heat required to change the temperature of the whole of it by 1 degree.

The **specific heat** of a substance is the amount of heat required to change the temperature of unit mass of that substance by 1 degree.

The **calorific value** of a substance is the heat produced when unit mass of that substance is completely oxidised.

Questions

(Unless otherwise stated, use as data the table of specific heats at the end of the chapter.)

1. Show that the thermal capacity of a mass m of specific heat s is equal to ms. Calculate the thermal capacity of (*a*) 120 g of lead, (*b*) 5 kg of iron, (*c*) 300 g of mercury, (*d*) an iron vessel, of mass 2 kg, containing 1·50 litres of water (sp.ht. of iron = 0·11).

2. Calculate the amounts of heat required to raise the temperature of (*a*) 12 kg of ice-cold water to boiling point, (*b*) 100 g of aluminium through 5 degC, (*c*) 500 g of aluminium from 60°C to 90°C, (*d*) 5 kg of aluminium from 20°C to 70°C.

3. Calculate the rise in temperature when 1000 calories are supplied to 100 g of each of the following. (*a*) Water. (*b*) Aluminium. (*c*) Copper. (*d*) Sand. (*e*) Lead.

4. 7000 cal can raise the temperature of 200 g of a metal from 10°C to 110°C. Calculate the sp.ht. of the metal.

5. 0·25 g of coal was burned in a calorimeter, of thermal capacity 50 cal/degC, containing 450 g of water. The rise in temperature was 4·0 degC. Calculate the heat evolved when 1 g of coal is burned.

6. A copper calorimeter containing 100 g of water at 10·0°C has 100 g of water at 39·3°C added to it; the final temperature is 20·0°C. Calculate the thermal capacity of the calorimeter. Calculate also the sp.ht. of copper if the calorimeter weighs 1 kg.

7. How would you determine the specific heat of a liquid by the method of mixtures?

An iron can weighing 300 g contains 690 g of water at 60°C. The water is gently stirred while it is left to cool, and the temperature falls to 30°C in 10 min. Find the average rate of loss of heat (sp.ht. of iron = 0·11).

8. Describe how you would compare the rates at which a given

gas ring and an electric hot-plate can each supply heat to a vessel placed on it.

9. 1 g of water, 1 g of concrete (sp.ht.=0·25) and 1 g of iron (sp.ht.=0·10) are each supplied with 10 cal of heat. Calculate the rise in temperature of each.

A shallow iron tank containing water is embedded in concrete, and is heated by the sun's rays. Explain the fact that after a time the iron and the water are slightly warm and the surface of the concrete is noticeably hot.

10. A block of metal weighing 180 g and having a thermal capacity of 20 cal/degC is observed to cool at the rate of 0·15 degC per second when placed in a refrigerator. Calculate (*a*) the rate at which the block is losing heat, (*b*) the specific heat of the metal.

11. A piece of copper weighing 14 g is heated in a bunsen flame and then transferred to a copper calorimeter, of mass 50 g, containing 95 g of water. The temperature of the calorimeter and contents rises from 11·0°C to 21·0°C. Calculate the temperature of the bunsen flame, and explain why an experiment such as this can give only an approximate value of the temperature of the flame. (Mean sp.ht. of copper=0·100.)

12. (*a*) Calculate the heat supplied per minute by an electric immersion heater which raises the temperature of 1·80 kg of water from 10°C to 85°C in 8 minutes. (Neglect heat losses from the vessel.) (*b*) A can containing 400 g of water at 18·0°C is put in a refrigerator which takes out heat at the rate of 320 cal/min. Calculate the time taken for the water to become ice-cold. (Neglect the heat taken from the can.)

13. An alcohol thermometer and a mercury thermometer each contain 0·50 c.c. of liquid. Calculate the heat taken in by each liquid when the temperature rises 10 degC. (Density of alcohol =0·80 g/c.c. Density of mercury=13·6 g/c.c.)

CHAPTER 17

Change of State. Latent Heat

17.1. Latent heat. Heating a substance usually raises its temperature. But this is not so when a substance changes its state. Water running away from melting snow during a thaw is ice-cold; the heat which reaches the snow from the sun or from the surrounding warmer air does not raise the temperature of the snow and water. If you heat a can, full of crushed ice, over a small flame you will find—if you keep the ice and water mixture well stirred—that the temperature does not rise above 0°C until the ice is nearly all melted. Any pure substance behaves like this at the definite temperature called its **melting point,** and the heat which melts it without warming it is called **latent heat** (latent = hidden).

When water is heated it becomes warmer until the boiling point is reached. The water then ceases to rise in temperature, the heat from the heater being used to make steam, which is no hotter than the boiling water. Stronger heating only boils away the water more quickly. As in the case of melting, the heat required to vaporise the water is spoken of as latent heat.

For all pure substances a change of state occurs at a definite temperature, the **melting point** or the **boiling point.** During melting or boiling, heat is absorbed without any change of temperature; the reverse occurs, i.e. heat is given out, during the freezing of a liquid or the condensation of a vapour. This heat, the latent heat of change of state, is measured by the **amount of heat required to change the state of unit mass of the substance without change of temperature.**

17.2. Fusion. Melting point and freezing point. The graph of Fig. 17.1 shows the result of heating a solid to a temperature above its melting point and then letting it cool. The graph has the same shape for all substances, but the particular one in the diagram refers to naphthalene, slowly heated in a water-bath in the first part of the experiment and allowed to cool in air in the second part. The following deductions can be made from the experiment. (i) The melting point of naphthalene is 80°C. (ii) The first horizontal part of the graph shows that heat is taken in without rise of temperature during the melting. (iii) The freezing point of naphthalene is also 80°C. (iv) The second horizontal part of the graph shows that heat is given out without fall of temperature during the solidification.

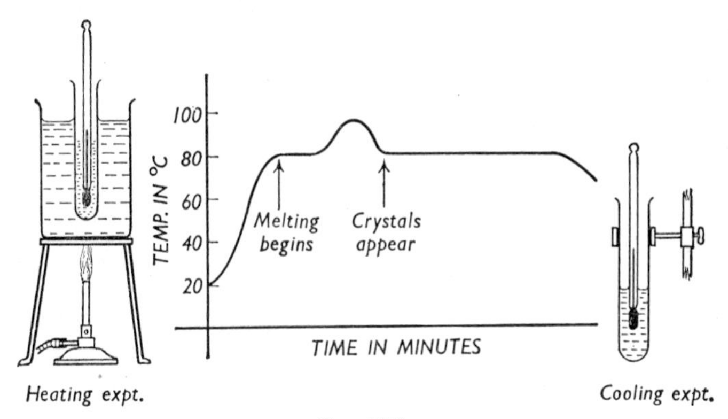

FIG. 17.1

Heating and cooling of naphthalene

In fact, the latent heat taken in during (ii) is equal to the latent heat lost in (iv); but this can only be proved by actual measurement. In the naphthalene experiment the heating-rate was greater than the cooling-rate, and so the first flat part of the graph was shorter than the second.

Melting points of pure substances are often found by melting the substance and then allowing it to cool in air. Conditions during solidification are much steadier than during the heating, and it is also easier to stir the liquid form. The temperature corresponding to the flat part of the cooling graph is the melting point.

When a liquid is cooled below its freezing point without solidifying it is said to be **overcooled,** and the effect is known as **surfusion** or **overcooling.** Thus if some photographic hypo (sodium thiosulphate) is melted in a test-tube and allowed to cool without being stirred, it is likely that the liquid will not solidify. It can be made to crystallise by very vigorous stirring or by the addition of a crystal of hypo—the smallest speck is sufficient. As a result the temperature rises rapidly to the melting point of hypo and remains steady until the hypo is completely solid.

17.3. Effect of dissolved substances on melting point. A solution has a lower freezing point and therefore a lower melting point than the pure substance. Thus if some camphor is added to molten naphthalene and the mixture is allowed to cool, crystals of pure naphthalene separate out at less than 80°C (the m.pt. of pure

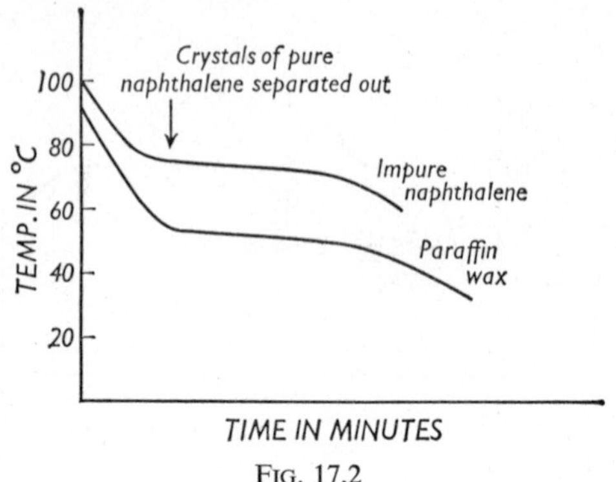

FIG. 17.2

Cooling curves for impure substances

naphthalene) and the cooling graph is as shown in Fig. 17.2. The same type of graph is obtained with paraffin wax, showing that paraffin wax is not a pure substance. Note that the temperature falls slightly while the substance is solidifying. The crystals which separate out as the mixture freezes are crystals of the pure substance, and this leaves the 'melt' with a higher percentage of dissolved substance. This makes the melting point even lower, and so the temperature drops as time goes on.

Milk, in addition to containing tiny drops of fat in suspension, contains dissolved substances (salts, sugars, proteins); its freezing point is $-1{\cdot}03$°C, and one of the ways of testing milk, to check that it has not been diluted, is to find its freezing point.

Sea water has a freezing point below 0°C, and the ice-floes which come from the freezing of it are not salty ice but pure ice. Strong solutions of common salt may freeze as low as -21°C. So that when salt is mixed with wet ice the mixture is above its freezing point; some of the ice therefore melts and takes the necessary latent heat from the mixture, which becomes very cold. A mixture of ice and salt is thus a **freezing mixture**; an even colder one can be made by mixing calcium chloride with ice.

Alloys are made by melting a mixture of metals, and the alloy has a lower melting point than the metals which compose it. Soft solder, an alloy of tin (m.pt. 232°C) and lead (m.pt. 327°C), can have any melting point between 327°C (pure lead) and 183°C (37% lead) according to the proportions of lead and tin it contains. The properties of alloys are often quite different from the metals of which they are made, and the range of usefulness of a metal can be increased by alloying it with other metals.

17.4. Changes in volume during melting and freezing. Most substances contract during solidification, and in doing so become

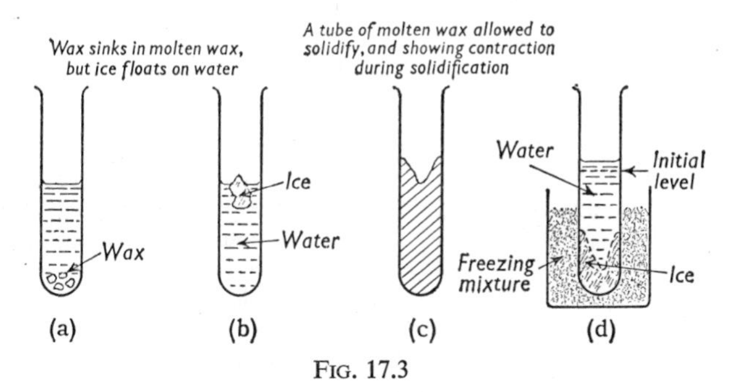

FIG. 17.3

more dense. As a result the solid form sinks in the liquid form. This can be shown by melting some wax, sulphur, naphthalene or hypo in a test-tube; before all of the solid is melted, some of the solid will be seen at the bottom of the liquid. There are some exceptions to this general rule. Ice floats on water, and from this it follows that water expands during freezing and ice contracts during melting; 10 c.c. of water give nearly 11 c.c. of ice. Diagrams illustrating these effects are shown in Fig. 17.3.

Owing to this fairly large expansion, precautions have to be taken to prevent damage to water-containers in frosty weather. Freezing of water in the cooling system round the engine of a car may cause a burst in the radiator or a crack in the cylinder casings; so 'anti-freeze', e.g. glycerin, ethylene glycol, is added to give a low freezing-point solution. Exposed water pipes may burst in frosty weather. The risk of a burst depends partly on the position of any ice which has formed. Thus a freezing of the water just behind the tap may not cause a burst; the expansion in this case just pushes a small amount of water back along the pipe (Fig. 17.4*a*). But if there is water entrapped between two points, e.g. between A and the tap in Fig. 17.4*b*, a burst is likely somewhere between these two points. The burst will not be discovered immediately, for the ice block A has stopped the water flow; it is quite usual for a burst in a pipe not to be discovered until the thaw sets in.

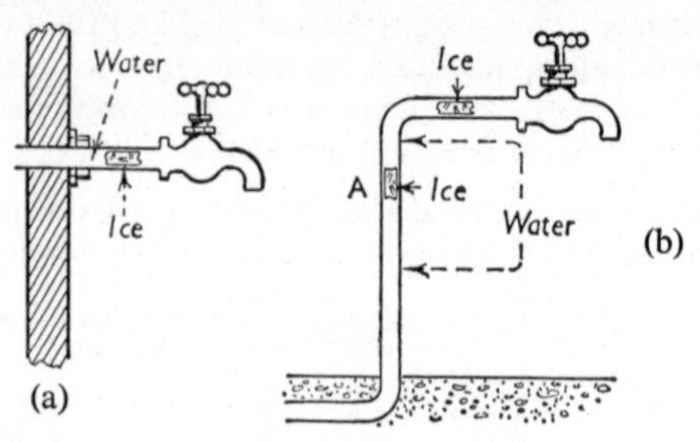

FIG. 17.4

17.5. Effect of pressure on melting point. Most substances, when put under pressure, have a higher melting point than usual. Ice, and other substances which expand on freezing, is exceptional. When ice is under pressure, its melting point is lower than usual; but a pressure of 140 atmospheres is needed to lower the m.pt. by 1 degC.

If two flat pieces of ice at 0°C are squeezed together tightly, and then the pressure is released, the pieces will stick together. The ice under pressure has a melting point below 0°C, so a small amount of it melts, taking in latent heat as it does so. When the pressure is released, the melting point is again 0°C, so the ice-water freezes once more, giving up its latent heat; and so the pieces are firmly joined. This re-freezing is called **regelation.** The effect is to be observed when walking on snow, provided that the snow is not much below 0°C. Under one's footprints are firm lumps of snow, held together by regelation after the pressure of the foot has been removed. In the same way, heavy wheeled vehicles on snow-covered roads can leave a track of solid ice from the binding together of snow-crystals after compression. In extremely cold conditions snow will not bind well because it is not possible to depress the freezing point below the snow temperature.

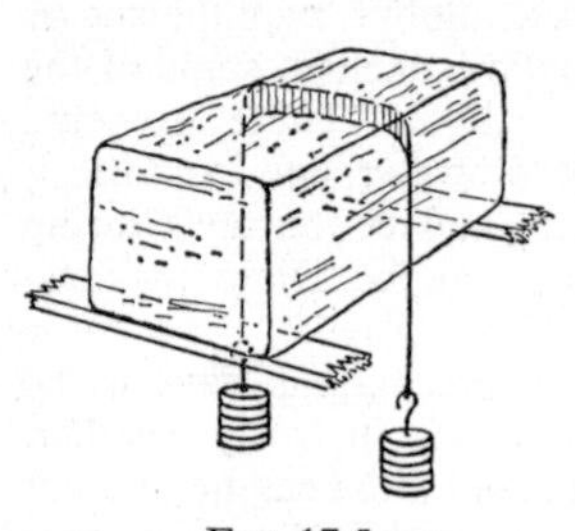

FIG. 17.5

Regelation. A thin weighted wire cutting through ice; water, formed from ice melted under pressure, re-freezes above the wire

Regelation can be shown in the laboratory by means of the apparatus illustrated in Fig. 17.5. The heavy weights and small area of the copper wire in contact with ice produce a high pressure, which depresses the freezing point. Some of the ice melts, and water which is below 0°C slips past the wire and appears on top, where it can be seen to be freezing again. The wire eventually passes through the block, leaving it in one piece. Latent heat, given out during the regelation, passes downwards through the copper wire and is taken in by the ice which is melting below it. A poor conductor of heat such as string will not cut through the block.

17.6. Latent heat of fusion. Definition. The latent heat of fusion of a substance (or the latent heat of its liquid form) **is the quantity of heat required to change unit mass of the substance at its melting point to liquid at the same temperature** (or vice versa). The units are usually cal/g.

The latent heat of fusion of ice is 80 cal/g; another way of expressing this fact is to say that it takes 80 times as much heat to melt a mass of ice at 0°C as is required to heat the same mass of water 1 degC. This fairly large value for latent heat accounts for the fact that thawing is a fairly slow process after a heavy fall of snow. It is also one of the factors which contribute to the slow increase in the thickness of ice on ponds in frosty weather.

Some other latent heats, in cal/g, are as follows (m.pt. given in brackets).

> Naphthalene (80°C) 35, bromine (−8°C) 16, tin (232°C) 14, sulphur (115°C) 9, mercury (−40°C) 4.

In terms of the kinetic theory, these numbers represent the relative energies needed to free the molecules from the forces which bind them in the space lattice of the solid form (p. 26).

17.7. Determination of the latent heat of fusion of ice. One way of finding the latent heat of fusion of ice is by the method of mixtures. A copper calorimeter is weighed empty and then about three-quarters full of cold water. The calorimeter and water are heated to about 10 degC above room temperature, lagged, stirred and the initial temperature taken. Small lumps of ice are dried on blotting paper and added one at a time, with continual stirring, until all the ice has melted and the final temperature is about 10 degC below room temperature. The final temperature is taken and the calorimeter and contents re-weighed to find out how much ice has been melted.

Specimen results:

Weighings		*Temperatures*	
Calorimeter (copper)	52·32 g	Initial	28·2°C
Cal + water	153·63 g	Final	12·1°C
Cal, water, melted ice	173·23 g		
Water	101·31 g	Fall	16·1 degC
Ice	19·60 g	Rise	12·1 degC

Let L cal per gm be the latent heat of fusion of ice. Then heat gained by ice in melting to water at 0°C and by the melted ice in rising to 12·1°C = heat lost by calorimeter and water.

$$19{\cdot}6L + 19{\cdot}6 \times 12{\cdot}1 = 103{\cdot}31 \times 16{\cdot}1 + 52{\cdot}35 \times 0{\cdot}1 \times 16{\cdot}1$$
$$19{\cdot}6\,(L + 12{\cdot}1) = 16{\cdot}1 \times 106{\cdot}5$$
$$L + 12{\cdot}1 = 87{\cdot}5$$
$$L = 75{\cdot}4$$

$\therefore$ Latent heat of fusion of ice = 75·(4) cal/g

17.8. Latent heat of vaporisation. Definition. The latent heat of vaporisation of a substance (or the latent heat of its vapour state) **is the quantity of heat required to change unit mass of the liquid to vapour at the same temperature.** The latent heat of condensation of a vapour is the quantity of heat given out by unit mass of the vapour in condensing to liquid at the same temperature; it is numerically equal to the latent heat of vaporisation.

The latent heat of vaporisation of water, or the latent heat of steam, is approximately 540 cal/g at 100°C. The value at other temperatures is different; water evaporating at 20°C, for example, needs 580 cal to convert each gram of it to vapour at the same temperature.

Some other latent heats, in cal/g, are as follows (b.pt. given in brackets).

Alcohol (78°C) 205, benzene (80°C) 93, ether (35°C) 90, mercury (357°C) 65, bromine (60°C) 46.

Most of the energy of the latent heat of vaporisation is used, not in making the molecules move faster (for the temperature of liquid and vapour is the same), but in increasing the distance between the molecules against the forces of attraction they exert on each other. When a liquid is boiled the issuing vapour takes up much space, pushing against the surroundings as it does so. This means that the vapour is doing work, and some of the latent heat goes in supplying the energy for this work.

17.9. Determination of the latent heat of steam.

(*a*) **From the heat required for vaporisation.** Water is boiled in a conical flask, fitted with a glass-wool or a cotton-wool plug to retain any spray and covered with an upturned beaker to surround the flask with steam and so reduce heat losses (Fig. 17.6).

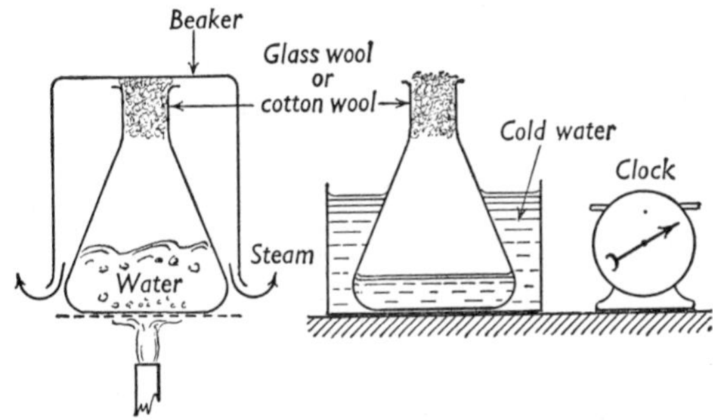

FIG. 17.6

The flask and plug are weighed alone, water is put in the flask and the arrangement re-weighed to find the weight of water added. After taking the initial temperature, the arrangement is put on a gauze heated by a bunsen, and the time taken for the water to boil is observed. Heating is continued for the same length of time and then the flask is put quickly into cold water to condense the steam still in the flask. When cold, the arrangement is wiped dry and weighed. From the loss in weight the latent heat of steam can be calculated.

Specimen results

Weighings (g)		Temperatures (°C)	
Flask+plug . .	81·0	Initial . . .	10·0
Flask+plug+water (i)	231·8	Final	100·0
Water . . .	150·8	Rise	90·0
Flask+plug+water (ii)	204·4	(Heating time and boiling time were equal, actually 5 min 35 s)	
Water boiled away .	27·4		
		Specific heat of glass .	0·2

Calculation. Heat supplied to flask and to water during 'heating time' $=(81\times 90\times 0{\cdot}2)+(150{\cdot}8\times 90)=15{,}030$ cal.

Assuming that the same quantity of heat was supplied during the boiling-away time,

27·4 g of water at 100°C were vaporised by 15,030 cal.

∴ 1 g of water at 100°C is vaporised by 15,030 ÷ 27·4 = 548 cal.

∴ Latent heat of vaporisation of water, or the latent heat of steam = 548 cal/g

This result selected from a set of experiments giving answers from 540 to 560 cal/g is reasonably close to the accepted value of 540 cal/g.

(*b*) **From the heat given out in condensation.** A calorimeter is weighed, chilled water is added, and the calorimeter reweighed. The calorimeter is jacketed and the initial temperature taken. Steam is generated in a boiler fitted with a spray-trap and a jacketed exit-tube (Fig. 17.7), and is passed into the calorimeter until the final temperature is in the region of 40°C. The calorimeter and contents are cooled, and reweighed to find the mass of steam condensed.

Specimen results (barometer 76·0 cm Hg.; steam temperature 100·0°C):

Weighings (g)		*Temperatures* (°C)
Calorimeter (sp.ht. 0·1)	110·0	
Calorimeter and water	320·38	10·3
Water	210·38	
Calr, water and steam	330·84	38·5
Steam	10·46	100·0

Rise in temperature 28·2 degC
Fall in temperature 61·5 degC

Let L cal/g = latent heat of steam.

Then heat lost by steam in condensing to water at 100°C = 10·4L cal.

Heat lost by condensed steam cooling 61·5 degC = 10·4 × 61·5 cal.

$$\therefore 10{\cdot}4\ (L+61{\cdot}5)=(210{\cdot}4+11{\cdot}0)\ 28{\cdot}2$$

$$L+61{\cdot}5=\frac{221{\cdot}4\times 28{\cdot}2}{10{\cdot}46}=597$$

$$L=535{\cdot}(5)$$

In spite of the fact that the weighings are to two places of decimals, the mass of steam may be wrong due to a drop of water on the end of the pipe; this itself could introduce an error of 1%.

Latent heat of steam = 535 ± 5 cal/g.

Note that in the above calculation an allowance is made for the fact that the condensed steam has a final temperature below 100°C.

Whenever calculations are made involving a **change of state and a change of temperature,** an additional $ms\theta$ term, or terms, must be added on to the mL term to give the total heat change.

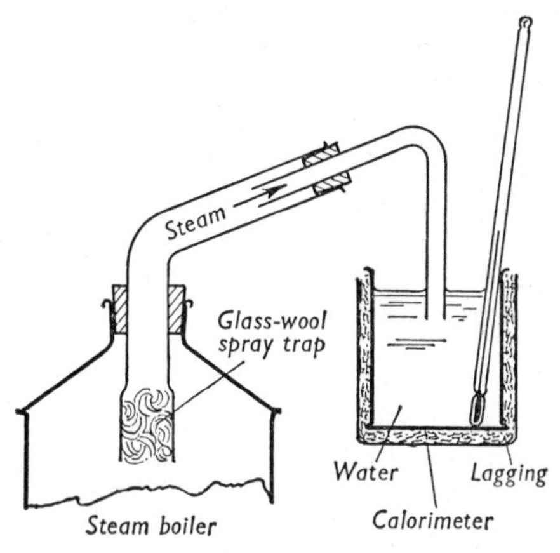

FIG. 17.7

EXAMPLE 1. *Calculate the heat given out by* 10 *g of naphthalene cooling from* 100°*C to* 20°*C.* (*Latent heat*=35 *cal/g. Melting point* =80°*C. Specific heats of liquid and solid naphthalene,* 0·45 *and* 0·40.)

Heat lost from 100°C to 80°C $= 10 \times 0{\cdot}45 \times 20 = 90$ cal
Heat lost in change of state $= 10 \times 35 = 350$ cal
Heat lost from 80°C to 20°C $= 10 \times 0{\cdot}40 \times 60 = 240$ cal
Total $= 680$ cal

EXAMPLE 2. *Calculate the mass of steam at* 100°*C required to melt* 10 *g of ice at* −20°*C.* (*Latent heats of steam and water,* 540 *and* 80 *cal/g. Specific heat of ice*=0·50.)

Let m g of steam be required.

$$\text{Heat lost by steam} = m \times 540 + m \times 1 \times 100 = 640m \text{ cal.}$$

$$\text{Heat gained by ice} = 10 \times 0{\cdot}5 \times 20 + 10 \times 80 = 900 \text{ cal.}$$

$$640m = 900$$

$$m = 1{\cdot}406$$

Mass of steam required = 1·41 g

SUMMARY

The **melting point** of a substance is the temperature at which its change from the solid to the liquid state occurs.

The **latent heat** of any change of state is, for a given substance, the amount of heat required to change the state of unit mass of that substance without change of temperature.

Dissolved substances lower the freezing point of a substance. When the freezing of dilute solutions commences, the crystals which form are crystals of the pure solvent.

Most substances contract during freezing, the solid form being more dense than the liquid form; exceptions are water and type metal. Increase of pressure lowers the melting point of ice; the phenomenon of **regelation** is related to this fact.

Questions

(Unless otherwise stated, take the latent heat of steam as 540 cal/g, of water as 80 cal/g.)

1. What is meant by change of state? Describe one experiment to show that during a change of state the temperature of the substance undergoing the change remains constant.

2. What is meant by latent heat? Describe a simple experiment to show that more heat is available from a mass of molten naphthalene at its melting point than from an equal mass of solid naphthalene at the same temperature.

3. Steam at 100°C is passed at the rate of 10 g per min into 320 g of ice-cold water. Calculate the time taken to heat the water (*a*) to 50°C, (*b*) to 100°C. (*Hint.* In the case of (*a*) each gram of steam gives out 540 cal in condensing to water at 100°C and a further (100-50) cal. in cooling to 50°C.)

4. (*a*) Define (i) the latent heat of fusion, and (ii) the latent heat of vaporisation, of a substance. (*b*) 1 gram of lead at 0°C and 1 gram of ice at 0°C are heated separately until they melt. Calculate the quantity of heat given to each. (Latent heat fusion of lead = 5 cal/g, specific heat of lead = 0·03, melting point of lead = 327°C.)

5. What is meant by regelation? Explain the fact that a snow-covered road becomes ice-covered after heavy vehicles have driven over it.

6. A simple form of calorimeter devised by Joseph Black consists of a block of ice with a cavity in the top. 600 g of iron at 100°C, put into the cavity of Black's calorimeter, caused 84 g of ice to melt. Calculate the specific heat of iron.

7. Steam at 100°C was passed into a mixture of ice and water at 0°C, and 10 g of the ice melted. Calculate how much steam was condensed.

8. Account for the fact that water at 60°C well mixed with an equal weight of ice at 0°C gives a mixture which is still at 0°C.

9. Calculate the weight of steam needed to raise the temperature of 24 g of ice-cold water to 40°C.

10. A copper can of negligible weight containing 250 g of water at 16°C is placed in a refrigerator which takes away heat at the rate of 320 cal/min. Calculate the time taken for the water to be converted to ice at 0°C; explain the fact that this time would not be much affected even if the can were as heavy as the water.

11. A copper calorimeter containing water at 30·2°C weighs 146·31 g, the calorimeter itself weighing 50·11 g. Ice at −4·0°C is added and the mixture stirred; when all the ice has melted the temperature has fallen to 10·2°C. The calorimeter and contents now weigh 168·31 g. Calculate the latent heat of fusion of ice. (Specific heat of copper = 0·093. Specific heat of ice = 0·50.)

12. How does the kinetic theory account for the fact that energy is needed to change a solid to a liquid, and a liquid to a vapour?

13. Do you consider the following statement to be reliable? Give reasons for your answer.

'If a kettle of ice-cold water takes 10 min to come to the boil it will be at least an hour before it boils dry.'

14. Certain types of stone are slightly pervious to water. After a severe frost the surface of such stone is liable to flake off. Give an explanation of this effect.

CHAPTER 18

Change of State. Evaporation

18.1. Evaporation and boiling. The evaporation of water from puddles, or the boiling of water on a stove is a matter of everyday experience; in both cases water disappears into the air as steam or water vapour. The chief difference between the two is that *evaporation* takes place only from the exposed **surface of the liquid,** whereas in boiling the vaporisation occurs also **in the body of the liquid.**

The temperature at which a liquid will boil depends on the pressure of the surroundings. Thus water at room temperature, or even water at 0°C, will boil if connected to a vacuum pump; but under atmospheric conditions water will only evaporate at these temperatures. Under standard atmospheric pressure the boiling of a liquid occurs at a definite temperature known as the **normal boiling point.**

The rate at which a liquid will evaporate also depends on the surrounding conditions. Thus in the apparatus of Fig. 3.5*a* the release of a liquid into a vacuum produces an evaporation which seems almost instantaneous; in air the evaporation is slower.

In evaporation it is the faster molecules which escape from the attraction of those around them, but they are retarded as they leave the meniscus. The kinetic theory assumes that, when a liquid is in equilibrium with its vapour, the average speed of the molecules both in the vapour and in the liquid is the same; the difference is one of spacing, not of speed.

18.2. Vapour pressure. The vapour from a liquid is in the gaseous state and it shows many of the properties of a gas. For example, it exerts a pressure. The pressure of any gaseous substance is the result of the action of many millions of molecules, moving with high speeds, which collide with the walls of the containing vessel. Fig. 18.1 shows molecules which have escaped from a liquid, moving about as vapour in an enclosed space. The molecules not only collide with the walls and produce a pressure but some of them re-enter the surface, becoming part of the liquid. A stage is reached when the number of molecules leaving the liquid per

second is equal to the number entering it per second; the vapour is **then** said to **be saturated.** The existence of vapour pressure can be

FIG. 18.1

FIG. 18.2
Effect of vapour pressure

shown as illustrated in Fig. 18.2. A glass bulb (its size is exaggerated in the diagram) contains a volatile liquid, such as ether or pentane, which will float on water. It is connected by rubber tubing, closed with a clip C, to a flask containing air, water and an exit pipe. C is opened to allow the liquid to enter the air space. Its evaporation produces a vapour pressure sufficient to blow a jet of water out of the exit pipe.

The **saturation vapour pressure (s.v.p.)** of a liquid can be

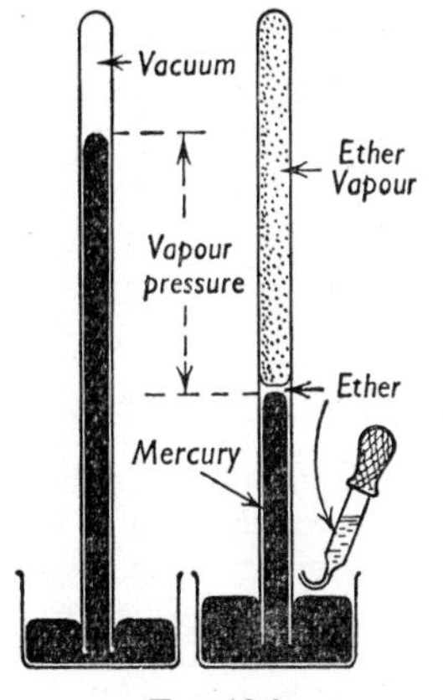

FIG. 18.3
Vapour pressure

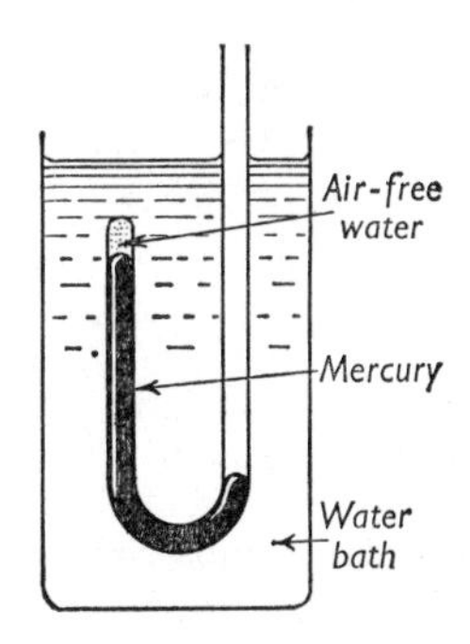

FIG. 18.4

measured by introducing a small quantity of the liquid into the space above the mercury in a simple barometer (Fig. 18.3). At 15°C the s.v.p. of water is 1·2 cm Hg, of ether 25 cm Hg. Warming the liquid increases the s.v.p. At the higher temperature the molecules move faster, more of them evaporate into the space; and the combined effect of greater speed and greater numbers causes an increase in the s.v.p. If the temperature is raised to the normal boiling point of the liquid the s.v.p. becomes equal to the pressure of the surroundings. This can be illustrated by heating the apparatus of Fig. 18.4; when the water in the bath is boiling, the water entrapped in the J-tube produces vapour and this pushes the left-hand mercury column downwards until the two mercury columns are at the same level.

18.3. Cooling by evaporation. Refrigerators. Evaporation of a substance causes cooling of the substance. Latent heat is needed for the change of state, and so the substance cools—unless heat can reach it from the surroundings as quickly as the latent heat is required.

Fig. 18.5*a* shows thermometers, their bulbs surrounded by

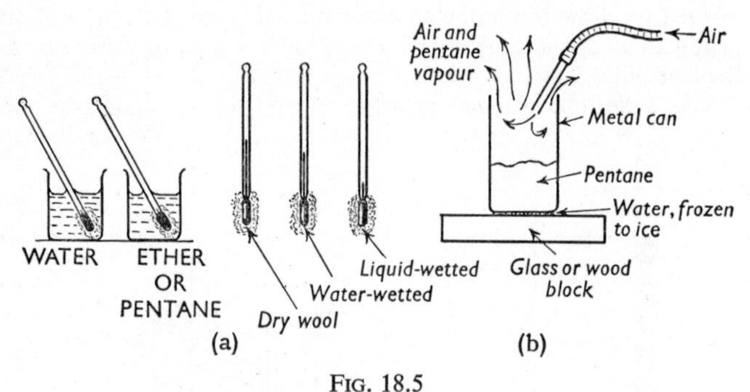

FIG. 18.5

Cooling by evaporation

cotton wool, which have been dipped, one into water and the other into a volatile liquid. When they are allowed to stand in the air, with a dry thermometer for comparison purposes, the temperatures of the wetted bulbs show a fall in temperature which is quite marked in the case of the volatile liquid. The cooling is due to evaporation of the liquid from the large area of the cotton wool.

Fig. 18.5*b* shows that water can be frozen to ice by the rapid extraction of heat caused by the evaporation of a volatile liquid. The evaporation is made more rapid by blowing air across the surface of the volatile liquid; water put under the containing vessel soon becomes frozen to ice.

Rapidity of evaporation is increased by lowering of the pressure, or by making the area of exposed surface large, or by making sure that the vapour is quickly carried away from the surface. Anyone who stands about in a wet bathing costume experiences this cooling effect, for the large surface of fabric exposed gives a high rate of evaporation; any wind or draught which carries the vapour away makes the effect more noticeable. Similarly a damp fabric wrapped round a bottle of milk will keep it relatively cool in hot weather; porous earthenware coolers for milk and butter are sold for the same purpose.

Cooling by evaporation is put to use in refrigerators. Most refrigerators contain a gas, such as ammonia, which can be liquefied fairly easily by pressure. Fig. 18.6 illustrates a refrigerator

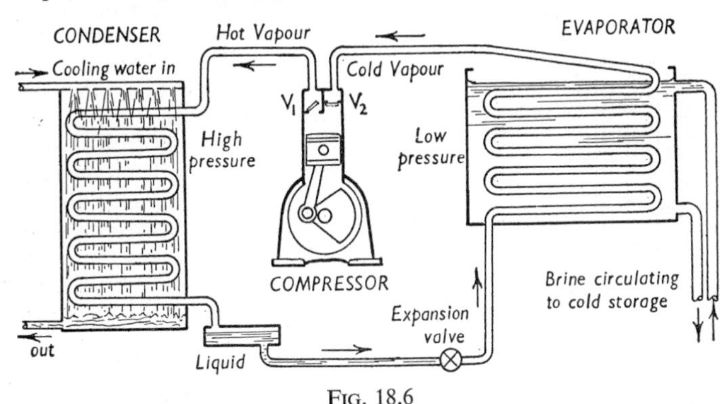

FIG. 18.6

A refrigerator circuit

circuit. Cooling is caused by allowing the liquefied gas to flow out through a valve into the low-pressure side of the circuit. Here the liquid evaporates quickly, taking in the latent heat needed for the change of state. At a cold-storage depot the cooling pipes are surrounded by a strong solution of calcium chloride (calcium chloride brine), which can be cooled to a very low temperature without freezing. The cold brine is kept circulating in pipes through the cold-storage rooms; or, if ice is being made, it goes to a huge tank into which are lowered the smaller tanks containing the water to be frozen. In a domestic refrigerator the cooling pipes cool the air in the upper compartment of the refrigerator.

The vapour is recovered and liquefied by the action of the compressor and condenser. On the downstroke of the piston, vapour is drawn into the cylinder through a valve, V_2; on the upstroke, it is driven through the valve V_1, as a hot vapour—heated by the action of the compression stroke. In the condenser pipes it is cooled and condenses to liquid again.

18.4. Water in the atmosphere. Humidity. There is always a certain amount of water vapour in the atmosphere, formed by evaporation from ponds, lakes and seas. Except during heavy rainstorms or when there is a mist in the atmosphere, the water vapour is very rarely saturated. Cooling a sample of damp air can cause the vapour to become saturated and then some of the moisture is deposited on the surroundings as dew. The temperature at which the moisture in the air is just sufficient to saturate it is known as the **dew point;** the higher the dew point, in relation to the temperature of the surroundings, the greater is the humidity of the air.

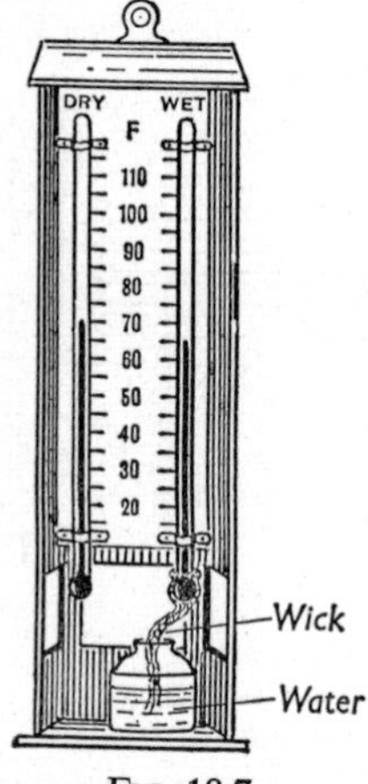

FIG. 18.7
Mason's hygrometer

Instruments for testing humidity are called **hygrometers.** One such instrument is Mason's wet-and-dry bulb hygrometer (Fig. 18.7). The evaporation from the wet bulb is greater in dry than in humid air, so the drier the air, the greater is the difference between the temperatures of the two thermometers. No difference in their temperature shows that the surrounding air is saturated, or has a *relative humidity* of 100%. Using special tables, and the values of (i) the dry-bulb temperature and (ii) the difference in temperature of the two thermometers, the relative humidity of the atmosphere is found. Relative humidity affects a person's sense of comfort; it is also a factor which has to be controlled in certain industries such as cotton-weaving, paper manufacture, the artificial seasoning of wood.

SUMMARY

A **saturated vapour** is one which is in equilibrium with its liquid or solid form. In terms of the kinetic theory the equilibrium occurs when as many molecules leave the liquid or solid per second as enter it per second.

When an **unsaturated** vapour is in contact with its liquid or its solid form, evaporation takes place.

A liquid is said to be **boiling** when evaporation occurs within the body of the liquid. The temperature at which this occurs is known as the **boiling point;** at this temperature the s.v.p. is equal to the pressure on the liquid.

Evaporation produces cooling; when a liquid evaporates the latent heat necessary for the change of state is provided by the surroundings and by the liquid itself.

Hygrometers are used to measure the relative humidity of the atmosphere.

Questions

1. A closed flask has a thin glass tube inside it, the tube containing a volatile liquid. Use the ideas of the kinetic theory to forecast what happens when the tube is broken (*a*) when the flask is evacuated initially, (*b*) when the flask contains a gas at atmospheric pressure. Give a reason why, in (*b*), the final pressure in the flask is greater than atmospheric.

2. Butane is a liquid with a normal boiling point of 0°C. It is usually *stored in strong metal vessels.* If the liquid is put into a beaker in a warm room, *the liquid boils* and *becomes colder* in doing so. Give an explanation of the features printed in *italics.*

3. Distinguish between evaporation and boiling. State the conditions favourable to the evaporation of water in the open air.

4. Why does a muddy road dry more quickly on a warm windy day than on a cold calm day?

5. A flask containing water at 60°C is connected to a vacuum pump. Account for the fact that the water commences to boil.

As the water continues to boil, the temperature of the water drops more rapidly than when the flask is not connected to the pump. Explain this.

6. Two thick-walled vessels of the same size, one made of glass and the other of copper, stand in the same room. Each is filled with a freezing mixture at -20°C. The glass vessel becomes coated with dew, which later becomes a coating of ice; the copper vessel becomes coated with hoar-frost. Explain these facts and point out how the thermal conductivity of the vessel affects what happens.

7. Draw a labelled diagram of a simple refrigerator circuit. Explain the action of the chief parts of the circuit.

8. Draw a labelled diagram of a wet-and-dry bulb hygrometer. If the temperature of the dry-bulb went up, but the temperature

difference did not change, how would the humidity of the air have altered? Give a reason for your answer.

9. What would you expect to notice about the readings of a wet-bulb and a dry-bulb thermometer on (*a*) a cold dry day, (*b*) a warm dry day, (*c*) a warm moist day, (*d*) a cold misty day?

10. Describe, with the aid of a diagram, any one experiment which shows that a vapour exerts a pressure. State how, if at all, the experiment would be affected if the room temperature were to rise during the course of the experiment.

11. Describe an experiment to determine which of two liquids, e.g. alcohol and pentane, could give the greater degree of cooling. State (i) how you would try to make conditions the same for both liquids, (ii) what you would do to make the degree of cooling as great as possible.

12. 5·0 g of a liquid of specific heat 0·25 and latent heat 50 cal/g, is made to evaporate at the rate of 1·00 g/min by passing air through it. Calculate (*a*) the rate at which the liquid loses heat, in cal/s, (*b*) the initial rate of cooling, in degC/s.

CHAPTER 19

The Nature of Heat. Heat Engines

19.1. The caloric theory. Heat was at one time considered to be an invisible weightless fluid. The fluid was called **caloric**, and the theory which assumed its existence was called the caloric theory. But the large quantities of heat which can be obtained from friction, or from operations such as filing and drilling of materials, are difficult to explain on this theory unless the materials contain an inexhaustible supply of the caloric fluid. Overcoming friction, the operations of filing and drilling, involve the use of energy. Present-day theory considers heat to be a form of energy; and this is borne out by the fact that whenever heat is produced from mechanical energy, the heat is directly proportional to the amount of energy used to produce it. The relation between the two is known as **Joule's equivalent,** since much of the research work on the subject was done by James Prescott Joule (1818–89).

19.2. The mechanical equivalent of heat or Joule's equivalent (J). This constant is the amount of mechanical energy which, when converted into heat, produces 1 unit of heat. It has been measured experimentally in many different ways, and the value of the constant is the same by whichever method is determined. This is one of the most important pieces of evidence that heat is a form of energy. One very simple method of determining J is the shot-tube method. Lead becomes distorted and warmer, if dropped from a great height on to a hard surface such as steel. The steel, which recovers its shape after the impact, becomes hardly any warmer. This fact has been used in the shot-tube method for finding J.

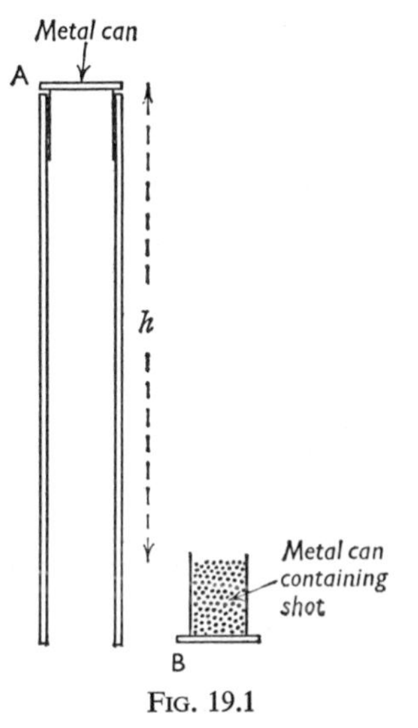

FIG. 19.1

A cardboard tube, about a yard long, has its ends closed by metal cans. One of the cans is full of lead shot which is allowed to fall by abruptly inverting the tube several times (Fig. 19.1). The distance h is first measured, the tube is put over the can of shot and the arrangement is inverted a few times to mix the shot. The tube is then pulled off, and the temperature of the lead shot taken with a sensitive thermometer. The tube is put back and the arrangement inverted abruptly some thirty or forty times, always such that the tube rests on a hard surface. Then the final temperature of the shot is taken—it usually takes about a minute for the thermometer to reach the temperature of the lead. It is unnecessary to find the weight of the lead provided that it is much larger than the metal cans, the thermal capacities of which are ignored in the specimen results which follow.

Specimen results. The calculations are shown using two different systems of units. The specific heat is taken as 0·030.

	Metric System	British System
Initial temp. 15·00°C		
Final temp. 16·18°C		
Rise in temp. . .	1·18 degC	$1{\cdot}18 \times \frac{9}{5} = 2{\cdot}12$ degF
Mass of lead: let this be	M kg	W lb
Height of fall (h) 32·3 in.. . .	=0·82 metres	2·8 ft
Number of falls .	20	20
Potential energy lost	$20 \times 0{\cdot}82M$ metre-kgf $= 20 \times 0{\cdot}82M \times 9{\cdot}8$ joules	$20 \times 2{\cdot}8W$ ft lbf
Heat produced .	$1000M \times 1{\cdot}18 \times 0{\cdot}03$ cal.	$W \times 2{\cdot}12 \times 0{\cdot}03$ Btu
J	$\frac{20 \times 0{\cdot}82M \times 9{\cdot}8}{1000M \times 1{\cdot}18 \times 0{\cdot}03}$ =4·6 joules per cal	$\frac{20 \times 2{\cdot}8W}{W \times 2{\cdot}12 \times 0{\cdot}03}$ =880 ft lbf per Btu

A more accurate apparatus for finding J is illustrated in Fig. 19.2. It is a modification of the brake-band method originally devised by Callendar. Heat is produced by the friction of a silk band against a cylindrical copper block, thermally insulated from the driving shaft and surrounded by a light metal shield to reduce heat loss to the surroundings. A heavy weight (W gf) pulls on one end of the silk band, and a spring balance (tension T gf) pulls on the other; the hand-wheel is turned at a steady rate so that the weight W is just lifted clear of the bench. The resultant friction

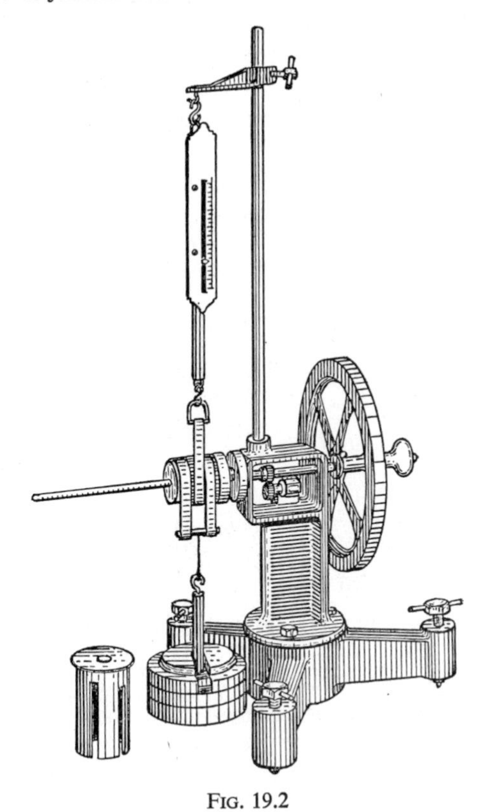

FIG. 19.2

An apparatus for finding J by a brake-band method.
(Griffin & Tatlock, Ltd.)

force is then $(W-T)$ gf or $(W-T)\ g$ dynes. The surface of the cylinder, of radius r, moves a distance of $2\pi r$, against this force, for each revolution; so the work done during n revolutions is $2\pi rn(W-T)$g ergs. n is determined from a revolution counter and r by using callipers.

A sensitive thermometer, which fits into a hole in the copper cylinder, is used to determine the rise in temperature $(\theta_2 - \theta_1)$ produced. The copper cylinder is weighed (m gm) and as its specific heat (s) is known, the heat produced is $ms(\theta_2 - \theta_1)$ cal. Whence

$$J = \frac{2\pi rn(W-T)g}{ms(\theta_2 - \theta_1)}$$

If r is in metres, m in kg and g in metres/s², J will be in joules/cal.

EXAMPLE 1. *A lump of lead falls freely from a height of* 300 *metres on to a rigid surface. Assuming that all the heat developed remains in the lead, calculate the rise in temperature of the lead.* (J=4·2 *joules/cal.* g=9·8 *metres/s². Sp.ht. of lead*=0·031.)

Let the wt. of the lead $= M$ kgf
Then loss of potential energy

$$= 300M \text{ metre-kgf}$$
$$= 300 \times 9{\cdot}8M \text{ metre-newtons or joules}$$

$$\text{The heat equivalent of this} = \frac{300 \times 9{\cdot}8M}{4{\cdot}2} \text{ cal}$$

Let the rise in temperature of the lead be θ degC.

$$\text{Then } 0{\cdot}031 \times (1000M) \times \theta = \frac{300 \times 9{\cdot}8M}{4{\cdot}2}$$

Whence $\theta = 22{\cdot}6$

∴ Rise in temperature of the lead = 22·6 degC.

EXAMPLE 2. *An electric drill of output* 200 *watts is used to drill a hole in a piece of iron of mass* 150 *grams. It takes* 25·0 *s to drill the hole. Calculate the rise in temperature of the iron, assuming that all the heat produced is absorbed by the iron.* (J=4·2 *joules/cal. Sp.ht. of iron*=0·11.)

Work done by drill $= 200 \times 25{\cdot}0$ joules
Heat equivalent $= 5000 \div 4{\cdot}2$ cal.

Let θ degC = rise in temperature

$$\text{Then} \quad 150 \times 0{\cdot}11 \times \theta = \frac{5000}{4{\cdot}2}$$

Whence $\theta = 72{\cdot}2$

∴ Rise in temperature of the iron = 72·(2) degC.

EXAMPLE 3. *Calculate the heat developed when a mass of* 200 *kg, travelling at* 40 *metres/s, is stopped by a frictional force.* (J=4·2 *joules/cal.*)

In this problem it will be convenient to make use of the fact that the formula $\frac{1}{2}mv^2$, used with the metre-kilogram-second system of units, will give the kinetic energy in joules.

$$\text{Kinetic energy} = \tfrac{1}{2} \times 200 \times 40 \times 40 \text{ joules}$$
$$= 160{,}000 \text{ joules}$$
$$\text{Heat produced} = 160{,}000 \div 4{\cdot}2$$
$$= 38{,}100 \text{ cal.}$$

19.3. Compressed gases. When a gas is compressed, work is done on it. The energy used appears as heat in the gas. You can test this by putting your finger over the end of a bicycle pump and using the pump handle to drive air past your finger. The air coming out feels quite hot. The compression of a gas is different from the compression of a spring; the spring stores potential energy and does not become hot. The difference is well illustrated by the fact that if a compressed gas is allowed to expend and so do work, it becomes colder. Compressed air released from a cycle or car tyre is colder as it comes out because it is doing work against the surrounding atmospheric pressure. The steam in a steam engine and the hot gases in a petrol engine also lose some of their internal heat as the piston is pushed along the cylinder.

19.4. Heat and molecular motion. Since Joule's time the molecular theory of matter has become well established. And it now seems that the **heat** in a body depends on the kinetic energy of the motion of its molecules, both straight-line motion and spin motion; its temperature depends on the kinetic energy of the straight-line motion of the molecules. In the cycle-pump experiment of the previous section, the piston of the pump acts as a battering ram, hitting the molecules and making them move faster and so raising their temperature. The application of the brakes to a moving vehicle makes the brake drums hotter; the kinetic energy of the moving vehicle is transferred, through the action of the force of friction, to the individual molecules of the brake drums. A hot solid hung in a cold gas has greater kinetic energy in its molecules; the moving gas molecules, hitting it, are set moving faster—the gas has become hotter. On this view heat is a mechanical effect. When we get burnt by touching something hot this theory suggests that the molecules of the skin have become damaged, probably decomposed, through being hit by molecules having a large kinetic energy.

The form of energy which we call heat exists as the **kinetic energy of the molecules.**

19.5. Heat engines. Heat engines are devices for making heat energy available for the purpose of doing work, e.g. hot-air engines, compressed-air engines, steam engines of both piston and turbine type, petrol engines and other internal-combustion engines such as the Diesel engine, and the jet propulsion engine. In most of these engines a pressure is formed which is applied to a piston. It thus seems as though the pressure or the material used in the engine does the work. This is partly true, for the thrust—due to pressure—does work as its point of application moves; but at the same time heat disappears from the system in direct proportion to the work done. It is the heat from within the material (i.e. from the kinetic energy of its molecules) which is the real source of the energy. The fact that in most types of engine there is a fresh supply of working material at each stroke does not alter the fact that it is the heat which is the source of energy.

In the internal-combustion engine, fuel such as petrol or other oil is burnt inside the cylinder itself. In a four-stroke engine (Fig. 19.3) there are four stages in the action. During the *induction stroke* vaporised fuel mixed with air is drawn from the carburettor into the cylinder as the piston moves down. The inlet valve closes and the *compression stroke* takes place; the piston moves up to compress the fuel-air mixture to a small volume. Next follows the *ignition stroke* or *power stroke*. The mixture is ignited, by spark in

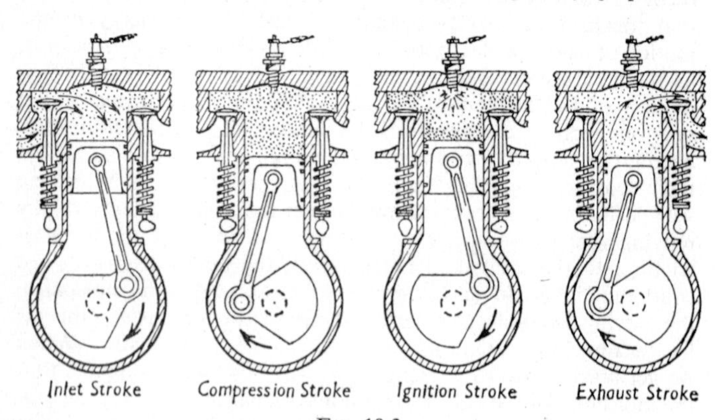

FIG. 19.3

Four-stroke petrol engine

some engines, by the high temperature caused during the compression stroke in the Diesel engine. The hot gases from the explosion do work as they push the piston down, becoming cooler in doing so. The exhaust valve then opens and the *exhaust stroke* takes place, discharging the gases as the piston moves up; the fact that the exhaust gases are still quite hot shows that not all the available heat has been used. This is a defect common to all heat engines.

The **thermal efficiency** of a heat engine is defined as the ratio

$$\frac{\text{Work done by the engine}}{\text{Work equivalent of the heat input}}$$

Approximate thermal efficiencies are as follows:

Steam engine, without condenser—less than 10%
Steam engine, with condenser—about 20%
Steam turbine, with condenser—about 30%
Internal combustion engine—about 30-35%

SUMMARY

Heat is a form of energy, since it can be applied to do work. The kinetic theory explains a **rise in temperature** as being due to an increase in the speed, and therefore in the **kinetic energy of the molecule.**

Whenever heat is used to do work, or whenever mechanical energy is converted into heat, the heat and work are found to be proportional. The constant of proportion is known as the **mechanical equivalent of heat (J)**, and is the number of units of work which are equivalent to one unit of heat.

$$J = 778 \text{ ft lbf/Btu}$$
$$= 4{\cdot}185 \text{ joules/calorie.}$$

The thermal efficiency of a heat engine is defined as the ratio

$$\frac{\text{Output of work}}{\text{Work equivalent of the heat input}}$$

Questions

1. What is meant by the statement 'mechanical equivalent of heat is 778 foot-pounds per Btu'?

Show that water at the bottom of a water-fall with a 778-ft drop should be 1 degF higher in temperature than at the top. Give one reason why the rise in temperature is likely to be less than 1 degF.

2. Describe an experiment, or the action of a machine or apparatus, to illustrate (*a*) the conversion of mechanical energy into heat energy, (*b*) the use of heat energy to do work.

3. A heavy steel cylinder falls freely down a vertical tube at the bottom of which is an equal mass of lead shot resting on a rigid surface. Describe the changes in energy which take place from the commencement of the fall; assume that the steel cylinder does not rebound. How do you account for the fact that the rise in temperature of the steel is almost negligible?

4. What is meant by the 'conservation of energy'? Apply the principle to the consideration of a moving vehicle brought to rest by the application of a brake.

Explain the fact that a piece of steel becomes steadily hotter as a hole is drilled in it.

5. A lump of lead becomes warmer if dropped from a height on to a hard surface. Assuming that all the heat energy available from the fall is retained by the lead, calculate the height of fall required to raise the temperature of the lead by 1·00 degC. (Sp.ht. of lead $=0{\cdot}031$; $J=4{\cdot}27\times10^{4}$ cm gf/cal.)

6. A bullet weighing 0·0200 kg travelling at 420 metres/s strikes a target. What is the maximum amount of heat that could be evolved? ($J=4{\cdot}2$ joules/cal.)

7. 5 litres of water are heated by a rotating paddle driven by a motor with an output of 200 watts. Assuming that all the output is converted to heat in the water, calculate the time required to raise the temperature of the water by 4 degC. ($J=4{\cdot}2$ joules/cal.)

8. A machine with an efficiency of 79% is driven by a motor with an output of 2·00 kW. Assuming that all the wasted power is distributed evenly over the whole machine (made of metal of mass 40 kg), find the rise in temperature after the machine has been running for 180 s. ($J=4{\cdot}2$ joules/cal; sp.ht. of metal $=0{\cdot}100$.)

9. Air is enclosed in a tall vertical cylinder by a light frictionless piston loaded with a 60-lb weight, the space above the piston being a vacuum. When the cylinder is heated the piston rises 18 in. If the heat supplied to the cylinder and the enclosed air is 4·0 Btu, what is the thermal efficiency of the process? ($J=780$ ft lbf/Btu.)

CHAPTER 20

Transference of Heat

20.1. Substances can lose heat by the process of **evaporation;** examples of this are given on page 164. Other modes of heat transfer have been grouped under the names of **convection, conduction** and **radiation.**

Convection is the conveyance of heat in fluids by the movement of hotter parts of the fluid from the source of heat. The movement is due to a change in density of the fluid.

The hot air current rising above a fire is an example of convection in a gas; the spreading of heat throughout a kettle of water placed on a heater is an example of convection currents in a liquid. Such movements are known as *free* or *natural convection*; if a fan or pump is used to help the movement, the process is known as *forced convection.*

Conduction is the transfer of heat through a material from regions of high temperature to regions of lower temperature but without transfer of any of the material from the hotter to the colder parts. This can be explained by assuming that molecules in the hotter regions have greater kinetic energy and pass on this energy to nearby molecules by collision with them.

A body can lose heat even if isolated in a vacuum. Under such conditions conduction and convection are impossible because there is no material medium. The loss is due to the change of some of the kinetic energy of the molecules into another form of energy. It is called **radiation** because it spreads out in all directions as rays. If the body is below red-heat the rays are known as *infra-red rays*; above red-heat *light rays* are given out as well; and at very high temperatures some *ultra-violet* radiation is also emitted. (Infra-red and ultra-violet radiations are invisible but, like light, they both have a warming effect on the skin.) These radiations which bodies give out because of their temperature are known as thermal radiation or **temperature radiation.** (These names distinguish it from other types of radiation such as X-ray radiation, radioactive radiation.) Because it has the property of **warming anything which absorbs it,** thermal radiation is often studied by absorbing it and noting the resulting rise of temperature.

20.2. Convection. A fine light dust shaken over an electric lamp or an electric fire will readily show the rising currents of heated air. And convection currents in water can be made visible by dropping a crystal of potassium permanganate into a beaker of cold water and heating it with a small flame.

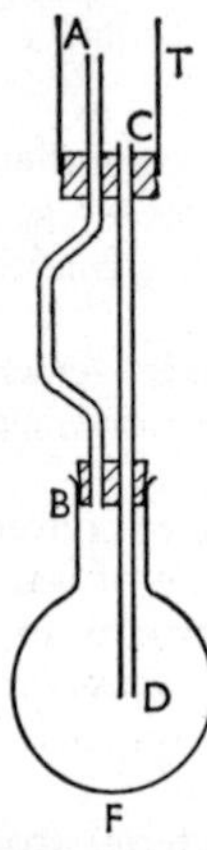

FIG. 20.1

Fig. 20.1 shows an apparatus in which the upper part (B and above) has been put into the lower flask, with the flask initially full of hot coloured water (nearly at its boiling point). The water columns in the tubes are at the same level, since the liquid is of the same density throughout. But if cold water is carefully put into the tube CD until the levels are nearly up to the cork, then the column in AB is a few mm higher than in CD; the less dense hot water is held up by the pressure of a shorter column of water of greater density. If more cold water is poured into the glass vessel B until the coloured water in AB is at A, the slightest extra amount put into B will set up a circulation in the system, which will be kept going as long as there is a pressure difference between the two pipes. This experiment clearly shows that convection currents are due to changes of density.

The previous experiment also illustrates the way in which convection currents are used to collect hot water from a fire-heated boiler in a domestic hot-water system (Fig. 20.2). In this system the hot-water storage tank H is closed at the top and is fitted with (i) a safety pipe S, (ii) an exit pipe E to hot-water taps, (iii) a cold-water supply pipe P leading from a cistern, which is high enough to produce a pressure to drive hot water out of H when a hot-water tap is opened. The cistern is fitted with a ball-cock; this arranges for refilling when the level of water in the cistern drops. Side pipes leading to hot-water 'radiators' are commonly fitted to such a system. These warm the air around them, setting up convection currents in the air; but a small proportion of heat is lost from them by thermal radiation. In large central-heating systems a pump is sometimes fitted. This forced convection is important in large systems. It reduces the warming-up period by speeding the flow; it also results in a more uniform temperature throughout the system.

Natural convection is used in refrigerator cabinets where the cooling coils are put near the top, so that cold air falling downwards may set up a circulation in the cabinet. On the other hand the air-conditioning units used in hot countries have to be fan assisted. The unit is a small refrigerator with cooling coils; without the help of a fan the cold air would sink downwards towards the floor and the cooling circulation would not be rapid. Similarly, in

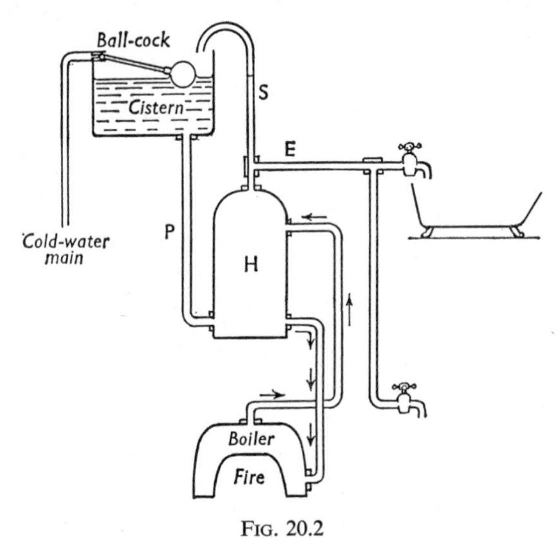

FIG. 20.2
A domestic hot-water system

cold countries, electric radiators are sometimes fan assisted to make the hot air circulate more quickly throughout the room.

The flow of flue gases up chimneys is a good example of gas-convection. Chimneys serve the double purpose of discharging unwanted smoke well away from buildings and setting up a draught for the fire. The draught is due to the pressure difference between the column of hot gases within the chimney and the corresponding column of denser cold air outside. Boiler and factory chimneys are made tall to increase this difference of pressure; the chimneys of a dwelling-house have the additional advantage of acting as ventilators to the rooms.

20.3. Conduction. The rate at which heat is conducted through materials differs from one material to another. A glass rod, heated at one end in a bunsen flame, can be held at the other end without any discomfort, but a rod of copper of the same dimensions very soon becomes too hot to hold. So that either the glass loses its heat more quickly to the surroundings, or else copper is a much better conductor of heat; a more carefully designed experiment shows the latter to be true. Metals are among the best conductors of heat, but even so there are marked differences between them; for example, copper is about seven times better than iron, which means that a copper bar will conduct seven times as many calories per second for the same temperature difference, length and cross-section. The apparatus of Fig. 20.3 shows one way of comparing the conductivities of two different metals. Two equal lengths of different wires of the same diameter are cooled at one end and heated at the other by the vapour from a boiling liquid. Loss of latent heat makes the vapour condense, and the rates at which the condensed liquid drips away from the rods gives a measure of their relative conductivities. There is hardly any heat lost from the sides of the rods since the cork which holds them is at all places at the same temperature as the rods.

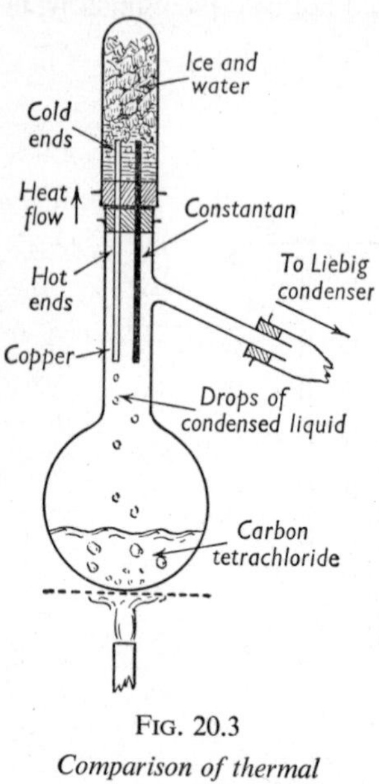

FIG. 20.3

Comparison of thermal conductivities

20.4. Conduction in fluids. When testing the conductivity of fluids it is necessary to avoid convection currents; this is done by having the heater at the top of the containing vessel. Liquids are found to be poor conductors (except for mercury, which is a metal).

Fig. 20.4 illustrates a simple experiment which shows that water is a bad conductor of heat. A large test-tube is nearly filled with cold water and is heated near the top. In due course the water boils at the top and heat is conducted downwards; but the thermometer which records the temperature at the bottom rises in temperature very slowly, showing that the rate of heat-flow through the water is small.

Gases are very bad conductors; cotton wool, felt, blanketing and similar fabrics owe their heat-insulating properties almost entirely to this fact. The fibres of the fabric stop the action of convection currents. The material itself (the cotton or the wool) is a bad conductor and there is also very little cross-section in the fibres for the passage of heat. Even steel wool is a bad conductor; so also is

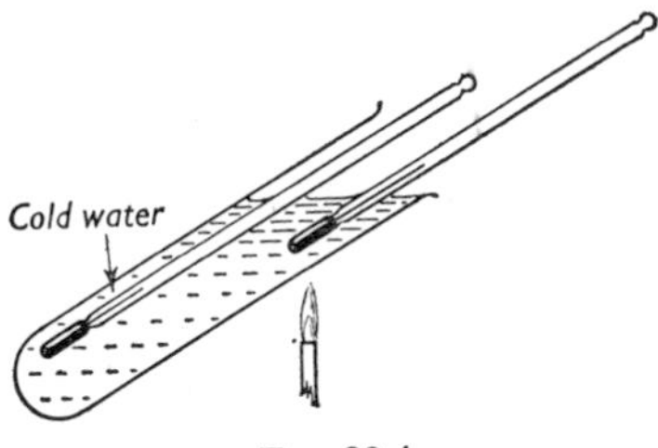

FIG. 20.4

crumpled aluminium foil, by reason of the large number of small air pockets within it. For the same reason snow is eight times as effective an insulator as solid ice; in frosty weather a layer of snow can give considerable protection to young crops.

20.5. Applications of conduction. Metals are good conductors; they are also fireproof and mechanically strong. These qualities make many of them suitable for boilers and for household heating utensils. As a rule all heating utensils are designed to offer as large a surface area as possible to the heat source and are made as thin as is possible without losing strength.

Wire gauze is often used as a heat-spreader when glassware is being heated. Conduction along the many channels provided by the wires of the gauze gives a more uniform heating. Wire gauze will also protect an inflammable gas from the action of a naked flame. This was first discovered by Sir Humphry Davy in his experiments on the design of a safety-lamp (Fig. 20.5) for use in mines. A gauze-enclosed flame can set fire to inflammable gases within the enclosure; but the conduction of heat in the gauze keeps the surface of the gauze below the *flash point* or *ignition temperature*. Fig. 20.6 shows how it is possible to have an inflammable gas near to a flame without catching fire. A bunsen-burner, with some wire gauze above it, has been lit above the gauze; but the gas below does not catch fire because the gauze does not get hot enough to reach the ignition temperature of the gas-air mixture below the gauze.

Nowadays electric lamps are used for illumination in mines; but the Davy lamp still has its uses. In air with a dangerous proportion of fire damp (methane) the gas which enters the gauze mesh can be seen burning harmlessly as a luminous cap above the main flame and so gives a warning of the dangerous conditions.

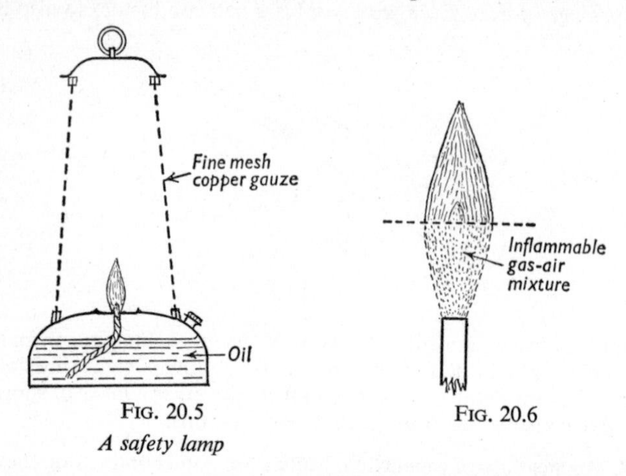

FIG. 20.5
A safety lamp

FIG. 20.6

Most non-metallic substances are poor conductors of heat. So that lagging materials, i.e. thermal insulators used for the retention or exclusion of heat, are made of such substances as wood, brick, cork, asbestos. As mentioned on page 178, their insulating properties can be increased by making them porous or fibrous (as in asbestos wool, wood shavings). The recently developed rigid foams are very good insulators, and have also the advantage of very low density—about 0·04 g/c.c.

20.6. Radiation. Thermal radiation travels so fast that to casual observation it seems to take no time at all. The light from an electric lamp seems to become visible at once when it is switched on. Anyone shielding himself from the glare of the sun by means of a shade finds that the effect of the shade seems to occur at once. Experiment shows that all types of thermal radiation (infra-red, visible light, ultra-violet) travel in a vacuum at the rate of 300,000 km/s.

Infra-red radiations follow the same laws of reflection as light (see Chapter 25). Fig. 20.7 illustrates an experiment which shows this. A powerful electric lamp is so placed in front of a concave reflector that the reflected beam is parallel to the axis of the mirror. A similar reflector is placed in the beam some distance away so that the reflected radiation is focused on to a piece of cork. The cork will begin to smoulder, and may catch fire. If a sheet of special dark glass, known as an *infra-red filter*, is placed in the path of the beam the light is cut off but the invisible infra-red radiation carries

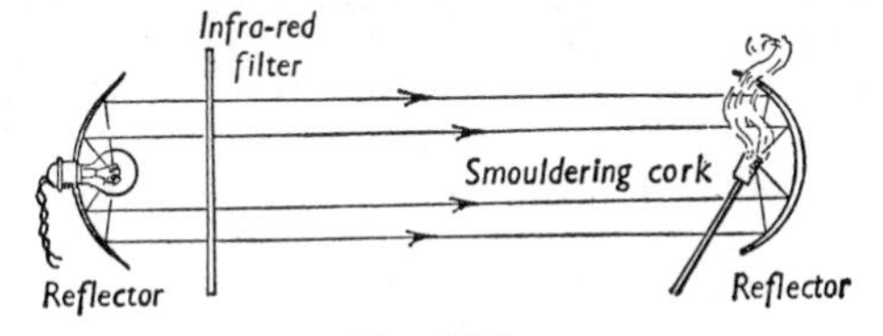

FIG. 20.7
Reflection of thermal radiation

on and is focused by the second reflector on to the cork, which smoulders as before.

A lens used as a burning glass illustrates another way of focusing radiation. The effect is due to refraction, the change in direction which occurs when radiation passes from one medium to another. Use is made of the concentration of solar radiation in the *sunshine recorder* (Fig. 20.8). As the sun moves across the sky the focus of its

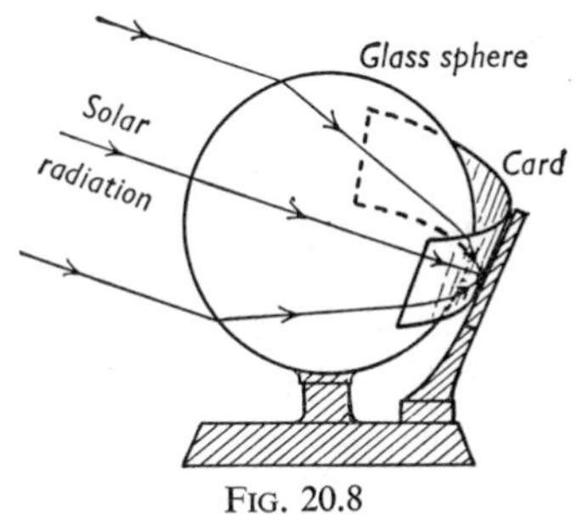

FIG. 20.8
Sunshine recorder

radiation scorches a track across the card when the sun is not obscured. The effect can be shown by using a large glass flask full of water, with a piece of thin card at the focus-point. The effect is not so noticeable as with a glass globe because the water absorbs some of the radiation. A dark-coloured card (e.g. dark green, dark red) is better than a white one because the darker colours are better absorbers of the radiation.

20.7. Absorption of thermal radiation. Any kind of radiation may either pass through a substance, in which case the substance is not warmed, or the substance may absorb some or all of the radiant energy, in which case the substance responds by a rise in temperature. With opaque substances the amount of radiation absorbed depends very much on the nature of the surface of the substance. Polished opaque surfaces are bad absorbers. Rough surfaces are good absorbers, and black rough surfaces are very good absorbers. The chemical nature of the material can have some influence, however; thus a clear varnish, in spite of its smooth surface, is a good absorber. A simple method of comparing the absorption of different surfaces is illustrated in Fig. 20.9, where two equal

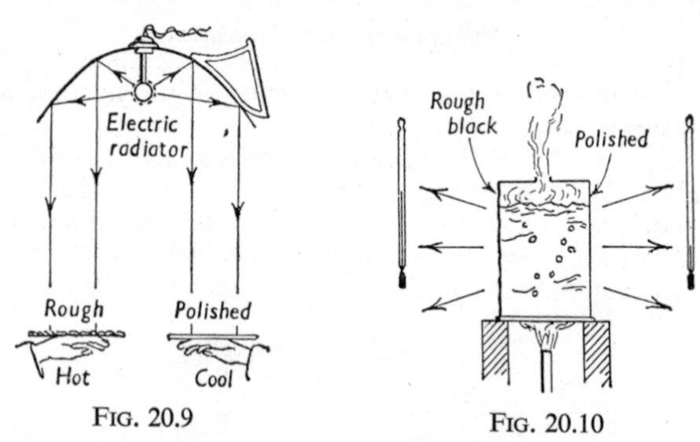

FIG. 20.9

FIG. 20.10

rectangles of metal foil, one of them coated with candle soot, are exposed to a radiation beam and the backs of the observer's hands are used as detectors. The sun's radiation can be used as a source in this experiment, if there are no clouds in the sky.

20.8. Emission of radiation from different surfaces. Measurements of the emission of radiation show that **good absorbers are good radiators,** poor absorbers are poor radiators. Black rough surfaces are very good radiators, silvery surfaces emit hardly any radiation. Something which absorbs, say, 40% of a radiation stream will emit 40% of the radiation which a black body gives in the same circumstances.

Fig. 20.10 shows a rectangular metal can with one side shiny, the other coated with candle soot. Both surfaces are kept at the same temperature by boiling water in the can. The back of your hand, at a distance of a few cm from each surface in turn, will easily detect the larger emission from the black surface. In the diagram the comparison is being made with thermometers (with blackened bulbs) placed equidistant from the two surfaces.

The vacuum flask or thermos flask (Fig. 20.11) is an excellent heat insulator in which the containing vessel is surrounded by another one, with a vacuum between them. The flask was originally designed by James Dewar for the storage of liquid air, but it is just as good for keeping liquids hot. Conduction and convection cannot occur in the empty space between the glass walls, and very little heat is conducted round the tops of the walls or through the cork. Radiation is possible across the vacuum, but the amount of it is much reduced by silvering the walls facing the vacuum; silvered surfaces are very poor radiators. When hot things are stored in the flask there is little radiation from the inner silvered surface; when cold things are stored there is little radiation sent to them from the outer silvered surface.

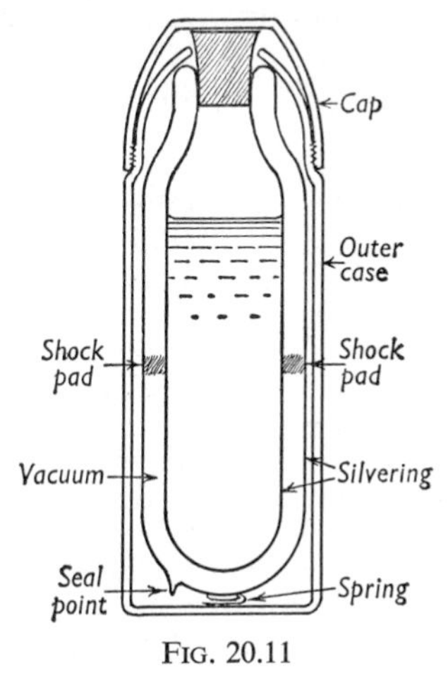

FIG. 20.11

A vacuum flask or Thermos flask

SUMMARY

Convection is the conveyance of heat in fluids by movement of the hotter parts of the fluid from the source of heat.

Conduction is the transfer of heat through a material medium from regions of high temperature to regions of lower temperature without any movement of the material from the hotter to the colder parts.

Thermal radiation, due to temperature, is the emission of energy in the form of electromagnetic waves. The range of this radiation includes ultra-violet light, the colours of the spectrum and infra-red radiation. Bodies which are not hot enough to be luminous emit only the infra-red radiation.

All forms of thermal radiation follow the same laws of reflection and refraction, but the deviation due to refraction is greater for the shorter wave-lengths.

A good absorber of any one type of radiation **is an equally good emitter** of that type of radiation.

Questions

1. Give three examples each of the application of (*a*) good conductors of heat, (*b*) bad conductors of heat.

2. Describe simple experiments to show (*a*) that copper is a better conductor of heat than iron, (*b*) water is a poor conductor of heat.

3. Give a reason why (*a*) the heating coil of an electric kettle is placed near the bottom of the vessel, (*b*) the cooling unit of a household refrigerator is placed near the top of the cabinet.

4. Draw a labelled diagram of a domestic hot-water system. Give an account of the flow of water (*a*) while the water is being heated, (*b*) when the hot tap is turned on.

5. In a vacuum flask used for the storage of ice-cream, what is the purpose of (*a*) the vacuum between the walls, (*b*) the silvering of the surfaces facing the vacuum?

6. Of two similar thermometers, one has its bulb coated with lamp black, while the other has a shiny bulb. How would their readings compare (*a*) if they were suspended in bright sunlight, (*b*) if they were suspended in a hole in a block of ice?

7. An electric fire has a heating bar with a *rough* surface; behind the bar is a *curved* piece of *polished* metal. Give reason for the use of the words in *italics*.

8. Explain the following, with special reference to the words printed in *italics*. (*a*) A block of ice will melt less rapidly if it is wrapped in *several layers* of *newspaper*, particularly if the layers are *loosely* wrapped. (*b*) Steel *wool* is a worse conductor of heat than *solid* steel. (*c*) The engines of motor-cycles are provided with *metal fins*. (*d*) A *portable* ice-storage box is made of a rigid *foam*.

9. One type of calorimeter consists of a polished copper can supported inside a larger can by a ring of felt at the top. Explain how this arrangement lessens but does not eliminate heat losses.

10. A chimney fitted to the fireplace of a boiler induces a draught through the burning fuel. Explain how this draught occurs. Explain the fact that increased height of the chimney induces a greater draught.

CHAPTER 21

Wave Motion

21.1. Waves. If a rope is lying on the ground, you can make a wave-form move along it by swinging one end of the rope up and down several times. A stone thrown into water makes the water swing up and down at the place where it hits the water; and ripples then spread out over the surface. If you sing a note, you make the air near your mouth vibrate; and a sound goes out in all directions as a sound wave. You will not be able to see the waves in this case, but instruments can detect a regular up-and-down pressure effect which suggests a wave-form. A radio aerial has an alternating current in it; this sends out electrical effects into the surroundings, making the voltage go up and down in a regular manner, so what is transmitted is called a radio wave.

In rope waves and water ripples we can see a shape or **wave-form** which seems to travel away from the cause of the waves. But the rope as a whole does not move away from the person swinging it; and it can be shown that water ripples make floating objects move only up and down—not forward. (The drift of floating objects in large sea-waves is due to causes such as wind, the tide, or the formation of breakers on a shelving beach.) The chief feature of a simple **wave motion is an oscillatory motion,** the oscillations of different parts of the wave being out of step with each other. The following experiment illustrates this.

Experiment 1. Draw a curve such as is shown in Fig. 21.1. It is actually a sine curve, and can be plotted as follows. At equally

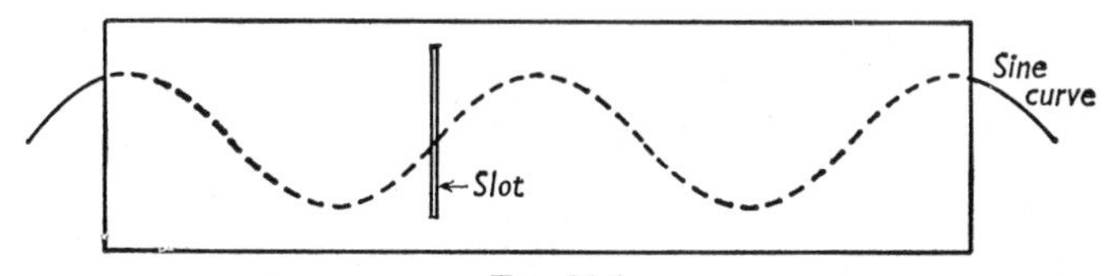

FIG. 21.1

spaced distances, plot points which are successively 0, 0·5, 0·87, 1·0, 0·87, 0·5, 0, −0·5, −0·87, −1·0, −0·87, etc., units from the x-axis. Move the curve at a steady speed beneath a fixed slot in a card. The part seen through the slot will appear to oscillate. Move the curve beneath two parallel slots, and two oscillations will be seen, which are not in step with one another. This is expressed by such terms as 'they are not in the same phase' or 'there is a difference of phase in their motions'.

Now move the curve beneath a set of equally spaced slots, e.g. a comb with equally spaced teeth; a whole series of points is now oscillating in the same kind of way, but each one differs in phase by the same amount from the next.

If you keep your attention fixed on any two slots you will be able to see the effect of phase difference; if you watch the appearance of the whole group of moving points, you get the impression of a moving wave-form.

The motion of each of the moving points in this experiment is a **simple harmonic motion (s.h.m.)**; it is one of the properties of s.h.m. that a graph of displacement against time is a sine curve.

The **amplitude** of the wave is the maximum displacement from the centre of the swing. The time of a complete oscillation, i.e. the **periodic time** T, depends on the rate at which the curve is pushed under the slots; so too does the number of oscillations done per second, known as the **frequency** f. f and T are reciprocals, for if a simple harmonic motion has a period of $\frac{1}{4}$ sec, it will do 4 oscillations per second.

So that $$f=\frac{1}{T} \text{ and } T=\frac{1}{f}$$

21.2. Speed of a wave motion. Wave-length and frequency. Fig. 21.2 shows a wave-form (continuous line) which has moved to a new

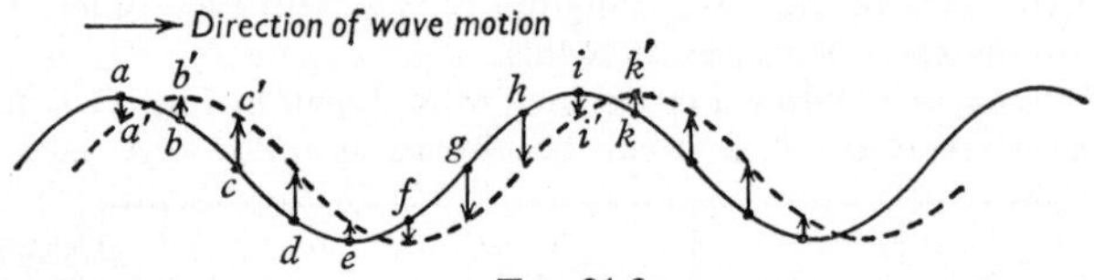

FIG. 21.2

position (dotted line) owing to an up or down movement of the parts of the wave; the movement is shown by arrows. The distance *a-i* or *b-k* is called the **wave-length** (λ).* Now the oscillations of *a* are in step with those of *i*; similarly for *b* and *k*. So the **wave-length** can be expressed as the **distance between any two consecutive points which are in the same phase** (i.e. have no phase difference).

* The Greek letter *lambda*.

Consider the movement of the wave-crest at a to b' and then on to the position of i. By the time it reaches i the particle at a will have gone down and up once, taking the periodic time T to do so. The wave travels a distance λ in the periodic time T. Therefore

$$\left.\begin{array}{c}\text{Speed at which the}\\ \text{wave travels } (V)\end{array}\right\} = \frac{\text{Distance gone}}{\text{Time taken}} = \frac{\lambda}{T}$$

But $$f = \frac{1}{T} \text{ and therefore } V = f\lambda$$

This is a general equation which **applies to all types of wave motion,** though here it has been deduced for a particular type. This type, where the direction of the oscillations is perpendicular to the direction of wave-travel, is called **transverse wave motion.** In sound, the to-and-fro vibrations of the medium are in the same direction as that of the course of the sound; such wave motion is called **longitudinal wave motion.**

21.3. Water ripples. Reflection and refraction. Water ripples are very convenient for a study of the general properties of waves. Special ripple tanks have been made for this (Pl. 6), but it is quite easy to study the simpler effects by using a bowl containing water and illuminated from above by a small lamp. Alternatively a glass-based shallow tank can be used with the lamp below it, and the ripple-shadows cast on the ceiling of the room. A sheet of glass with a wall of putty or plasticine round the edges forms a simple tank.

Experiment 2. Set up a simple ripple tank and lamp (preferably with a small filament) with the water about ½ cm deep. Touch the water surface with a rod, and remove the rod. A circular ripple-shadow or wave-front will be seen diverging from the point source. Repeat the experiment, but making two ripples start from two different points at the same time. The two ripples meet, cross over and go on unaffected by each other.

Sprinkle cork filings on the water and look at their shadows as the ripples pass; you will find that the bits of cork are not carried along by the waves.

Experiment 3. *Reflection of waves.* Strips of tinplate standing vertically in the tank can be used as reflectors of ripples. Fig. 21.3 shows the effect of reflectors of different shapes.

Experiment 4. *Refraction of waves.* Refraction, or change of direction, occurs when waves suffer a change of speed. This can be shown in the case of water ripples by having an abrupt change in the depth of the water by putting in a slab of some sort. The depth of water above the slab has to be adjusted to give the most noticeable effect. Fig. 21.4 shows the effect of a reduction of speed as the waves enter patches of shallower water.

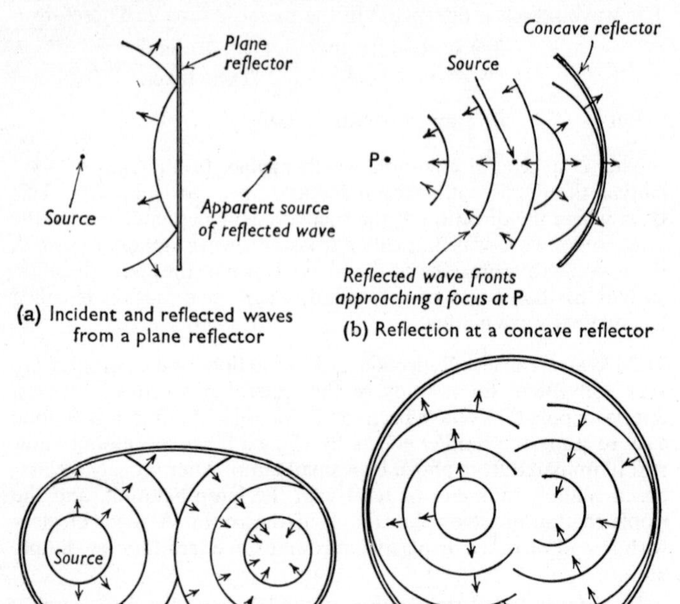

(a) Incident and reflected waves from a plane reflector

(b) Reflection at a concave reflector

(c) Reflection from an oval reflector e.g. a pie-dish

(d) Reflection from a circular reflector e.g. a circular bowl

FIG. 21.3

Reflection of waves

21.4. Super-position of waves. Interference patterns. When two wave motions are acting, each travels independently of the other, as was shown in *Experiment* 2. But in places where the waves overlap, the effect at any moment is the sum of the effects which each would have separately. Thus if both motions would produce a crest at a particular point, the combined effect is a doubly-large crest; if one wave motion would form a crest and the other a trough, the combined effect is to give no displacement. This is known as **super-position** of the waves, and when the waves have the same frequency this super-position causes a steady or **stationary** pattern; there are places where there is no displacement ever

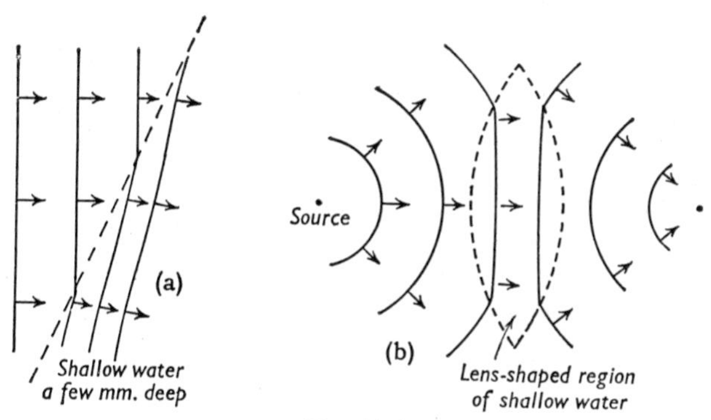

FIG. 21.4

Refraction of waves

(*nodes*) and places where there is always an extra-large amplitude (*anti-nodes*). Such patterns are called **interference patterns** or **interference effects.**

Experiment 5. Interference patterns with water ripples. Dip a vibrator (e.g. one prong of tweezers) into a ripple tank. You will not see the travelling ripples unless you view them through a stroboscopic disc (p. 193) to get a slow-motion view. Now dip two vibrators of the same frequency (e.g. both prongs of tweezers) into the tank. The super-position of the waves gives a stationary interference pattern such as is shown in Fig. 21.5*a*. A similar effect

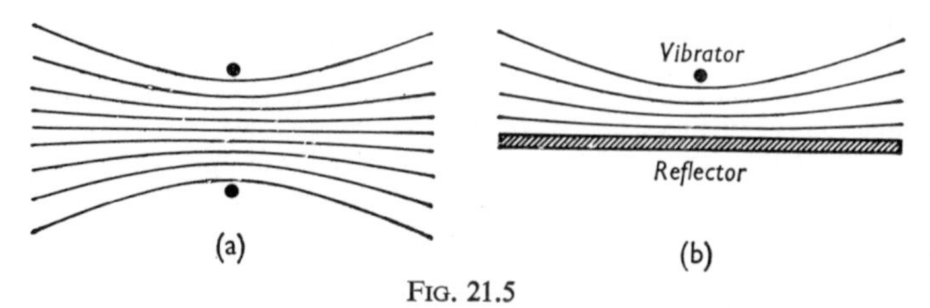

FIG. 21.5

Interference patterns due to super-position of waves

is obtained by using only one vibrator placed near a plane reflector to make two sets of ripples (Fig. 21.5*b*).

Fig. 21.6*a* shows how the stationary pattern arises from the super-position of crest-and-crest or trough-and-trough (giving

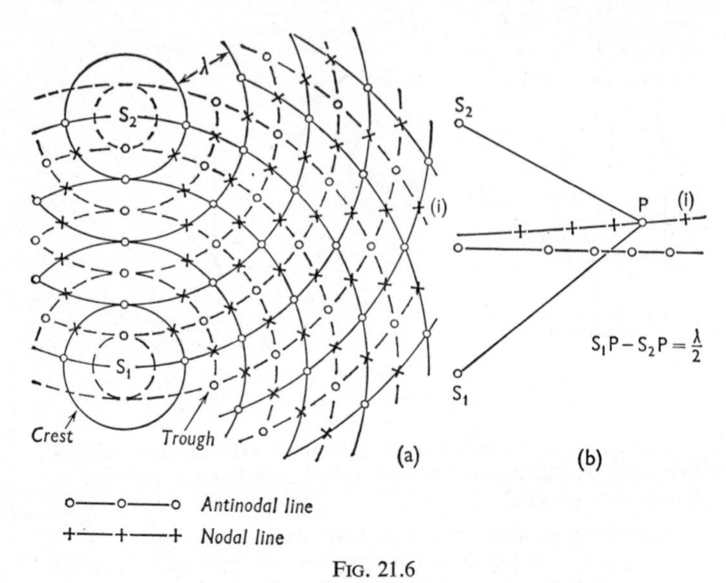

FIG. 21.6

Super-position of waves from two identical sources S_1. S_2

large oscillations or anti-nodes) and crest-and-trough (giving nodes, no displacement of the water at any time). Nodes occur where the waves always arrive out of step, i.e. in opposite phase. If the sources S_1 and S_2 are themselves in step, a node occurs at any point P when the journeys S_1P and S_2P differ by 1, 3, 5 etc. half wave-lengths. Fig. 21.6*b* illustrates this for the nodal line marked (i) in Fig. 21.6*a* where $S_1P - S_2P = \lambda/2$.

These interference patterns can be detected not only with water ripples but with sound waves, light waves and radio waves; forming an interference pattern is one of the ways of detecting a wave motion.

21.5. Stationary waves. Stationary waves occur when two waves of the same frequency travel in opposite directions. They give an interference pattern which is a series of equally-spaced nodes and anti-nodes, such as occurs along the line S_1S_2 of Fig. 21.6*a*.

Experiment 6. Fix one end of a length (2 metres or more) of rubber tubing or heavy cord to the end of a bench. Pull on the free end to give the cord a slight tension. Jerk the cord sideways and note the kink which moves along the cord; it is reflected at the fixed end and returns. Then swing the free end from side to side. For certain frequencies you will find that the moving cord takes up the shapes of Fig. 21.7. These are **stationary waves** of different

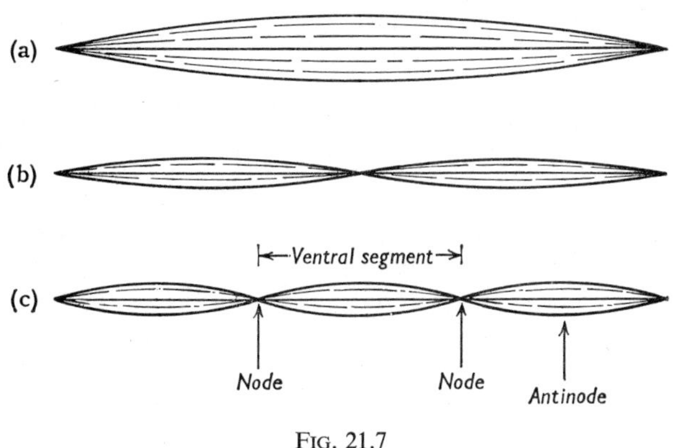

FIG. 21.7
Stationary waves in a string

wave-lengths. The names given to the parts of this stationary wave pattern are marked on the diagram.

In this experiment the stationary waves are due to superposition of the outgoing and reflected waves. In the resulting pattern the crest of the wave-form does not move onwards. The wave-form itself is still there, but is hidden in the blurred appearance of the moving cord. A slow-motion view of the movement can be obtained with the use of a stroboscopic disc, using the arrangement shown in Fig. 21.10. The successive positions taken up by the moving cord are shown in Fig 21.8, lines i, ii and iii. *The wave-form flattens to a straight line, becomes reversed in shape, and then repeats the process.*

Now the distance AB on the wave-form represents the wave-length. But AB equals CD, and this is the length of two ventral segments. Therefore

Length of one ventral segment = Half a wave-length
or
Distance between two nodes = Half a wave-length

This relation applies to all types of wave motion, so that if a wave motion is reflected back along its track and the nodal points are

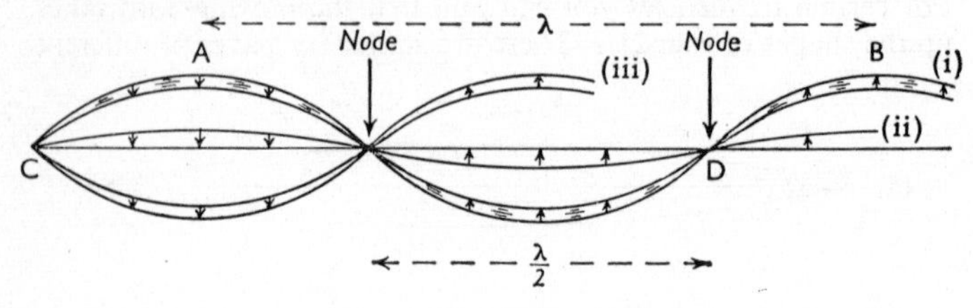

FIG. 21.8

Stages in the motion of stationary waves in a string

found experimentally, the wave-length can be found. Sound sent along a closed tube is reflected at the closed end and the nodes of the stationary waves can be detected. Fig. 21.9 shows an

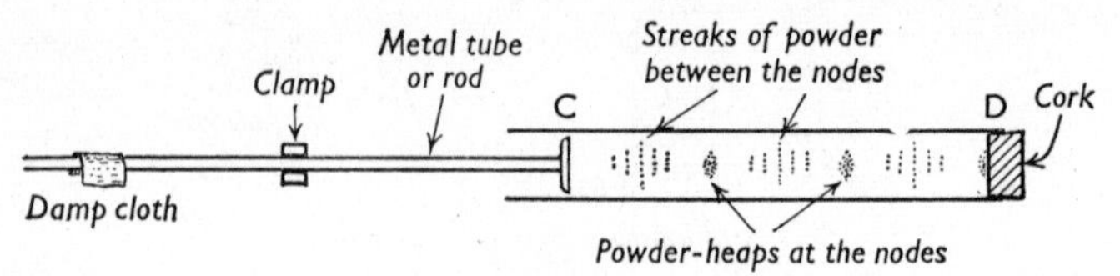

FIG. 21.9

Plan of the apparatus for the dust-tube experiment. Sound is made at C when the rod is stroked with the damp cloth

experimental arrangement, where some cork dust put into the tube is used as a detector of the nodes. Fig. 21.10 shows the formation of stationary waves in a string.

21.6. Diffraction. When waves pass by the edges of an obstacle they bend round the obstacle to some extent. The effect is known as **diffraction,** and can be seen quite easily in a ripple tank by putting obstacles in the tank. Fig. 21.11 shows what happens with different forms of obstacle. When waves meet a gap which is only a few wave-lengths in width, the waves spread out as though the gap were itself a source of waves.

The extent of the bending round an obstacle depends on the wave-length of the waves. The sounds of speech and music have wave-lengths which may be as long as a metre, and obstacles do not affect them much, i.e. there is no definite sound shadow. Light

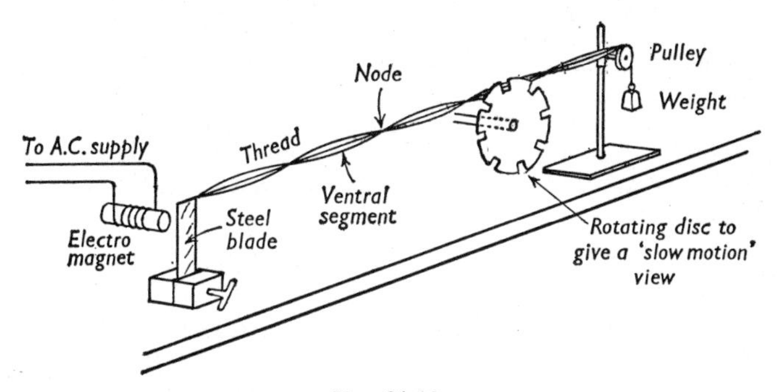

FIG. 21.10

Stationary waves in a length of thread. The rotating stroboscopic disc give 'snap-shot' views of the string. By adjusting its speed, and hence the frequency of viewing, the string can be seen at rest or seen moving slowly up and down

has such a very short wave-length that obstacles cast sharply defined shadows from a point source; some bending or diffraction does occur but it is much less noticeable.

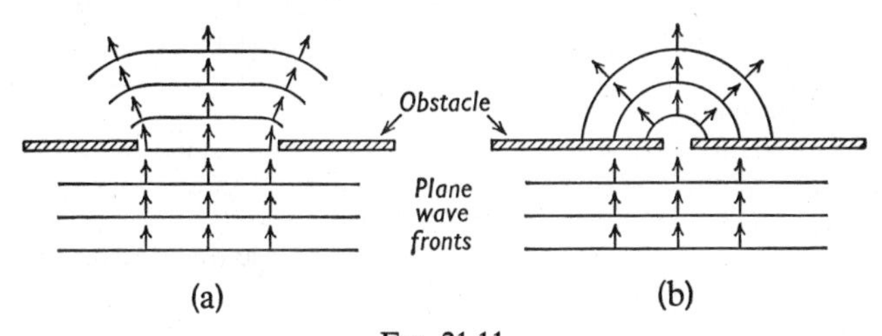

FIG. 21.11

Diffraction of waves

SUMMARY

The **frequency** (f) of an oscillation is the number of complete swings performed in one second.

The **wave-length** (λ) of a wave-form is the distance between two consecutive points in the same phase.

For all types of wave-motion, the speed of travel (V) is equal to the product $f \times \lambda$, i.e.

$$V = f\lambda$$

Waves can show the effects of reflection, refraction and diffraction. Refraction is due to a change in the speed of travel.

Super-position can give rise to interference patterns.

Two identical wave-forms travelling in opposite directions set up **stationary waves.** The nodes of stationary waves are **half a wave-length apart.**

Questions

1. Water ripples, of wave-length 2 cm, travel a distance of 19·3 cm in 1·08 s. Calculate (*a*) the speed of travel, (*b*) the frequency of the oscillations.

2. Draw a diagram to show a wave-form in a string, the wave-form having a wave-length of 5 cm. Assuming the wave to be travelling from left to right, mark on the diagram some points in the string which are (*a*) moving upwards, (*b*) moving downwards, (*c*) momentarily at rest.

Assuming the wave to have a speed of 0·50 metre/s, calculate the frequency of the oscillations.

3. Calculate the wave-lengths, in air and in water, of sounds which have frequencies of (*a*) 100, (*b*) 680, (*c*) 3400. Speeds of sound in air and in water are 340 and 1360 metres/s respectively.

4. Calculate the frequency of a radio station transmitting on a wave-length of (*a*) 60 metres, (*b*) 300 metres. Speed of radio waves $= 3 \times 10^8$ metres/s.

5. A radio wave from A to B can travel both along the line AB and also along a path ACB where C is a point in the upper atmosphere. The two waves reaching B may result in a weakening instead of a strengthening of the reception. Use the ideas of phase difference in wave motion to explain this.

6. Taking the wave-length of yellow light as 5000 Ångström units calculate (*a*) its frequency, (*b*) the number of wave-lengths in 1 mm. 1 Ångström unit $= 10^{-8}$ cm. Speed of light $= 3 \times 10^8$ metres/s.

7. A vibrator of frequency 100 cycles/s sets up stationary waves in a string 27·9 cm long; three ventral segments are formed. Calculate the speed of travel of the *transverse* waves in the string. Explain the meaning of the word printed in *italic* and describe the change in the appearance of the string if the frequency of the vibrator is trebled.

8. In what circumstances are waves refracted? Illustrate your answer by reference to an example of refraction of water ripples.

9. Draw three concentric circles of radii 1·4 cm, 2·8 cm, and 4·2 cm to represent the crests of ripples on a water surface. Draw two parallel lines BB′ and RR′, each 3·6 cm from the centre of the circles, BB′ representing the boundary of shallower water across which the ripples travel with only one-third of their initial speed, and RR′ representing an obstacle which reflects the ripples. Show on the diagram (*a*) the ripple-crest which has entered the shallower water, (*b*) the ripple-crest which has been reflected from RR′, (*c*) a ripple-trough which has been reflected from RR′.

10. Distinguish between the terms *longitudinal* and *transverse* as applied to waves. Give one example of each type of wave.

CHAPTER 22

The Nature of Sound. Pitch, Frequency and Wave-Length

22.1. Sound and vibration. Every source of sound is in a state of vibration. In many instances the vibration is clearly visible. If you twang a piece of stretched elastic you can see that the elastic is vibrating. So also you can see the vibrations of a ruler fixed at one end and set vibrating at the other. But the vibrations which are the cause of many common sounds are not always to be clearly seen, often because the vibrating system is a gas and therefore invisible —the toot of a ship's siren, the note of a whistle, the thunderous noise which succeeds a lightning flash. Experiments show that all such sounds are due to vibrations, and also that the vibrations are transmitted by the air or other surrounding material.

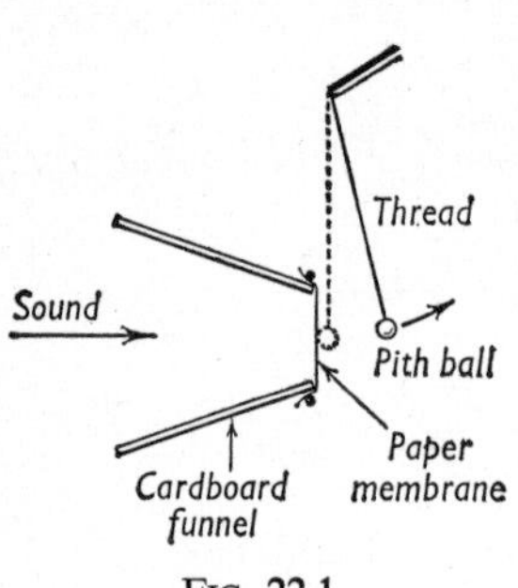

FIG. 22.1
Acoustic pendulum

Fig. 22.1 shows an apparatus known as the acoustic pendulum, which consists of a very light ball hung from a thread and touching a paper membrane. Any kind of sound which enters the cardboard funnel causes the membrane to vibrate, and the deflection of the small ball is easily seen.

If you rub a pin over the surface of a file you will hear the sound and feel the vibration which caused it. The pitch of the sound depends on the rate at which the movement takes place—the more rapid the movement the higher the pitch.

22.2. The transmission of sound. Vibration is not in itself sufficient to produce the sensation of sound; **there must be some material to transmit the effects** of the vibration to the ear of the listener—sound cannot travel through a vacuum. This can be proved by hanging an electric bell in a glass jar from which the air can be withdrawn by an exhaust pump (Fig. 22.2). The bell, with a battery tied to the back of it, is hung inside the jar by thin threads. The bell is set ringing and the jar placed over the base-plate which is connected to the exhaust pump. As the air is removed the loudness of the sound decreases; eventually the bell can be seen to be vibrating but no sound is heard; on letting air flow in again the bell is heard ringing once more.

All materials can transmit sound, but in some the sound dies away. Cloth fabrics and fluffy substances are good absorbers and are often used to deaden sounds. Water and metals transmit sound with very little absorption. If you put your head under water in a bath when the tap is running you will hear the splashing sounds particularly well; if you put your ear to a metal pipe or rail, the slightest knock on the metal is readily heard.

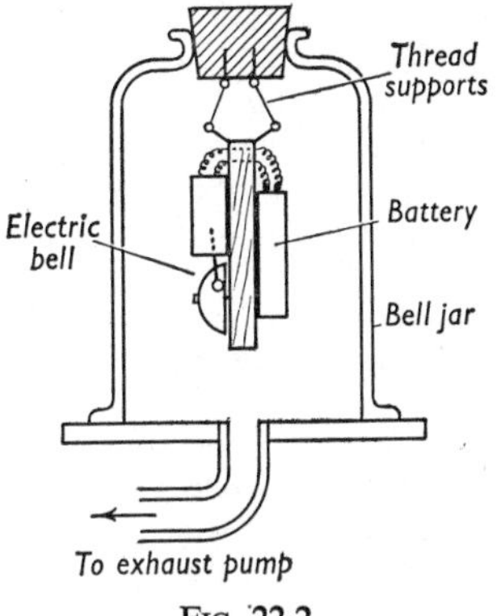

FIG. 22.2

22.3. The speed of sound. The flash and bang of a firework seem to occur at the same moment if you are standing nearby. But at a range of a hundred metres or more the sound is heard later than the flash is seen. The light from the flash, which travels at the enormous speed of 300,000 kilometres per second, reaches you practically at once even over a range of many kilometres; the sound takes an appreciable time. Experiment shows that the speed

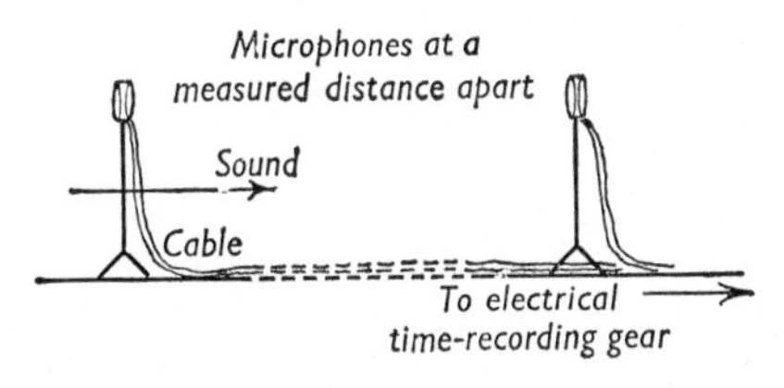

FIG. 22.3

of sound in air is about a third of a kilometre per second or a fifth of a mile per second. To measure such a speed with accuracy requires an accurate timing device and a long distance for the sound to travel; it is also necessary to time the sound in two opposite directions to allow for the effect of wind. One recent method uses two microphones, set in line with a source of sound, connected by cables to an electrical time-recorder (Fig. 22.3). In this way the time t taken by the sound to travel the measured distance s between the microphones is found; the speed is then $s \div t$. The average of a large number of results is found, and the temperature is also noted because the speed of sound depends on temperature.

Experiments show that the seeed of sound in air at 0°C is 331 metres/s (1090 ft/s). The speed increases by 62 cm/s (2 ft/s) for every degC rise in temperature. The speed in hydrogen gas and in water is about four times that in air, and the speed in steel is about sixteen times that in air.

22.4. The reflection of sound. Echoes. An echo is caused by the reflection of sound waves. A vibrating body sets up a series of compressions in the surrounding air (Fig. 22.7) and the effect of these is passed on, similar to the spreading of ripples when a stone is dropped into water. Whenever a compression wave meets the surface of another material, some of the energy is reflected as a compression wave. There is a strong reflection from hard substances such as wood, metal and stone; it is also quite noticeable from liquid surfaces.

Pl. 7 shows a flash-photograph of a sound pulse (actually the 'crack' of an electric spark) reflected from a plane surface. The compression is actually invisible, but if the air is illuminated by a sudden flash from a point source of light it casts a shadow on a photographic film and so can be recorded. The incident and reflected compressions are identical in shape with the wave-fronts seen in the reflection of water ripples (Fig. 21.3a). The track of the sound is such that the angle of incidence i is equal to the angle of reflection r (Fig. 22.4); the angle of incidence is the angle between the track of the incident sound and the perpendicular, or *normal*, to the surface.

If you clap your hands or stamp your feet when at a distance of 17 metres from a tall wall or building, the sound will travel the 34 metres journey (out and back) in a tenth of a second if the speed of sound is 340 metres/s. You may just be able to hear the original sound and the echo as separate sounds in this case. For time intervals of less than a tenth of a second the returning sound cannot be distinguished from the original, and no separate echo can be heard for distances less than 17 metres. If you shout in an empty room many echoes reach your ear very rapidly; the general echo-effect from the walls may last for a noticeable time. The time taken for sound to die away in a building is known as the **reverberation**

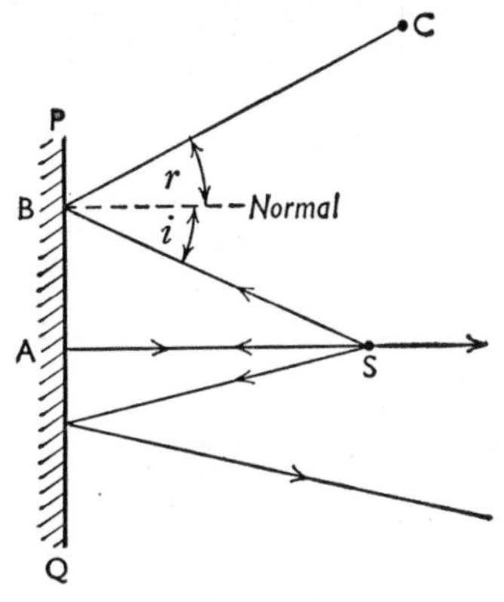

FIG. 22.4

time. In a large unfurnished hall this may be as long as several seconds; it is difficult to hear distinctly in a hall with a reverberation time as long as this. Soft furnishings act as absorbers of sound; their presence makes listening easier in an unfurnished hall.

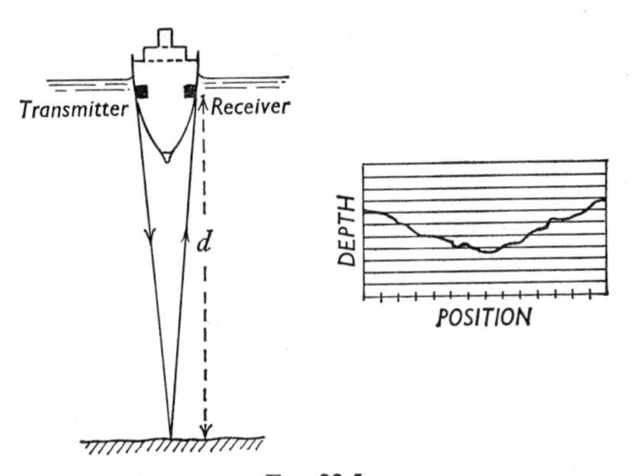

FIG. 22.5

Echo depth-sounding

A knowledge of the speed of sound in water has been applied in the **echo depth-sounding** equipment which is fitted to many ships.

A transmitter fitted to the hull of the ship sends out a sound-impulse and the echo is detected by a hydrophone (a microphone designed for use under water), also fitted to the hull and connected to an electrical recording circuit. In this way a continuous record can be traced on a chart showing the depth of water (Fig. 22.5). The equipment has also been used for finding submerged wrecks and for detecting the presence of shoals of fish.

22.5. Sound waves. Wave-length. The transmission of sound through a material is due to the springiness of the material through which it goes. If the stem of a vibrating tuning-fork is pressed against a wooden rod, as shown in Fig. 22.6, the end surface of the

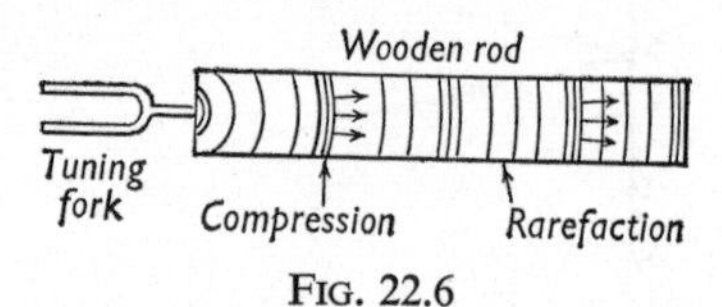

FIG. 22.6

rod is set vibrating too. This makes a series of compressions in the wood. Each compression as it is formed passes on the effect of the compression to the more distant sections of the wood. In this way a whole set of evenly spaced compressions is formed in the wood. The compressions can be considered to travel as waves do, and the distance between one compression and the next is known as the **wave-length** (λ). In a similar manner the moving prongs of the tuning-fork set up a series of evenly spaced compressions and rarefactions in the surrounding air (Fig. 22.7). These compressions

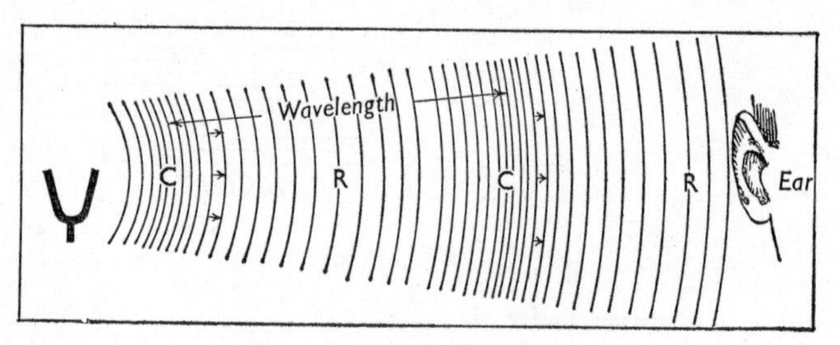

FIG. 22.7

Transmission of sound as a series of compressions, C, and rarefactions, R

and rarefactions result in the air vibrating to and fro; but the air does not move along with the travel of the sound. This again is

similar to the way in which waves travel. If you place some small corks on a large bowl of still water and then start some ripples by touching the water with your finger you will see the ripples move across the surface, but the corks only bob up and down as the ripples pass by.

Sound waves, however, differ from water waves in the direction of their vibrations. The to-and-fro vibrations of sound are along the line of travel of the sound itself. Waves of this sort are called **longitudinal waves.** In water waves the vibrations of the water surface are at right angles to the direction of travel of the waves. Waves of this sort are called **transverse waves.**

22.6. Pitch and frequency. The **frequency** of a vibrating system is the number of complete (to-and-fro) oscillations or **cycles** which it makes per second. The **pitch** of a note is its position on some chosen musical scale; we judge the pitch of a note by ear. Though it requires some musical training to judge the pitch of a particular note, most people can easily judge a change of pitch and can say whether the pitch has risen or fallen. Experiment shows that pitch is related to frequency; **the pitch of a note rises with increase of frequency.** If a piece of card is held against a rotating bicycle wheel the note which is produced rises in pitch when the rate of rotation of the wheel is increased; you can test this by holding the card either against the tyre or the spokes. At slow speeds you get only a clicking noise; faster, you get a deep-noted hum. The frequency corresponding to this hum is known as the **lower limit of audibility;** it is about 30 cycles/s.

The ear becomes less sensitive to sounds of frequency greater than 4000 cycles/s. Vibrations with a frequency of the order of 20,000 cycles/s can barely be heard; the beginning of this inaudible range is known as the **upper limit of audibility.** This limit varies with different individuals, but for most persons it is in the range 20,000–30,000 cycles/s. Some animals, dogs for example, can detect vibrations of a higher frequency than this. Bats are known to be able to emit and detect vibrations of very high frequency, and can use the echoes of their high-frequency ‘squeaks’ to help them locate and dodge obstructions when flying in the dark.

Seebeck's siren (Fig. 22.8) and **Savart's toothed wheels** (Fig. 22.9) are two pieces of apparatus which are used to study the relation between pitch and frequency. In Seebeck's siren a jet of air is blown against a ring of holes in a rotating disc. At low speeds the issuing air can be heard as a series of puffs. At higher speeds the separate puffs merge to give a definite note, rising in pitch as the speed of rotation is increased. By fitting the shaft with a revolution counter, and timing the revolutions with a stop-watch,

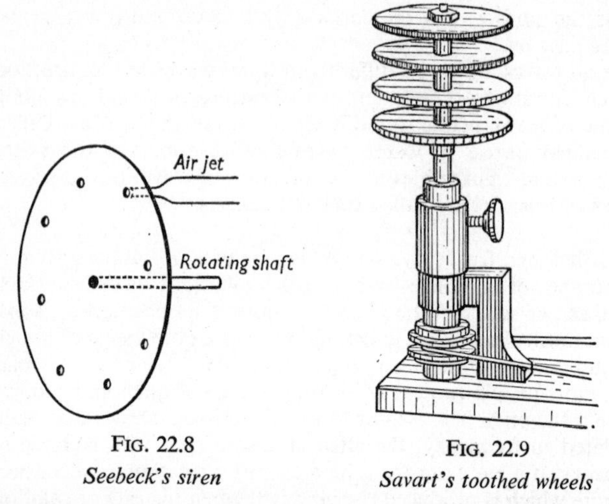

FIG. 22.8
Seebeck's siren

FIG. 22.9
Savart's toothed wheels

the frequency of a note can be found; the siren is kept in unison with the note whilst the timing is done. Thus if there are 12 holes in the disc, there will be 12 puffs per revolution, and if the disc does 20 revolutions every second the frequency of the note will be $12 \times 20 = 240$ cycles/s.

One of the most familiar musical scales of pitch is the **diatonic scale.** It comprises the eight notes known by the names

doh ray me fah soh lah te doh′ (or upper doh)

and the rise in pitch from the lower to the upper doh is known as an **octave**—a 'jump' of the eight notes of the scale. The rise in pitch from one note to another is known as an **interval.** It is found that the interval between two notes depends on the **ratio** of the frequencies of the notes. For example, the frequencies corresponding to the notes doh, me, soh and doh′ are in the simple numerical ratio,

doh	me	soh	doh′
4	5	6	8

22.7. Determination of frequency. Both the siren and the toothed wheel can be used, if the shaft is fitted with a revolution counter, to find the frequency of a note.

The frequency of a vibrating blade or of a tuning-fork can be found by making a trace of its motion on a rotating disc (Fig. 22.10).

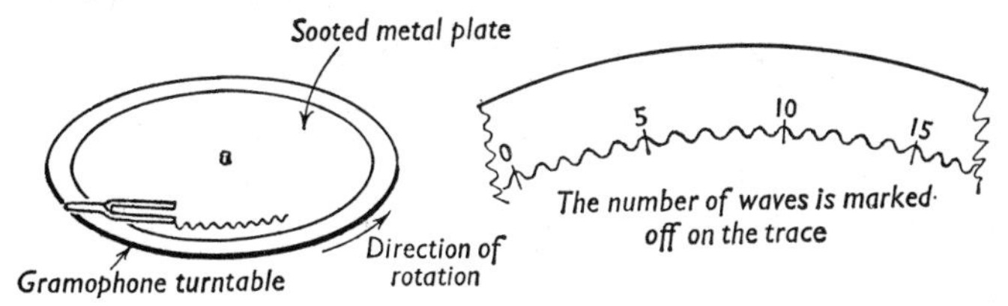

FIG. 22.10

A flat sheet of material (preferably metal) is chosen which will fit on to a gramophone turntable. (The sheet need not necessarily be circular.) The surface of the material is coated with soot from a candle flame, placed on the turntable and set in rotation. A light bristle or short piece of fine wire is fixed with sealing-wax to one prong of the fork. The fork is struck and the bristle touched against the rotating smoked surface. With a little practice it is possible to obtain a complete ring of wavy marks, and the number of complete wave-forms is then counted. The rate of revolution of the turntable is then found by timing a definite number of revolutions with a stop-watch. The frequency f of the fork is then calculated from the relation

$$f=\frac{\text{Number of complete waves in 1 revolution}}{\text{Time of 1 revolution}}$$

For example, for the D fork the following results were obtained.

Time for 50 revolutions = 38·5 s
Time for 1 revolution = 38·5 ÷ 50 = 0·77 s
Waves in three different traces = 218, 220, 219
Mean number of waves per revolution = 219

$$\text{Frequency of fork D}=\frac{219}{0\cdot 77}=285 \text{ cycles/s}$$

This is the frequency of the 'loaded' fork; without the bristle and the wax, the frequency would be slightly greater than this.

22.8. Quality. Notes of the same pitch, played on two different musical instruments such as the piano and the trumpet, are distinctly different. The difference in character or **quality** of the notes is due to the presence of a group of higher pitched notes which accompany the main note. These notes are a whole number of times the frequency of the main note; they are called **overtones** or **harmonics.** It is these overtones which give the note from a particular instrument its characteristic quality. Fig. 22.11 shows how

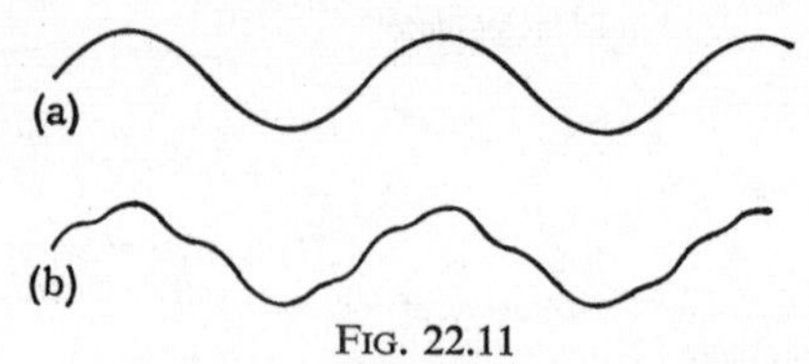

FIG. 22.11

Oscillograms of a vibrating tuning-fork: (a) illustrates the fundamental note, (b) shows the presence of an overtone

the displacement of a prong of a tuning-fork varies with time after the fork has been struck (*a*) gently, (*b*) vigorously. The effect of the additional overtone in the second case can be seen as a series of kinks in the pattern, and the slightly different quality of the note can be detected by ear.

22.9. Frequency and wave-length. The spacing of the successive compressions of a sound wave is known as the **wave-length** (**λ**) of the sound. The wave-length depends on the **frequency** of the source and also on the **speed** with which the compressions move outward from the source. Suppose that a tuning-fork has a frequency of 100 oscillations per second and that the compressions are transmitted at the speed of 1000 ft/s. Then the first compression to be formed will, after one second, be 1000 ft from the fork. Between it and the fork there will be many other compressions so

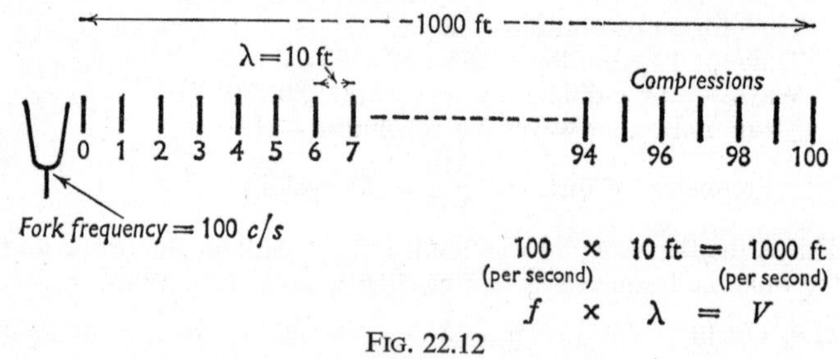

FIG. 22.12

Relation between speed, frequency and wave-length

placed that there are 100 compression-spacings or wave-lengths in the total distance of 1000 ft (Fig. 22.12). From this it follows that the wave-length in this case is $1000 \div 100 = 10$ ft. This illustrates the general formula

$$V = f\lambda$$

where V = speed of travel of the sound
f = frequency of the oscillations of the source
λ = wave-length

Applied to the previous example we therefore have

$$V(1000) = f(100) \times \lambda(10)$$

The wave-length of a note therefore depends on the material through which it is travelling, since it is found that the speed of sound is different in different materials. If in the previous example the speed of the sound had been 2000 ft/s the wave-length would have been 20 ft.

SUMMARY

The speed of sound in air at 0°C is 331 metres/s (1090 ft/sec); it increases with temperature, and for small changes in temperature the increase is 62 cm/s (2·0 ft/s) for each centigrade degree. A more exact relation, which applies to all gases, is

$$\textbf{Speed} \propto \sqrt{\textbf{Absolute temperature}}$$

An echo is caused by the reflection of sound waves. The directions of the incident and reflected lines of transmission make equal angles with the normal to the reflecting surface.

Sound is transmitted as a **longitudinal wave motion,** i.e. the vibrations are along the line of travel of the sound and they set up **compressions** and **rarefactions** in the medium.

The wave-length of a sound is the distance between two successive compressions or rarefactions,

$$V = f\lambda$$

The **pitch** of a note rises with increase of **frequency.**

The musical **interval** between two notes is determined by the **ratio** of their frequencies, which is 4 : 5 : 6 : 8 for the notes doh, me, soh, doh′.

The **quality** of a note is affected by the number and relative loudness of the **overtones** which are present.

Questions

1. How long will it take for a sound to travel 2000 metres in air (*a*) at 0°C, (*b*) at 20°C? (The speed of sound at 0°C is 331 metres/s and increases by 62 cm/s for each degC rise.)

2. Calculate the time taken for sound to travel 340 metres (*a*) in still air, (*b*) in a following wind of speed 25 metres/s, (*c*) in an opposing wind of speed 25 metres/s. (Speed of sound in still air = 340 metres/s.)

3. Describe how you would find experimentally a value for the speed of sound in the open air using thunderflash fireworks as the source of sound. State the principal sources of error in the experiment and show how they could be reduced.

4. You are provided with a gramophone turntable, turning at the rate of exactly 45 rev/min, as a timing device in measuring the speed of sound by a flash-and-bang experiment. Describe in detail how you would use this timing device. State, giving reasons, whether you consider it to be more accurate than a stop-watch reading to fifths of a second.

5. An explosion is made at the end of a steel tube 1·6 km long, and two sounds are heard at the other end with an interval of 4·4 s between them. If the speed of sound in the air is 340 metres/s, calculate the speed of sound in steel. (The speed of sound in steel is greater than in air.)

6. Give a brief account of echoes and their uses.

7. In Fig. 22.4 a person C claps his hands and a person S makes a squeak, both at the same time. Explain how it is that S hears 2 squeaks and 2 claps, C hears 1 clap and 2 squeaks. State the courses taken by these sounds; by making measurements on the diagram, deduce the sequence in which the sounds are heard by C and S.

8. Two ships A and B are 408 metres apart and each is 272 metres from the shore which is parallel to AB and consists of a vertical cliff. When a gun is fired on A the noise is heard twice by observers on B as well as by observers on A. Explain this, and calculate the time interval between the two noises heard (*a*) by an observer on A, (*b*) by an observer on B. (Speed of sound in air = 340 metres/s.)

9. Explain the reverberation of an empty room when someone shouts within it. Explain the effect on the reverberation time of the room of (*a*) opening all the windows, (*b*) covering the floor, walls and ceiling with felt, (*c*) introducing an audience to hear the effect of the shout.

10. If a bicycle wheel is set spinning the sound of a note can be heard when a card is touched against (*a*) the spokes, (*b*) the tyre. Explain this, and state, giving reasons, which of the two notes you would expect to have the higher pitch.

11. State a simple numerical relation between the frequencies of

the notes c, e, g, c′. If the frequency of the note c is 128 cycles/s, deduce the frequencies of the other three notes.

12. Describe, with the aid of a diagram, a simple type of siren. Explain its action.

13. Describe how the sound of the vibrations of a metal blade reach the ear of a person hearing the sound.

14. Describe an experiment to show that a material medium is necessary for the transmission of sound.

15. What is the frequency of the note given by a siren, with 15 holes in the disc, rotating at a rate of 960 rev/min? What change of pitch will result if the rate of rotation is (*a*) increased to 1440 rev/min, (*b*) decreased to 480 rev/min?

16. A vibrating bristle is touched against a sooted disc which is rotating at a uniform rate. The wavy trace so formed shows $62\frac{1}{2}$ oscillations and subtends an angle of 120° at the centre of the disc. If the disc performs 20 rev in a time of 15·0 s, what is the frequency of the vibrating bristle?

17. The musical interval between a note of frequency 216 cycles/s and one of f cycles/s is the same as that between f cycles/s and 384 cycles/s. Calculate the value for f.

18. State the factors which affect the *pitch* and the *quality* of a musical note.

19. What is meant by the wave-length of a note? Calculate the wave-length of a note of frequency 500 cycles/s sounding (*a*) in air, (*b*) in hydrogen. Assume the speed of sound in air and in hydrogen to be 1100 and 4400 ft/s respectively.

20. Calculate the frequency of the vibration which sets up a wave-length of 5 cm in air, the speed of sound in the air being 340 metres/s. State whether this frequency is within the limits of audibility of the human ear.

CHAPTER 23

Sound from Strings and Pipes. The Reproduction of Sound

23.1. The vibration of strings. Fig. 23.1*a* shows a **sonometer** or **monochord,** an instrument used for making tests on the vibration of strings. A simple version of it can be made from a length of wire stretched between two screws in a board as shown in Fig. 23.1*b*; the tension in the wire can be altered by turning the screws.

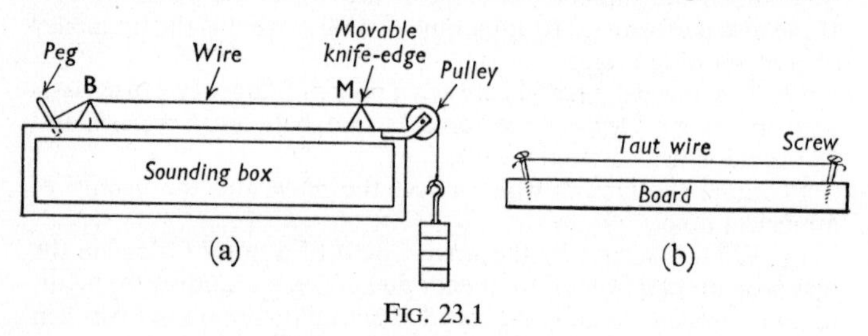

FIG. 23.1

Types of sonometer or monochord

The length of wire in use can be varied by putting a movable knife-edge, or bridge, underneath the stretched wire. Suppose that the bridge is put under the wire so that it just touches the wire half-way along. Then if you pluck either half of the wire you will hear a note which is the **octave** above the note given out by the wire before the bridge was put in place; **halving the length has doubled the frequency.** With the bridge one-third of the way along the wire, the longest section (two-thirds of the original length) gives the note soh if the original note is taken as doh; thus the frequency has increased in a proportion $\frac{3}{2}$ (see the frequency list on p. 202). Both these results are examples of inverse proportion. The **frequency** of a wire under constant tension is **inversely proportional** to its **length.**

Other experiments with the sonometer, varying the tension and using different wires, show that the frequency of vibration (f) is given by the formula

$$f=\frac{1}{2l}\sqrt{\frac{T}{m'}}$$

where T is the tension of the wire in absolute units, l is the length of the wire and m' is its mass per unit length or linear density.

Another way of setting a stretched string into vibration is by the method of **resonance.** Resonance occurs when a body is set into vibration by the application of small impulses having the same frequency as the natural frequency of the body itself; the final extent or **amplitude** of the swing is much greater than the applied amplitude. A simple example of resonance occurs when you set someone swinging on a garden swing; experience shows that you can do this with quite small forces if you time the application of them to coincide with the natural frequency of the swing.

If a sonometer wire is tuned to a slightly lower pitch than a tuning-fork of frequency, say, 256, a shorter length of that wire will be in unison with the fork. If the fork is sounded and moved with its handle in contact with the wire, slowly along the wire from one end, a point will be reached where the wire sings out with the same note. A small paper rider put across the wire can be flung off by the violence of the induced vibration. This is an example of tuning by resonance (Fig. 23.2*a*). The experiment can be repeated with a fork of double the frequency, 512. It is then

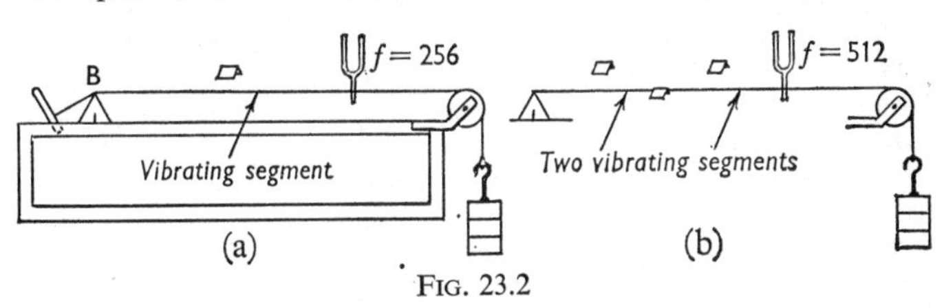

FIG. 23.2

Resonance of the same wire to different frequencies

found that, at exactly the same place as before, the wire sings out in resonance. But the note is the same note as the new fork—twice the frequency which the wire had in the first part of the experiment. That the wire is in fact vibrating in quite a different way can be shown by the use of paper riders. If three are placed as shown in Fig. 23.2*b*, it is found that two are thrown off but the middle one is not thrown off. **The wire has to vibrate in two sections in order to vibrate with twice its fundamental frequency.**

It is quite common for a sounding body to be capable of several different modes of vibration. The one with the lowest frequency is known as the **fundamental**; the higher frequencies are known as **overtones** (see p. 204). The frequencies of the overtones are always a whole number of times the frequency of the fundamental. Thus in the experiment just described, the fork was sounding one of the overtones of the stretched string.

23.2. Stringed instruments. In the violin the four strings are first tuned by altering the tension. A suitable mass per unit length is chosen by the manufacturer, the low-frequency G-string having the greatest linear density and the high-pitched E-string the least. The fingering of the player gets the required notes by altering the length of the string in use. The body of the instrument acts as a sounding board; the design of the body affects the quality of the notes.

In the piano the notes are 'ready-made' by tuning steel wires to the required notes. The low notes are produced by the longer wires; the piano tuner makes the final adjustments by altering the tension. The pressing of a key on the keyboard causes a felt-covered hammer to strike a group of wires (three in the case of the high notes) which sound the note.

23.3 Vibrations in tubes and pipes. Anything which causes a sudden change of pressure in a vessel of gas will usually set the gas in vibration and so cause a sound. The familiar 'pop' when a cork is pulled out of a bottle is an example of this. Blowing across the mouth of the bottle will also set the enclosed air into vibration; and you will find that the pitch of the note is the same as that given when the cork is pulled out. If you put water into the bottle, and so reduce the volume of air, you will find that the pitch of the note rises.

A test-tube will give out its fundamental note if you blow gently over the mouth of the tube. If you blow more vigorously another note will be given out, much higher up the scale. A very vigorous puff will give rise to a very shrill note of much greater frequency. This shows that a column of air can vibrate in more ways than one. The higher-pitched notes are harmonics of the low-pitched note or **fundamental.** They are **overtones,** and their frequencies are a whole number of times that of the fundamental. They are usually present to some extent even when the tube is blown gently, and they only become pronounced when the tube is overblown; their presence and relative intensities affect the quality of the note.

When an air column is set in vibration it does so in segments. These are illustrated in Fig. 23.3 for a closed pipe (a pipe which is closed at one end). At the open end of a pipe sounding its fundamental there is a large extent or **amplitude** of vibration, further in there is less amplitude and at the base of the tube there is no

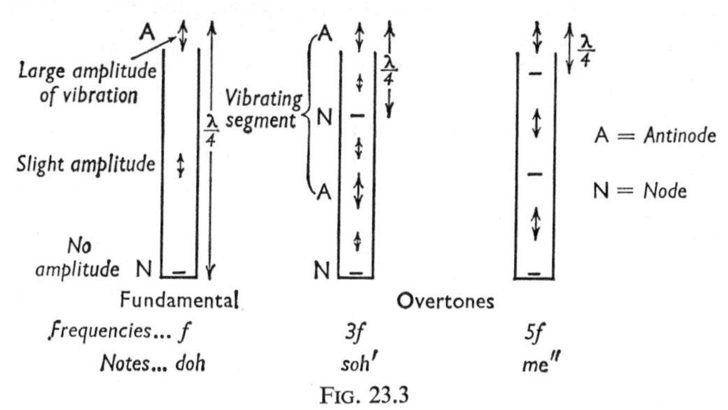

FIG. 23.3

Modes of vibration in a closed pipe

vibration. The place of maximum amplitude of vibration is called an **antinode;** the place of zero vibration is called a **node.** In the case of the overtones there are more of these node-antinode sections, and the air has to vibrate with greater frequency to produce these. The modes of vibration for an open pipe (a pipe open at both ends) are shown in Fig. 23.4. Here the segments are similar to the seg-

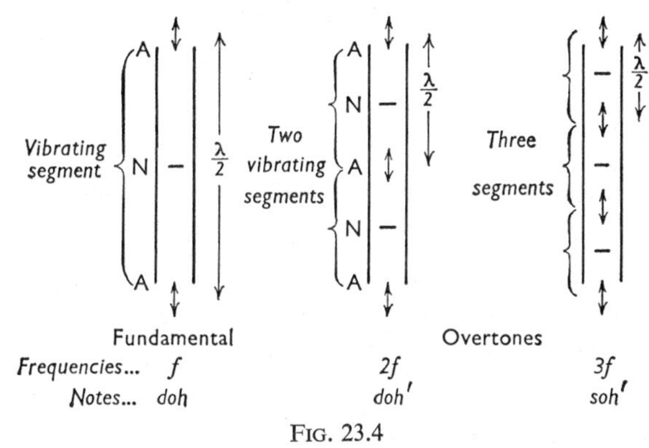

FIG. 23.4

Modes of vibration in an open pipe

ments shown by vibrating strings, except that a string has a node at each end.

Pipes can be set into vibration by resonance with a tuning-fork if the fork has the same frequency as the natural frequency of the pipe or of one of its overtones. This is illustrated in Fig. 23.5*a* which shows water being poured into a tall jar whilst a sounding-fork is held above the changing air column. A stage is reached at which the air column is set into vibration and a very loud sound is heard. If at this stage you stop the fork and blow over the top of the air column you will hear that it has the same natural frequency as the fork.

Fig. 23.5*b* shows a resonance tube in which the length of the air

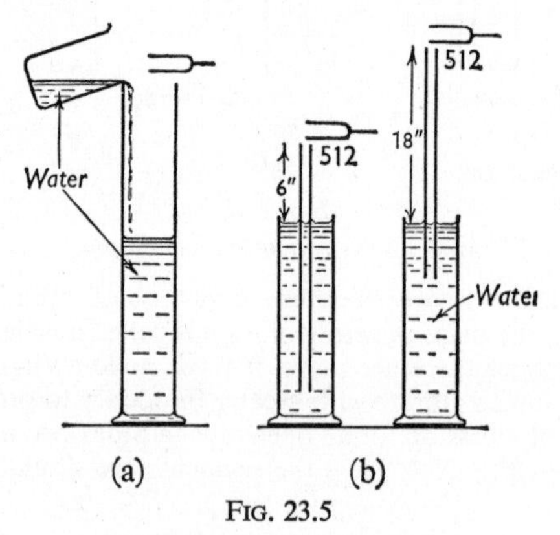

FIG. 23.5

Resonance in a column of air

column is varied by pulling a glass tube out from a tall jar of water. If the tube and jar are long enough, several lengths of air column can be found which resonate with the fork. Fig. 23.5*b* illustrates two of them; in the case of the longer air column, the fork is in resonance with an overtone of the pipe. Using a tube of about 1 cm diameter with a fork of frequency 512 cycles/s in air at a room temperature of 12°C, the two resonant lengths were found to be 16·5 cm and 49·5 cm. Now the speed of sound in air at 12°C is 338 metres/s. Applying the formula

$$V = f\lambda$$

we have $33800 = 512 \times \lambda$

whence $\lambda = 66{\cdot}0$

The wave-length of the sound is therefore 66·0 cm. The first resonant length is thus a quarter of a wave-length and the second resonant length is three-quarters of a wave-length. **The distance between a node and an antinode is a quarter of a wave-length.**

By having two tubes which slide inside one another we can make an open pipe of variable length and use it to produce resonance with a tuning-fork. The shortest open pipe to resound, in air at 12°C, with a fork of frequency 512 cycles/s is 33·0 cm long. Its length is half a wave-length and it has an antinode at each end (Fig. 23.6).

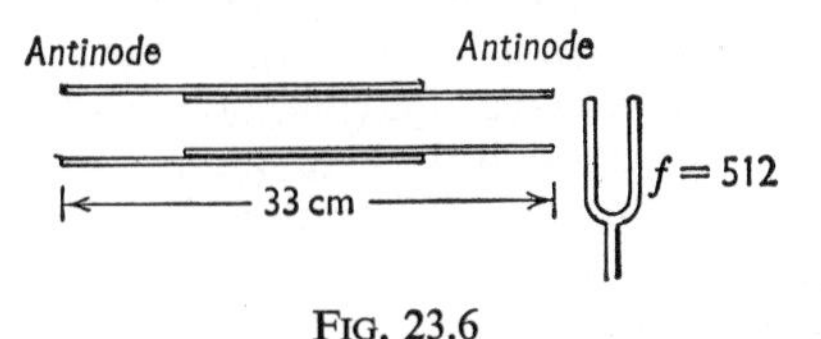

FIG. 23.6

The simple relationships, between wave-length and length of tube, apply only to narrow tubes. With wide tubes the antinodes are a short distance outside the open end of the tube. This distance is known as the *end-correction* of the tube; it has been found to be three-tenths of the diameter of the tube.

23.4. Wind instruments. Organ pipes, the tin whistle, the wood-wind and the brass of an orchestra are examples of musical instruments which give musical notes from the vibrations of columns of air. In the 'flute' or 'flue' pipes of an organ, a blade-like stream of air from the wind-chest passes from a slit or flue S over the sharp edge or lip E. This causes the air in the pipe to vibrate. There are

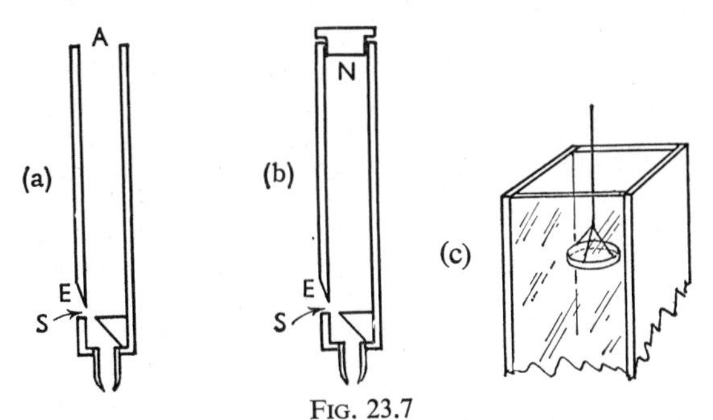

FIG. 23.7

(a) Open organ pipe. (b) Closed organ pipe. (c) Savart's tray used to detect antinodes

antinodes near the two openings of an 'open' pipe (Fig. 23.7*a*), and a node and antinode in a closed or stopped pipe (Fig. 23.7*b*).

The wave-length in an open pipe is approximately twice the length of the pipe; in a closed pipe it is approximately four times the length of the pipe. For pipes of equal length, the closed pipe gives the lower note—approximately an octave below that from an open pipe.

Experimental organ pipes have been constructed with glass fronts. The positions of the nodes and antinodes can be explored in such pipes by Savart's method of lowering a light parchment tray, containing fine sand, into the pipe (Fig. 23.7*c*). An agitation of the sand particles is detectable at the antinodes.

The notes of the simple tin whistle (Fig. 23·8) are sustained in a

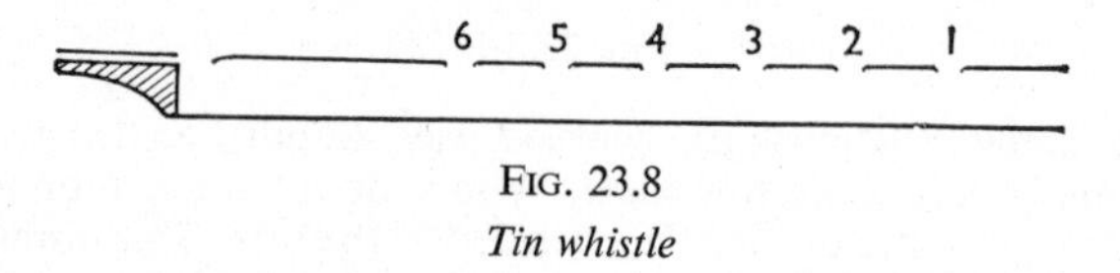

FIG. 23.8
Tin whistle

manner similar to that in the flue organ pipes. A flat air-jet is blown from the mouthpiece and passes over an edge of the metal tube. With all the holes 1–6 closed by the fingers the whistle sounds its lowest note, since the air column is then the full length. Opening any one of the holes reduces the effective length of the pipe, and this gives an increase in the frequency of the note. Similar controls with the fingers, with keys or with plungers, are used in many wind instruments, e.g. flute, clarinet, oboe, saxophone, orchestral horn, bassoon.

23.5. The reproduction of sound. There are many ways in which the effects of sound can be made permanent and then used to reproduce the original sound, e.g. gramophone records, the magnetic tape recorder, the sound track of films. Some part of the recording gear is kept in steady motion and on it in one way or another the wave form of the sound is imprinted. The early types of sound recorders were purely mechanical. In the early phonograph designed by Edison (1877) the recording surface was a sheet of tinfoil wrapped round a grooved cylinder; rotation of the cylinder caused a steel point, attached to a diaphragm at the end of a conical horn, to move over the tinfoil in the grooves. Sounds entering the horn caused the steel point to vibrate, and that made dents in the tinfoil. When the needle was driven over the same course again it reproduced the original sounds from the diaphragm, though the quality of reproduction was not very good.

From this was developed the gramophone, using disc records

with spiral grooves and the wave-form cut from side to side in the grooves (Pl. 8). The first recording was cut on a wax composition, and copies made from it. In these methods the sound itself had to supply the necessary energy to work the cutting point, so that sounds of low intensity were not always faithfully recorded. Nowadays electrical recording is used; a microphone receives the sound and an amplifier increases the variations of the electric current. It is these relatively large currents which work the cutting tool. The cutting point is geared to trace a spiral course on the wax disc. Reversed or negative copies are made from this; and from the negative moulds the finished record is made in a hydraulic press. The record can be re-played with the aid of a sound box or a gramophone pick-up and amplifier. Most pick-ups nowadays are of the crystal type; these have the advantage of being very light in weight so that the pressure of the needle or stylus does not damage the very fine grooves which are now used in the 'long-play' records. The vibrations of the needle or stylus cause variations in pressure on the surface of a crystal of Rochelle salt; the variations of pressure cause variations of voltage in the surface of the crystal.

The wave-form of sounds can also be recorded on **magnetic tape,** imprinted on it in the form of varying degrees of magnetisation. The tape is made of plastic material impregnated with a magnetic powder. The tape is wound from one reel to another by a small motor, and on its journey it passes between the pole pieces of an electro-magnet which carries the amplified currents from a microphone. When the magnetised tape is re-wound between the pole pieces of the electro-magnet it induces variations of voltage in the coil of the electro-magnet; these voltage variations are amplified to produce currents in a loud-speaker which thus gives a reproduction of the sound.

In the case of the cinema film the sound is recorded on a narrow strip along the edge of the film, the strip being known as the **sound track.** A microphone converts the original sound to corresponding current variations; these can be made to affect either (*a*) the brightness or (*b*) the area of a narrow strip of light which falls on the moving film; in (*a*) the resulting record is known as a **variable density** track and in (*b*) as a **variable area** track (Pl. 9). For reproduction of the sound, light is passed through the track and on to a light-sensitive surface—the metal cathode of a photoelectric cell. The fluctuations of light intensity reproduce, in the output from the cell, the current variations caused by the original sound at the microphone, and a valve-amplifier system supplies the necessary power to give the reproduction at loud-speaker strength.

Questions

1. Describe simple experiments, one in each case, to show that the frequency of vibration of a stretched string depends on the length of the string and on the tension of the string. State one other factor which affects the frequency.

2. State the effect, on the pitch of an open organ pipe, of closing its end. Give a brief explanation of this change of pitch.

3. A whistle is fitted with a plunger which can be moved along the length of the barrel. Describe in general terms the changes of pitch which result as the plunger is moved from half-way along the barrel to the far end, and then pulled out of the end so that the end is open.

4. If a column of air, free at both ends, is set in vibration so that it sounds its fundamental note, how does the motion of the air vary along the length of the column? What is the frequency of vibration if this length is 33 cm and the speed of sound in the air is 330 metres/s?

5. Give an account of the production of sound in two of the following cases: (i) from a gramophone record, (ii) from an organ pipe, (iii) from a vibrating tuning-fork with its stem in contact with a wooden board.

6. What is meant by the term *resonance*? How would you demonstrate the resonance of an air column to the vibrations of a tuning-fork? Describe, with the aid of a diagram, the motion of the air in the column at the stage where resonance occurs.

7. Describe simple experiments, one in each case, to show (*a*) a stretched wire set into vibration by resonance with a tuning-fork, (*b*) the presence of overtones in a stretched wire which has been plucked.

CHAPTER 24

Light Radiation. Shadows. Eclipses

24.1. Light radiation. Electro-magnetic radiation. Sources of light are generally hot. In the case of things such as a filament lamp or the surface of molten iron, the nature of the light depends mainly on the temperature of the source. The following is an approximate guide to colour-temperature for surfaces which are good radiators:

Very dull red .	500–550°C	Yellow . .	1050–1150°C
Dark red . .	650–750°C	Yellow-white	1250–1350°C
Bright red . .	850–950°C	White . .	1450–1550°C

Light of all types travels through space at a speed of 300,000 km/s. This was first discovered by Roemer in 1674. He found that light from outside the earth's orbit (he observed the eclipse of light from one of Jupiter's moons) took 1000 s to cross the earth's orbit of 300,000,000 km. The speed is the same for light of all colours. It is also the same for all types of thermal radiation, for X-rays and for radio waves whether of long or short wave-length. The name **electro-magnetic radiation** has been given to all these radiations, and they have the properties of a wave motion. They are reflected and refracted as waves would be; and they show diffraction effects—the ability to bend round the edges of an obstacle in their path. In the case of light the bending is hardly noticeable, and this is due to the very short wave-length of light. But you can test the effect yourself in the following manner.

Experiment 1. *The diffraction of light*. Set up a very small lamp, such as an electric torch, about 3 metres from you in a darkened room. Hold a strip of card, about 2 cm wide, at arm's length in front of one eye, the other eye being closed. Move the card slowly across your line of view, so as to obscure the lamp. You will find that the light is not suddenly cut off as the card moves across. Even more remarkable is the fact that when the middle of the card is on the line of sight to the lamp (Fig. 24.1*a*), the edges of the card appear lit up, showing that some of the light energy from the lamp can still reach your eye.

Now hold two strips of card close to your eye, as shown in Fig. 24.1*b*, and view the lamp through the slot between them. If you make the slot narrower a stage is reached when the spot of light appears to broaden, showing that the light has bent round the edges of the slot.

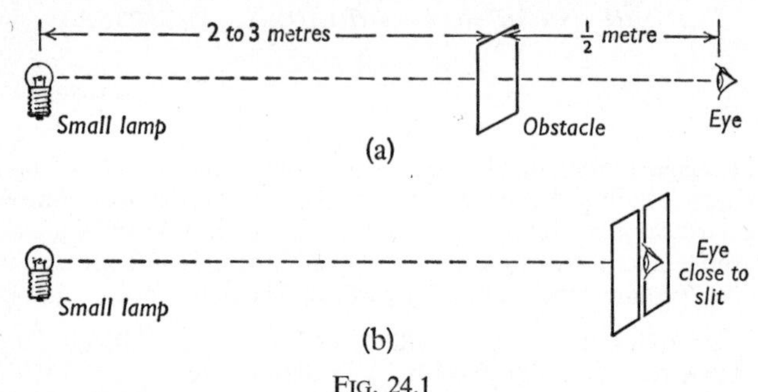

FIG. 24.1

Diffraction of light

Fig. 21.6*a* shows the interference pattern caused by the overlapping of water ripples. A similar effect occurs with two overlapping beams of light, provided that both beams have started from the same source. You can see the effect by allowing the diffracted beams, from two pinholes, to overlap inside your eye as in the following experiment.

Experiment 2. *An interference effect with light.* Set up the lamp arrangement shown in Fig. 24.1*b*. Make two *very small* pinholes, about half a millimetre apart, in a piece of paper or in metal foil and view the lamp with the pinholes held *very close* to your eye. The light from the lamp will appear as a set of parallel light and dark bands, and these are the antinodes and nodes of the waves of light. The bands are known as **interference fringes.** Although they are formed on the retina of the eye, the brain interprets them as being in the region of the lamp.

24.2. The wave-length of light. The wave-length of light can be found from interference effects. Thus the previous experiment can be modified so as to measure the **fringe-width** (the spacing of the bright or of the dark fringes); and with the arrangement shown in Fig. 24.2 you can make measurements to find, approximately, the wave-length of light.

Experiment 3. *Wave-length by the double-slit method.* Set up a line source of light, e.g. a straight-filament lamp, well above the bench to avoid unwanted reflections. About 2 metres from it arrange two slits, about 1 mm apart and parallel to the lamp filament. The slits can be ruled, with two needles fixed together, on a sheet of glass coated with Aquadag (colloidal graphite). View the interference

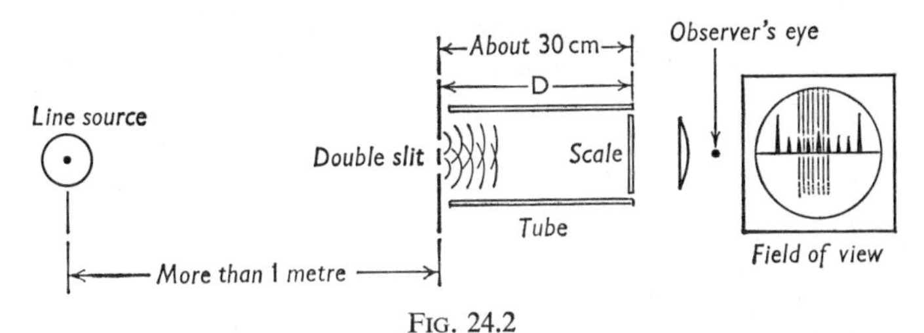

FIG. 24.2

Plan of apparatus for estimating the wave-length of light

fringes against a celluloid mm scale in the manner shown in Fig. 24.2. Measure the fringe-width w and also the distance marked D. Then place the scale across the slits and, with the help of a magnifying glass, measure their separation s.

Calculation. Fig. 21.6*a* shows that on the line S_1S_2 the antinodes are half a wave-length apart, and that they become much further apart at the other side of the diagram. It can be shown (see Question 2) that the spacing at the distance D from the sources is increased by the factor $D \div \frac{1}{2}s$, where $s = S_1S_2$. At this distance the spacing or fringe-width w becomes $\frac{1}{2}\lambda \times (D \div \frac{1}{2}s)$, i.e. $w = \lambda D/s$ or $\lambda = ws/D$.

In an actual experiment there were 4 fringe-widths to the mm, so $w = \frac{1}{4}$ mm, s was 0·5 mm and D 250 mm.

$$\therefore \lambda = \frac{0{\cdot}5}{4 \times 250} = \frac{0{\cdot}5}{1000} \text{ mm} = 0{\cdot}5 \text{ micro-metre (micron)}$$

This is an average value for the wave-length of white light. Using coloured light, it is found that the wave-length ranges from 0·35 micro-metre for violet light to 0·70 micro-metre for red light.

Another interfering effect which has been used to find λ is that due to a **grating.** One type of grating consists of many parallel equally-spaced lines on glass or transparent plastic; the grating effect can also be studied with petrol-filter gauze, a fine-mesh handkerchief or umbrella fabric. When parallel light falls on such a grating, each gap in the grating acts as a fresh source of light waves, all in step with each other. This is shown in Fig. 24.3. One effect of these waves is similar to a plane wave-front such as PP;

and if a lens is put beyond the grating the light is focused just as if the grating had not been there. But on each side of the focus

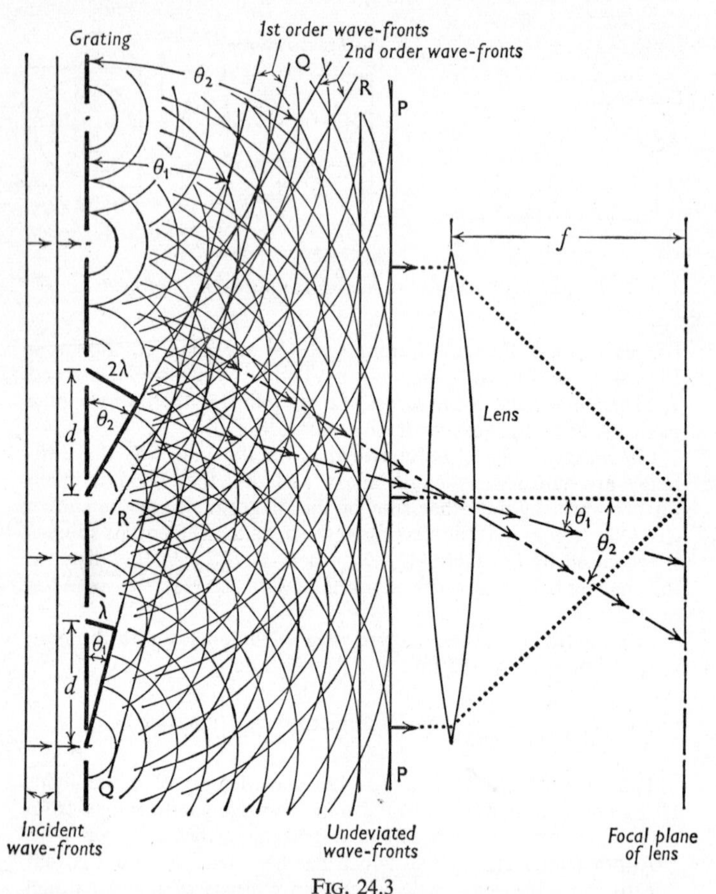

FIG. 24.3

Effect of a grating on plane wave-fronts

there are other images. These are due to the fact that the waves re-inforce each other to give wave-fronts such as QQ and RR which are focused, by the lens, off-centre. (You will see these wave-fronts more clearly if you look across the diagram with your eye nearly in the plane of the paper.) The names given to the foci of PP, QQ, and RR are the **undiffracted image,** the **1st order spectrum** and the **2nd order spectrum** respectively. From the angles of deviation of the spectra, the wave-length can be found. Thus an inspection of the diagram will show you that

for QQ $\lambda = d \sin \theta_1$ (1st order spectrum)
for RR $2\lambda = d \sin \theta_2$ (2nd order spectrum)

Experiment 4. *Wave-length by the grating method.* Clamp a grating with its lines vertical and look through it at a distant vertical slot illuminated by a lamp—preferably a sodium lamp because this emits light of one particular wave-length (monochromatic light). Each side of the slot you will see several images of the slot, the 1st, 2nd, 3rd, etc. orders of spectra. Place two pointers so that they are in line with the 1st order spectra (the ones nearest the slot). Measure the distances x and h (Fig. 24.4). Then

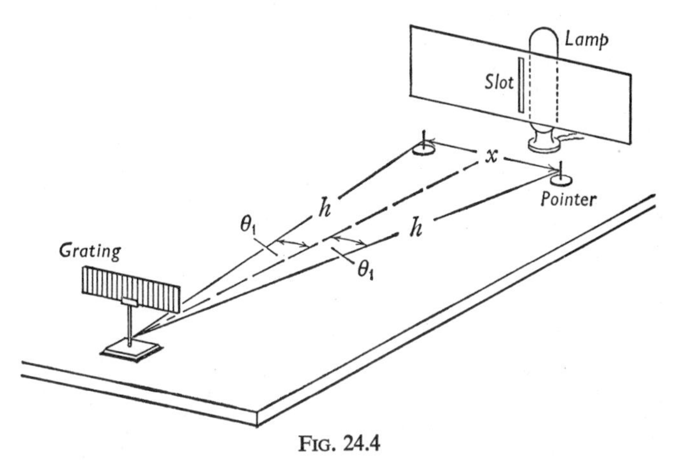

FIG. 24.4

Finding the wave-length of light with a diffraction grating

place an accurate mm scale across the grating and look at them through a powerful magnifying glass. Count the number of grating spaces in several mm of the scale; from this you can calculate the grating spacing d. Then for the 1st order spectrum $\lambda = d \sin \theta_1 = dx/2h$.

24.3. Electro-magnetic waves. Present-day theory assumes that light is a disturbance similar to that sent out from a radio aerial. But whereas the electrical oscillations in an aerial have a frequency of a few million per second, the electrical oscillations set up in the atoms of a source of light have a frequency of several thousand million million per second. The wave-length is far too short to be 'picked up' with an ordinary aerial; but the molecules of matter can act as aerials as far as light radiation is concerned, and electrical as well as heating effects are to be observed when light falls on materials.

The frequency of oscillations in light can be calculated from the general formula for wave motion $V=f\lambda$ where V is the speed of travel, f is the frequency of the oscillations and λ the corresponding wave-length. For electro-magnetic radiations

$$V=3\times10^{10}\text{ cm/s}=3\times10^{8}\text{ metres/s}$$

Taking an average wave-length of $0{\cdot}60\times10^{-6}$ metre

$$f=\frac{3\times10^{8}}{0{\cdot}6\times10^{-6}}=5\times10^{14}=500\text{ million million}$$

The speed of light is the same for the various colours only in a vacuum. In transparent substances the speed is less for violet light than for red.

The following table gives values of wave-length and frequency for various types of electro-magnetic radiation *in vacuo*; the frequency is given in megacycles/s, a megacycle being a million oscillations.

Radiation	Wave-length	Frequency (megacycles/s)
Long-wave radio	1500 metres	$\frac{1}{5}$
Medium-wave radio	300 metres	1
Short-wave radio	30 metres	10
Radar	3 cm	10,000
Long-wave infra-red	30 μ	10 million
Short-wave infra-red	3 μ	100 million
Orange light	0·6 μ	500 million
Ultra-violet	0·3 μ	1000 million

1 μ = 1 micron or micro-metre

24.4. Chemical and electrical effects. Light affects a number of chemicals. The chemical effect of light is particularly noticeable in silver salts. This fact is applied in photography. The glass plate or plastic film on which the negative is formed is coated with an emulsion of silver chloride, bromide or iodide in gelatin.

Chemical actions occur in the green leaves of plants. Part of the energy of sunlight is absorbed by the chlorophyll in the leaves and is used in the building up of complex compounds from relatively simple ones.

Light—and other short wave-length radiation—has an electrical effect. If it falls on a plate of iron coated with selenium, a voltage is formed. The arrangement is called a **photo-voltaic cell,** and the voltage depends on the illumination falling on the cell. This cell is used in illumination meters in photographic work; it is also used for the measurement of illumination in rooms and workshops (Fig. 24.5). Another type of cell is the **photo-electric cell** (Fig. 40.10).

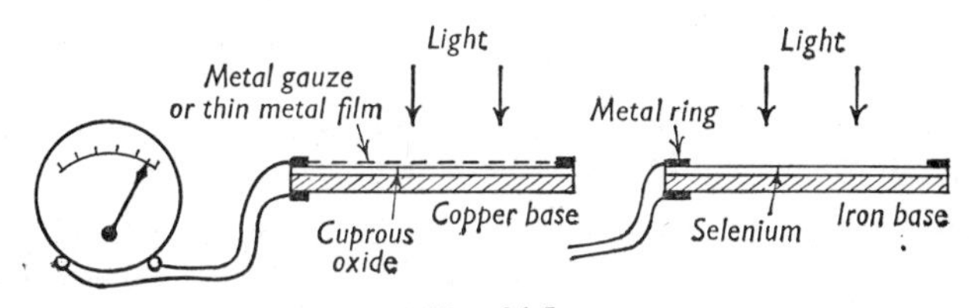

FIG. 24.5

Photo-voltaic cells

This consists of an evacuated glass bulb lined with a film of metal such as sodium or potassium; it also contains a terminal connected to the positive pole of a battery. When light falls on the metal, negative particles of electricity (electrons) are emitted and are attracted to the positive terminal, so setting up an electric current. This current can be used to work counting devices, burglar alarms, automatic switches.

The number of electrons emitted per second, and hence the photo-electric current which flows when a voltage is applied, depends on the strength of the light; but the *speed* with which electrons are ejected from a metal does not depend on the strength of the light but only on the kind of light or, more precisely, the frequency of its oscillations. A weak light of a particular frequency gives an electron the same speed as a more intense light, so that the energy associated with a light wave seems to be available in 'packets'; each such packet is called a **quantum** or **photon.** The energy of a light wave seems to have a corpuscular nature.

24.5. Shadows. The effect of diffraction in light is so small that for most practical purposes we say that light travels in straight lines.

The size and shape of shadows fit the idea of straight-line travel, i.e. they have the size and shape you would get by drawing straight lines, from points on the source, over the edges of the object and then on to the receiving screen. If the source of light is very small, the edges of the shadow are clear-cut. With a larger source, such as is shown in Fig. 24.6, it is found that there are two distinct regions of shadow, the **umbra** or complete shadow and the **penumbra** or partly illuminated shadow. If you make a hole in the screen in the umbra region you will not see the lamp through it; but a hole in the penumbra region will give you a view of part of the lamp. The views obtained are similar to the large-scale effects of total and partial eclipses of the sun.

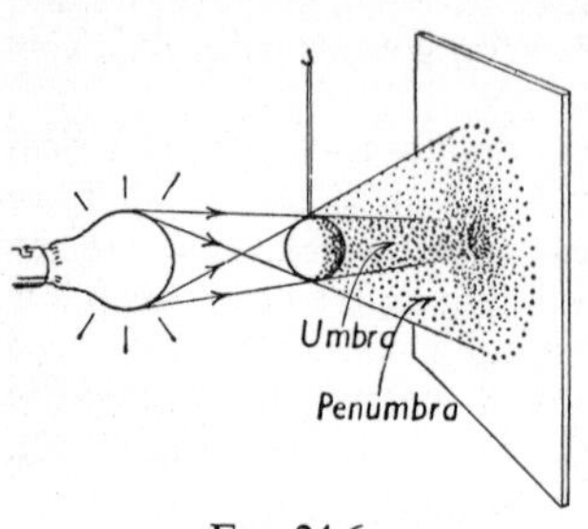

FIG. 24.6

24.6. Eclipses. There are long shadows cast in space by sunlight passing over the edges of the planets. We do not see them as there is nothing in space to show up the course of the light; but we see the result of them in eclipses of the sun or moon, or (through a telescope) in the eclipses of Jupiter's moons.

Eclipse of the moon. The moon is approximately 0·4 million km away from the earth, but the earth's shadow or umbra extends to

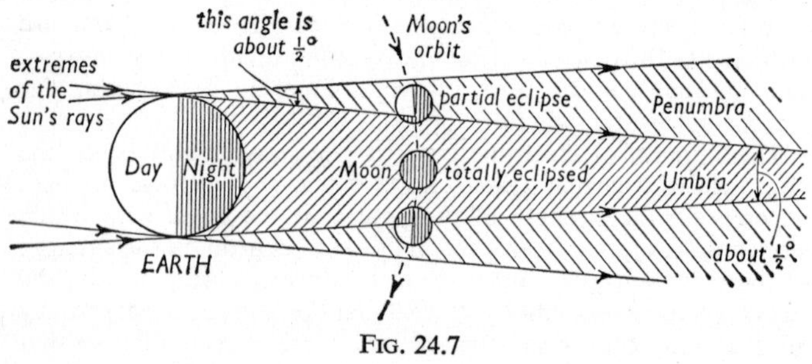

FIG. 24.7

Conditions for a lunar eclipse (*not to scale*)

1·6 million km. If the path of the moon round the earth were in the same plane as the path of the earth round the sun, the moon would enter the earth's umbra every twenty-eight days, and there would be an eclipse of the moon once a month. But the moon's path, or orbit, is inclined at 5° to that of the earth, so there is an eclipse of the moon only twice a year; even then the moon is sometimes not completely hidden in the earth's shadow and so is only partly eclipsed. Fig. 24.7 shows how an eclipse of the moon takes place.

Eclipse of the sun. The sun and moon appear to occupy a region of sky which subtends an angle of about $\frac{1}{2}°$ to an observer on the earth. At times the moon in its orbit comes between us and the sun and it then acts like a shutter, cutting out the sunlight either completely or partially (Fig. 24.8). When this happens, astronomers

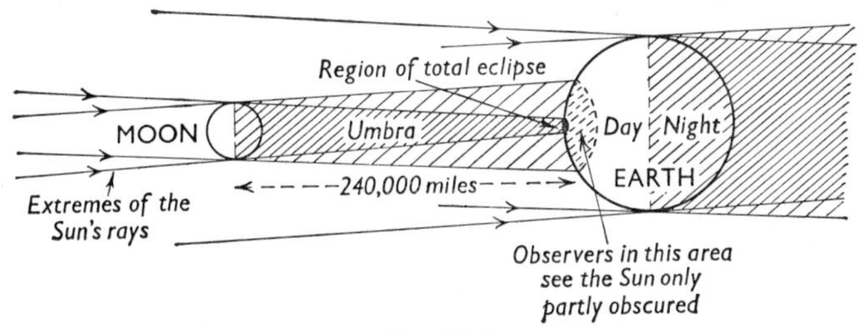

FIG. 24.8

Conditions for a solar eclipse (*not to scale*)

can view the outer regions of the sun without the interfering glare of the main sunlight.

Because the moon travels in an elliptical orbit it is sometimes further off than the average; if a solar eclipse occurs then, the moon does not completely cover up the sun and we get an **annular** eclipse, a ring of sunlight being visible even when the eclipse is most complete.

24.7. The pinhole camera. Light passing through a small hole can form pictures of the source of light. Fig. 24.9*a* shows a simple form of apparatus for seeing pinhole pictures. If the tube is pointed towards any brightly-lit object an inverted image appears on the screen. The size of the image on the screen is exactly what would be expected if rays of light from the object reach the screen by travelling in straight lines through the hole. Every point on the object gives a small patch of light, slightly larger than the hole, on the screen; so the picture loses its sharp outlines if the overlapping patches are large.

Photographs can be taken with a camera which has, in place of the lens, a thin metal sheet with a needle-hole in it. Pl. 10 was photographed in this way. Exposures with pinhole cameras are rather long because the pinhole does not let much light through.

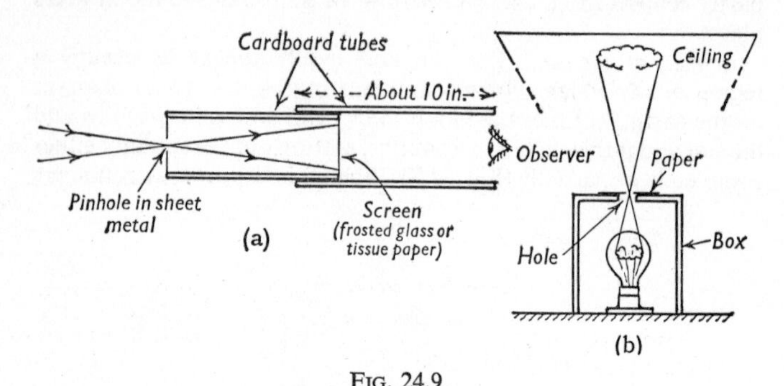

FIG. 24.9

Pinhole-camera effects. (a) Viewing a distant scene on a screen. (b) Projection of an image on a ceiling

Questions

1. Construct a diagram similar to Fig. 21.6*a*, showing only the crests of the waves. Make the wave-length $\frac{1}{4}$ in. and the distance S_1S_2 3 in.; omit the first five wave-fronts, i.e. make the first arcs have a radius of $1\frac{1}{2}$ in. Draw the straight central antinodal line, and draw the nearest antinodal line on each side of it. Measure the fringe-width at a distance of $20\frac{1}{2}$ wave-lengths from the line S_1S_2.

2. Find, by graphical construction, the fringe-width of the interference pattern at a distance of 160 mm from two sources, 20 mm apart, the wave-length being 6 mm. Use the following method.

Mark out two sources, 20 mm apart. With each in turn as centre, draw long arcs of radius 157 mm; repeat the process to get arcs of radius 163 mm. The four arcs should cross to give a diamond-shaped pattern. Measure the distance between the points of the diamond; this is twice the fringe-width.

Compare your result with that given by the formula on page 219. Then check the formula again with the sources about 25 mm apart, making the first arcs of radius 160 mm, and the second arcs about 7 mm more than this, measuring D, s, λ and w from your diagram. The measurements should be made, with the aid of a magnifying glass, using a good-quality mm scale.

3. Construct a diagram similar to Fig. 24.3, making the grating spacing 25 mm and the wave-length 5 mm. Draw lines to show the number of possible resultant wave-fronts and measure the angles which these lines make with the grating. Compare your results with the theoretical values which are 11·5°, 23·6°, 36·9° and 53·1°.

What would happen to the waves from the grating if a concave reflector, of radius 30 cm, were put in their path?

4. A parallel beam of monochromatic light falls perpendicularly on to a grating, passes through it and falls on a screen beyond the grating. Explain the following facts: (*a*) No interference pattern is seen on the screen. (*b*) A line of bright spots is seen on the screen when a convex lens is put, at its focal distance, in front of the screen.

5. A line source gives out light of two wave-lengths only; one wave-length is a red colour, the other green. How, by looking at the source through a grating could you tell whether green or red light has the greater wave-length? Give your reasoning.

6. Calculate the speed of radio waves by multiplying the wave-length and frequency of any broadcasting station. (The information can usually be obtained from a daily newspaper.)

7. Calculate the time taken for a radio wave to travel (*a*) round the circumference of the earth, (*b*) from the earth to the moon and back. (Radius of the earth = 6400 km. Distance of the moon from the earth = 384,000 km. Speed of travel = 300,000 km/s.)

8. 'The listener at home hears the sounds of a broadcast concert slightly earlier than a member of the audience in the hall.' Explain this.

9. Calculate the time for radiation from the sun to reach the earth. (Distance of the sun = 150 million km.)

10. Calculate the wave-length of a green light of frequency 720 million megacycles/s (*a*) *in vacuo*, (*b*) in a medium where the speed of light is two-thirds that *in vacuo*.

11. The alternating voltage in a radio aerial oscillates at the rate of 2 megacycles/s. What is the periodic time of the oscillation? How far will the radio waves have travelled in this time?

12. A radiation containing three frequencies, whose megacycles/s are 10 million, 100 million and 500 million meets a sheet of glass. Which of these frequencies will be transmitted by the glass, and what will happen to the energy of any which are not transmitted?

13. A powerful flash is made, at a point outside the earth's orbit,

every 24 hours. Explain the fact that, to an observer on the earth, the flash would not always seem to occur at 24-hour intervals.

14. Name any one instrument in which light produces an electrical effect. What practical application has been made of the effect?

15. A luminous disc 15 cm in diameter is 30 cm from a cardboard disc of the same size; their line of centres is perpendicular to each disc. A white screen is placed 15 cm from the card on the shadow side. Find, by calculation or scale diagram, the diameters of the umbra and penumbra. Describe and explain the appearance on the screen if a small hole is made at the centre of the card.

16. The shadows cast on a wall by the setting sun are clear-cut if the objects are near the wall, blurred when the objects are far away. Explain this, bearing in mind that the sun is not a point source of light.

17. Shadows of a horizontal rod are cast on a vertical wall by two small coloured lamps, a red one above the level of the rod and a green one below the level of the rod. Explain, with the aid of a ray diagram, the positions and colours of the shadows.

18. Explain, with the aid of a diagram, the camera-like action of a pinhole. Explain the disadvantages of using a pinhole camera for taking photographs. Describe and explain the effects of using, instead of a pinhole, (*a*) a small triangular hole, (*b*) a hole of about 2 mm diameter.

19. A disc 8·7 mm in diameter, held 1 metre from the eye, just eclipses the sun. Calculate (*a*) the diameter of the sun, (*b*) the diameter of the penumbra around the eye. (Distance of the sun from the earth = 150 million km.)

20. Draw a diagram to illustrate the conditions which give rise to an eclipse of the sun. Mark clearly on the diagram the regions of the earth where the eclipse appears (*a*) a total eclipse, (*b*) a partial eclipse.

21. Eclipses of the moon can occur only at about the time of 'full moon'; an eclipse of the sun can never occur then. Explain why this is so.

22. Draw a diagram to show the regions of the earth's umbra and penumbra. On your diagram show the positions the moon could occupy to be (*a*) totally eclipsed, (*b*) half-eclipsed. What would an observer on the moon, facing the earth, see in each of these positions?

23. Draw a diagram to show one set of circumstances in which a person on the earth could watch the eclipse of an artificial satellite. For example, draw a diagram to show the earth and its umbra, the direction of rotation of the earth, the position of an

observer for whom the sun has set for 3 hours, the position of an artificial satellite which is just coming into view, and the course the satellite takes before being eclipsed.

From your diagram estimate how long the satellite will be in view, assuming that it goes round the earth once in 90 minutes.

CHAPTER 25

The Reflection of Light

25.1. Laws of reflection. When light is reflected from a smooth surface the reflected light takes a definite course. Anyone who has played with a mirror, using it to reflect sunlight to a particular spot, soon gets the knack of placing the mirror to direct the beam. The expression which states the course of the reflected light is known as the law of reflection because it is true for all positions of the reflector. In stating the law it is convenient to refer to the line which is perpendicular to the part of the surface which the incident ray hits; this line is called the **normal** at the point of incidence (P in Fig. 25.1). The effect can be stated in the following manner:

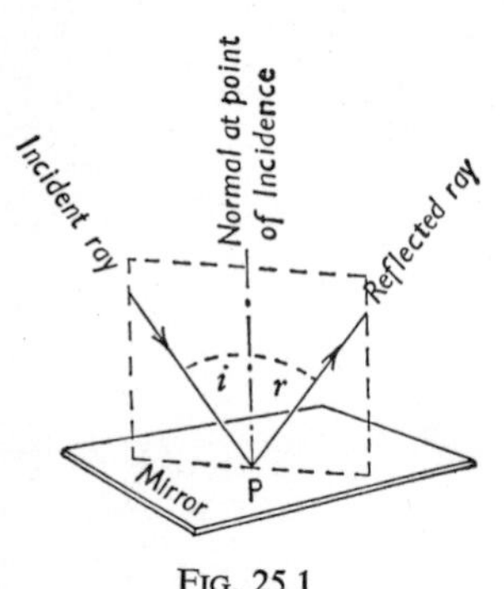

FIG. 25.1

(i) **The incident and reflected rays make equal angles with the normal at the point of incidence.**
(ii) **The two rays are on opposite sides of the normal and are in the same plane as the normal.**

The angle between the incident ray and the normal is called the **angle of incidence (i)**, the angle between the reflected ray and the normal is called the **angle of reflection (r).** So that another way of stating the first law of reflection is: 'The angle of reflection is equal to the angle of incidence.'

Fig. 25.2 shows an experimental way of tracking the directions of an incident and reflected beam on a sheet of paper. By varying the angle of incidence and measuring the angles of incidence and reflection it can be shown that the two are equal.

Ray-tracking can also be done with two pins or with a ruler to mark the direction of an incident ray, another two pins or another ruler being placed in line with the reflection to mark the course of the reflected ray (Fig. 25.3).

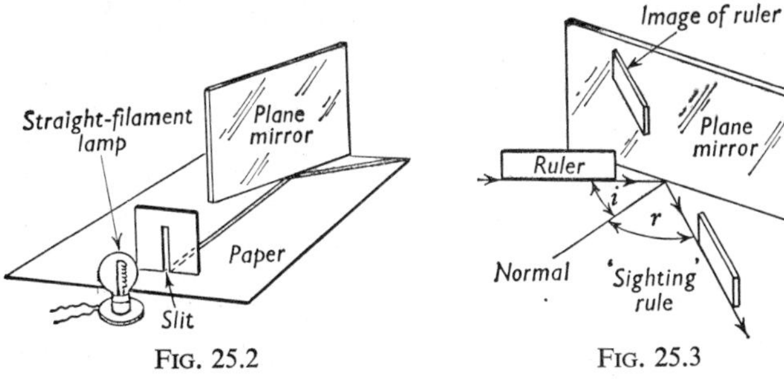

FIG. 25.2

Ray-tracking using a lamp and slit

FIG. 25.3

Ray-tracking using two rulers. Two well-spaced pins could be used in place of each ruler

25.2. Diffuse reflection. A piece of paper may appear smooth, but actually its fibres slope in many directions. A regular reflection occurs at any one point on a fibre, but the overall effect is a scattering of light in all directions (Fig. 25.4). This is called **diffuse**

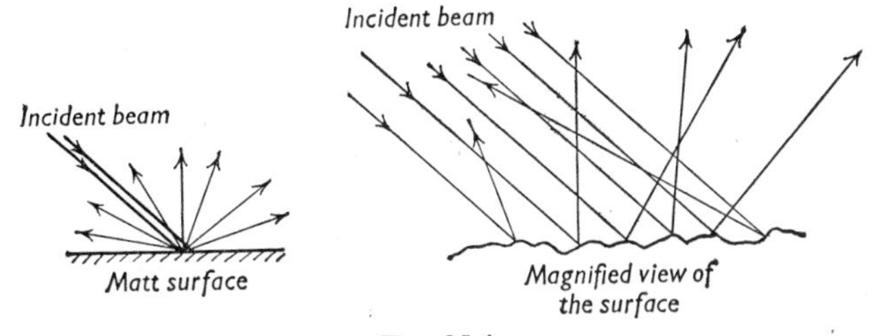

FIG. 25.4

Diffuse reflection from an irregular surface

reflection; reflection from polished surfaces, such as can be seen occurring in the table-top of Pl. 18, is known as **specular reflection.** Transparent substances may show diffuse reflection when they are in the form of small particles, presenting many differently sloping surfaces to the light, e.g. powdered glass, snow, soapsuds, clouds.

25.3. 'Reflections' or images in plane reflecting surfaces. It follows from the laws of reflection that if a point source of light is in front of a plane reflecting surface, all the reflected rays will appear to diverge from a point behind the surface. This point is known as the **image** of the source; a 'reflection' of the source appears there. The image (I in Fig. 25.5) is as far behind the surface as the object O is in front, and the line OI is perpendicular to the surface. The image is called a **virtual** image because the rays of light do not really come from this image but only appear to do so.

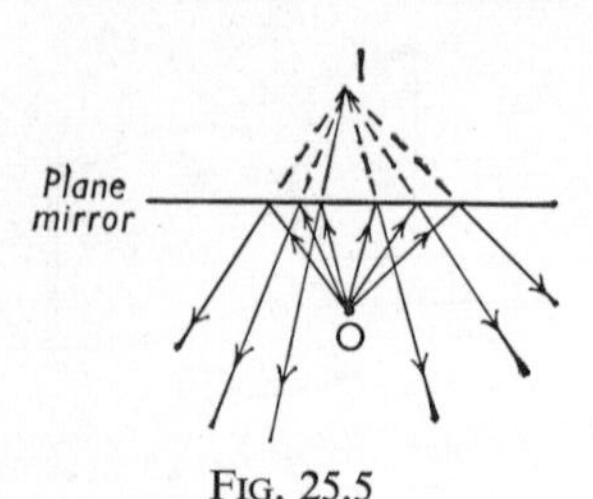

FIG. 25.5
Virtual image formed by reflection

Fig. 25.6*a* shows a simple way of locating the image formed by reflection. Two plumb-lines are arranged, one on each side of a vertical plane mirror; the plumb-bobs can be in small vessels of water to stop them from swinging. The mirror is moved to the position where the image-finder (seen above and below the mirror) coincides with the image of the object-line (seen reflected in the mirror) as shown in Fig. 25.6*b*. It is then checked that this is so from all viewpoints. When the distances of the two lines from the reflecting surface of the mirror are measured it is found that they

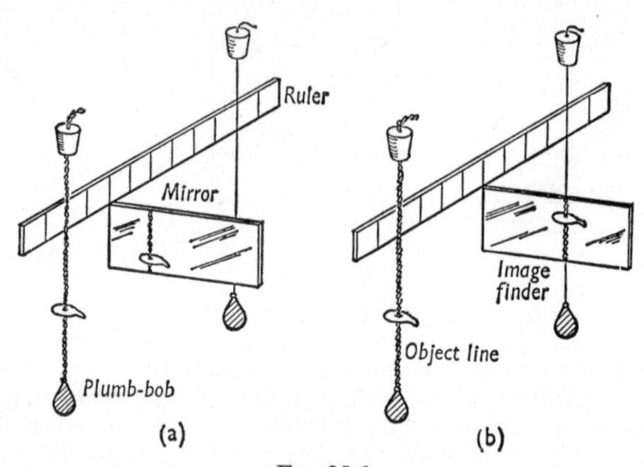

FIG. 25.6
Locating the image formed by a plane mirror

are equal, and that this is also true for different settings of the lines and the mirror.

From the viewpoint of Fig. 25.6*a* the image-finder and the image are said to show **parallax,** i.e. they subtend an angle at the observer's eye. In Fig. 25.6*b* they show **no parallax,** so this method of finding images is sometimes known as a **no-parallax method.**

Parallax errors have to be avoided whenever a reading is taken from a pointer which moves over a scale. The correct viewing-line is perpendicular to the scale, and one way of ensuring this is to have a mirror set alongside the scale. Fig. 25.7 shows the pointer

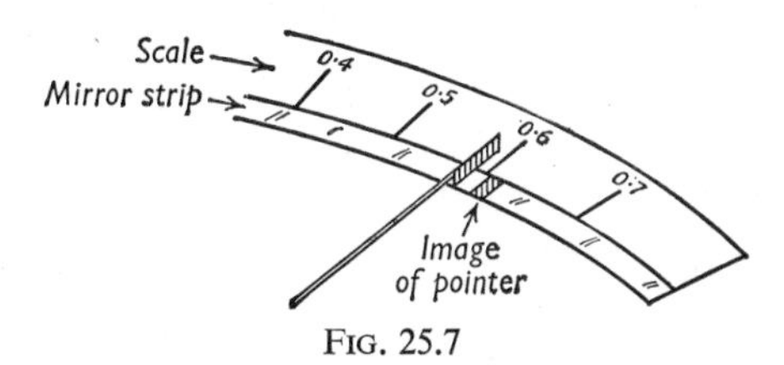

FIG. 25.7

of an ammeter, which is actually over the 0·60 mark, seen from the wrong viewpoint; by moving your eye so that the pointer and its image are in line, i.e. show no parallax, the correct reading can be taken since then your viewline is perpendicular to the scale.

Plane mirrors are commonly used in a vertical position. As a result the image is the same way up as the object—we say that the image is **erect.** In a direction perpendicular to the mirror-surface,

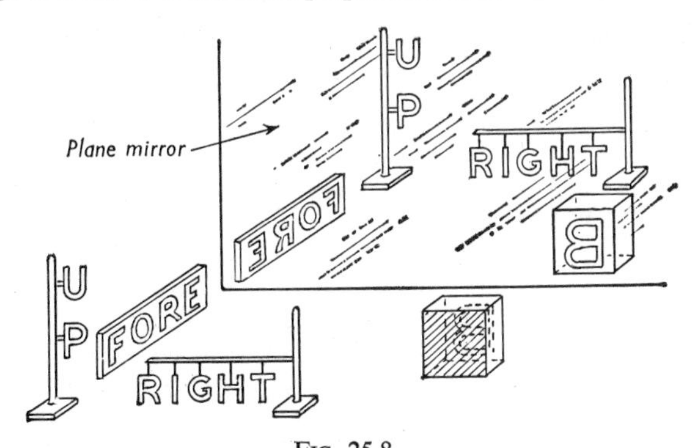

FIG. 25.8

Images in a plane mirror

images appear reversed despite the fact that they are erect. This is shown in Fig. 25.8. Reversal occurs in the fore-and-aft direction;

the lettering of the word FORE appears laterally inverted or sideways reversed. Another **lateral inversion** occurs when paper with printing faces a mirror, but the effect is due to a different cause; the mirror gives a back-view of the object, as in the letter B in Fig. 25.8. It is this type of lateral inversion which prevents people, looking in a mirror, from seeing themselves as others see them; for example, hair parted on the left appears to be on the right-hand side of the mirror-image person.

When mirrors are used horizontally, the fore-and-aft inversion acts in an up-and-down direction. In this case the image appears upside down. This is to be seen when objects are viewed reflected

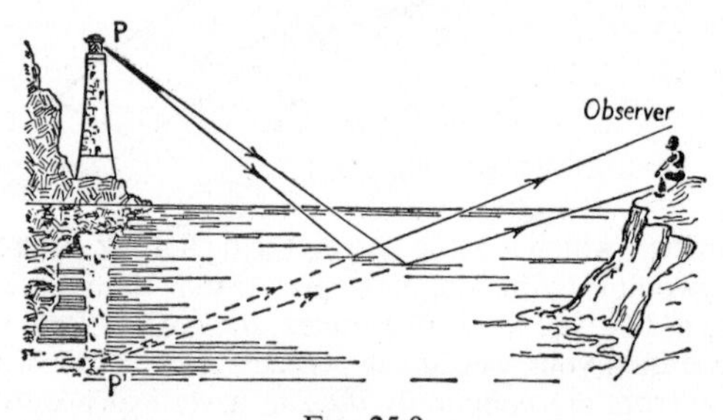

FIG. 25.9

Images formed by reflection from still water

in the still water of a pond or lake. Fig. 25.9 gives an illustrative diagram.

25.4. Rotation of a mirror. Mirrors at an angle. Fig. 25.10 shows a mirror set to reflect light back along its own path, and then tilted to turn the reflected beam through 90°. The mirror has had to be turned through an angle of 45°. This is a particular case of the following general rule. **If a mirror is turned through an angle, any reflected beam of light coming from it is turned through twice that angle.** This property of mirrors is used in some types of galvanometer. A small mirror is fixed to the moving part and a beam of light is sent on to the mirror which reflects it to a scale; small rotations of the moving part are thus doubled by the action of the mirror.

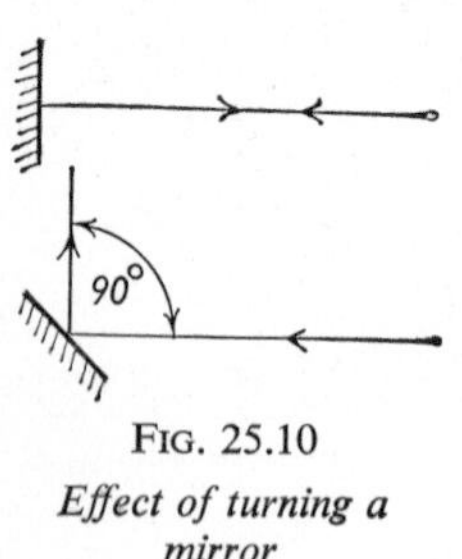

FIG. 25.10

Effect of turning a mirror

Mirrors set at an angle to each other give rise to many images. Fig. 25.11 illustrates the effect obtained with two mirrors at right

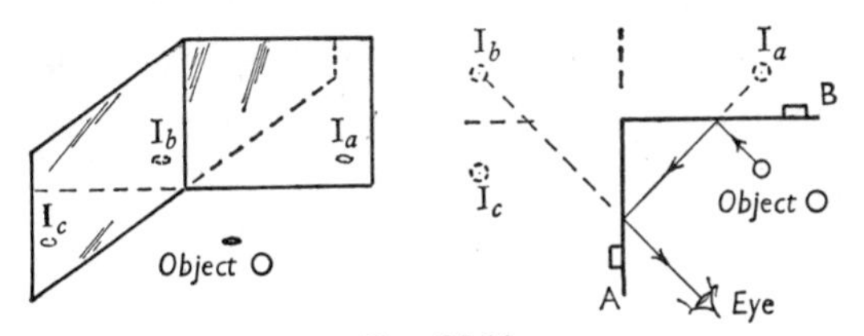

Fig. 25.11

Images formed by mirrors at right angles

angles; one of the images is formed by rays which have suffered two reflections. A person standing between two mirrors gets views of himself which are different from those obtained with only one. For this reason dressing-table mirrors are often fitted with side mirrors; and tailors make use of two mirrors to let a customer have a view from the side or the back. The multiple images and the differing views given by two mirrors inclined at 60° are shown in Pl. 11. The multiple images formed by mirrors at 45° or 60° have been made the basis of a toy called a *kaleidoscope*.

Another property of mirrors at an angle is that they deflect or deviate a ray of light through a constant angle (independent of the angle of incidence) provided that the ray has been reflected once by each mirror. Thus the ray shown in Fig. 25.11 has been deviated through 180° and emerges parallel to its original direction. This also occurs when three mirrors are set up at right angles to each other as in the corner of a box (Pl. 12). A ray reflected from each mirror in turn comes back parallel to its original course. This arrangement is used in some types of road reflector-signs which appear lit up by the reflection of light from car headlights. Pl. 13 shows the back surface of the rear-reflector of a bicycle, in which the reflecting surfaces are arranged in box-corner pattern.

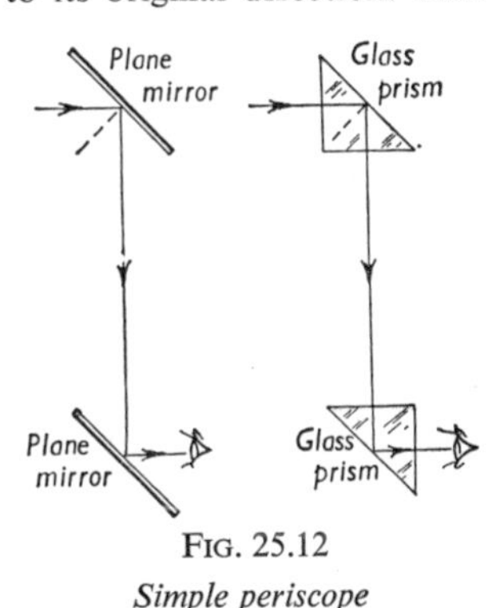

Fig. 25.12

Simple periscope

In periscopes, light is reflected downwards and sideways by mirrors or reflecting-prisms with their surfaces arranged as shown in Fig. 25.12. Simple types, such as are used for sightseeing over the heads of a crowd, consist of little more than two mirrors held in a framework, but in others a telescope system of lenses is put into give a magnified image.

25.5. Curved mirrors. The laws of reflection apply to reflectors of any shape. The incident and reflected rays make equal angles with the normal even when the reflector is curved. In the case of a curved reflector the normal at any point is the line from that point to the centre of the circle of which the reflector is a part. Thus in the curved surfaces of Fig. 25.13, C represents the centre of the curve;

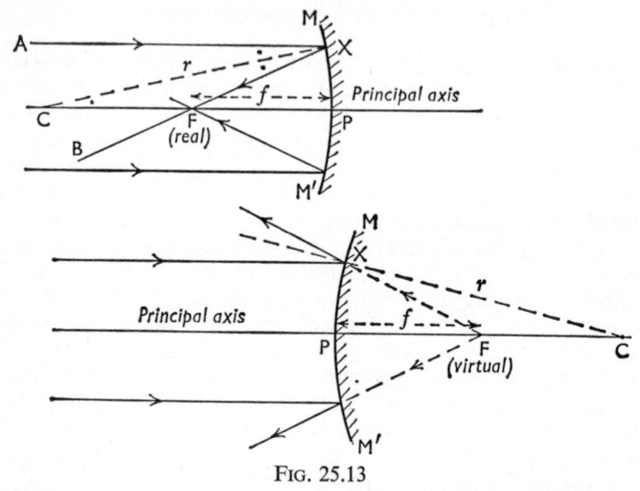

FIG. 25.13

Curved mirrors. P=pole; C=centre of curvature; F=principal focus or focal point; CX is the normal at X; r=radius of curvature; f=focal length

CX is the normal at the point X. In the top diagram, AX is an incident ray, XB is the reflected ray; the angles of incidence and reflection have been marked with a dot.

Pl. 13 shows the reflection of parallel beams of light from concave and convex strips of mirror. The concave one has a converging or focusing effect, and the point at which the rays cross is known as the **principal focus** or **focal point**. It is found to be half-way between the mirror and the centre of the curve; the focus is called a **real** focus because the rays of light do really reach it and cross over there. The convex mirror has a diverging effect; the rays of light only *appear* to come from a focal point and such a focus is called a **virtual** focus. The distance of a principal focus from a mirror is called the **focal length** of the mirror.

In Pl. 13, the width of the mirror was only part of a full circle. With wider mirrors, the outlying rays are not reflected through the focal point. The rays are reflected around a curve known as a **caustic** (Pl. 14). The formation of a reflection caustic can be seen on the surface of a cup of tea when light from a lamp to one side is reflected on to the liquid by the curved surface of the cup.

Concave mirrors are useful for focusing beams of light, or of thermal radiation, or of radio waves—all of which follow the same law of reflection. To get the greatest effect, the reflector needs to be wide, and the reflected energy should be brought to a single point focus. Pl. 14 shows that a circular-section mirror is not ideal for this. But mirrors can be made to a shape which will focus all the oncoming rays to a point, no matter how wide the mirror may be. One such shape is the parabola, and Pl. 15 shows parallel rays falling on a wide parabolic mirror; all the reflected rays go through one point, the focus.

The mirrors of large reflecting telescopes, such as the 200-inch reflector at Mount Palomar, have a parabolic section because they give more accurate focusing. Concave radio-telescopes (Pl. 16) have a parabolic section. They collect radio waves from distant stars and focus them on an aerial, or they can concentrate the signals sent out by radio-transmitters in artificial satellites. Another application of the focusing effect of a parabolic reflector is the solar furnace (Pl. 17). Here the reflector is made of a large number of panels of curved mirror, and the concentration of the sun's radiation produces extremely high temperatures. A concave mirror one metre across is sufficient, in sunlight, to give enough heat to set a thick stick of wood alight immediately. The idea has been applied, in tropical countries, to the making of solar cookers. One type is made of sheets of aluminium which can be opened out like an umbrella and fixed to a stand so that the arrangement faces the sun. A small oven or a fry-pan is at the focus of the reflector.

The path of light in any optical system is reversible. So a point source of light at the focal point of a concave reflector sends out a reflected beam which is parallel. This idea is applied in searchlights, in the reflector mirror of electric torches, and the reflector mirror at the back of some types of electric fire. And just as light can be beamed in this way, so too can radio waves. Television and radar transmitter aerials are sometimes placed at the focus of a concave metal reflector to concentrate the waves in a beam to some distant receiving point.

Convex mirrors have their chief application in giving a wider field of view than is given in plane mirrors. Their action, when fitted to motor-cars to give the driver a wide view, is illustrated in Fig. 25.14.

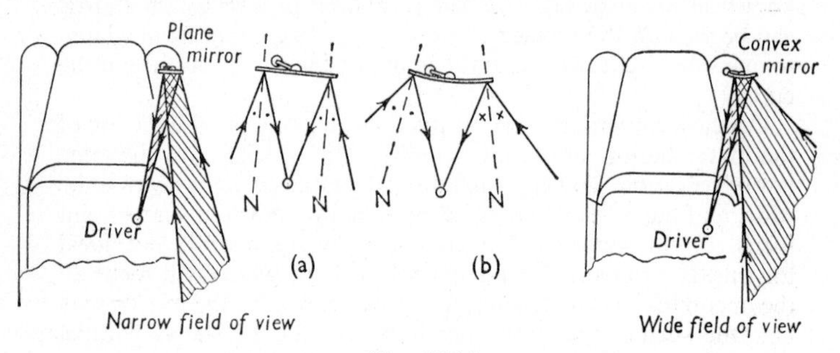

FIG. 25.14

Plane and convex driving-mirrors: N, N are the normals to the mirror surfaces. (a) shows the relatively narrow field of view obtained with a plane mirror. (b) shows the wide field of view obtained with a convex mirror

25.6. Images formed by curved mirrors. If you hold a concave reflecting surface such as a concave mirror, a watch-glass or a metal spoon some distance away from you, you will see a diminished image of your face, inverted. (The image is likely to be distorted in the spoon, since the spoon's surface is not truly spherical.) If you move the reflector towards you the image appears bigger. And if you bring the reflector quite close to your eye you will see a magnified erect image of your eye, which seems to be behind the mirror. This magnified view has been put to use in the concave dentist's mirrors for examining teeth, and in concave shaving mirrors.

In a convex mirror the image is always erect and appears behind the mirror surface.

The way in which such images are formed can be shown by ray diagrams (Fig. 25.15). These diagrams are known as scale diagrams, and the horizontal scale is more reduced than the vertical one. To allow for this the reflected rays have been drawn as though reflected from a vertical plane through the pole. The resulting images are thus those which would be obtained from rays close to the axis. Some or all of the following rules have been used in constructing these diagrams.

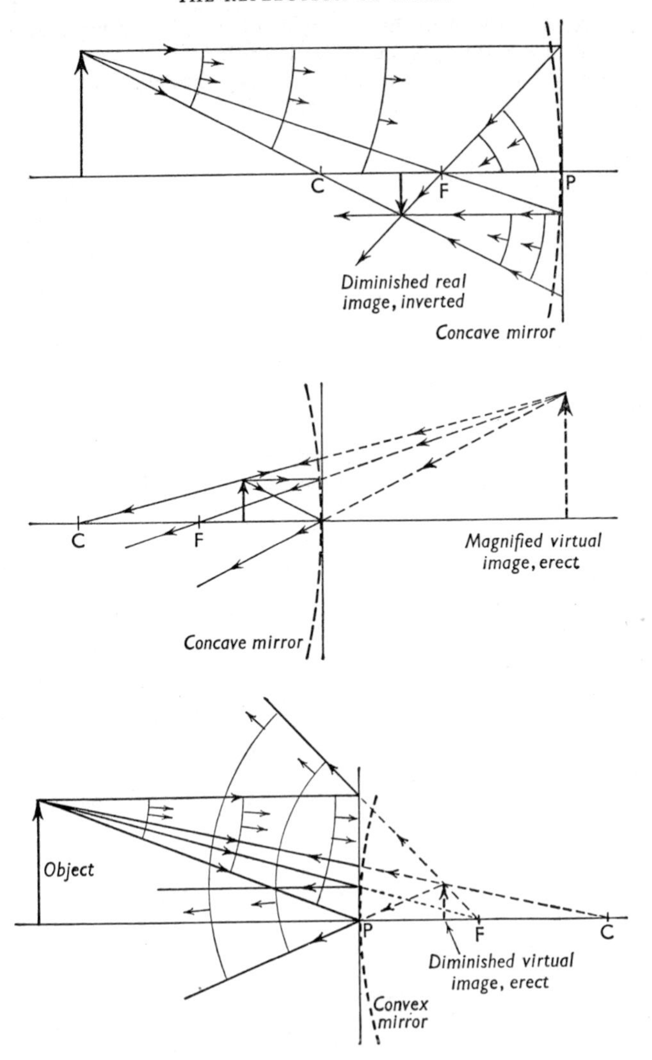

FIG. 25.15

Formation of images by curved mirrors

(1) A ray parallel to the principal axis is reflected towards or away from the principal focus (focal point).

(2) A ray actually or apparently passing through the principal focus is reflected parallel to the principal axis.

(3) A ray actually or apparently passing through the centre of curvature is reflected back along its own path.

(4) A ray incident at the pole gives a reflected ray making an equal angle with the principal axis.

In Fig. 25.15 rays are shown coming from one point on the object. The point of intersection of the reflected rays (real or virtual) gives the image of that point on the object. The image of the object as a whole is deduced from the fact that the image, like the object, is vertical and not curved.

SUMMARY

Laws of reflection. (i) **The angle of incidence is equal to the angle of reflection.** (ii) **The incident ray, reflected ray, and the normal at the point of incidence are co-planar.**

The image in a plane mirror is virtual and erect. It is as far behind the mirror as the object is in front. Lettering on paper suffers **lateral inversion.**

A **real image** is one through which rays of light actually pass; it can be formed on a screen. A **virtual image** is one through which rays do not actually pass, but from which they appear to come.

The rotation of a reflected beam by a mirror is equal to twice the angle of rotation of the mirror.

Mirrors at an angle give multiple images; the smaller the angle, the greater the number of images.

The focal length of curved mirrors is half the radius of curvature.

Questions

1. State the laws of reflection. Describe an experiment to verify one of these laws.

2. Draw a ray diagram to explain the fact that the image of a small lamp formed by a plane mirror appears to be behind the mirror. Describe an experimental method for finding the position of the image formed by a plane mirror.

3. A small lamp is placed 50 cm in front of a plane mirror which is 10 cm long. Find, by calculation or by scale diagram, the length of the reflected patch of light on a large screen which is parallel to the mirror and 180 cm in front of the mirror.

4. Two plane mirrors A and B are parallel and 12 metres apart. Between them, 4 metres from A, is a small lamp. A person at O, 8 metres from the lamp and 4 metres from the mirror A, sees many images of the lamp. Show, on a diagram drawn to scale, the positions of the three images of the lamp which are nearest to the person, and show the tracks of the rays of light by which he sees the images.

5. A person standing in front of a vertical plane mirror can just see the whole of his reflected image if the mirror-length is half his height and if the mirror is suitably placed. Explain this, and find the heights of the top and bottom of the mirror from the floor for a person 2·00 metres tall with an eye-level at 1·90 metres.

6. A lighted candle stands close to a dish of water. Draw a ray diagram to show how an observer, on the opposite side of the dish, sees a reflected image of the candle flame.

7. Two plane mirrors, AD (vertical) and DE (horizontal), are each 3 units long. An object O is 1 unit from AD and 3 units from DE. Draw a ray diagram, to scale, to show the tracks of two rays which start from O and fall on AD at the points B and C, where AB=BC=1 unit. Find the point I from which the final reflected rays appear to come. (Theoretically I, D and O are in line; the paper on which this diagram is drawn should be at least 6 units square.)

8. Explain why several images can be seen if an object is held between two plane mirrors which are at right angles. Draw a diagram to show the positions of the images and show the tracks of light, one in each case, which give rise to these images.

9. When two mirrors are set at an angle θ° with an object between them, the object and its images total $360/\theta$, fractions counting as whole numbers. Check this by reference to Fig. 25.11 and Pl. 11. Calculate the number of images formed by mirrors when the angle between them is (*a*) 80°, (*b*) 100°, (*c*) 50°, (*d*) 44°.

10. A plane mirror 10 cm long is placed 45 cm in front of the driver of a car. Through what width of rear window, 135 cm behind him, can he see when looking into the mirror?

11. Pl. 5 shows part of the rod of a retort stand reflected in the surface of molten lead. Draw a ray diagram to show (*a*) how this image is seen, (*b*) the fact that the image is inverted. Why does the image look to be part of the actual retort stand?

12. A pointer-reading instrument, such as an ammeter, may have any of the following fittings. (i) An arrow-head, fitted to the pointer, parallel to the scale. (ii) A thin flag, fitted to the pointer, perpendicular to the scale. (iii) A mirror alongside the scale. (iv) The

scale engraved on a mirror. Explain how each of these can assist the accuracy with which a reading is taken and state how the observer's eye should be situated in each case. Why, in (iii), should the mirror be accurately parallel to the scale?

13. In a darkened room, a person directs the beam from an electric torch on to a strip of plane mirror lying on a table. Half the length of the mirror-strip is covered with white paper. Explain how rays of light from the paper can reach the person's eye, and explain the fact that the uncovered part of the mirror looks dark.

14. Draw a labelled diagram to illustrate the optical arrangement in a searchlight giving a parallel beam, and explain the adjustment needed to give a diverging beam. By day, searchlights should never be left in such a way that they might point at the sun; explain this fact.

15. Draw a ray diagram to show how a concave mirror can give a magnified image of an object placed near it.

16. What do you understand by the terms *centre of curvature*, *principal focus* and *focal length* of a spherical mirror? Illustrate your answers with labelled diagrams for (*a*) a concave mirror, (*b*) a convex mirror. An object 2 units high is placed 10 cm in front of a curved mirror of radius of curvature 30 cm. Draw ray diagrams, to scale, to show the position and size of the image when the mirror is (*a*) concave, (*b*) convex.

17. An object is placed in front of a concave mirror so that the centre of curvature is mid-way between the object and the pole of the mirror. Draw a diagram, to scale, to show the position and size of the image.

18. An object is placed in front of a concave mirror so that it is mid-way between the mirror and the principal focus. Find, by scale diagram, the position and size of the image; state whether the image is real or virtual.

19. Draw diagrams to show how it is that a convex mirror has a wider field of view than a plane mirror of the same size. Draw a ray diagram to show how a person sees the image of his face reflected in a convex mirror.

CHAPTER 26

The Refraction of Light

26.1. When light meets a boundary between two transparent media, some of the light is reflected and some is transmitted. The transmitted light suffers an abrupt change in direction, except when it is travelling along the normal; the name **refraction** is given to this occurrence. The effects of refraction in substances such as water and glass are a matter of everyday observation; examples are shown in Pl. 18. The actual refraction can be shown only by making the track of the light show up; Pls. 19, 20 and 21 show some of the experimental ways of doing this.

Fig. 26.1 shows the angles of refraction (the angle between the

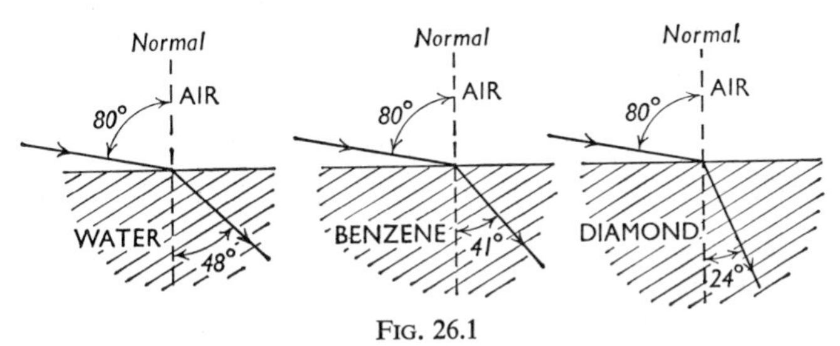

FIG. 26.1

Refraction of light by different substances

refracted ray and the normal) in three different substances when the angle of incidence is 80°. The bending is greater for diamond and for benzene than it is for water. These two substances are therefore said to be **optically denser** than water.

26.2. Laws of refraction. In the seventeenth century Snell discovered a geometrical relation between the incident and refracted rays. He found that the following construction applies to all cases of refraction.

Draw a line, AB in Fig. 26.2, parallel to the normal at the point of incidence P. Produce the incident and refracted rays to meet AB in C and D respectively. Then PD/PC is a constant for all positions of the incident ray. Later, the mathematician Descartes showed that this is equivalent to stating that sin i/sin r is a constant.

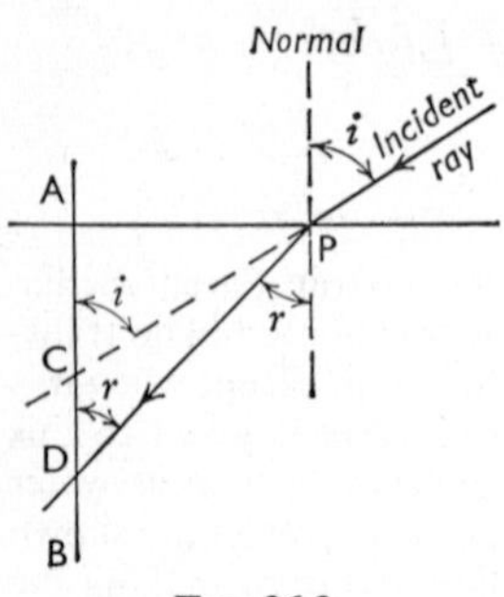

FIG. 26.2

1st law of refraction. The incident and refracted rays are in the same plane as the normal at the point of incidence, and are on opposite sides of the normal.

2nd law of refraction (Snell's law). When light passes from one medium to another, the ratio of the sine of the angle of incidence to the sine of the angle of refraction is a constant (which depends on the two media concerned, and on the colour of the light).

If light enters a medium from a vacuum, the constant value of sine i/sin r is known as the *absolute refractive index* of the medium; this is very nearly the same as the value of the constant when light enters from air—a constant known as the **refractive index** of the medium and denoted by the letter n.

Refractive Index of Materials

Material	n	Material	n
Ice	1·31	Benzene	1·50
Water	1·33	Crown glass	1·52
'Hypo' solution, saturated	1·42	Flint glass	1·65
Glycerin	1·47	Methylene iodide	1·74
		Diamond	2·42

The values given in the above table are average values; they do not show the slight variation in refractive index with colour (or wave-length).

26.3. An explanation of refraction. The refraction of light can be explained by considering light as a wave motion, travelling slower on entering an optically denser medium. Measurements of the speed of light in materials bears this out; for example, Foucault showed in 1850 that the speed of light in water is less than in air.

When a plane wave-front of light approaches an optically denser medium obliquely, the course of the wave-front is swung round towards the normal. In Fig. 26.3 the edge of the wave-front at A travels to P in the same time as the edge of the wave-front at B travels to Q.

$$\frac{\text{Speed of light in air}}{\text{Speed of light in the medium}}=\frac{BQ}{AP}$$

From the geometry of the diagram it follows that

$$\frac{BQ}{AP}=\frac{\sin i}{\sin r}=n \text{ (refractive index)}$$

$$\text{Refractive index}=\frac{\text{Speed of light in air}}{\text{Speed of light in the medium}}$$

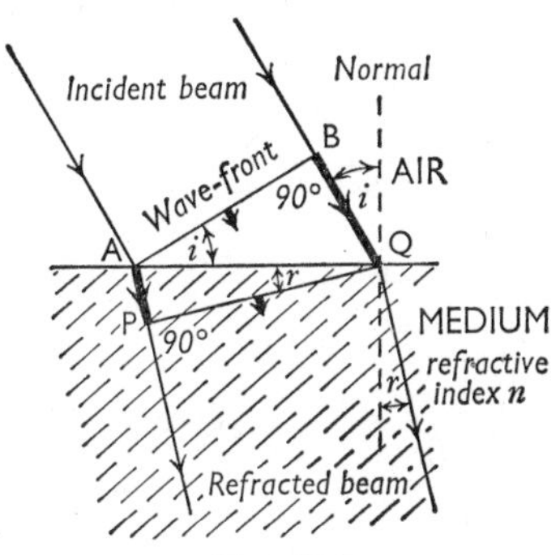

FIG. 26.3

26.4. Images formed by refraction. It is a common observation that objects under water do not appear to be in their real positions. Ponds, swimming baths, tanks of water, all appear shallower than their true depth. Note, in Pl. 18, that the base and far side of the glass block appear narrower than the top and near sides.

For a view at right angles to the surface, there is a simple relation between the real depth of an object and its apparent depth. The ratio

$$\frac{\text{real depth}}{\text{apparent depth}}$$

is equal to the refractive index of the material, as is shown in the following paragraph.

For a ray-track such as OXY (Fig. 26.4),

Refractive index $(n)=\sin\beta\div\sin\alpha$

$$\therefore n=\frac{NX}{XI}\div\frac{NX}{XO}$$

$$=\frac{XO}{XI}$$

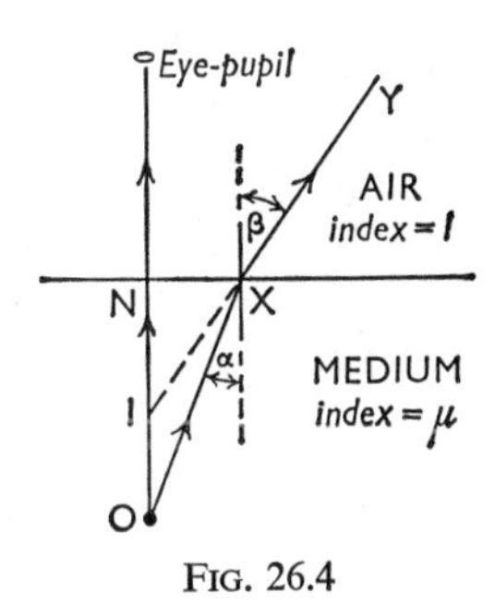

FIG. 26.4

Now the pupil of the eye is very small, only a few mm in diameter. So that if the observer's eye is on the normal ON, then a ray such as XY can enter the eye only if X is very close to N. In such a case the ratio XO/XI will scarcely differ from NO/NI.

$$\text{Hence} \qquad n \simeq \frac{NO}{NI} \text{ or } \frac{\text{Real depth}}{\text{Apparent depth}}$$

For other directions of view this formula does not apply. Thus Fig. 26.5 shows some of the refracted rays coming out of water, the

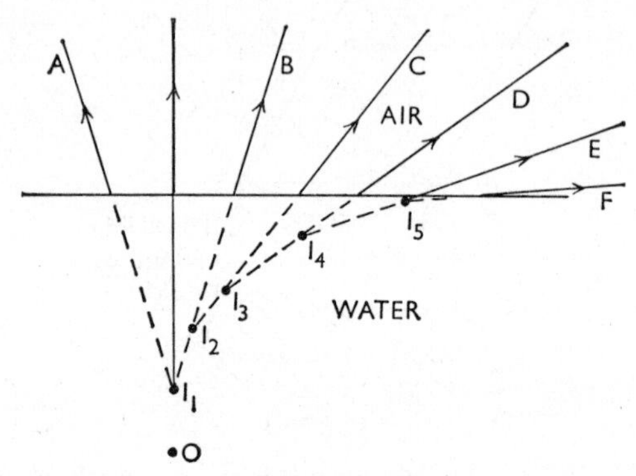

FIG. 26.5

Refracted rays leaving a water-surface

source of the rays having been at O. These refracted rays do not all come from the same point, so the position of the image varies with the position of the observer. Rays such as A and B, which are close to the normal, appear to come from I_1. Rays such as D and E appear to come from I_4, so that when one looks in this direction the image is even nearer the surface and is also nearer the observer. You can see the effect by putting a coin in a shallow dish which is full of water. View the coin from above, and then move your head till you are nearly looking along the water surface; the coin will then appear to be only just below the surface.

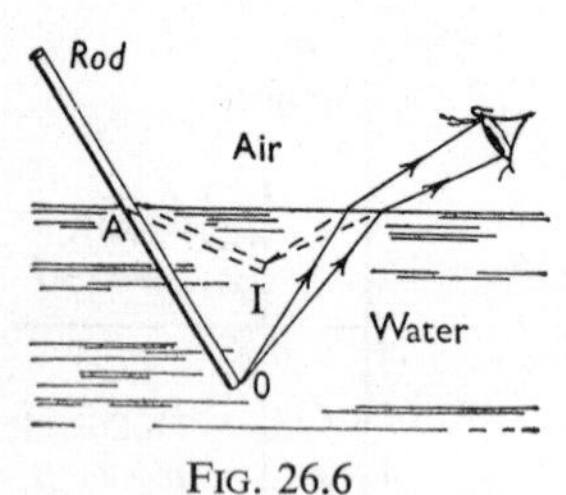

FIG. 26.6

The 'bent-stick' effect

When a stick is held at a slant under water, the immersed part of it appears bent up towards the

10. *Images formed by two plane mirrors at an angle of 60°. This photograph was taken with a pinhole camera. The disc of metal, which contains the pinhole, can be seen reflected in the picture.* [p. 235]

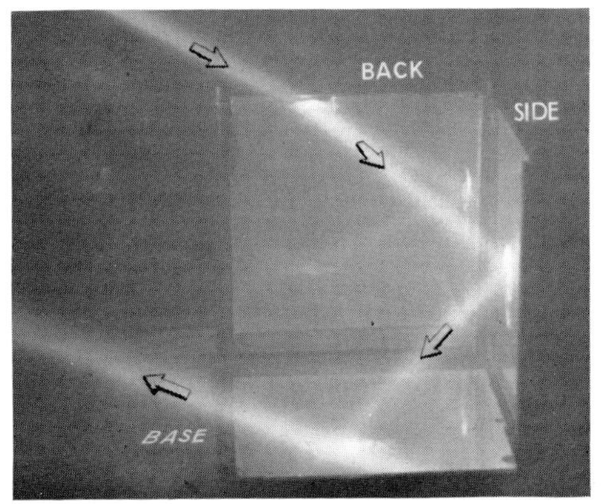

11. *Box-corner reflection; the incident ray, which is reflected from each of the mirrors in turn, returns parallel to its original course. The effect here is seen in a smoke-box. Arrows have been added to show the course of the light. The fainter white lines are images of the beam seen in the back mirror.* [p. 235]

12. *The back surface of a rear-reflector such as is used on cycles and cars. The front surfaces act as box-corner reflectors.* [p. 235]

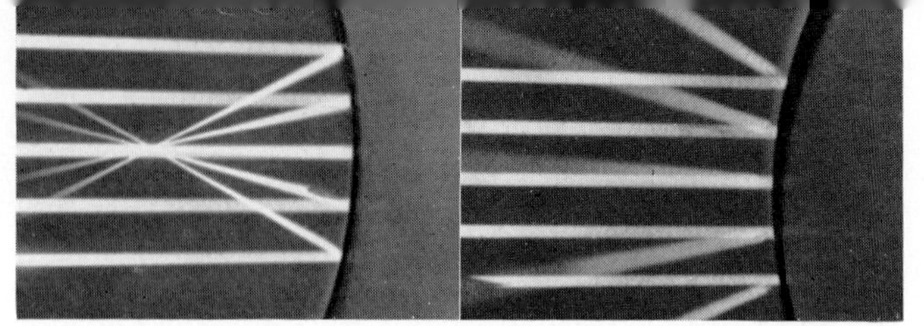

13. *Parallel rays of light reflected from concave and convex mirrors.* [p. 236]

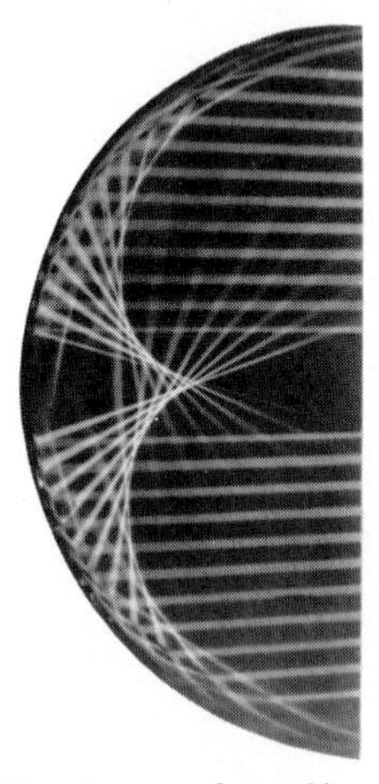

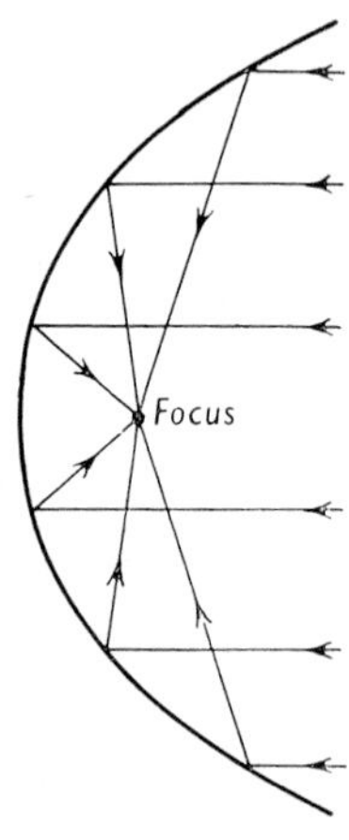

14. *Caustic curve formed by reflection of rays of light from a concave mirror, of wide aperture.* [p. 237]

15. *Reflection of a parallel beam from a parabolic reflector.* [p. 237]

16. *Radio-telescope at Jodrell Bank. Concave reflector with aerial at the focus.* [p. 237]

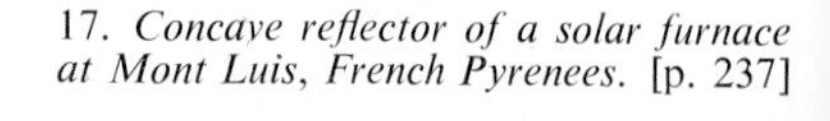

17. *Concave reflector of a solar furnace at Mont Luis, French Pyrenees.* [p. 237]

surface. Fig. 26.6 shows how rays from O give rise to an image at I. Similarly, light from other points on AO appears to have come from AI, so that the stick appears bent at A.

26.5. Critical angle. Total internal reflection. When light in one medium meets the surface of another which is optically less dense, part of the light is refracted away from the normal and part of the light is reflected (Fig. 26.7*a*, Pl. 20). As the angle of incidence is

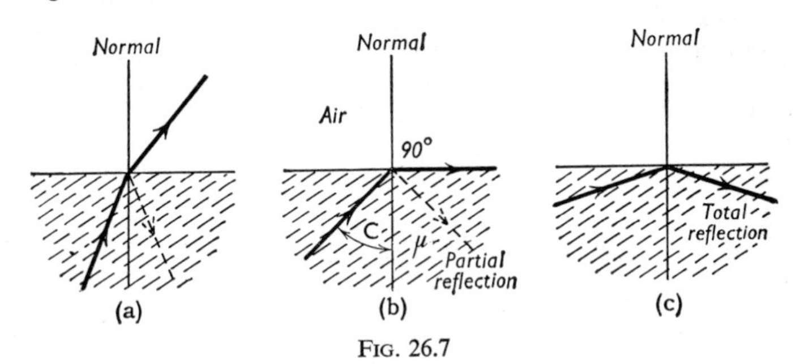

FIG. 26.7

Critical angle and total internal reflection

increased, the angle of refraction increases until it is 90°, and the refracted ray then skims the surface (Fig. 26.7*b*). The angle of incidence, in the optically denser medium, for which the angle of refraction is 90°, is known as the **critical angle.** Experiment shows that any further increase in the angle of incidence results in all the incident light being reflected back into the denser medium, there being no refraction at all (Fig. 26.7*c*).

Since the path of light is reversible the refracted ray in Fig. 26.7*b* can be treated as an incident ray; it then follows that

$$\frac{\sin 90^\circ}{\sin C}=n \text{ or } n=\frac{1}{\sin C}$$

By taking n for water as $\frac{4}{3}$, we have $\sin C=\frac{3}{4}$, whence C for water $=48^\circ 36'$. A similar calculation for glass of refractive index 1·52 shows that the critical angle for this glass is nearly 41°.

Conversely, the determination of C for any medium enables the refractive index to be calculated. Commercial refractometers measure refractive index from a determination of the critical angle. The refractive index of substances such as oils, fats, waxes, syrups and jams can be used to test either their purity or their concentration.

Total internal reflection can also be observed in any rectangular block of glass. Light can pass through any pair of opposite sides in any direction, but it cannot pass through two adjacent sides. If you look through any side, an adjacent one looks silvered and opaque (see Pl. 18). A similar silvery appearance can be seen if you fill a rectangular perspex box with water; but in this case, owing to the larger critical angle, there are certain directions of view for which it is possible to see through two adjacent sides.

Light which enters the end of a transparent rod at small angles of incidence meets the sides at large angles of incidence. It suffers repeated internal reflection and travels along the rod—even a bent rod—without escaping from the sides. Fig. 26.8 shows a bent

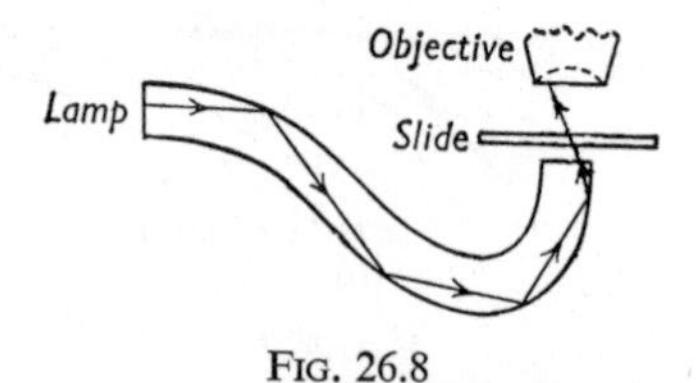

FIG. 26.8

A microscope-slide illuminator

glass rod used as a microscope-slide illuminator; in similar fashion a bent glass or perspex rod, attached to a small pocket lamp, is used by doctors for illuminating the back of a patient's throat.

Total reflecting prisms have a variety of uses in optical instruments; some of these are illustrated in Fig. 26.9. The angle of

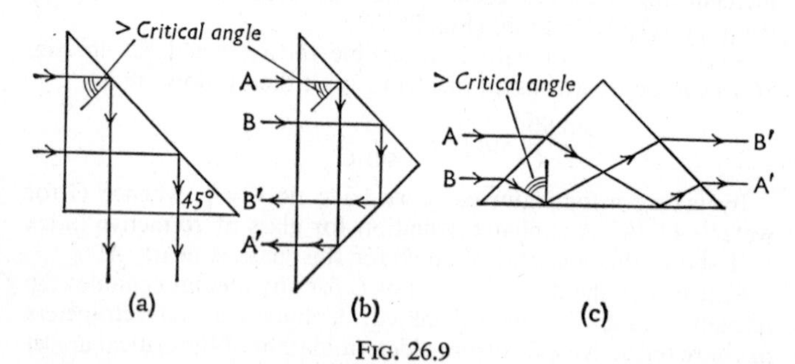

FIG. 26.9

Reflecting prisms. (a) Is used in periscopes, prismatic compasses, (b) is an erecting prism, used in prismatic binoculars, (c) is an erecting prism which can be fitted to projection lanterns

incidence on the reflecting face is in each case greater than 41°, the critical angle for crown glass. These prisms have a great advantage over the corresponding plate-glass mirror systems; they avoid the multiple images which can occur with back-silvered mirrors (Fig. 26.10).

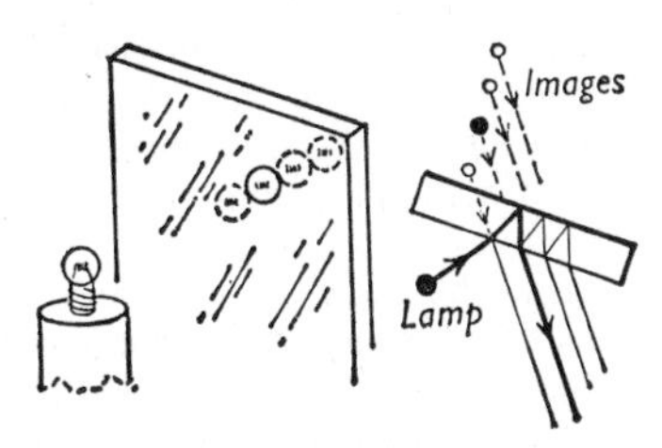

Fig. 26.10

Multiple images in a back-silvered mirror

26.6. Atmospheric refraction. Astronomers have to allow for the effects of refraction in the earth's atmosphere when observing the position of sun or stars. The effect is most marked (a deviation of 36′) near the horizon, since the angle of incidence is then greater. The refraction in the upper atmosphere is very slight, but the light becomes more and more refracted as it meets the layers of denser air near the earth's surface.

A variety of types of **mirage** are caused by variation in the density of the air due to variations of temperature. The commonest occurs when there is a region of hot air near the ground and cooler air above it (Fig. 26.11). The warmer air has the smaller optical

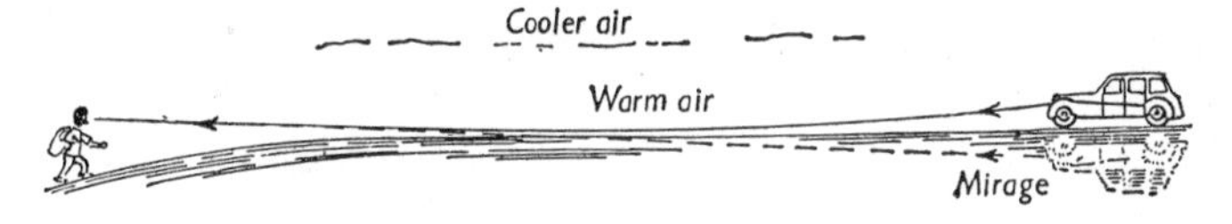

Fig. 26.11

Formation of a mirage

density and the incident rays are continuously refracted in the manner shown in the diagram. Low-lying distant objects appear reflected, inverted, in what appears to be a puddle of water or a lake. The effect occurs on a large scale over deserts, and over the mud-flats or sand-flats of estuaries. It can also be seen when driving along a road on a calm hot day. Pools of water seem to appear on the road, and they appear either bright or dark depending on whether the distant scene is the sky or a dark background.

26.7. Refraction by a triangular glass prism. If a ray-box is used to send a bright narrow beam of light through a glass prism, the ray is found to be *deviated* (see Pl. 21); the *angle of deviation* is the angle between the incident and emergent rays. The light is also found to be *dispersed*, forming a band of colour known as a *spectrum* (Pl. 22). Red light is the least deviated, violet light the most. Violet light is refracted more than red because its speed in materials is less than that of red light.

By rotating the prism, the angle of incidence can be altered and this causes a change in deviation. It is found that whatever the angle of incidence, the deviation never becomes less than a certain value, which is known as the *angle of minimum deviation* for the prism. Experiment shows that for a prism in the *position of minimum deviation*, the ray passes symmetrically through; the prism in Pl. 21 is nearly in this position.

26.8. Determination of refractive index

(i) *Slab and ray-track method.* A rectangular perspex box is filled with the liquid under test or a rectangular slab of the material is used if solid. The course of rays of light is tracked through the slab, either by using a ray box to obtain the necessary narrow beams (Pl. 19) or else by arranging four pins (two each side of the slab) to be in line as seen through the block. After several such tracks have been marked out on paper which is put under the apparatus, the values of the angles i and r are measured; the average value of $\sin i/\sin r$ gives n.

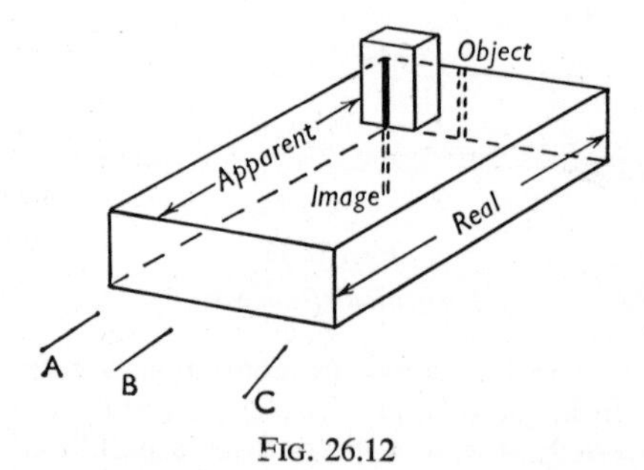

FIG. 26.12

(ii) *Real and apparent depth method.* Fig. 26.12 shows the application of this method to a slab of material. The object is a narrow strip of paper at one end of the block. The image-finder is a thin line on a small block standing on the glass. If the image and the image-finder line appear to tally when viewed from positions such as A, B and C, the two are in the same place. By measuring the real and apparent thickness of the block the refractive index can be calculated.

(iii) *Prism method.* A ray of light is sent through the prism so that the ray is least deviated. The angle of minimum deviation D and the refracting angle of the prism A are then measured. At the position of minimum deviation the ray passes symmetrically through the prism as shown in Fig. 26.13. It is left as an exercise to the student to show that $D=2(\alpha-\beta)$ and $A=2\beta$ and that therefore $n=\sin\frac{1}{2}(A+D)/\sin\frac{1}{2}A$. (*Hint.* The angle marked with a dot is equal to A.)

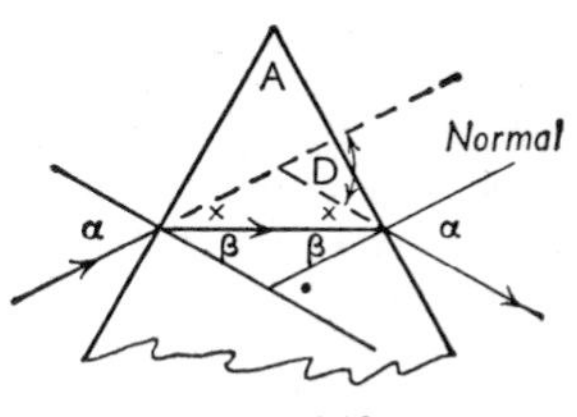

FIG. 26.13
Minimum deviation

SUMMARY

Laws of refraction

(i) **The incident and refracted rays are in the same plane as the normal, and are on opposite sides of the normal.**

(ii) **When light passes from one medium to another, the ratio of the sine of the angle of incidence to the sine of the angle of refraction is a constant** (which depends on the two media concerned, and on the colour of the light).

$$\sin i/\sin r=n$$

The position of an image due to refraction at a plane surface depends on the position of the observer. For a bird's eye view,

$$\text{Real depth/Apparent depth}=n$$

The **critical angle** C is the angle of incidence (in the denser medium) for which the angle of refraction is 90°. An angle of incidence greater than C results in total internal reflection.

$$n\sin C=1 \text{ or } n=\operatorname{cosec} C$$

Refraction through a prism causes **deviation** and **dispersion.** At the position of **minimum deviation,** the ray passes symmetrically through the prism.

Questions

1. Construct a ray diagram to show the refracted ray when light meets a water surface at an angle of incidence of 40°. (Refractive index of water=4/3.)

Proceed as follows, preferably using squared paper:

(a) *Light incident in the water*. Draw the incident ray to meet the surface at P. Produce it to Q and make PQ=4/3 units. Drop a perpendicular QN on to the surface. With centre P and radius 1 unit, draw an arc to cut QN in R. PR is then the refracted ray.

(b) *Light incident in the air*. Use the same construction, but make PQ=1 unit and PR=4/3 units. NQ will have to be produced beyond Q in this case.

2. Check, by calculation, your answers to Question 1.

3. Describe how you would determine the refractive index of either water or glass. From the data of Fig. 26.1 calculate the refractive indexes and critical angles of the substances named.

4. A thick sheet of glass rests on a page of printing. As one side of the sheet of glass is lifted the printing seems to move. Explain this with the aid of a ray diagram.

5. An observer looking at a fish which is in a cubical glass tank full of water sees two images of the fish. Draw a ray diagram to show how this can happen; assume the fish to be in the middle of the tank, the observer's eye being above the water level and in a direction of a diagonal of a mid-section of the tank.

6. A heavy can stands in a dish which is full of water. Seen from above, the bottom of the can seems to be below the bottom of the dish. Explain this with the aid of a ray diagram.

7. Explain, with the aid of diagrams, how a suitable glass prism can act as a reflector and be used to turn a ray of light through (*a*) 90°, (*b*) 180°.

8. To an observer looking normally at one face of a glass cube, the adjacent faces appear to act as mirror. Explain this by means of a labelled ray diagram.

9. An observer looking through a glass slab sees an object on the other side slightly displaced from its true position. Draw labelled ray diagrams to show how this can happen when the line of sight is (*a*) perpendicular to the slab, (*b*) oblique to the slab.

10. Explain the formation of a *mirage*.

11. State the laws of refraction of light. How is refraction explained in terms of the wave theory of light? Illustrate your answer with a diagram.

12. Define *angle of refraction* and *refractive index*.

A microscope is focused on a mark on a horizontal card. When the mark is covered by a slab of glass 2·40 cm thick the microscope has to be raised 0·78 cm for the mark to be in focus again. Explain why the microscope has to be raised; calculate the refractive index of the glass.

13. Explain, with the aid of a diagram, why a pool of water appears to be shallower than it is.

A small lamp is held 120 cm above the surface of a pond. When viewed from nearly overhead the image of the lamp, seen by reflection in the surface, appears to coincide with the image of the bottom of the pond. Calculate the depth of the pond. (Refractive index of water = 4/3.)

14. What is meant by the statement 'the critical angle for water is 49°'? To a fish in a pond, the still surface of the water appears silvered except for a circular patch which makes an angle of 98° at the eye of the fish. Explain this statement.

15. Draw a diagram to show a parallel beam of light entering and leaving adjacent sides of a triangular glass prism which is in the position of minimum deviation. Show, on your diagram, some of the wave-fronts of the light waves both in the air and in the glass. Deduce from the diagram that the wave-fronts travel slower in the glass, and make an estimate of the refractive index.

16. Copy the prism and ray tracks shown in Pl. 21. Measure the angles of *incidence* and *reflection* at the first face. Draw the track of a reflected ray (inside the glass) which could occur at the second face. Show the direction in which you would expect this ray to be refracted when it hits the base of the prism. Examine Pl. 22 to see if there is any indication of the presence of this emergent ray.

CHAPTER 27

Lenses

27.1. A lens is usually made of glass, but can in fact be made from any transparent material. Thus a spherical flask filled with water or other transparent liquid will act as a lens; so also will a watch-glass or a wine-glass containing transparent liquid (see Pl. 18). A beaker of liquid or a test-tube of liquid will act as a lens—a cylindrical lens in this case.

The curved surfaces of lenses are usually spherical; but ray-box lenses are cylindrical, and spectacle lenses may be partly spherical, partly cylindrical. The action of a lens depends on the refraction which takes place at each of its surfaces. An incident ray is deviated, towards the thicker parts of the lens, in much the same way as a ray is deviated towards the thicker parts of a prism. Because the sides of a lens slope together more at the edges of the lens the deviation is greater there. The shape of a lens is such that the different deviations at different places result in a common focus-point for all the rays of a beam.

27.2. Terms used in connection with lenses. Lenses are named bi-

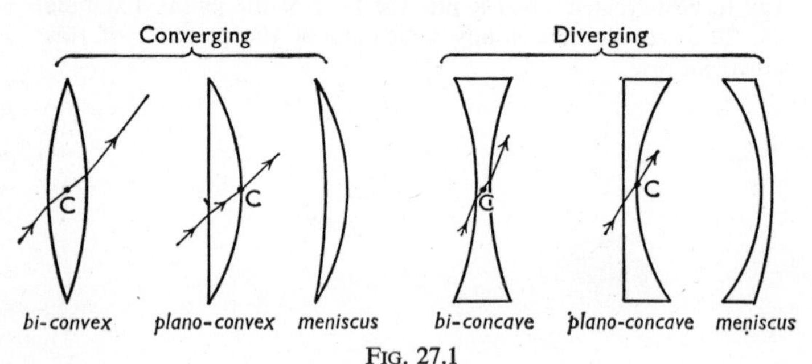

FIG. 27.1

Types of lenses. C = optical centre

convex, plano-convex, etc., according to the shape of their section, as shown in Fig. 27.1. They are also classified as either **converging** or **diverging** according to their action on parallel beams of light (Pls. 23 and 24).

The principal axis of a lens is a line joining the centres of curvature of its faces. Rays which are parallel to this axis either converge to a point or diverge as if coming from a point after passing through the lens. This point is known as a **principal focus** or **focal point;** its distance from the optical centre of the lens is known as the **focal length.** Light which passes through the optical centre, C in Fig. 27.1, emerges parallel to the incident light, i.e. it is not deviated.

A lens can be considered to have two principal foci, depending on whether light is incident on one side of the lens or the other. For thin lenses the two foci are symmetrically placed with respect to the optical centre of the lens, even though the curvatures of the faces may not be the same; the focal length of a lens is not affected by turning it round so that the other side faces the light.

Fig. 27.2 shows the action of a converging lens on rays which

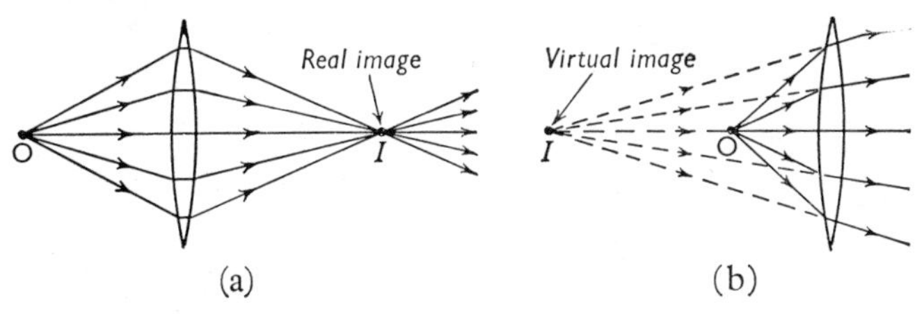

FIG. 27.2

are not parallel; light from a small source O gives rise to an image at I. Points such as O and I are known as conjugate foci.

27.3. Images formed by lenses. If a small lamp and a screen are placed about a metre apart and a convex lens, focal length 10–20 cm, is put between them, it is possible to find two positions of the lens which give a focused image on the screen (Fig. 27.3). One of the images is magnified, the other diminished. The distances marked *a* and *b* in the upper diagram have become interchanged in the lower diagram; the larger image is magnified b/a times and the smaller one diminished in the same proportion. Both images are real and are formed in the manner shown in the first and third ray-diagrams of Fig. 27.4.

The ability of a converging lens to form diminished or magnified real images is put to a number of practical uses. For example, it is used in taking pictures of a distant scene by photography, and in the projection of magnified pictures on a screen in the cinema-projector.

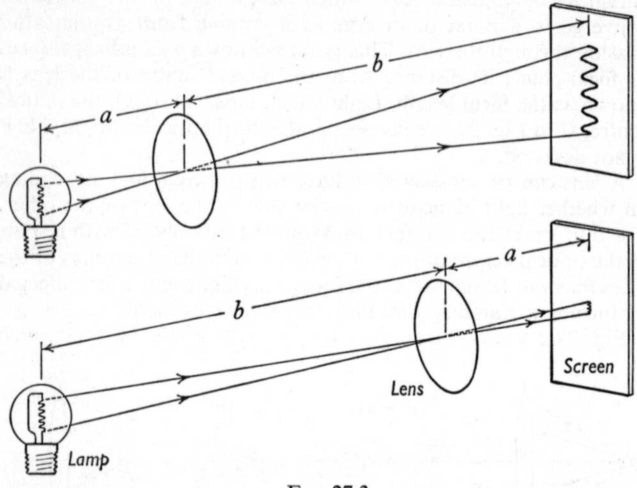

FIG. 27.3

If the lens is held at less than its focal length from the lamp or from the page of a book, a magnified image is formed which appears to be behind the lens. This is a virtual image; the rays leaving the lens diverge as if from a point behind the lens. The course of the rays is shown in the fourth ray-diagram of Fig. 27.4.

In the ray-diagrams of Fig. 27.4, only two of all the rays which spread out from the top of an object have been shown. These two rays are

(1) A ray parallel to the principal axis. After refraction this ray converges to or diverges from the corresponding principal focus (focal point).

(2) A ray directed to the optical centre. This ray is undeviated.

A real image occurs where these rays meet; a virtual image occurs where these rays diverge on leaving the lens (Fig. 27.4, last two diagrams). To simplify these diagrams the deviation of the rays has been shown as though it occurred at the central line of the lens instead of at the actual lens surfaces.

Note that in the first four diagrams the ray through F takes the same course in each. The ray through the centre makes increasing

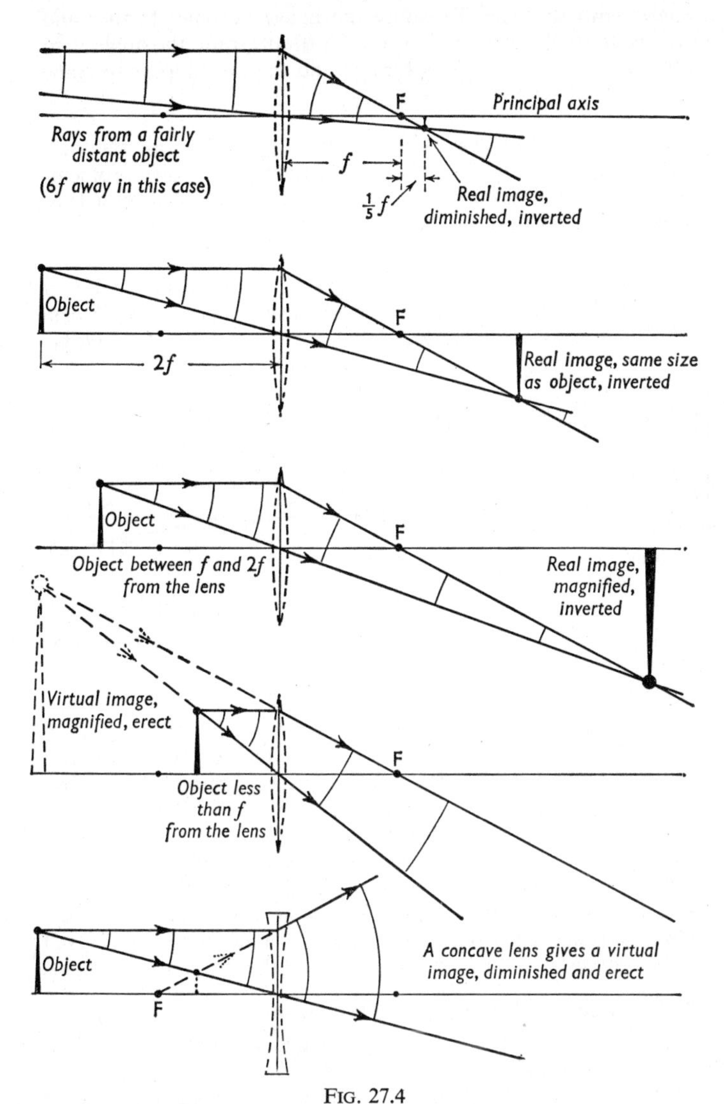

FIG. 27.4

Ray diagrams illustrating the formation of images by lenses

angles with the axis. Therefore the image becomes further and further from the lens until, in the fourth diagram, the angle is so great that no real image is formed and the rays appear to come from behind the lens.

27.4. Lens-problems solved graphically. By making ray diagrams such as those of Fig. 27.4 to scale, it is possible to solve problems on the position, size and nature of the image formed by a lens. It is convenient to draw such diagrams on squared paper.

EXAMPLE 1. *An object,* 8 *units high, stands vertically on the axis of a convex lens. The object is* 40 *cm from the lens, and the focal length of the lens is* 11 *cm. Find the position, size and nature of the image.*

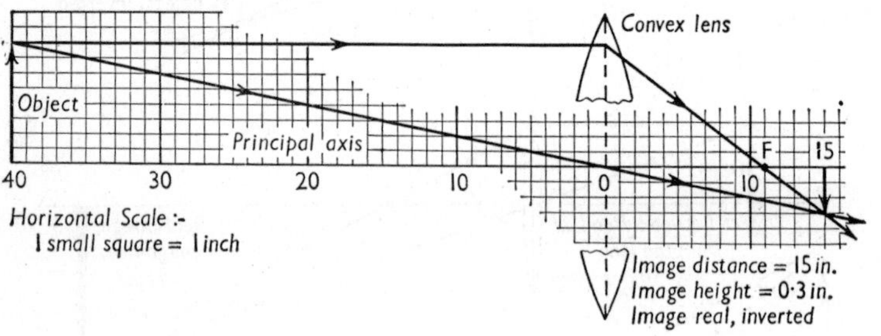

FIG. 27.5

The graphical solution to this problem is shown in Fig. 27.5. The height of the object has been made equal to 8 small squares; on the horizontal scale, each small square represents 1 cm. Two rays are sufficient to fix the position of the image; other rays could be drawn, if desired, from the tip of the object to the lens-line; they would be deviated, so that all passed through the tip of the image. Note that the image has a length of 3 small squares, so that its height is 3 units. The image is at a distance of 15 small squares from the lens-line; so the image distance is 15 cm. Rays of light actually pass through the image, so the image is a real one.

27.5. Formulae for lenses and curved mirrors

(i) **Lenses,** The distances of object and image from a lens or mirror are usually given the letters u and v respectively. The *magnification* (length of image ÷ length of object) is given the letter m; experiment shows that this is equal to v/u.

The variation of u and v can be found experimentally, e.g. as described in section 27.6 (iii). If a graph is plotted of v against u a curve such as that shown in Fig. 27.6*a* is obtained. This sort of

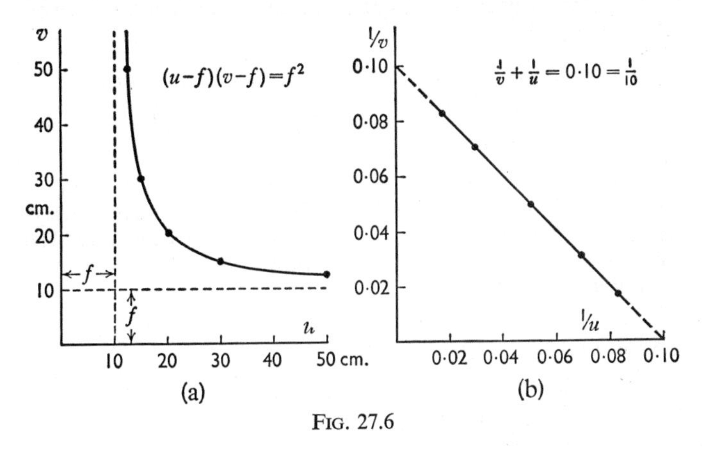

FIG. 27.6

graph is typical of an inverse proportion between two quantities, i.e. two quantities whose product is constant. For this particular graph the product $(u-f)(v-f)$ is constant and equal to f^2. So that

$$(u-f)(v-f)=f^2,$$

a formula derived by Newton and known as Newton's formula. This formula can be rearranged to give the form

$$\frac{1}{v}+\frac{1}{u}=\frac{1}{f}$$

The formula can be checked, for a given lens, by plotting $1/v$ against $1/u$; the points are found to lie on a straight line as shown in Fig. 27.6*b*.

To make sure that the formula shall apply to all types of lenses and to all the images they form, it is necessary to choose (i) an origin from which measurements of u and v are made, (ii) a convention concerning the meanings which shall be given to + and − signs.

For thin lenses the origin is the optical centre. There are two main types of sign convention. There are the **Cartesian conventions,** in which the sign depends on which *side* of the origin the measurement is made. Another convention is the **real-is-positive** convention. In this, distances measured to *real* foci, images and objects are *positive*; distances measured to *virtual* foci, images and objects are *negative*.

The lens-formula is different according to the convention you choose.

Real-is-positive convention	*Cartesian conventions*
$\frac{1}{v}+\frac{1}{u}=\frac{1}{f}$	$\frac{1}{v}-\frac{1}{u}=\frac{1}{f}$

The convention used in the following examples is the real-is-positive one. In studying these examples, note that a sign is always given to a known quantity, never to an unknown quantity. The sign of the final answer then tells you the sign of the unknown quantity.

EXAMPLE 1 (*see Example* 1, p. 258).

$u=+40;\ v=v;\ f=+11$ (real focus)

$$\therefore \frac{1}{40}+\frac{1}{v}=\frac{1}{11}$$

$$\frac{1}{v}=\frac{1}{11}-\frac{1}{40}=\frac{29}{440}$$

$$\therefore v=+15{\cdot}2$$

The image is 15·2 cm from the lens. The + sign shows it to be real. It must therefore be to the right of the lens in Fig. 27.5.

EXAMPLE 2. *Find the position of the image of an object placed* 4 *cm from a convex lens of focal length* 6 *cm.*

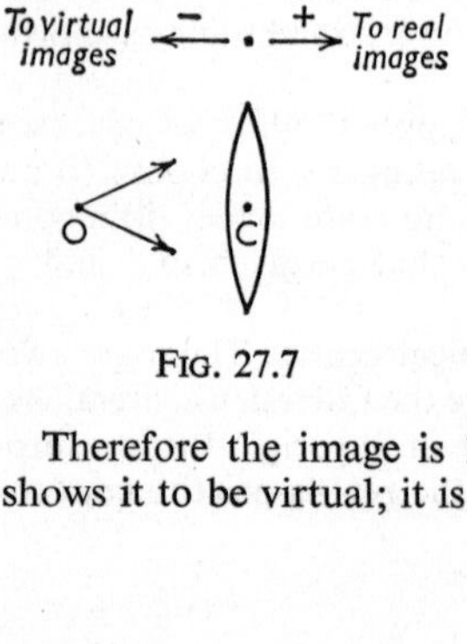

FIG. 27.7

$u=+4;\ v=v;\ f=+6$ (real focus)

$$\therefore \frac{1}{4}+\frac{1}{v}=\frac{1}{6}$$

$$\frac{1}{v}=\frac{1}{6}-\frac{1}{4}=-\frac{1}{12}$$

$$\therefore v=-12$$

Therefore the image is 12 cm from the lens. The minus sign shows it to be virtual; it is therefore to the left of C in Fig. 27.7.

EXAMPLE 3. *An object 1·2 cm high stands on the principal axis of a concave lens of focal length 20 cm. The distance of the object is 60 cm. Find the position and nature of the image.*

$u=+60;\ v=v;\ f=-20$ (virtual focus)

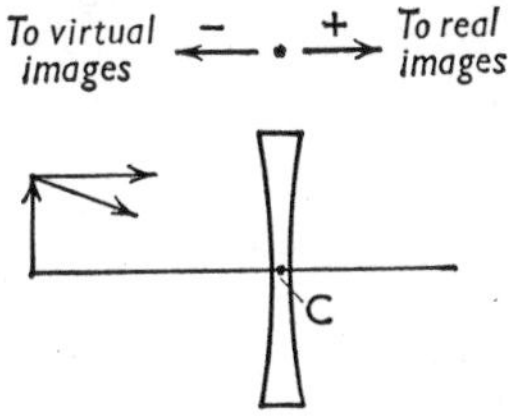

$$\therefore \frac{1}{60}+\frac{1}{v}=-\frac{1}{20}$$

$$\frac{1}{v}=-\frac{1}{20}-\frac{1}{60}=-\frac{4}{60}=-\frac{1}{15}$$

$$\therefore v=-15$$

FIG. 27.8

The image is 15 cm from C. It is virtual and therefore to the left of C (Fig. 27.8).

(ii) **Curved mirrors.** For curved mirrors the origin from which distances are measured is the *pole* of the mirror. The magnification m is given by the formula $m=v/u$. The formula for u, v and f is

$$\frac{1}{u}+\frac{1}{v}=\frac{1}{f}\left(=\frac{2}{r}\right)$$

This formula applies for both real-is-positive and Cartesian conventions.

EXAMPLE 4. *An object 30 cm from a curved mirror gives a virtual image which is 10 cm behind the mirror. Find the focal length and the nature of the mirror.*

$u=+30;\ v=-10$ (virtual image)

$$\frac{1}{f}=\frac{1}{30}-\frac{1}{10}=-\frac{2}{15}$$

$$f=-7{\cdot}5$$

The negative sign shows that the focus is virtual. Therefore the mirror is a diverging or convex one of focal length 7·5 cm.

27.6. Determination of the focal length of a convex lens

(i) *Distant object method.* A piece of card is cut to slip over a ruler as shown in Fig. 27.9. A distant scene or cloud is chosen as an object and the ruler pointed to it. The lens is put against the scale, and is moved to and fro until a clearly focused image is obtained. The difference in the scale-readings of the lens-edge and screen gives f. Each point on the object gives a diverging pencil of light to the lens, but over such a long range the rays which arrive at the lens are very nearly parallel. Several sets of readings should be taken and the mean focal length found.

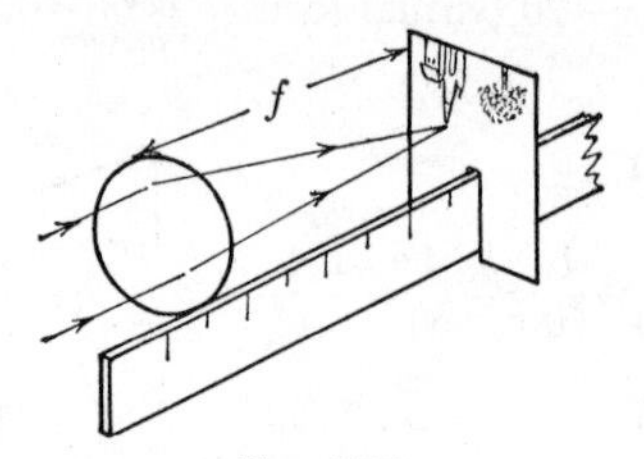

FIG. 27.9

(ii) *Plane mirror method.* An illuminated object, e.g. a card with a hole covered by a piece of tracing paper with a simple design on it, is set vertically over a horizontal scale. The lens is mounted with its axis horizontal, and a plane mirror is held behind the lens as shown in Fig. 27.10. The distance lens-to-object is adjusted until a clearly focused image is formed alongside the object. The only beam which a plane mirror can reflect completely unchanged is a parallel one; therefore the object is at the principal focus. A set-square put against the scale can be used to find the positions of the lens and object on the scale; the difference of the scale readings gives f; the mean of several sets of readings should be taken.

(iii) *$u-v$ method.* The apparatus of Fig. 27.10 can be used, the

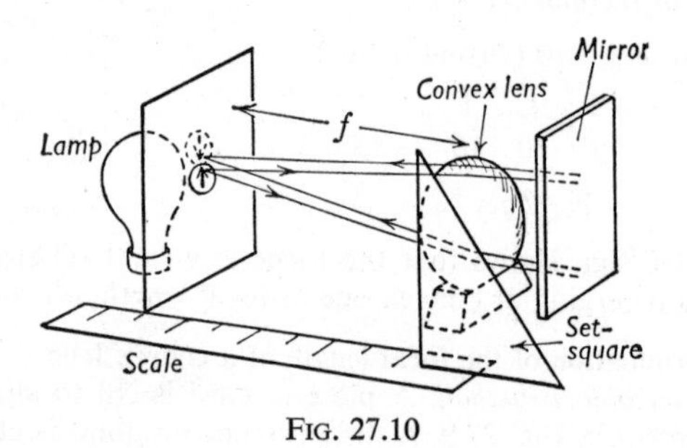

FIG. 27.10

mirror being replaced by a vertical screen on which real images can be focused by adjusting the positions of lens and screen. The positions of the object, lens and screen are found on the scale with the help of a set-square, and the values of u and v found by difference. Substitution in the lens formula enables the value of f to be calculated from a series of such results.

27.7. The power of a lens. The power of a lens is the reciprocal of its focal length. If the focal length is measured in cm, the unit is cm^{-1}. In stating the power of a lens it is more usual to express the focal length in metres and find the reciprocal of that. The unit for the power is then $metre^{-1}$ or the **dioptre**. Thus a lens with a focal length of +20 cm or 0·20 metre has a power of +5 dioptres.

SUMMARY

A **principal focus (focal point)** of a lens is a point to which rays parallel to the principal axis converge, or from which they appear to diverge, after passing through the lens.

The **focal length** of a lens is the distance of a principal focus from the optical centre of the lens.

Using the real-is-positive convention, the following formulae apply to both lenses and mirrors.

$$m=\frac{v}{u} \qquad \frac{1}{u}+\frac{1}{v}=\frac{1}{f}$$

where the origin of measurement is the optical centre of the lens or the pole of the mirror, and distances measured towards **real** foci, images and objects are positive.

Questions

(*Note.* Where scale diagrams are asked for, it is usually simpler to draw them on squared paper.)

1. A bi-convex lens rests flat on a table with a point source of light high above it. Explain the fact that the lens casts very little shadow on the table unless the lens is lifted up. Describe and explain the changes in shadow appearance as the lens is raised.

2. What is meant by the terms *principal focus* (*focal point*) and *focal length* of a lens? Illustrate your answer with labelled ray diagrams for (*a*) a convex lens, (*b*) a concave lens.

An object is placed on the principal axis of a convex lens of focal length 10 cm. Find by scale diagram or by calculation the position, size and nature of the image formed when the distance of the object from the lens is (*a*) 12 cm, (*b*) 8 cm.

3. A convex lens can be referred to as (*a*) a burning glass, (*b*) a magnifying glass. Draw labelled ray diagrams to show its action in each of these respects.

4. In what circumstances will a converging lens form (*a*) a magnified real image, (*b*) a magnified virtual image? Illustrate your answer by ray diagrams.

5. Light from a small lamp on the axis of a converging lens gives a real image which is 50 cm from the lens. Another lens is placed 5 cm from the image, and the light then leaves this lens as a parallel beam. Illustrate, by means of ray diagrams, how this effect could be produced by (*a*) a converging lens, (*b*) a diverging lens.

6. Describe two methods of producing a parallel beam of light.

A lamp with a straight filament, 1·0 cm long, is arranged with the filament upright and 4·5 metres from a wall. A convex lens, held 1·5 metres from the filament, gives a clearly focused image on the wall. Explain the fact that there is another position, nearer the wall, at which the lens will form a focused image of the filament on the wall. Compare the length of the first image with that of the second.

7. A rod, 18 cm tall, stands with its centre point on the axis of a convex lens of focal length 12 cm. The distance between the centre of the rod and the centre of the lens is 50 cm. Draw a ray diagram, to a scale of one-fifth, to show how and where the image of the top of the rod is formed. Show four rays starting from the top of the rod, one of the rays being that which reaches an observer's eye situated on the axis at a distance of 50 cm from the lens-centre. Deduce from the diagram the least diameter of the lens which will let the observer see the image of the top of the rod.

8. Find, by scale diagram, the position, size and nature of the image formed in each of the three following examples, where u = distance of the object from a convex lens, f = focal length of the lens, h = height of object.

	(i)	(ii)	(iii)
u	20 cm	12 cm	15 cm
f	12 cm	20 cm	9 cm
h	6 units	6 units	8 units

9. A vertical illuminated object, 1·80 cm high, is 56 cm from a vertical screen. A convex lens, placed between the object and the screen, forms a real inverted image of length 1·00 cm. Find (*a*) the position of the lens, (*b*) the focal length of the lens.

10. A convex lens is used to produce an image, four times the size of the object, on a screen which is 3 metres from the lens. Sketch the arrangement and find the focal length of the lens.

11. Describe how you would determine the focal length of a convex lens.

A convex lens of focal length 12·0 cm is placed with its principal axis horizontal, at a distance of 36·0 cm from a vertical screen. When a point source of light is placed on the axis and 48·0 cm from the screen, a circular patch of light, of the same diameter as the lens, appears on the screen. Explain this. Find the position to which the source must be moved in order that an image of the source may appear on the screen.

12. What is meant by the *power* of a lens? Calculate the power, in dioptres, of (*a*) converging lenses of focal length 2 metres, 0·25 metre, 0·20 metre, 8 cm, (*b*) diverging lenses of focal length 50 cm, 16 cm.

13. Calculate the focal lengths of lenses which have powers of +5 dioptres and −1 dioptre. Given that the power of two thin lenses in contact is the sum of the powers of each, calculate the focal length of these two lenses in contact.

14. BCD is a horizontal line which is the principal axis of a convex lens whose centre is at C. B is a point source of light and D its image; BC=CD. Draw a diagram to illustrate this.

Describe the appearance of the illumination on a vertical screen placed mid-way between C and D. Given that the diameter of the lens=3 cm and that BD=56 cm find (*a*) the widths of the bright and dark regions on the screen, (*b*) the focal length of the lens.

CHAPTER 28

Optical Instruments

28.1. The camera. A camera consists of a light-tight box fitted with a convex lens at one end, and a sensitive film or plate at the other. The interior is painted black to absorb any stray light. To control the amount of light admitted through the lens, it is provided with a shutter of variable speed, and a circular hole or 'stop' of adjustable diameter. Such a camera is a **fixed-focus camera;** as a rule the focal length is 8 cm or less. The lens-to-film distance is the focal length of the lens; thus objects on the horizon are sharply in focus. But objects much nearer than this are practically in focus too. Although they are really focused slightly behind the film, their focus-point is so near the film that the final picture appears quite sharply defined. Thus when an object is $101f$ from a convex lens (a matter of some 8 metres for a fixed-focus camera), its image is $\frac{1}{100}f$ beyond the photographic film. Instead of giving a point image on the film, the rays are spread over a small circular patch. In this case the patch is so small that it scarcely differs from a point, and the image appears in focus (Fig. 28.1).

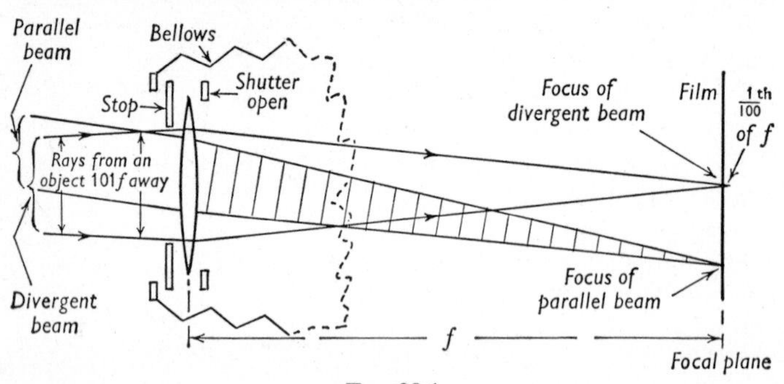

FIG. 28.1

Action of a fixed-focus camera

In the focusing type of camera, the lens is movable so that the image-distance may be adjusted to suit the corresponding object-distance.

The exposure-time is affected by the brightness of the image, which depends on the amount of light passing through the lens. This depends on the area of the stop used. Stops are quoted as $f/8$, $f/16$, etc., where $f/8$ means that the diameter of the stop is one-eighth of the focal length of the lens. Reducing the diameter of the stop from $f/8$ to $f/16$ means halving the diameter, and this gives a quarter of the area. So the exposure at $f/16$ must be four times that at $f/8$.

Lens-combinations with apertures as large as $f/1$ or $f/2$ are sometimes used for cine and television cameras, where light-collecting power is of great importance.

28.2. The eye. In some respects the human eye is like a miniature camera (Fig. 28.2). The inside of the eye is black, and a lens-system

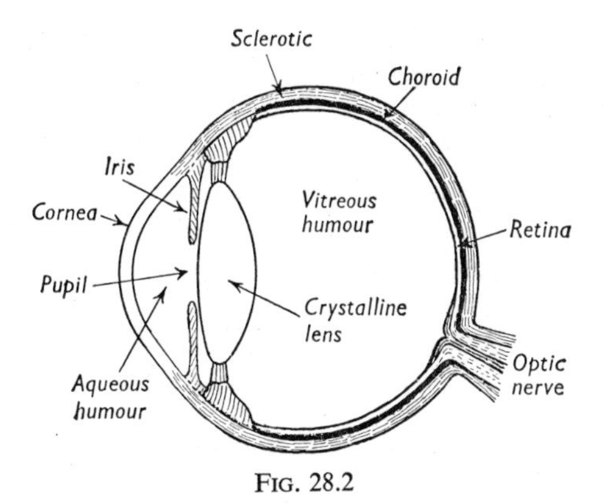

FIG. 28.2

Horizontal section of the human (right) eye

with an adjustable stop forms a very small inverted real image on a light-sensitive tissue. In this tissue, called the **retina,** is a network of nerves lining the sides and back of the eye, which leads away as a nerve-bundle—the **optic nerve.** The nerve passes through a hole on the nose side of the bony eye-socket, and leads to the brain. The outer covering of the eye is a tough opaque white tissue called the **sclerotic**—the 'white' of the eye. It bulges at the front, and is also transparent there; this part is called the **cornea.** Between the sclerotic and the retina is a black layer of cells called the **choroid,** which absorbs stray light and forms a background to the transparent retina. Near the front of the eye is the **crystalline lens,** of jelly-like substance, held in place by ligaments, and altered in curvature by a ring-shaped **ciliary muscle.** In front of the lens is the **iris**—the coloured part of the eye—which has a self-adjusting hole, the **pupil,** at its centre. The pupil contracts or widens to suit the brightness of the light.

In front of the lens is a chamber filled with a fluid called the **aqueous humour,** and behind it in the ball of the eye is a jelly-like substance known as the **vitreous humour.**

The cornea, the humours and the lens refract the light and focus it on the retina. Most of the refraction takes place as the light enters the cornea.

The eye in its relaxed state is focused 'on infinity', i.e. it is ready to focus light from a distant object. Focusing of light from nearer objects is done by the ciliary muscle, which increases the curvature of the lens, thus shortening its focal length. This control is known as **accommodation.** Most people can accommodate from infinity (the normal **far point**) to a point 25 cm from the eye (the standard **near point**). Young people have the near point closer to the eye than 25 cm. The power of accommodation decreases with age.

28.3. Defects of vision. Spectacles. Fig. 28.3 illustrates defects which may occur in the eye; the defects can be corrected by the

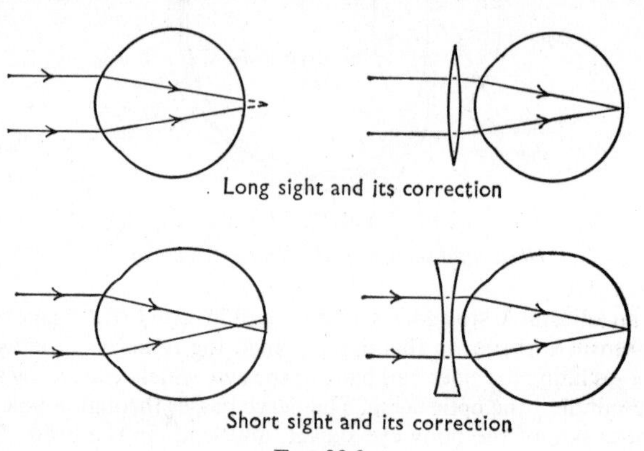

FIG. 28.3
Defects of vision

use of suitable spectacles, or by contact lenses which fit close against the cornea.

Short sight (*myopia*). The focus point for parallel light falls short of the retina; the far point is short of infinity, and the near point is closer to the eye than usual. This means that the optical system is too powerful for the length of the eyeball. It can be corrected by the use of a lens of negative power, i.e. a diverging lens.

Long sight (*hypermetropia*). The focus point for parallel light is beyond the retina. Distant objects are seen clearly only by using the power of accommodation; the near point is often more than 25 cm from the eye. This means that the optical system is not sufficiently powerful. It can be corrected by the use of a lens of positive power, i.e. a converging lens.

Loss of accommodation. With increasing age the far point usually approaches the eye and the near point recedes. This can only be overcome by two pairs of spectacles, one for distant and one for near objects. Sometimes bifocal lenses are used; they consist of two lenses cemented together, the top and bottom parts having different powers.

28.4. Persistence of vision. Binocular vision. For a short time the brain retains the impression of things seen by eye. If you look at a card which is set spinning about a central axis, both sides of the card can apparently be seen at the same time; you can test this by having different pictures on opposite sides of the card. It is this persistence of vision which gives cinema pictures the impression of steady motion, though what is projected on the screen is a series of pictures, each slightly different. The picture on a television screen is formed from a rapidly moving spot of light; persistence of vision enables the viewer to see the picture as a whole.

Sight with two eyes, or binocular vision, gives the brain the sense of depth in a scene. The two separate images, one formed on each retina, are not quite identical since they are formed from different viewpoints. But the brain manages to combine the effects of the two to give a three-dimensional picture. One way of getting this effect with the flat pictures on a cinema screen has been to project two pictures at once; viewers are provided with spectacles which transmit the light from one picture to the left eye and from the other picture to the right eye.

28.5. Simple microscope or magnifying glass. The action of a convex lens as a magnifying glass is illustrated in the fourth diagram of Fig. 27.4. An object placed at or just less than the focal length from the lens gives a virtual magnified image. The main purpose of a magnifying glass is to help your eye to view objects at very close range. The shorter the focal length of the lens, the nearer the object can be; if you try out lenses of different focal length, you will find that the shorter-focus ones are the more effective magnifiers.

28.6. Projection apparatus. In lantern projectors a convex lens is used at a distance slightly greater than its focal length from the object, to form a magnified real image on a screen. The converging lens-systems of optical lanterns, episcopes, film-strip and cine projectors, and photographic enlargers act in this way (see the third diagram of Fig. 27.4). To get a bright image a lamp-house is used

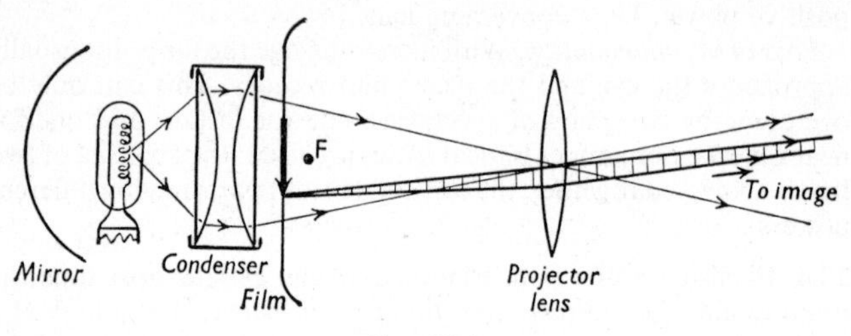

FIG. 28.4

A projector system

to illuminate the object, as in Fig. 28.4. Large-diameter convex lenses, an arrangement known as a **condenser,** are used to concentrate the light from the lamp through the object to light it up brightly. This convergent beam of light is arranged to go through

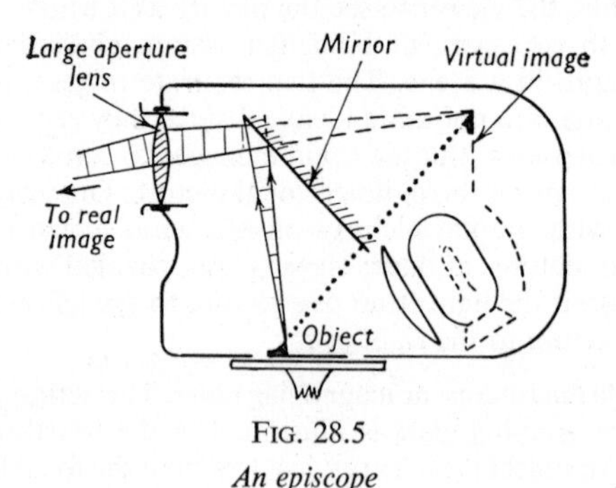

FIG. 28.5

An episcope

the centre of the projector lens so that it cannot form an image of the lamp on the screen.

In an **episcope** (Fig. 28.5), used for projecting images of opaque

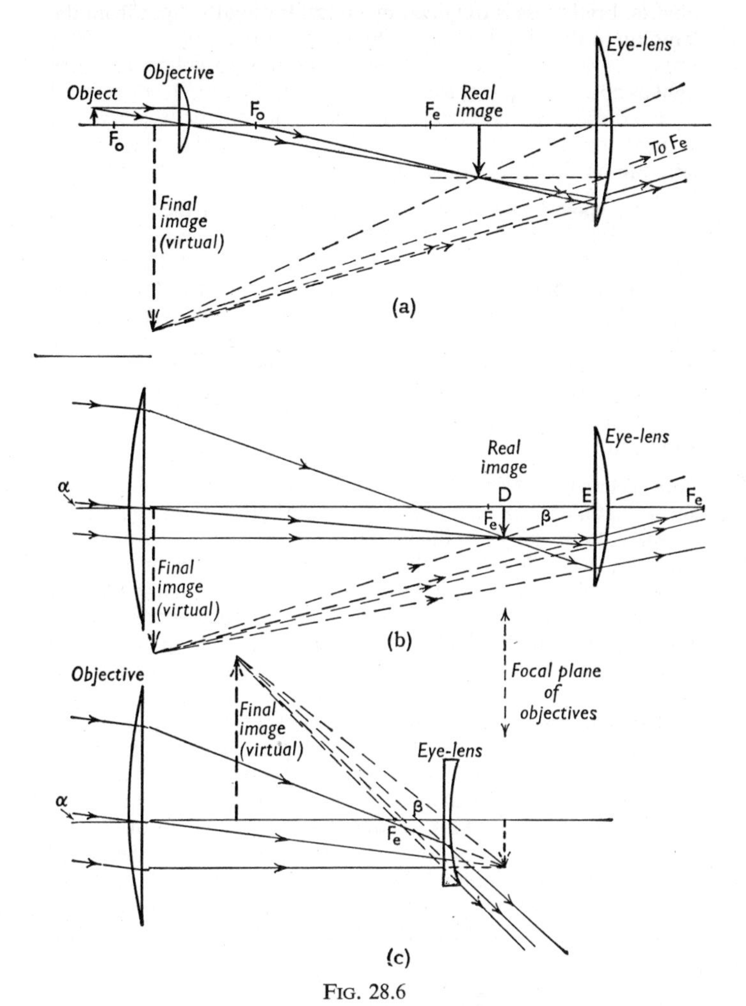

FIG. 28.6

(a) Compound microscope. (b) Astronomical telescope. (c) Opera glass. F_o and F_e represent the principal foci, or focal points, of the objective and eye-lens respectively

objects, brightness is obtained by concentrating the light from the lamp on to the object with a system of mirrors or condensers. The projection-lens is made with a wide aperture to collect as much light as possible. Most episcopes have a plane mirror, front-silvered to avoid multiple reflections. The use of the mirror means that a vertical image can be obtained from a horizontal object; and lettering on the object appears the right way round on the image.

28.7. Compound microscope. In its simplest form the compound microscope consists of two short-focus converging lenses separated by a distance of about 10 cm. They are known as **objective** and **eye-lens;** the objective is often a compound lens, and the eye-lens is usually a combination of lenses known as an **eyepiece.** The objective acts similarly to the lens of a projection-lantern, forming a real magnified image of the object. The eye-lens acts as a simple magnifying glass, giving the observer a closer view of the image than would be obtained with the naked eye. A ray diagram is shown in Fig. 28.6*a*.

28.8. Telescopes. Telescopes consist of a **converging system of long focal length,** to form an image of a distant object, and a **short-focus eyepiece,** to magnify this image. They are classified as refractors or reflectors according to whether the objective is a lens or a mirror. The image formed by the objective is always much smaller than the object, but because it is viewed at close range the apparent size of the image (the angle which it subtends at the eye) is greater. Note for instance, in Fig. 28.6*b* and *c*, that the angle β is greater than the angle α.

Astronomical refractor (*Kepler telescope*). This consists of a long-focus convex lens with a short-focus eye-lens. In simple forms the lenses are plano-convex, situated as shown in Fig. 28.6*b*. This diagram shows the telescope in *near-point* adjustment. In *normal adjustment* the distance DE is equal to the focal length of the eye-lens. The rays then come out parallel to each other, and the virtual image is formed 'at infinity'. The eye is then in a relaxed condition, suited to long periods of viewing without eyestrain. The image is inverted, but this is not a serious disadvantage when observing the sun, moon or planets.

Opera glass (*Galileo telescope*). This is a low-power telescope in which a concave eye-lens is used to catch the rays from the objective before they are brought to a focus. Fig. 28.6*c* illustrates its action for near-point adjustment. The image is erect, which is convenient; but much light is lost because the rays turn away from the axis on leaving the eye-lens, and the instrument is not capable of a very high magnifying power. It is, however, compact, since the separation of the lenses is approximately the difference of the focal lengths of the lenses.

Prism binoculars. These are telescopes of the Kepler type in which reflecting prisms have been introduced (Fig. 28.7). What

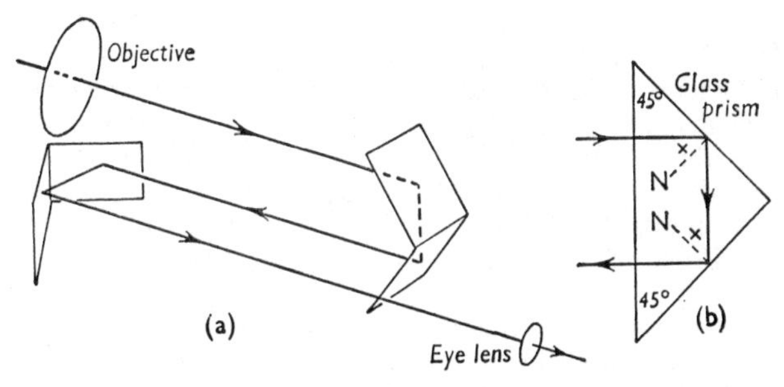

FIG. 28.7

Action of a prismatic telescope. (a) shows the reflecting surfaces of the prisms, and the course of the central ray through the instrument. (b) shows the course of the ray through one of the prisms: N, N are normals, and the angles marked with a cross are greater than the critical angle, so total internal reflection occurs

would otherwise have been an inverted image is made an erect image by the action of these prisms. One prism causes reversal of the rays in the plane of the triangle but not in a plane perpendicular to this; to turn the image the right way up and to reverse it left-to-right as well, two prisms are used. And by 'folding up' the beam of light the prisms also make the instrument much more compact for a given magnifying power.

SUMMARY

The optical systems of the eye and the camera both have a **black interior,** a **lens system** with an **adjustable aperture** which forms an inverted diminished **real image** on a **light-sensitive surface.**

Focusing is done in a camera by movement of the lens; in the human eye it is done by **accommodation** of the curvature of the crystalline lens.

Short sight is due to too short a focus. The too-powerful optical system can be weakened by a lens of negative power.

Long sight is due to too long a focus. The weak optical system can be strengthened by the use of a lens of positive power.

A convex lens can be used to give a magnified virtual image or a magnified real image. The two effects are combined in the compound microscope.

Questions

1. Describe, with the aid of a diagram, a simple type of fixed-focus camera. Explain why objects in the foreground and objects on the horizon all appear to be in focus with this type of camera.

Explain the fact that a fixed-focus camera can photograph clearly an object at a distance of 1 metre if an extra lens of focal length 1 metre is placed just in front of the camera.

2. Draw a labelled diagram of the human eye. Show in front of the eye the type of lens used to correct for short sight, and show the path of a parallel beam of light, incident on the lens, passing through the eye to the retina.

3. What is meant by the terms *long sight, short sight, accommodation*? A person has a far point at 100 metres and a near point at 10 cm. What type of spectacle lens would correct the far point? What effect, if any, would such a lens have on the near point?

4. Draw a ray diagram to show the passage of two rays, from a point P on a distant object, through a simple astronomical refracting telescope, the point P not being on the axis of the telescope.

5. Make a list of the similarities of the eye and a camera.

6. Describe the optical system of a projection lantern. Explain where the slide must be placed in relation to the projection lens in order to give a focused image on the screen. What would be the appearance on the screen, and where would you expect to find the image of the lamp, if the projection lens and the slide were removed?

7. Show by means of a labelled diagram how a converging lens and a plane mirror can be used to form a magnified image on a vertical screen of a well-lit horizontal picture.

8. You are supplied with five lenses marked A, B, C, D and E whose focal lengths in cm are as follows.

Convex lenses: A 30, B 10, C 5.
Concave lenses: D 30, E 10.

State which pairs of lenses you would select to set up (*a*) an astronomical telescope, (*b*) an opera glass or Galileo telescope, (*c*) a compound microscope. State, in each case, the lens you would use as an eye-lens and state the approximate distance between the lenses.

9. Explain, with the aid of a diagram, the action of a prism telescope.

10. Draw a ray diagram to illustrate the action of a compound microscope.

Two convex lenses are set up to act as a compound microscope and are adjusted so that they will give a magnified virtual image of a small lamp in front of the objective. Describe what will be seen on a white card which is put between the lenses and is moved from the objective to the eye-lens. What will be seen on the card if it is moved to the other side of the eye-lens?

11. Draw a ray diagram to show the action of a projection lantern in which the height of an object on the slide is 1 inch, the distance of the slide from the lens is 6 inches and the magnification =4. Deduce the focal length of the lens. (Horizontal scale = one-sixth. Vertical scale = full size.)

12. A convex lens is used to form a real image of a tower. The tower is 35 metres high, is 500 metres away and so subtends an angle of 4°. The image, 3·5 cm high, is viewed with the naked eye placed 25 cm from the image. Find (*a*) the ratio of the angle subtended at the eye by the image to the angle subtended at the lens by the object, (*b*) the focal length of the lens.

13. Explain each of the following. (*a*) The spokes of a rapidly revolving wheel cannot be seen separately by the naked eye. (*b*) The spokes of a rapidly revolving wheel seen on a cinema screen may appear stationary. (*c*) A snapshot photograph of a television screen showed only half the picture. (*d*) If you walk past a row of palings, with slots between them, you can see the distant scene almost as well as if the palings were not there. (*e*) If a person stands near some well-spaced vertical railings which are joined by a horizontal cross-bar, the railings do not obstruct the person's distant view but the cross-bar does.

CHAPTER 29

The Spectrum. Colour

29.1. The composition of white light. When a narrow beam of white light is refracted it is spread out or dispersed into colours. The resulting band of colour is known as a **spectrum;** the prominent colours in the spectrum of white light are violet, indigo, blue, green, yellow, orange and red, beginning with the most deviated colour. The effect is also to be seen in the rainbow, and in precious stones such as the diamond, where bright flashes of colour seem to have been added to the light. The colour is not really an addition to the light but is already present in it.

Fig. 29.1 shows an arrangement of prisms and a ray box for

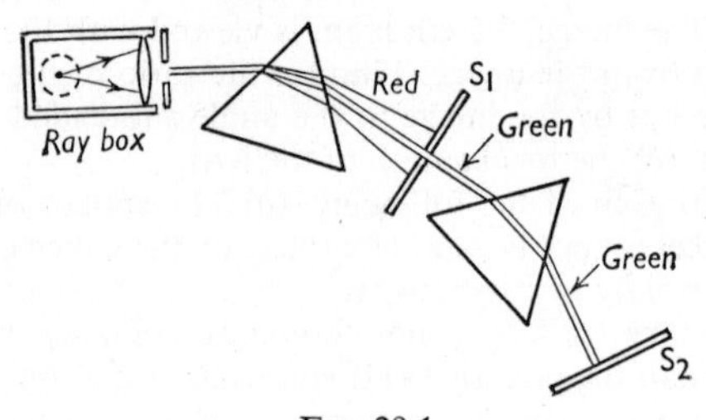

FIG. 29.1

tests on the spectrum. The first prism causes the formation of a spectrum on a screen S_1. If a narrow slot is cut in S_1 any colour from the spectrum can be made to pass through it. If another prism is put in the path of the coloured light, it is found that the light is refracted again but is not dispersed into any fresh colours. This suggests that white light has been split up into the different colours. More evidence for this comes from the fact that it is possible to make white light from coloured lights. If a concave mirror is placed at S_1 it will focus all the colours together again, and the result is white. It is also possible to combine the colours of the spectrum to form white light by painting these colours as coloured sectors on a circular disc. When the disc is spun rapidly all the colours are seen together. This gives a neutral tint—a grey which can be considered as a white of low intensity; if the disc is illuminated by a bright lamp it appears white.

29.2. The spectrum. The spectrum formed as in Fig. 29.1 is impure, owing to the overlapping of the colours. A spectrum in which the coloured images of the slit do not overlap is called a **pure spectrum.** This can be obtained by using a very narrow slit with a lens system to increase the illumination and also to focus the image of the slit. Fig. 29.2 shows one way of doing this. The Lens L_1 acts as a

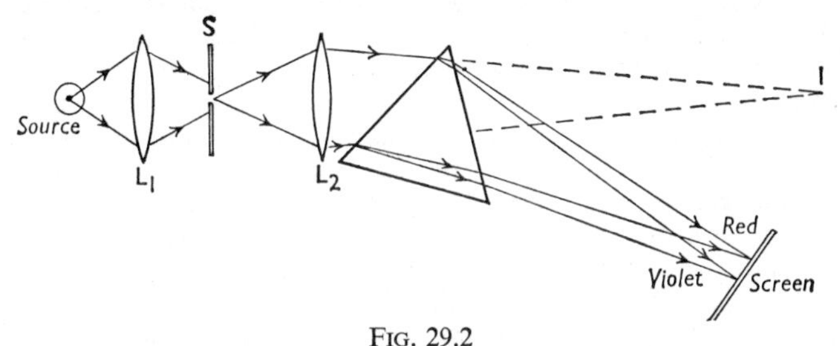

FIG. 29.2

Formation of a bright spectrum on a screen

condenser, illuminating the narrow slit. L_2 acts as a projection lens, set so that it would form a real image at I. The prism is placed to intercept the converging beam, and is turned to be in the position of minimum deviation. A screen is placed at the focus point of the colours of the spectrum. (A wide test-tube filled with water can be used as a condenser in place of L_1.)

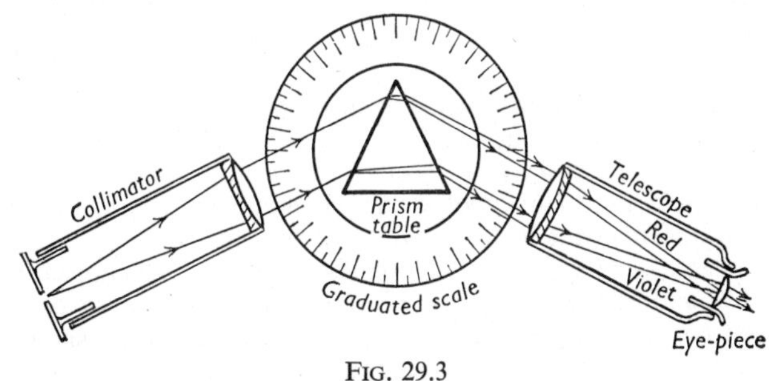

FIG. 29.3

Plan of a spectrometer

The optical system of the **spectrometer** (Fig. 29.3) gives a pure spectrum. This instrument has many applications. It can be used to analyse the light reflected or transmitted by coloured materials, the light given out by lamps, discharge tubes and flames coloured by the introduction of chemicals, and the light from the sun, stars and nebulae. In ordinary use the eyepiece of the telescope gives a virtual image of the spectrum, but by adjusting the position of the eyepiece it is possible to get a real image on a screen. For photographic work the eyepiece is removed and the film put at the focal point of the telescope lens.

Experiment 1. *The eye and a prism as a simple spectroscope.* Spectra can easily be seen with a prism held close to the eye. It is convenient to fit a cardboard tube to the prism to restrict the field of view, as shown in Pl. 25. A 60° crown-glass prism is suitable; greater dispersion is obtained with a flint-glass prism. Instead of a slit, a well-lit knitting-needle against a dark background can be used; it should be viewed from a distance of about a metre. Or a stick of blackboard chalk or a strip of white paper can be viewed from a distance of several metres.

(*a*) View the object through the prism, turning the prism if necessary to get the brightest spectrum. Observe the effect of covering the top half of the prism with a colour filter. In this way the full spectrum and the filtered spectrum can be compared.

(*b*) Try the effect of (i) illuminating the object with sodium light, (ii) using strips of coloured paper, illuminated by white light, as the object.

(*c*) View, through the prism, a *wide* strip of white paper. What you see will be the effect of many spectra overlapping each other.

(*d*) View a luminous bunsen flame through the prism. Introduce some common salt or some borax into the flame and note the change in appearance.

29.3. Infra-red and ultra-violet. The spectrum continues, beyond the red and violet ends, in the form of invisible radiations whose presence can be shown by special tests. Thus, suppose that the spectrum of the filament of a car headlamp bulb is formed by placing the filament in the position of the slit in Fig. 29.2. In a darkened room the screen will look dark, and on it will appear the bright band of the spectrum. If certain chemicals are put on the screen beyond the violet colour, the chemicals will glow showing the presence of an invisible radiation there. Quinine compounds, vaseline and motor oil, anthracene, and the mineral fluorspar all show the effect, which is known by the name **fluorescence.** A photographic film, put beyond the violet colour, behaves as if it had been exposed to visible light, i.e. it becomes black when put into a

18. *Optical effects resulting from refraction. A corner of the table-mat, viewed through the glass block, does not appear in its true position. Light from a lamp is refracted by the water in the wine-glass and is focused on the table-mat; an image of part of the mat is also to be seen by refraction through the top surface of the water. A 'bent-stick' effect is clearly visible; this is due to refraction at the curved sides of the tumbler of water. A shorter section of bent-stick is just visible at the top water-surface; this is because the apparent depth (p. 231) here is less than the real depth.* [See also pp. 245, 248, 254]

19. *Light, from a ray-box, refracted by a glass block. The photograph also shows a partial reflection of the incident light.* [pp. 243, 250]

20. *Demonstration of refraction using rays passing through a smoke-box to water, containing fluorescein to show the track of the rays. Note the partial reflection at the water-surface.* [pp. 243, 247]

21. *Deviation of light by a triangular glass prism.* [pp. 243, 250]

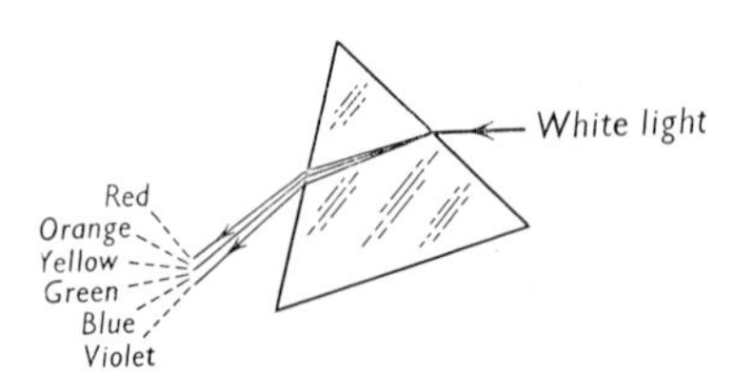

22. *The spectrum of white light.* [p. 256]

photographic developer. Another effect is the small heating effect to be detected when a blackened surface is used to absorb the radiation. The radiation which causes these effects is known as **ultra-violet radiation** and is of shorter wave-length than the colours of the spectrum.

In the region beyond the red end of the spectrum there is also some radiation. Like the ultra-violet it is invisible: it, too, gives a heating effect when absorbed; it can also affect specially sensitised photo-films and certain types of photo-electric cell. An example of its action in photography is illustrated by Pls. 26 and 27. Because of its position in the spectrum it is known as **infra-red radiation** (*infra* = below). Just as there is a great variety of colour radiation, so there is a great variety of wave-lengths of infra-red. In an elementary study of them it is usual to consider the radiation to consist of two main groups—the short-wave infra-red and the long-wave infra-red. It is the short-wave infra-red which is put to use in photography.

29.4. Types of spectra. Glowing solids and glowing liquids (e.g. molten iron) give a **continuous** spectrum, i.e. a continuous band of colour with no gaps in its range of wave-lengths. Substances in the gaseous state give out light when they are at a high temperature or when an electric discharge is passed through them. The spectra which they give are characteristic of the elements of which the gases are composed. Only a few wave-lengths are emitted as a rule; each appears in the spectroscope as a coloured image of the slit. These emission spectra are known as **line spectra** (Fig. 29.4). By studying the positions of these lines it has been possible to detect what elements are present in the stars and nebulae.

White light which has passed through coloured materials gives a spectrum in which certain bands of colour are missing. The materials have not in fact added colour to the light, they have absorbed some of it. The resulting spectra are known as **absorption spectra.** The last five diagrams of Fig. 29.4 are absorption spectra. The materials themselves are called **colour filters** because they filter or let through only certain colours of white light. Glass and gelatin colour filters have many applications in stage lighting and in photographic work.

The spectrum of sunlight is not continuous but is crossed by many dark lines. Fraunhofer mapped over 500 of them. The lines are now called **Fraunhofer lines;** the most prominent of them were labelled A to K by their discoverer (see Fig. 29.4). Kirchhoff (1824–87) put forward the theory that they are **absorption lines.**

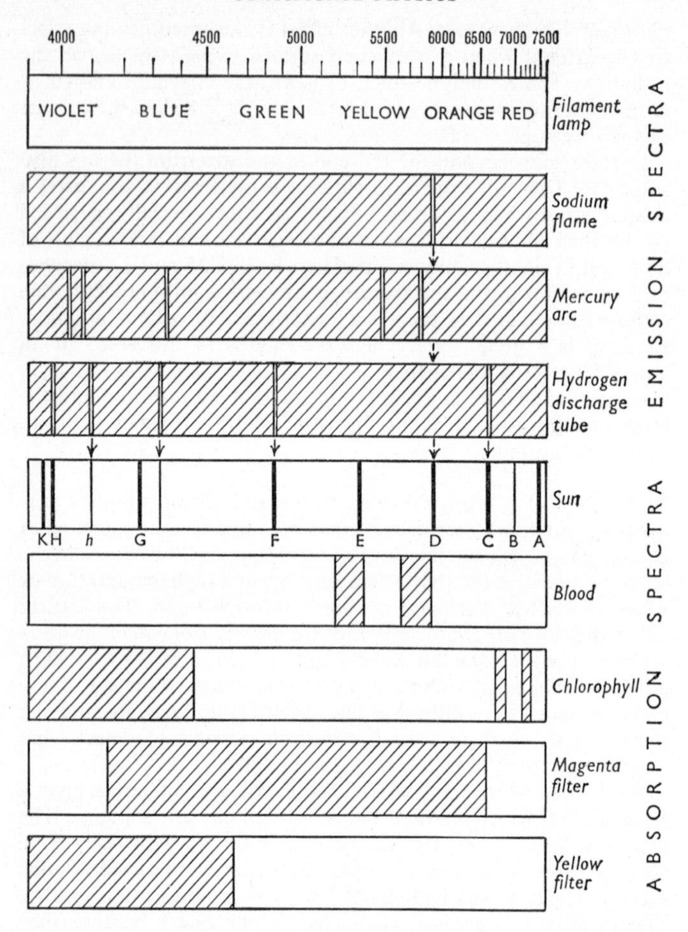

FIG. 29.4

Types of spectra. *The scale shows wave-lengths in Ångström units (Å).* 1 Å $= 10^{-8}$ *cm. In the solar spectrum, only the prominent Fraunhofer lines are shown.* C, F *and* h *are due to hydrogen,* H *and* K *to calcium, and* E *to iron, in the sun.* A *and* B *are due to absorption by oxygen in the earth's atmosphere*

Only the brightest of the lines in the mercury arc are shown, and the two violet lines are not as bright as the other three lines

He showed that if a spectrometer slit is illuminated by white light and a sodium flame put in the path of the light, then the resulting spectrum is darker where the sodium line should be. Sodium atoms can absorb the same light as they themselves emit, re-radiating in all directions the energy which would otherwise have gone straight on towards the spectrometer. Kirchhoff's theory is that the hot surface of the sun, called the *photosphere*, is surrounded by a layer of less intensely hot gases each of which absorbs the same wave-lengths as it emits. On this theory the solar spectrum is an absorption spectrum.

29.5. Colour mixing. Colour mixing can be either additive or subtractive according to whether the incident *radiations* are mixed or the coloured *materials* are mixed. The results are quite different in the two cases. Fig. 29.5 shows one of the results of projecting

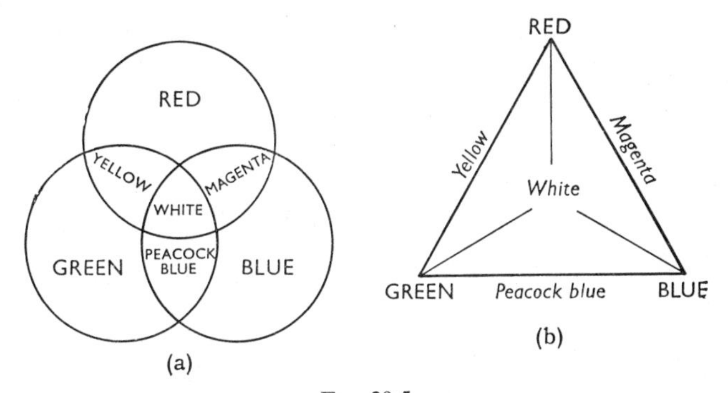

FIG. 29.5

(a) Overlapping beams of red, green and blue lights. (b) The colour triangle; the sides represent two-colour additive mixing, the centre shows three-colour mixing. A side and its opposite corner are complementary colours

three different-coloured beams of light on to a white screen so that they overlap. This is an example of additive mixing. By varying the relative brightness it has been found possible to match any colour in one of the overlapping regions. Red, green and blue are therefore called **primary colours** as far as *additive* mixing is concerned. (They are not the same as the artist's primary colours.) The two-component colours yellow, magenta and peacock-blue are known as **secondary colours.** The results are summarised in the colour triangle of Fig. 29.5*b*. Secondary colours additively mixed with the primary at the opposite corner of the triangle give white. Any two such pairs of colours are known as **complementary colours.**

Experiment 2. *Additive mixing of colour.* A simple way of colour mixing is to put a small-filament lamp in each of the sections of a box with three partitions (a cardboard shoe-box is a convenient size). Over an opening in each section is put a colour filter. This gives three overlapping beams of light, and these are allowed to fall on a white screen. A solid obstacle in front of the screen can be moved about to give a variety of coloured shadows, some lit by one colour only, some by two, whilst the background is lit by all three. Spectacular colour effects can be obtained from the overlapping shadows of a sheet of paper full of irregular holes.

Experiment 3. Paint two differently coloured semicircular patches on a circular card. Rotate the card on a gramophone turntable. This is an example of the *additive* mixing of the colours; if the two paints are themselves mixed together, *subtractive* mixing occurs and a different colour effect is obtained.

Subtractive colour mixing occurs in the mixture of paints and dyes, and in the superposition of colour filters. In general, two

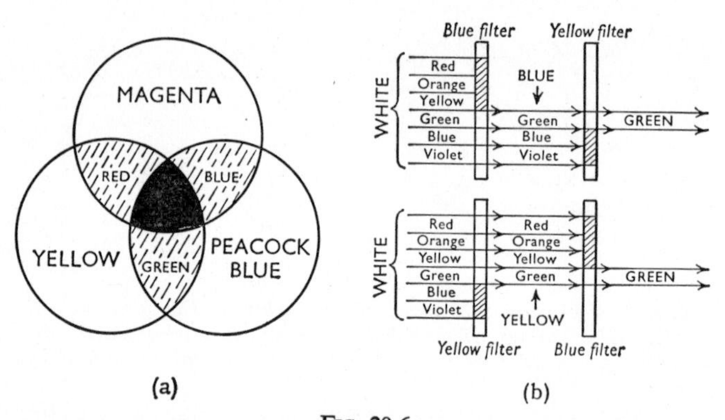

FIG. 29.6

Subtractive mixing. (a) Three overlapping secondary-colour filters. (b) Diagrammatic representation of the passage of white light through blue and yellow filters in sequence: each filter is polychromatic in this case. If the yellow had been monochromatic, no light would have passed through the combination

colour filters will transmit **only those colours which are common to the spectrum of each.** This is illustrated in Fig. 29.6*b* for some particular filters. Paints and powdered pigments follow the same rule. When mixed they reflect only the colours which are common to their two spectra.

Experiment 4. Draw two pictures, one in red and one in green. View them through red glass and then through green glass. Describe and explain the effects.

Experiment 5. View, in a darkened room, a number of coloured objects illuminated by sodium light. All will appear in different shades of yellow-grey depending on how much of the yellow light they can reflect. Their natural colours will not show.

The nature of the colour of an opaque object can be found by illuminating it with white light, and examining the spectrum of the reflected light. Alternatively the object can be held in different parts of a large spectrum. A red poppy, for example, looks red in the red part of the spectrum, but black in the others; this shows that the pigment in it absorbs all the colours except red. The colour of an object therefore depends on the nature of the light which illuminates it. In sodium light a person's face looks yellow-grey; in mercury light it looks purple and blotchy—the rosier tints are lost because there is no red in the incident light.

SUMMARY

Emission spectra

White-hot bodies:	I-R	R	O	Y	G	B	I	V	U-V
Yellow-hot bodies:	I-R	R	O	Y	G	B			
Mercury vapour lamp:				Y	G			V	U-V
Sodium flame:				Y					

Additive colour mixing is the mixing of different-coloured lights. Any colour can be obtained by suitable mixing of red, green and blue lights (known as the three **primary colours** for additive mixing).

Complementary colours are pairs of colours which add together to give white light.

Subtractive mixing occurs in the mixing of paints and pigments, and in overlapping colour filters. Mixtures of pigments **reflect only the colours which are common to the spectra of each.**

Questions

1. What is meant by a *pure spectrum*? Describe, with the aid of a diagram, how you would produce a pure spectrum of white light on a screen.

2. Describe the spectra of the light from (*a*) red-hot coke, (*b*)

white-hot iron, (*c*) a sodium flame, (*d*) an electric filament-lamp with a green glass bulb, (*e*) the sun.

3. What is meant by the term *complementary colours*? When blue and yellow paints are mixed, the resulting colour is green; but if blue and yellow beams of light fall together on a white screen the resulting illumination is white. Account for these effects.

4. A picture, on a *white* background, shows a *green* ball hanging from a *red* chain. It is viewed through (*a*) red glass, (*b*) green glass. Describe and explain the appearance of the picture in each case.

5. White light is viewed through pieces of blue and of yellow glass in contact with each other. The yellow glass transmits red, orange, yellow and green. Describe the view (*a*) if the blue glass transmits green, blue and violet, (*b*) if the blue glass transmits red, green and violet.

6. What is meant by the *dispersion* of light? An observer looking through a triangular glass prism at a magenta line on a dark background sees two lines, one red and one violet. Draw a labelled ray diagram to illustrate this, and explain the action of the prism.

7. Make a list of the different types of spectra. Give one example of each.

8. Describe experiments, one in each case, to show that (*a*) white light is composed of many colours, (*b*) when these colours are recombined, white light is formed.

9. Draw a narrow rectangle to represent the extent of a spectrum of white light. Mark one end of the rectangle with the letter R to represent the position of the red light, and then mark the positions of violet, yellow, infra-red and ultra-violet. If such a spectrum were formed on a screen in a darkened room, what experiments would you do to try to detect the presence of infra-red and ultra-violet?

10. Two pieces of yellow glass, labelled A and B, look alike; but one transmits only yellow light, the other a mixture of red and green. Describe and explain how you would identify each of the yellow pieces of glass using (*a*) a piece of pure green glass, (*b*) a sodium lamp.

CHAPTER 30

Current Electricity. Static Electricity

30.1. Electricity. Electric current. Even today we are not certain as to what electricity really is, though we know a great deal about what it does. Take, for example, the common supplies to an office or a factory—water, gas and electricity. The water we can see and feel, and hear it when in motion. Coal gas, though invisible, has a distinctive smell; and we can hear it coming out when a tap is turned on. With electricity we see only its effects. When you press a switch in an electric circuit you do not see or hear the electricity moving in the wires; you can see, hear or feel only the effects in the lamp or the vacuum cleaner or the oven which you have switched on.

The nearest we get to having electricity by itself, free from all wires, is in a television tube. Travelling from the back of the tube towards the screen is a stream of tiny electrical particles, far smaller even than atoms; these particles make patches of light when they hit the chemicals on the screen. The particles are called **electrons.** But if you were to view the back of the television tube, looking into the vacuum which is inside it, you would not see the electrons travelling across the space. The electrons themselves are quite invisible.

The turning-on of a switch is like the turning-on of a tap, and the flow of electricity in wires is somewhat similar to the flow of water in pipes. But there are several important differences. Thus the switch is a connector rather than a tap; it contains a bar of metal which connects two wires when you switch it on, and it thus completes a circuit. Electrical particles then flow right round the circuit, moving freely among the atoms of the wiring, and the particles are never lost from the circuit. We do not really use up the electricity itself; we use only the effects of its flow; a battery, or a machine of some sort, is needed to keep up the flow if we are to continue to use the effects. In this respect electricity is quite different from materials such as water and gas.

Some of the effects of electricity were first recorded over 2000 years ago, but it is only in the last hundred years or so that electricity has been put to so many practical applications. The electric battery was not discovered until about 1800; household supplies through cables were not common until after 1880. The use of electricity for railways, for radio transmission and for television has all happened since 1900. Though we are uncertain about the precise nature of electricity, it is reasonably certain that the molecules of matter are partly made up of electricity; and that when we put electricity to use we are extracting it out of matter or else driving the electricity, which is already present in the atoms of wires and cables, round a conducting circuit. To be able to use electricity we do not really have to make it; we have to make it move. And when this happens we say that we have a *current* of electricity.

30.2. Positive and negative electricity. If you rub a blown-up balloon or a strip of polythene on your sleeve it will stick to the wall of a room as though attracted to it. This is about the nearest you will get to making electricity or to 'having electricity'. The rubbing will have caused some electricity to come out of the rubber of the balloon or the material of your sleeve. When electricity is separated from matter by rubbing it, two different kinds of electricity are to be found. They are opposite in character, for they neutralise each other and give a state of no-charge. The names **positive** and **negative electricity** have been given to them. They also have the property of attracting each other. But electricity of any one kind repels electricity of the same kind. It is this property of electricity which causes it to flow freely when a conducting channel, such as a metal, is available.

The two kinds of electricity were first discovered by du Fay. He experimented with glass rubbed with silk, and rubbed resin; and he called the electrifications *vitreous* and *resinous*. *Vitreous* electricity we now call **positive** and *resinous* electricity **negative. Polythene,** ebonite and many plastics give **negative electricity** when rubbed with fabrics; but **perspex,** rubbed with dry hands, gives **positive electricity.**

When electricity is separated by rubbing, equal and opposite charges are produced. Thus when a piece of polythene is rubbed against your hand, negative particles—*electrons*—are removed from the molecules of your skin and the polythene becomes negatively charged. For a moment your hand becomes positively charged, but the human body is a conductor of electricity and electrons quickly flow in from the ground to neutralise the positive charge. If you rub polythene against a piece of metal on an insulating handle, you can detect that both the polythene and the metal become charged.

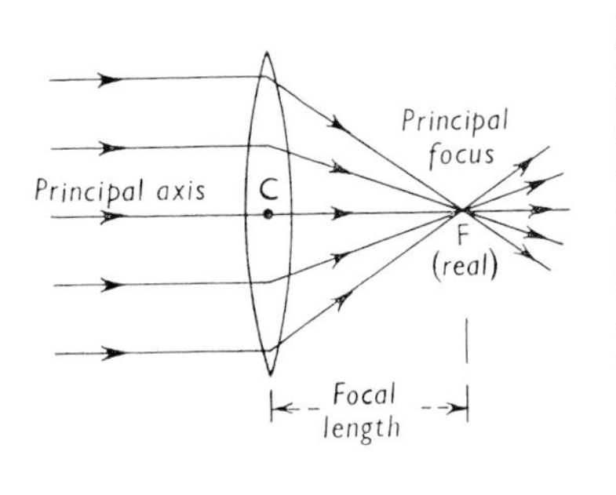

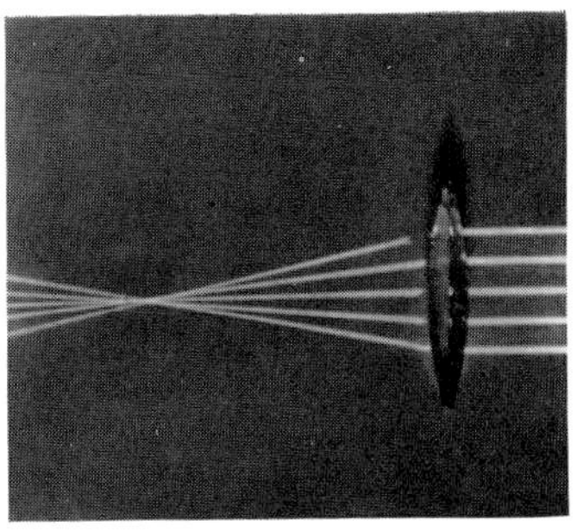

23. *Action of a converging (convex) lens.* [p. 255]

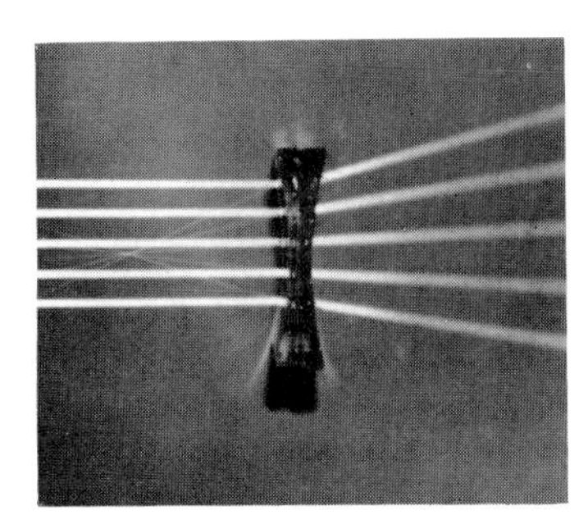

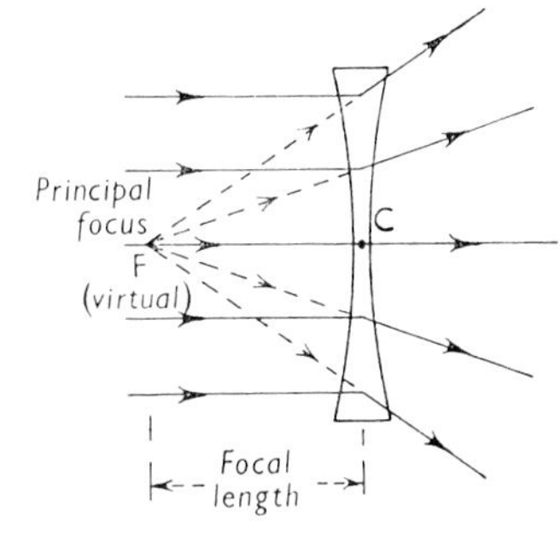

24. *Action of a diverging (concave) lens.* [p. 255]

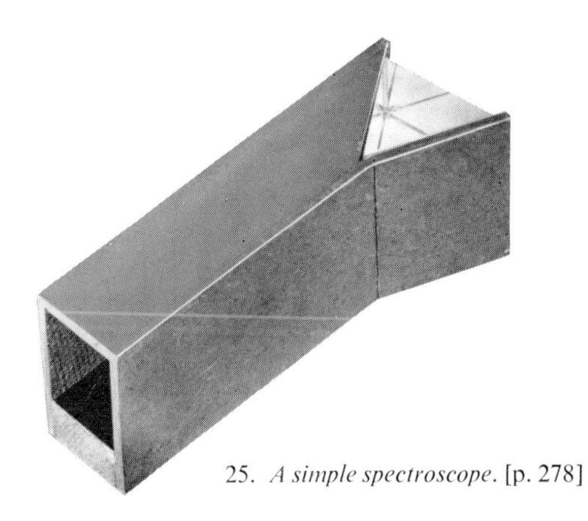

25. *A simple spectroscope.* [p. 278]

26. *Normal photograph of a river scene on a hazy day. The horizon appears to be just above the top of the bridge.* [p. 279]

27. *The same scene photographed at the same time on an infra-red plate, using an infra-red filter over the lens. It is now possible to see the lake into which the river runs and also the farther shore. Note also the prominent scattering of infra-red by the foliage of the trees and by the clouds, the strong absorption of infra-red by the water and the fairly strong absorption by part of the stone-work of the bridge.* [p. 279]

30.3. Electrical terms. Units

(i) **Current, I.** A current is a flow of electric charge. It can be a flow of negative particles (as in a television tube), or of positive particles (as in certain types of discharge tube), or a flow of both positive and negative particles (as in an electrolyte or in an ionised gas).

Whatever may be the actual sign of the moving particles, the *direction* of the current in electric circuits is assumed to be a flow of positive electricity from the positive terminal of the supply to the negative terminal. This is known as the *conventional* current, but the word conventional is usually omitted, and we simply refer to 'the current'.

Sometimes we wish to refer to the movement of the actual particles. Thus a flow of electrons is called an *electron current*, and it acts like a conventional current flowing the other way.

The unit of current is the **ampere** or **amp.** Currents are usually measured by putting an **ammeter** in the line of flow.

(ii) **Quantity or charge, Q.** When a current flows, electric charges flow past any point in the line of flow. Unit charge, the **coulomb,** is the quantity of electricity which passes any point when 1 amp flows for 1 second.

1 coulomb = 1 amp-second; $Q = It$
1 amp = 1 coulomb/second; $I = Q/t$

(iii) **Electromotive force, E. Potential, voltage, V.**

The electrical condition which can set electric charges in motion has been known by several names. At one time it was called electric tension, and we still use the terms *low-tension* (l.t.), *high-tension* (h.t.) and *extra-high-tension* (e.h.t.) with reference to electrical supplies. More common terms are electromotive force (e.m.f.), potential, potential difference (p.d.) and voltage.

The term **electromotive force** is applied to supplies of electric power, e.g. cells, dynamos, thermocouples. The term means that these things have the ability to set electricity in motion (see also p. 301).

Potential, a word meaning *ability*, is used in connection with the electrical condition of a point in an electrical system; and the term **potential difference (p.d.)** is used to indicate a difference of electric-tension between two points. This is often called the **voltage** between the two points because it is measured in **volts.** A higher p.d. increases the current flowing in a given conductor; it also demands more energy to send a coulomb through the conductor.

Voltages are generally measured with a **voltmeter,** the terminals of which are connected to the two points whose p.d. is to be measured. Voltmeters are not connected in the line of flow as ammeters are; they are connected in parallel with the direction of flow.

(iv) **Capacitance, C.** Insulated conductors have the capacity to retain an electric charge; the charge they can hold is proportional to the voltage to which they are charged. The unit for measuring their capacitance is the **farad.** A system which retains a quantity of 1 coulomb when charged to 1 volt has a capacitance of 1 farad. This is a very large system; the capacitor (condenser) components of a radio set are only a few microfarads or thousandths of a microfarad according to their uses in the set.

If you were to stand on an insulating stool, and become charged by connection to a 1000-V supply, your body would carry a charge of only about a millionth of a coulomb

$$C = Q/V;\ Q = CV$$

30.4. The gold-leaf electroscope. The gold-leaf electroscope is a type of voltmeter, but it is not a sensitive one and needs a hundred volts or so to work it. But it requires very little electric charge to deflect the leaf and it is commonly used in the study of electric charges.

The instrument consists of a box with glass windows and containing an insulated metal plate from the side of which hangs a narrow strip of gold leaf. The plate is connected to a metal disc or cap outside the case (Fig. 30.1). The sides of the case are usually of metal, fitted with a terminal to enable the case to be earthed; for most purposes the instrument is sufficiently well earthed merely by standing it on the bench. If one of the windows is covered with tracing paper, a small lamp on the other side can be used to cast a shadow of the leaf on the screen. The arrangement is known as a shadow electroscope; a scale can be marked out on the screen to measure the deflection of the leaf.

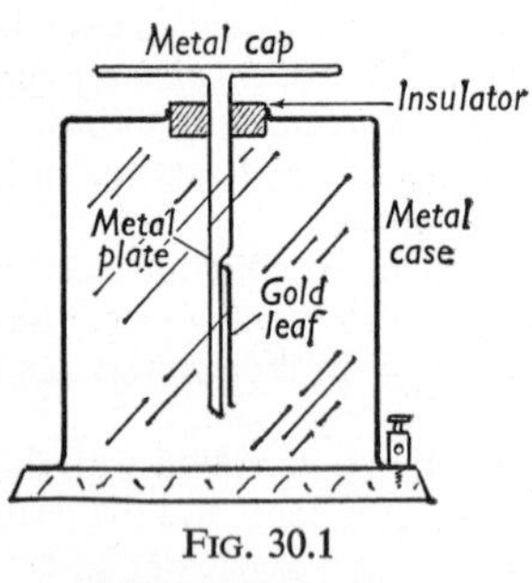

FIG. 30.1
Gold-leaf electroscope

In some types of electroscope a vertical metal plate, attached to a rod passing through the side opposite the leaf, can be adjusted to be near the leaf to increase the sensitivity. In some experiments this plate is used to discharge the instrument when it has acquired a definite charge (see pp. 431, 441).

Aluminium leaf can be used instead of gold leaf, but the instrument is not then so sensitive. Aluminium leaf is easier to handle than gold leaf, and is sufficiently strong to allow a fine glass fibre to be stuck to it for use as a pointer.

When the insulated system of the electroscope is given a charge of electricity, the leaf becomes deflected. The charge spreads over the plate and leaf, and repulsion occurs between the charged plate and the charged leaf. The following is a list of the uses of the electroscope.

(i) Detection of the sign of an electric charge, i.e. whether positive or negative.

(ii) Testing the quality of an insulator.

(iii) Comparison of the sizes of quantities of electricity.

(iv) Measurement of voltages; it is an electrostatic voltmeter.

(v) Measurement of the ionisation current caused by radioactivity, or X-rays, or cosmic rays. Air is not normally conducting. The formation of charged particles, or **ions,** in the air makes it able to conduct, and the air is then said to be **ionised.** An electroscope slowly loses its charge in ionised air, and the rate of loss of charge, or **ionisation current,** is a measure of the activity of whatever caused the ionisation.

The deflection of a charged electroscope is affected by bringing earthed objects near the cap; they cause a change in the *capacitance* of the system (see pp. 293, 294). It is therefore advisable to have the observer's hands well away from the cap when experimenting on electric charges; the electroscope can only be used for comparing charges when the capacitance of the system remains unchanged. The electroscope is really an indicator of potential or voltage; a deflection of about 45° usually results from a potential difference between leaf and case of 400 volts. In such circumstances an electroscope with a capacitance of 10^{-10} farad holds a charge of 400×10^{-10} coulomb.

An electroscope can be charged in the following ways.

(i) *By rubbing.* Flicking the cap of the electroscope with fabric gives the electroscope a negative charge. This can be shown by bringing rubbed polythene (negative) near the electroscope; this results in a greater deflection of the leaf if the electroscope is negatively charged.

(ii) *By conduction.* A piece of metal on an insulating handle can be charged by rubbing it. When the metal is touched against the cap of the electroscope, part of the charge on the metal is conducted to the electroscope.

(iii) *By induction.* A charged body is brought near the electroscope, which is then earthed for a moment by touching it with your hand. When the charged body is removed, the electroscope is charged with the **opposite** kind of charge to that on the charged body. Fig. 30.2 shows how this happens.

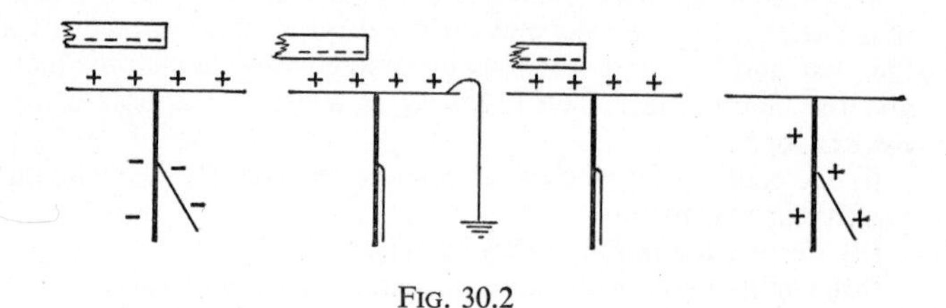

FIG. 30.2

Charging an electroscope by induction

(iv) *From a high-voltage supply.* Figs. 30.3 and 30.5 illustrate this method. Using a high-tension battery, the electroscope becomes charged at once. Using a gas-filled lamp connected to the main supply, the charging is slower. The hot filament gives off electric particles, called **ions**; the effect is known as the **thermionic effect.** The charged particles travel to the surface of the glass and give it a charge. The glass is a very bad conductor, and so the charge is only slowly conducted to the electroscope.

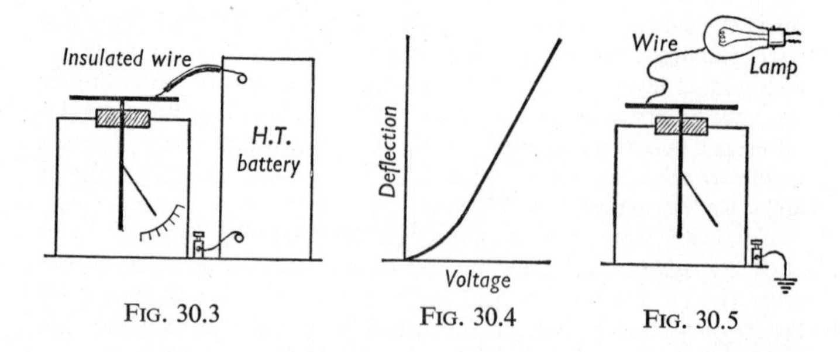

FIG. 30.3 FIG. 30.4 FIG. 30.5

The charging of an electroscope from a battery is part of the evidence that 'battery electricity' and 'frictional electricity' are the same. By using a set of batteries of known voltage, it is possible to calibrate an electroscope; a typical set of results is shown graphically in Fig. 30.4. A shadow electroscope, fitted with a volt-scale, can be used as an electrostatic voltmeter; but it is not suitable for low-voltage measurements.

30.5. The discharge of electricity. Charged conductors can be discharged quickly by earthing them. A charged insulator cannot be treated in this way; the insulator keeps its charge. The rubber tyres of cars and lorries can get to a high voltage in dry weather owing to road friction. To prevent people from getting a shock, manufacturers add some carbon (a conductor) to the rubber to allow the charge to leak away to earth. Charged insulators in the laboratory can be discharged simply and rapidly merely by passing them over the top of a bunsen flame or a candle flame. The molecules in the gases above a flame are electrically charged. The charged molecules are known as **ions,** and the gas is said to be **ionised.** The charged insulator attracts to it the ions of opposite sign, and so it quickly becomes completely discharged.

Pointed conductors will also act as discharging agents. The voltage around a charged point falls off very abruptly and the stress caused by this makes the surrounding air ionised and therefore conducting. The effect has been made use of in lightning conductors and in the collecting combs of some electrical machines.

30.6. Equal and opposite charges produced by friction. Electrification by rubbing always produces opposite charges. In the ordinary way, one of the two kinds of electricity escapes to earth. In the experiment illustrated in Fig. 30.6, this escape is prevented. A

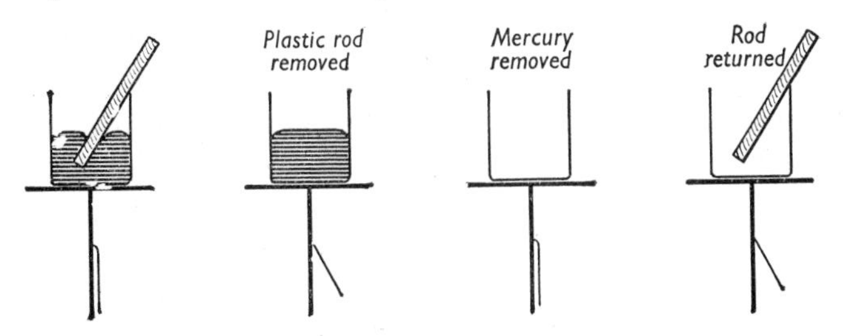

FIG. 30.6

Friction produces equal and opposite charges

plastic rod is put into a tall can containing dry mercury (or dry metal filings) standing on an electroscope. The rod is stirred round in the metal, but there is no sign of any charge being produced. The fact that charges are there is shown when the plastic rod is removed, the electroscope being deflected. When the electroscope is discharged and the rod returned inside the can, an equal deflection is obtained, showing that both metal and rod have had equal charges.

The idea of using a tall can in this experiment is to make sure that any charge formed inside the can is fully registered by the electroscope; equal deflections are not obtained if the charged rod is brought back to the outside of the can. The use of a hollow nearly-closed conductor to show all of the charge within it was first demonstrated by Faraday.

This experiment illustrates the following facts about electrification by friction.

Equal and opposite charges are produced by rubbing.
Equal and opposite charges of electricity neutralise each other.

30.7. Capacitors, condensers. Capacitance. The capacitances of hollow metal vessels can be compared by adding a number of small equal charges to the inside of them until they reach the same voltage. (Faraday found that charges put inside a hollow conductor go entirely to the outside of the conductor.)

Fig. 30.7 shows how this is done. Drops of water (or of mercury)

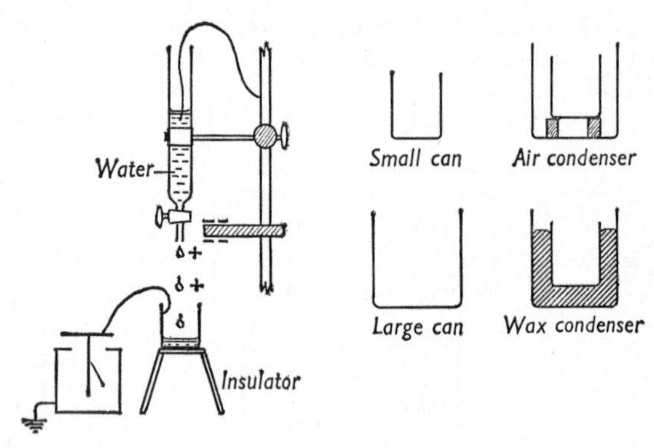

FIG. 30.7
A water-dropper used to test capacitance

are given equal charges by the action of a negatively charged polythene rod placed near the jet of the burette which delivers the drops. This attracts positive electricity into the drops and drives negative electricity away through the wire connected to the metal retort stand. The process is known as **electrostatic induction.**

The drops are counted, as they fall into the can, until the leaf of the electroscope reaches some fixed mark on its scale. The experiment is repeated with a larger can and also with cans which are surrounded by an earthed can (so forming a condenser).

Specimen results

Small can	30	Small can in earthed can (air condenser)	180
Large can	65	Wax condenser	610

The results show that different conducting systems need differing amounts of charge to bring them to the same potential. Each of the systems is known as a **capacitor** system, since it has the capacity for storing electricity. The **capacitance,** C, of a capacitor is defined as the quotient Q/V, where Q is the charge given to the capacitor and V is the resulting potential difference.

$$C = Q/V \text{ or } Q = CV$$

If Q is in coulombs and V in volts, C is in farads; so 1 farad can hold 1 coulomb at a potential of 1 volt.

An insulated conductor with an earthed conductor nearby is known as a condenser. The capacitance of a condenser depends on the area of the plates, their separation and the nature of the insulating medium or *dielectric* between them. This can be shown with the apparatus of Fig. 30.8. A metal plate P is laid on the cap of an electroscope which is then given a charge. An earthed plate E is then moved in the direction shown by the arrow and it is found that there is a steady fall in the deflection of the leaf. This means that more charge would have to be added to P to bring the deflection (and therefore the potential) back to its former value. Removal of E shows that no charge has been lost by the system. Therefore the capacitance of the system has increased with the area of overlap of the two plates.

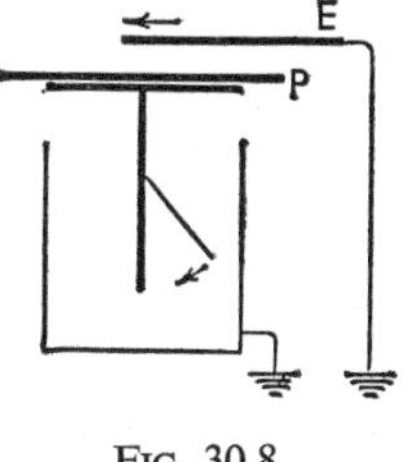

FIG. 30.8

If E is moved nearer to P a further decrease of deflection shows further increase of capacitance. And if a dry uncharged slab of wax or perspex is put between P and E, the leaf falls still further, but its position is restored when the slab is removed.

In these experiments there is no loss of charge from the system, i.e. Q is constant. Since $Q = CV$, a fall in the value of V denotes an increase in the value of C.

A person's hand brought near the cap of a charged electroscope causes a decrease of deflection, the hand acts as an earthed conductor. This is known as the **hand capacitance effect.** In making experiments in electrostatics it is important to guard against this effect.

30.8. The structure and uses of condensers. One of the earliest forms of condenser was the Leyden jar (Fig. 30.9) first discovered in 1745. In its early form it was merely a bottle of water fitted with a dry cork carrying a nail dipping into the water. If held in the hand it was capable of giving a person a shock, after sparks from an electrical machine had been passed to the nail. The water acts as one plate of a condenser, the hand as the earthed plate. Larger capacitance and better insulation resulted from coating the inside and outside of the jar with metal foil. Nowadays the jar itself is made of polythene. The capacitance of the 'pint' size is approximately 0·001 microfarad (μF). Charged to, say, 30,000 V from a spark machine it holds about 30 microcoulombs, enough to cause a serious shock if discharged through a person. If it is necessary to discharge such a highly charged jar, discharging tongs should be used.

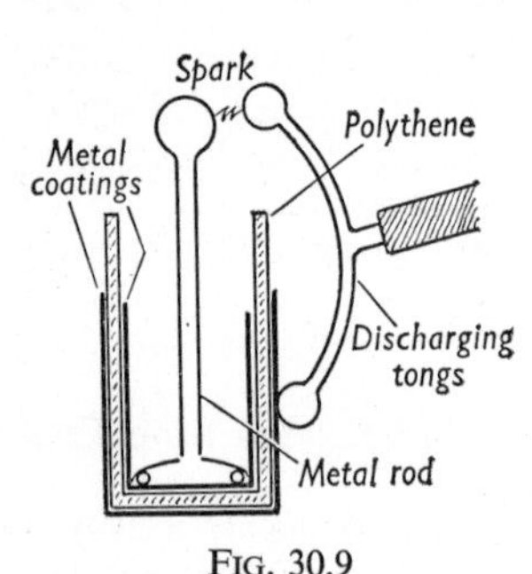

FIG. 30.9
A Leyden jar being discharged

Condensers, both fixed and variable, have important uses in radio and television sets. The **variable condensers,** used for tuning a circuit to a particular wave-length, are usually air condensers (Fig. 30.10*a*). There are two interleaved sets of plates, the two sets being insulated from each other. The capacitance can be varied by turning the control knob so as to alter the area of overlap of the plates.

Fixed condensers vary greatly in range of capacitance. Some are made of a thin strip of **mica,** silver coated. **Paper condensers** are made from long strips of waxed paper, foil coated. Two strips, arranged paper-foil-paper-foil, are put together and then rolled up; wire connections are made to the two layers of foil (Fig. 30.10*b*).

Condensers of this type range from 0·01μ F to several microfarads. The larger ones are used as storage condensers in the power-pack supplying high-tension to the valves of a radio set. Also used for

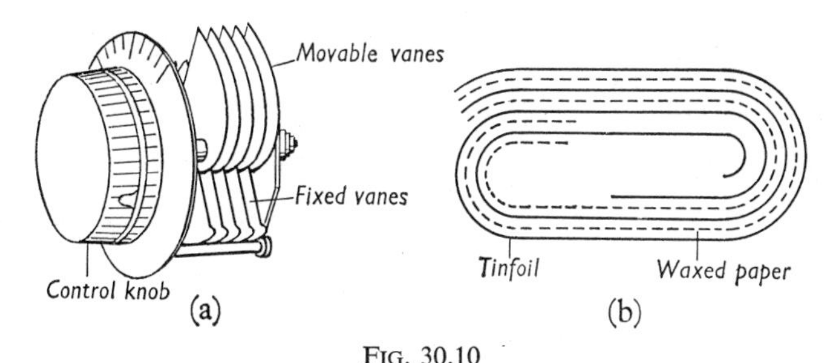

FIG. 30.10

(a) Air condenser, variable. (b) Paper condenser, fixed

the same purpose are condensers of the **electrolytic** type. In the electrolytic condenser both plates are of aluminium, separated by a solution or a paste of ammonium borate; the action is due to chemical changes which occur when a potential is applied. Unlike the other condensers, their poles act differently; they must always be connected with the terminal marked + on the positive side of the circuit.

30.9. Electrical machines. A simple induction machine is Volta's electrophorus. This consists of a slab of insulator, usually fitted with a metal base or *sole*. Quite a satisfactory one can be made by pinning a sheet of polythene to a wooden baseboard. The insulator is rubbed to give it a charge, and a metal plate, usually circular, with an insulating handle, is placed on top. A large round tin-lid, with a sealing-wax or plastic handle stuck to it, does quite well. The plate is then earthed for a moment by touching it. When the plate is lifted it is found to be highly charged, sufficient to give a spark; a piece of cotton wool, placed on the plate before lifting, is violently repelled when the plate is raised. If the plate is tested with an electroscope, it is found to be charged with the opposite sign to the base. The process can be repeated many times without loss of charge from the base, which loses hardly any of its charge by contact with the plate.

The stages of charging are shown in Fig. 30.11. If you follow the set of pictures you will see that the machine does not really make electricity. It only separates the electricities which are present in the metal of the plate. The machine also shows another important aspect of electricity. The charge which is shown in the third picture

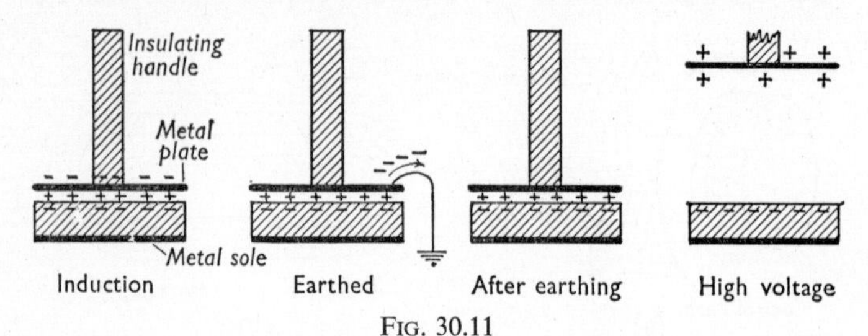

FIG. 30.11

Stages in the charging of an electrophorus

cannot be used until it is pulled away from the charge which is opposite to it. So that work is done in separating the opposite charges, and it is this work which supplies the energy of the resulting spark. Whenever electricity is put to a useful purpose, some form of energy has to be supplied.

The **van der Graaff generator** is capable of giving outputs of the order of several million volts; it has been used in atomic research

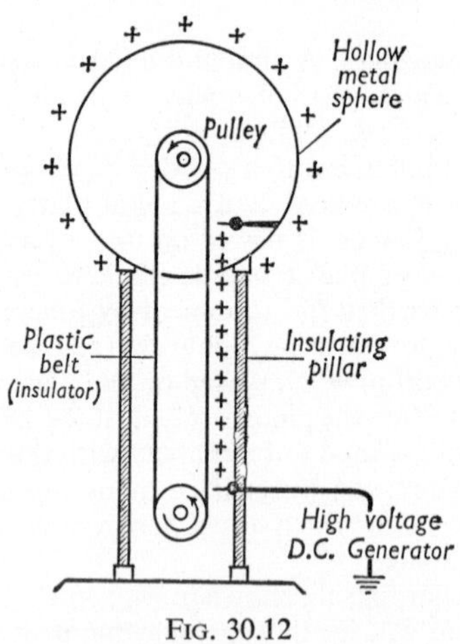

FIG. 30.12

A van der Graaff generator

to make electrical particles move at high speed. A moving endless belt of insulating material (paper, or silk or plastic) has charges 'sprayed' on it from a set of discharging points kept at about 20,000 V by a direct current generator (Fig. 30.12). The moving belt enters a large sphere to which it gives up its charge, and so in time the sphere gets to a very high voltage. Work has to be done to drive charges into the sphere against the repulsion of the charge which is already there. In the original van der Graaff generator a power of 30 hp was needed to work the machine.

SUMMARY

Electrical charges are present in all materials; they are of two kinds, **positive** and **negative.**

Equal and opposite charges of electricity neutralise each other.

Equal and opposite charges of electricity are formed by rubbing.

Equal and opposite charges are separated when electrostatic induction takes place.

An electric current is a flow of electric charge. When **positive** electricity **flows away** from a place (or if negative electricity flows towards a place), that place is said to be at a **higher potential** than the other place.

In electric circuits the *direction* of the current (i.e. the conventional current) is the direction of flow of *positive* electricity. An *electron current* is a flow of electrons (negative charges), and is equivalent to a conventional current flowing the other way.

A **gold-leaf electroscope** is an electrostatic **voltmeter,** the deflection depends on the **potential** of the system. Provided that the capacitance of the system is unchanged, the electroscope can be used to compare **charges;** comparison of charges is usually done by inserting them, in turn, inside a metal can which stands on or is connected to the electroscope.

The **capacitance** of a system is the charge needed to change the potential of it by unity. A **farad** needs a charge of 1 coulomb to change its potential by 1 volt.

$$Q=CV$$

The capacitance of an air condenser is increased by increasing the **area** of its plates, decreasing the **distance** between them, introducing a **dielectric** (insulator) between them.

Questions

1. A charged metal plate carrying a charge of 200 microcoulombs is discharged through a wire and the discharge takes

place in 10 milliseconds. Calculate the average current in the wire during the discharge.

2. Draw a labelled diagram of a gold-leaf electroscope. Describe how you would charge the electroscope (*a*) negatively, (*b*) positively.

3. How would you use an electroscope (*a*) to discover whether an insulated body were charged or not, (*b*) to discover the sign of the charge on a charged body, (*c*) to compare the insulating qualities of two materials supplied in rod form of the same diameter?

4. What is meant by the term *electrostatic induction*? Describe any one simple experiment to illustrate this. Describe any one method of charging an electroscope positively by induction. Draw diagrams to illustrate the stages of the process.

5. A stream of lead shot rolls down an earthed metal trough into an insulated metal can connected to an electroscope. Near the exit end of the trough is a negatively charged rod. Explain the fact that the electroscope shows a steadily increasing deflection as the shot pours into the can.

6. Describe the electrophorus and explain how it works. When the charged metal plate is brought near to an earthed conductor, a spark passes. Explain this, and give an explanation of the source of the energy shown in the spark.

7. Describe an experiment to show that equal and opposite charges are produced by friction.

Describe what happens to the equal and opposite charges when a moving vehicle, with insulating tyres, stops to let a person get out of the vehicle.

8. How would you use an electroscope to determine (*a*) which of two insulated charged conductors had the higher potential, (*b*) which of two small insulated charged spheres had the larger charge?

9. State the factors on which the capacitance of a condenser depends. Describe experiments to show how these factors affect the capacitance.

10. Draw a labelled diagram of a Leyden jar. Suggest a reason why the discharge knob of a Leyden jar is usually rounded, rather than flat or pointed. Explain the fact that a Leyden jar cannot be charged appreciably when it is standing on a slab of wax.

11. Calculate (*a*) the charge held by a 20 μF condenser charged to 300 V, (*b*) the p.d. required to give a 20 μF condenser a charge of 1000 microcoulombs, (*c*) the capacitance of a condenser which has a charge of 0·003 coulomb when charged to 5000 V.

12. What is an *electric current*? A stream of electrons passes from A to B, carrying a charge of 100 microcoulombs in a

thousandth of a second. What is (*a*) the magnitude of the current, (*b*) the direction of the conventional current?

13. An electrophorus is set up with the metal plate resting on the charged insulator. A very sensitive ammeter, with its zero at the centre of the scale, has one terminal earthed and the other is then joined by a wire to the metal plate of the electrophorus. Explain the fact that, at the moment of joining the wire, the ammeter registers a current. When the plate is then moved up and down several times, the pointer of the ammeter swings to and fro. Explain the cause of this.

14. An electroscope is constructed so that its leaf touches the earthed case when the deflection is 45°, the potential required to do this being 900 volts. Describe and explain the movements of the leaf in the following circumstances. (*a*) The electroscope is connected to a battery supplying 900 volts. (*b*) A charged rod is brought near to the electroscope and then removed. Consider the cases where the rod causes a deflection of (i) 30°, (ii) 45°.

15. What is meant by an *ionised gas*? Describe how you would use an electroscope to demonstrate the fact that the air around a candle flame conducts electricity.

CHAPTER 31

Sources and Effects of Current

31.1. Sources of current. The electric currents obtainable from the discharge of static electricity are small because the electric charges are small in amount. As a rule the currents do not last for more than a fraction of a second because there is nothing to keep up the flow of charge; once you have discharged an electrophorus plate, for example, you can get no more current until you have re-charged the plate.

The commonest sources of electrical power today are chemical batteries (such as car batteries and torch batteries) and rotary generators. It is a rotary generator which supplies the power-main of a house or factory. The generator itself consists of electromagnets mounted on a shaft and set spinning past insulated coils of copper wire (see Fig. 37.1). This action sets up a voltage in the coils, and this voltage is an **alternating** one; not, as in batteries, a **direct** or steady one. As the electromagnets approach the coils they tend to drive a current in one direction, and as they move away they tend to drive a current in the other direction. This is illustrated graphically in Fig. 31.1. A circuit connected to such a generator

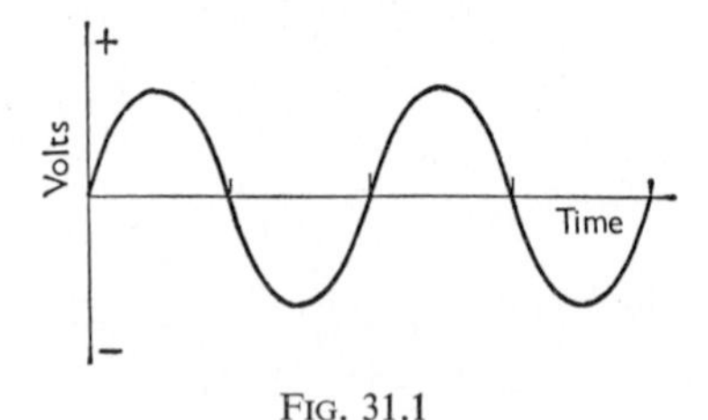

FIG. 31.1
Voltage output of an alternator

carries an **alternating current (a.c.).** A generator running at constant speed gives a supply at a definite **frequency,** depending on the rate at which the shaft is turning; most commercial supplies give the alternations at a frequency of 50 cycles/second.

One of the advantages of an a.c. main is that it is a simple matter to increase or decrease the peak voltage which it normally supplies. This is done by **transformers** (see p. 309). Some electrical appliances have power-packs inside them, e.g. radio sets, television sets, laboratory supply packs. These power-packs usually do two things; they have in them a transformer to give a variation of the supply-voltage, and they also have a rectifier to change the a.c. supply to a direct current (d.c.) supply. A **rectifier** is a device which will allow current to flow through it in one direction only. A simple type consists of plates of copper in contact with plates coated with cuprous oxide. Pl. 38 shows the components of a power-pack, and Fig. 39.8 shows the corresponding circuit diagram.

31.2. Cells and batteries. A steady flow of current can be obtained from **electric cells;** two or more such cells connected together form an **electric battery.** Electric cells were first discovered by Volta about the year 1800. A simple cell (Fig. 31.2) consists of two separate and different conductors dipping in an acid, or an alkali or a salt—usually in the form of a solution. The liquid into which they dip will be referred to as the **electrolyte** (see p. 397). It is found that one of the conductors becomes positively charged and the other negatively charged; the former is called the positive pole, the other the negative pole. When the conductors are allowed to touch or are joined by a conducting wire, electricity flows in the wire and also in the electrolyte. Such an arrangement is called an electric circuit, because electric flow can be detected all the way round it, outside the cell (the *external circuit*) and inside the cell (the *internal circuit*). In some way the poles can keep up a flow of electric charge; the discharge is not abrupt as is the discharge of an electrophorus plate. For this reason the poles are said to have an **electromotive force** or electricity-moving force. This is not a force in the mechanical sense for it cannot move uncharged matter; it can only move electrical particles. It is measured in **volts.** Energy is required to send a charge round a circuit, and a volt is defined such that an electromotive force of 1 volt needs 1 joule of energy to send 1 coulomb round a circuit.

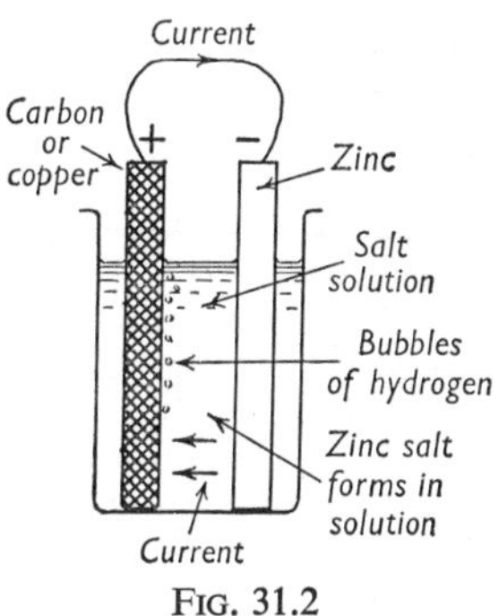

FIG. 31.2
A simple cell

Initially the poles gain their charges from the chemicals of the cell. When joined by a wire they set electricity moving in the wire and in the electrolyte; any charge which the poles themselves may lose is made up by the collection of more from the chemicals. The process is always accompanied by chemical changes, at the poles or in the electrolyte around the poles. The energy for keeping the current flowing comes from the chemical energy of these changes which, if they had occurred without the formation of a current, would have produced heat. In an electric circuit the cell itself rarely becomes hot; most of the energy appears in the external circuit, where the electric charges, moving among the molecules of the conductor, give kinetic energy to the molecules and so give them a faster oscillation which appears as heat.

When no further chemical action is possible, the current stops and the cell is said to be run-down. It is then thrown away unless the chemicals can be replaced or re-made. Re-making of the chemicals is possible in **accumulators,** where a current is sent backwards through the cell to do so. The process is called **re-charging.**

Many improvements have been made on the simple cells of Volta's time. The ones which are in common use today are the **dry cell** which is a compact form of a cell originally devised by Leclanché (Fig. 38.3), the **lead accumulator** and the **nickel-iron accumulator.**

Dry cells are compact, clean and contain no liquid; they find common use in electric torches, hearing-aid outfits, portable radio sets. Accumulators are used for the current-supply to motor cars and to telephone exchanges. The poles and electrolytes of these cells are shown in the following table. Their structure is shown in

Cell	Poles		Electrolyte
	Positive	Negative	
Leclanché	Carbon	Zinc	Sal-ammoniac (Ammonium chloride)
Accumulators	Lead dioxide	Lead	Sulphuric acid (approximately 1 vol. strong acid added to 3 vol. water)
	Nickel oxide	Iron	Caustic potash solution

28. *Magnetic poles caused by the flow of current in a coil. The thick wires in the picture were connected to a car-battery. The ends of the coil then attract iron filings.* [p. 305]

29. *A magnetised razor-blade floating on water. The blade finally settles with one of its poles towards the north. In England, the centre-line of the blade lies in a direction which is slightly west of true north.* [p. 330]

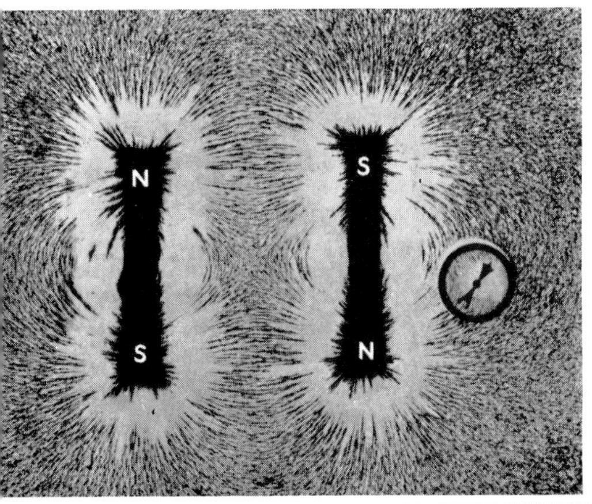

30. *The combined magnetic field of two bar magnets, placed so that they attract each other.* [p. 335]

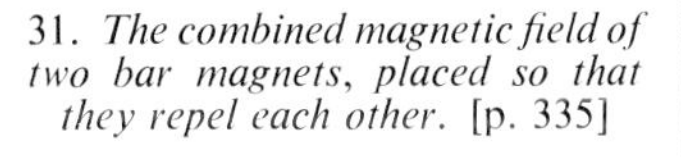

31. *The combined magnetic field of two bar magnets, placed so that they repel each other.* [p. 335]

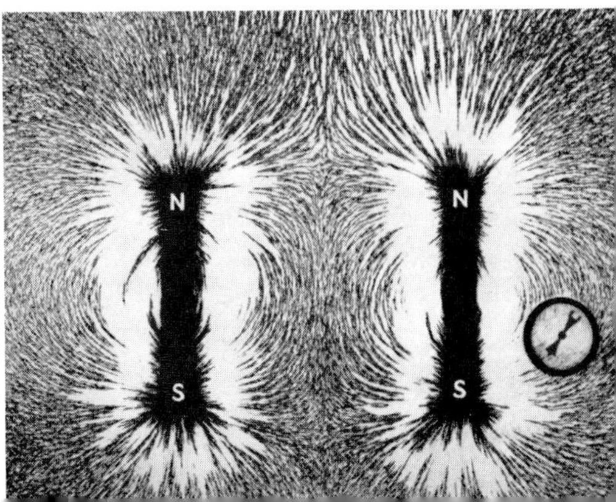

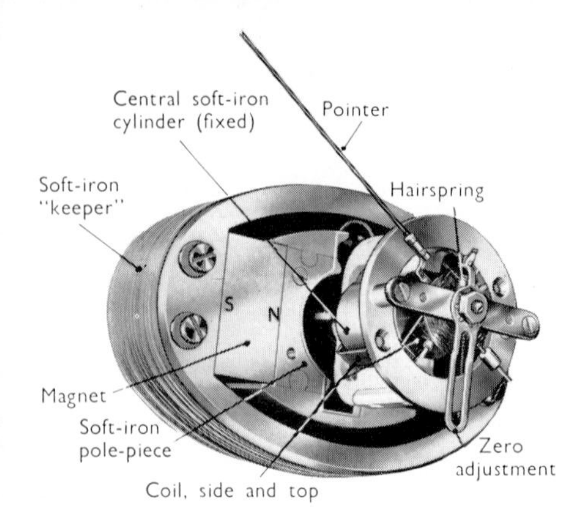

32. *The movement of a moving-coil galvanometer shown removed from the magnetic field. There is another short permanent magnet making a S-polar pole-piece, to the right of the coil assembly. Both these short magnets are made of special steel.* [pp. 337, 356]

33. *A coiled filament and a coiled-coil filament, magnified about 50 times. A human hair is shown in the picture for comparison.* [p. 376]

34. *A 60,000-kilowatt alternator being erected for test. The stator is being lowered into position; the thick copper straps which form the ends of the stator windings can be seen in the picture. The rotor has 14 poles. Installed at Aura in Norway, the machine is driven by a Pelton wheel (a horizontal water-turbine driven by a water jet). The head of water used at this site is 3,200ft.* [p. 380]

Fig. 38.3, Pl. 37; a further explanation of their action is given in Chapter 38.

31.3. Effects of an electric current

(i) **The shock effect.** Of all the effects of an electric current, its ability to give a person a shock was one of the first to be discovered. The electrical machines of the eighteenth century, and the discharges from Leyden jars, provided a certain amount of amusement in this respect. Such shocks could be taken without danger, partly because the current was small and did not last for long, and partly because the supply was direct current (d.c.). An alternating current is more dangerous, for the nerves of the body are much more affected by changes of current than by a steady one. The electrical supply in the mains to nearly all houses is an alternating one. The e.m.f. rises to over 300 volts, falls to zero and then reverses the process; this occurs 50 times per second. The resulting changes in current are very dangerous to the nervous system, and it is quite possible to be killed by electricity from the household mains. That is why household wiring systems are fitted with safety devices (p. 374) to prevent contact with the live wires of the system.

(ii) **The heating effect.** The spark which can be got from a charged electrophorus plate shows that heat is produced by the passage of electricity. A torch battery produces heat as well as light in the bulb. If a current is passed from a torch battery through a coil of thin insulated copper wire, you can feel the coil becoming warmer; by wrapping the coil round a thermometer-bulb you can show the rise in temperature (Fig. 31.3).

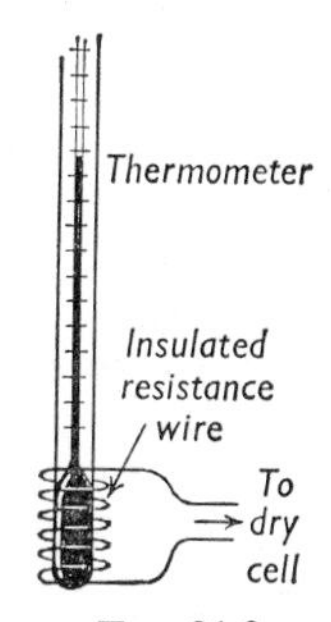

FIG. 31.3
Heat produced by an electric current

(iii) **The chemical effect.** When current passes through an electrolyte a chemical change takes place. New substances are formed at the **electrodes,** the conductors by which the electricity enters and leaves the electrolyte.

Fig. 31.4 shows the spark from a positively charged electrophorus plate passing through starch-iodide test paper which has been made damp. (The test paper is made of filter paper which has been soaked in a mixture of potassium iodide solution and starch emulsion.) If several sparks are passed through the arrangement it is found that where the current entered the paper there is a dark blue-black colour, showing a liberation of iodine from the potassium iodide. Potassium iodide consists of potassium atoms carrying a positive charge and iodine atoms carrying a negative charge. The positive electricity entering the test paper attracted the negative iodine atoms to the copper electrode, neutralised their negative charge and set free the uncharged iodine.

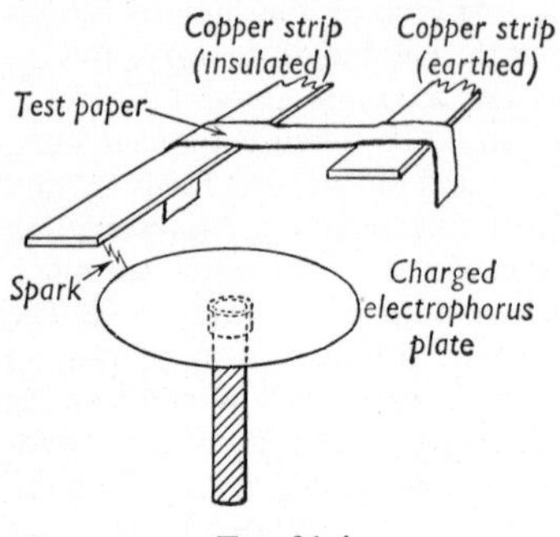

FIG. 31.4

Decomposition when electricity passes through an electrolyte

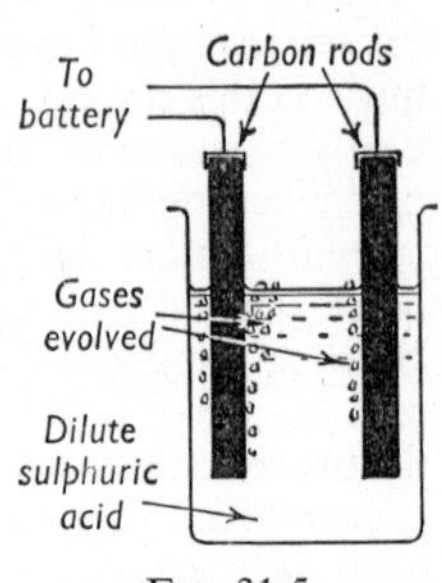

FIG. 31.5

Electrolysis of water

If wires leading from a dry cell are touched down on a strip of wet starch-iodide test paper, you will get the blue-black colour almost at once. In fact you can use the result of the test to show which of the poles of the cell is the positive. Test paper used in this way is called **pole-finding paper.**

If two carbon rods, put into dilute sulphuric acid as shown in Fig. 31.5, are connected to a d.c. supply of about 4 volts, gases are evolved around each carbon electrode. One of the gases comes off in greater volume than the other. It is inflammable, as can be shown by bringing a lighted taper up to the bubbles; this gas can be proved to be hydrogen. A glowing splint, brought near the bubbles of the other gas, glows brighter; and this gas can be proved to be oxygen. The hydrogen is found to be given off at the **cathode,** the electrode connected to the **negative** of the supply. Chemical analysis shows that in this experiment the sulphuric acid is unchanged in amount. The hydrogen and oxygen are the decomposition products of the water present; the sulphuric acid is needed only to make the liquid a better conductor—nitric acid or caustic soda could equally well have been used for this purpose.

If this experiment is done with copper sulphate solution instead of acid, evolution of gas at one of the electrodes shows that chemical decomposition or **electrolysis** is taking place. The other electrode, which is the cathode, becomes copper-plated; whenever electro-plating occurs it is found that the **metal** of the salt **seems to travel in the direction of the current,** i.e. towards the negative terminal or cathode.

If you continued the plating experiment long enough, all the copper from the copper sulphate would be deposited. In commercial plating this loss of the electrolyte is made good by using a copper plate for the electrode at which the current enters. There is then no evolution of gas at this electrode; instead, the electrode wears away and the strength of the copper sulphate stays unchanged. You can test this by reversing the current after you have deposited some copper on one of the electrodes.

(iv) **The magnetic effect.** A magnetic effect of an electric current was discovered in 1819 by Oersted, professor of physics at Copenhagen. He found that a current, passing over a compass needle and parallel to it, causes a deflection as shown in Fig. 31.6. It

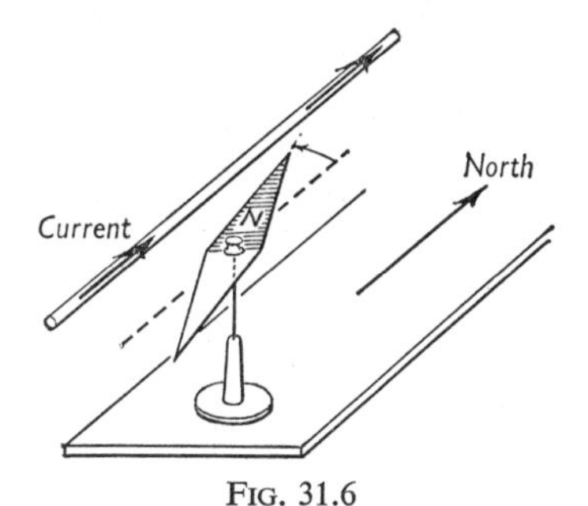

FIG. 31.6

Magnetic effect of an electric current

illustrates what may be called the 'SNOW' rule, i.e. a current flowing S.–N., *over* the needle, drives the north-seeking pole to the *West*. Reversal of the current, or putting the wire under the needle, reverses the deflection.

A coil of wire carrying a current behaves as though it were itself a magnet of the same size and shape as the coil. This is shown in Pl. 28, where a strong current in a coil causes it to attract iron filings to its ends, as a magnet would. The wire of the coil, the insulation, and the material of the tube on which the coil is wound have no magnetic properties of their own at all. It is only when the current flows that the coil behaves as a magnet. This seems to suggest that magnetism itself is really due to electric currents. One theory of magnetism assumes that in a magnet the electrons of its atoms are spinning in orbits in such a way as to produce the effect of a swirl of current round the outside edges of the magnet.

31.4. Current and charge. The ampere and the coulomb. The fact that a current in a coil acts as a magnet means that two current-carrying coils exert forces on each other, as magnets would do. The unit of current, the **ampere** or **amp,** is defined from the force that one current exerts on another under definite conditions of length and distance apart (see p. 345). Balances, called **current balances,** have been made to measure the force which one coil exerts on another; from the force and the sizes of the coils, the current can be calculated in amperes. These balances are generally used only in standardising laboratories. In the ordinary way currents are measured by sending them through instruments called ampere-meters or **ammeters.** Some of these act through the heating effect of the current (Fig. 35.8), but in most of them a pointer is caused to move over a scale by means of a magnetic effect. The scale put on by the manufacturers is checked against a current balance or against a standard ammeter.

Fig. 31.7 shows a circuit for testing an ammeter against a

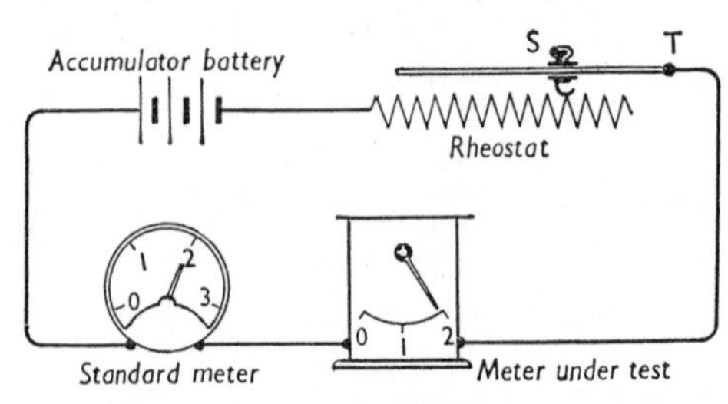

FIG. 31.7

Series circuit for testing an ammeter against a standard ammeter

standard ammeter. The standard and the ammeter under test are put together in a series circuit. The current is varied by a **rheostat,** a device for altering the resistance to the flow by adding more wire in the circuit. The order in which the meters are placed does not affect the current, nor does the position of the rheostat—it could, for instance, be put between the two meters. The rheostat controls the size of the current, weakening it if the slider is moved away from the terminal T, but it does so at all places in the circuit. **In a series circuit the current at any moment is everywhere the same.**

This fits in with the idea that a current is a flow of electric charge and that no charge is lost as it flows round the circuit. It also gives a method of defining charge or quantity of electricity. Thus if a steady current of 1 amp flows in a circuit for 1 second, a certain quantity of electricity must have flowed past each point in the circuit. This quantity is called an **amp-second** and is also known as a **coulomb.** A larger unit of charge is the **amp-hour;** since there are 3600 seconds in 1 hour, an amp-hour represents a charge of 3600 coulombs. If an accumulator is labelled 'capacity 50 amp-hours' it means that it can maintain a current of 1 amp for 50 hours, or 2 amp for 25 hours, before it needs to be re-charged.

Another way of checking the scale of an ammeter is to use an electro-plating method, but to obtain reasonable accuracy by this method requires a plating-time of half an hour or more just to check one mark on the scale. It has been found that the rate at which a metal is deposited in electro-plating is proportional to the current. Thus a steady current of one amp deposits silver from silver salts and copper from cupric salts at the rates of 1·118 mg/s and 0·3294 mg/s respectively.

Any apparatus used for measuring an electro-chemical effect is known as a **voltameter. A copper voltameter** consists of copper plates dipping into copper sulphate solution. A **silver voltameter** has silver plates and silver nitrate solution; in the standard pattern the silver is deposited on a platinum bowl instead of on a silver plate. It is on the *cathode* that the metal deposit occurs. In electro-plating experiments a certain *current density* (current per unit area) should not be exceeded, or the deposit does not adhere well. The maximum current density for copper is 0·01 amp/sq. cm. By shaping the anode so that current passes to both sides of the cathode, the effective area of the cathode is doubled. The following is a description of an experiment using a copper voltameter to calibrate an ammeter.

Experiment. Calibration of an ammeter. The anode was a sheet of copper, cut as shown in Fig. 31.8, bent to fit a rectangular vessel containing copper sulphate solution. (The solution should be strong, but not saturated; it should contain about 1 % sulphuric acid to prevent the formation of basic salts.) The copper cathode, its surface well cleaned, was held by a stand and clip between the double-anode. The voltameter was put in series with the circuit, the switch S closed and the rheostat adjusted to bring the pointer of the ammeter to the 1·10 mark. The current was allowed to flow for a few minutes to give an initial plating. Then the cathode was removed, washed with water and then with alcohol, dried over a small bunsen flame, allowed to cool, and weighed. It was then

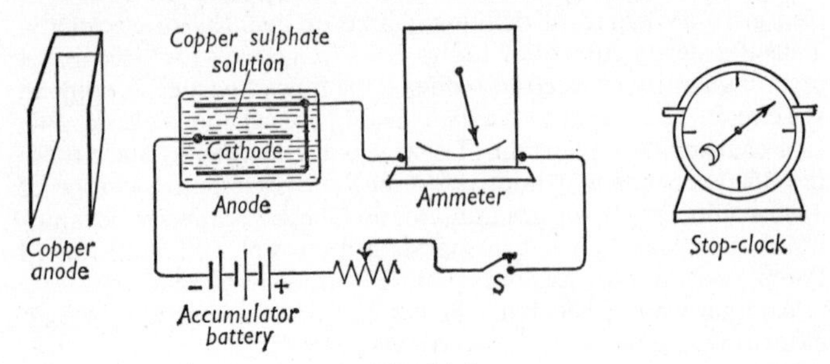

FIG. 31.8

Testing an ammeter by finding the rate at which copper is deposited by the current

replaced in the voltameter, S closed, and the stop-clock started at the same instant. The current was observed at regular intervals for about half an hour. S was then opened and the clock stopped. The cathode was removed, washed and dried as before, and reweighed to find the mass of copper deposited. (Subsequently the stop-clock was checked against a standard clock.)

Specimen results

Meter reading at five-minute intervals:

1·11, 1·11, 1·10, 1·10, 1·09, 1·09 Mean reading 1·10 A

Initial mass of cathode	25·143 g
Final mass of cathode	25·882 g
Mass of copper deposit	0·739 g
Time of current flow	33 min 20 s = 2000 s

Since

1 amp flowing for 1 s deposits 0·0003294 g copper,

I amp flowing for t s deposits 0·0003294 It g

$$\therefore\ 0{\cdot}0003294 \times I \times 2000 = 0{\cdot}739$$

whence $I = 1{\cdot}122$

True current = 1·12(2) A

Meter reading = 1·10A

Error = −0·02A

Correction = +0·02A, at the 1·1 mark

SUMMARY

Electric cells supply **direct current** (d.c.). An alternator supplies **alternating current** (a.c.); a.c. can have its voltage altered by a **transformer,** and can be converted to d.c. by a **rectifier.**

The **electromotive force** of a supply is measured in **volts.** An e.m.f. of E volts uses E joules in sending 1 coulomb round a circuit.

A current can produce a shock, produce heat, cause chemical decomposition, make a magnet.

In a series circuit the current at any moment is everywhere the same.

The accuracy of an ammeter can be checked by putting it in series with a standard ammeter, or by an electro-plating method.

Questions

1. Describe simple experiments, one in each case, to show that an electric current has (*a*) a magnetic effect, (*b*) a chemical effect, (*c*) a heating effect. How, if at all, does the time for which the current flows affect each of these effects?

Describe how you would use one of these effects to find out which of the poles of a battery is the positive pole.

2. Three ammeters A, B and C are connected in series in a circuit and register 1·2, 1·1 and 1·0 A respectively. Describe a simple experiment to show that this is not due to any real decrease of current as it flows from one meter to the other.

3. Name the materials of the positive and negative poles of (*a*) a dry cell, (*b*) a lead accumulator. State some of the uses for which each of these cells is particularly suitable, and give in each case a reason for their suitability.

4. What is meant by the marking 'capacity 40 amp-hours' on an accumulator? What weight of silver plating could be deposited by such an accumulator before it needed a re-charge? (1 amp deposits silver at the rate of 0·001118 g/s.)

5. Distinguish between a d.c. and an a.c. electrical supply. State any **one** advantage of an a.c. supply. What is the meaning of the marking 240 V 50~ on an a.c. supply?

6. A faulty ammeter is put in series with a copper voltameter. When the meter reads 1·00 A, 1·966 g of copper is deposited in the voltameter in 5000 seconds. Find the correction which must be given to the meter at the 1 A mark. (1 amp deposits copper at the rate of 0·0003294 g/s.)

7. A cell of e.m.f. 2·0 V, connected to a circuit for 10 seconds,

maintains a current of 1·2 A. Calculate (*a*) the charge sent round the circuit, (*b*) the energy required for the discharge.

8. A cell of e.m.f. 2 V and a battery of e.m.f. 4 V are joined in series to light a 6-volt lamp which takes exactly half an amp. When the lamp has been alight for 1 minute, how much charge has passed through (*a*) the cell, (*b*) the battery? Calculate the energy supplied to the circuit by (*c*) the cell, (*d*) the battery.

9. Two fully charged accumulators X and Y are marked 4 V 10 amp-hour and 2 V 30 amp-hour respectively. State, giving your reasons, which of the two will (*a*) supply the greater charge, (*b*) supply the greater amount of energy, (*c*) keep a current of 3 A flowing for the longer time.

10. A U-tube containing dilute sulphuric acid has a carbon rod in each limb. Draw a diagram to show how you could use it, with a battery of three dry cells, to obtain (*a*) a sample of hydrogen, (*b*) a sample of oxygen.

After such an experiment it is possible to show that the weight of the battery is unchanged and that the weight of the zinc casings of the battery has become less. Suggest an explanation of these facts.

If the hydrogen and oxygen are mixed and lit, there is an explosion. Where, in the electric circuit, is a possible source of the energy of the explosion?

11. A coil carrying a current of electricity can attract iron filings and it becomes warmer as the current flows. How do these facts fit the idea that there is energy in a flow of electricity?

12. Describe, with the aid of a diagram, how you would copper-plate a carbon rod. State the precautions you would take to ensure that the plating was firm and uniform.

CHAPTER 32

Power. Current and Potential. Ohm's Law. Resistance

32.1. Electrical power. Power is the rate of doing work or the rate of using energy (p. 68). To run electrical appliances, energy is fed at a certain rate or power into the supply-cables from a generator. This energy is converted into heat (in cookers), or into light and heat (in lamps), or into mechanical energy (in motors) at a rate or power which is usually printed on the appliance.

In electric circuits **power** is connected with the **current** which flows and also with the **potential difference** which drives the current; the power used depends on the product (current × p.d.). This can be illustrated by test-circuits with identical lamps, each lit to their normal brightness and so emitting energy at the same rate, i.e. they give out equal power.

Fig. 32.1 shows an accumulator lighting a pea-lamp. The ammeter in the circuit registers the current flowing, which is the same

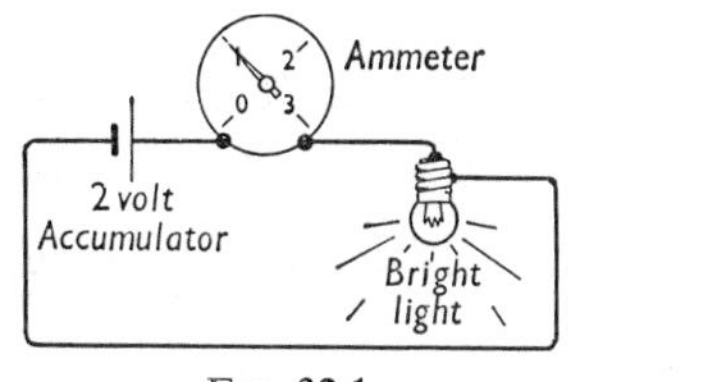

FIG. 32.1

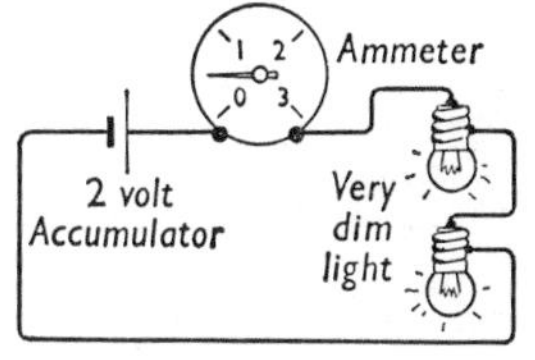

FIG. 32.2

at all points in the circuit. The lamp gives out light energy and heat energy, but it does not use up the electrical particles whose flow is indicated on the ammeter. Fig. 32.2 shows the effect of connecting two such lamps in series. The current drops, due to there being more resistance in the circuit. The power looks to be less, for the light output is very much less. There are two ways in which the brightness of the lamps can be restored so that each lamp is as powerful as before, and so that the circuit is given twice the power it had before. These are to be seen in Fig. 32.3. Double power is

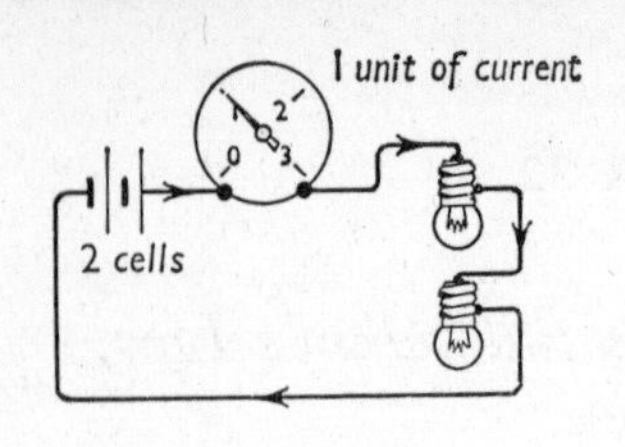

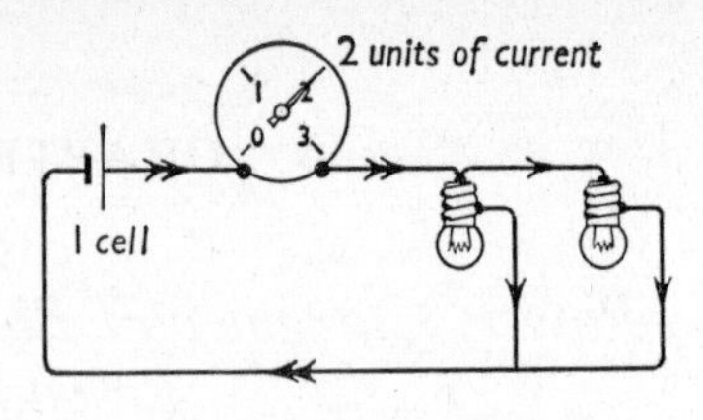

FIG. 32.3

Different ways of lighting two lamps to their normal brightness

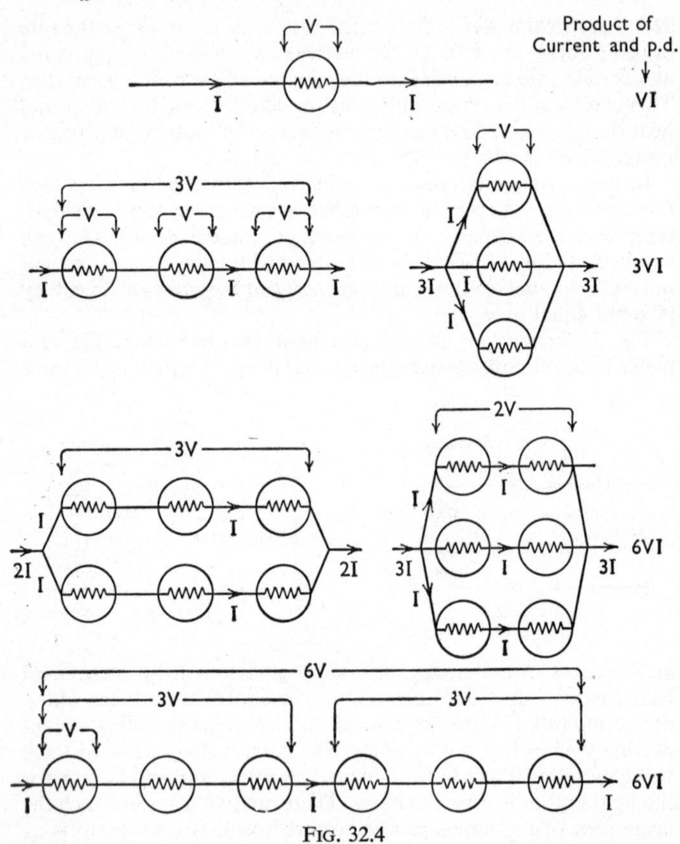

FIG. 32.4

Identical lamps, or identical heaters, connected to show that electrical power *depends on the product* VI

given by either (*a*) using two accumulators in series which gives twice the e.m.f., as explained on page 316; or (*b*) connecting the lamps in parallel and joining them to one accumulator, when the ammeter shows that the accumulator supplies twice the current it did before.

Fig. 32.4 shows different ways of connecting identical fittings, such as lamps or heaters, so that the power output is 1, 3 or 6 units. The corresponding products of current and voltage are VI, $3VI$, and $6VI$. The power depends on the product (p.d. × current). Now units of power (p. 68) were defined before electric power came into common use. So units of potential (volts) were chosen to be of such a size that the following equation applies to power in electric circuits:

Power (in *watts*) = **Potential** (in *volts*) × **Current** (in *amps*).

This follows from the fact that 1 volt uses 1 joule of energy in moving 1 coulomb of charge (p. 287), and therefore uses 1 watt (1 joule/s) in driving 1 amp (1 coulomb/s).

The measurement of potential differences and electromotive forces is usually done with voltmeters. When the manufacturers put the scales on these instruments they have to make sure that the scales agree with the definition given above.

EXAMPLE 1. *Calculate the power taken from the supply by* (a) *an electric lamp which takes a current of* 0·5 *A from a* 240-*V supply,* (b) *an electric fire which takes* 4·2 *A from a* 240-*V supply.*

(*a*) Power = 240 × 0·5 = 120 watts
(*b*) Power = 240 × 4·2 = 1008 watts ≃ 1 kilowatt (kW)

EXAMPLE 2. *Two electric kettles are both rated at* 1000 *W, but one is intended for use on a* 250-*V supply and the other on a* 100-*V supply. Calculate the current taken by each.*

On 250 V. 1000 = 250 × current Current = 4 A
On 100 V. 1000 = 100 × current Current = 10 A

EXAMPLE 3. *When the p.d. across a radio valve is* (a) 200 *V,* (b) 300 *V,* (c) 400 *V, the corresponding currents are* (a) 200 *mA,* (b) 250 *mA,* (c) 250 *mA. Calculate the power used in each case.*

(*a*) Power = 200 × 0·200 = 40 watts
(*b*) Power = 300 × 0·250 = 75 watts
(*c*) Power = 400 × 0·250 = 100 watts

32.2. The cost of using electrical power. People commonly speak of 'paying the electricity bill' as though they were paying for the electricity supplied. Actually the electricity they use is already present in the atoms of the wiring and the electrical appliances. The power station supplies the voltage to set the electricity in motion, and the energy for keeping up the current. The account rendered is not so much an electricity account as an *energy account*. The joule or watt-second is too small a unit for dealing with household or factory demands. A larger unit is the **kilowatt-hour (kWh).** This is the energy needed to maintain a power supply of one kilowatt (1000 watts) for a period of one hour.

1 kilowatt-hour = 1000 watt-hours
= 1000 × 3600 watt-seconds or joules

The cost per kWh often varies with the nature of the demand; the cost-schemes (tariffs) are generally different for domestic use and industrial use.

EXAMPLE 4. *Calculate the cost of using a 4-kW electric heater for 3 hours at a cost of* $1\frac{1}{2}$*d. per kWh.*

Number of kilowatt-hours $= 4 \times 3 = 12$.
Cost $= 12 \times 1\frac{1}{2} = 18$d.

32.3. Relation between current and potential. Usually, the higher the potential difference applied to a system, the greater is the current which flows. For many substances the current is proportional to the potential difference. This is certainly true for metallic conductors provided that their physical conditions, such as temperature, do not change. The fact was first discovered by Georg Simon Ohm and is expressed as **Ohm's law** in the following way.

The current (I) flowing between any two points in a metallic conductor is proportional to the potential difference (V) between these points, provided that the physical conditions (such as temperature, physical state) remain constant.

Expressed mathematically,

$$V/I = \text{a constant}$$

Not all substances have this simple relation between current and potential. Gases, for instance, pass no current until a certain sparking potential is reached. Semi-conductors (e.g. selenium, germanium, silicon carbide) do not show a simple current-voltage relation, nor do rectifiers which allow current to pass one way only. A diode valve has a non-linear relation between current and potential; and a stage can be reached where increase of potential causes no increase of current (see Fig. 40.9).

The investigation of the current-voltage variation for a given test-piece can be done with an ammeter and a voltmeter connected in circuit as shown in Fig. 32.5*a* or 32.5*b*. Note that the ammeter is

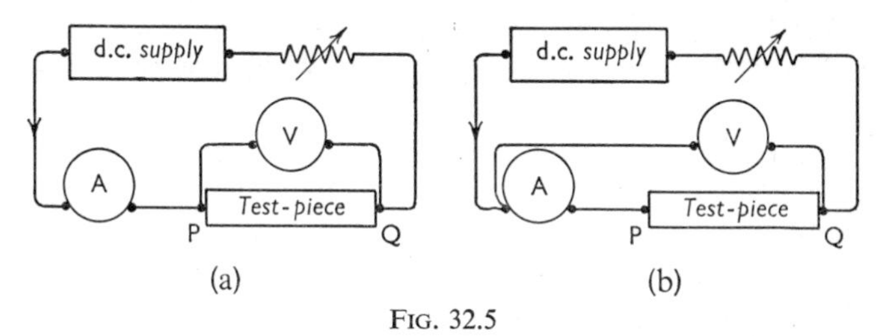

FIG. 32.5

Test-circuits for the relation between current and p.d.

connected in series with the circuit, the voltmeter in parallel. Although in *a* the voltmeter is connected directly to the test-piece at P and Q, the circuit of *b* is generally to be preferred. Even a high-resistance voltmeter takes some current to work it, and in circuit *a* the current registered by the ammeter divides at P, not all of it going through PQ. In circuit *b* the ammeter registers the actual current going through PQ. The voltmeter registers slightly more than the p.d. across PQ, but the p.d. across the ammeter is usually negligible; if necessary its value can be calculated if the resistance of the ammeter is known.

32.4. Verification of Ohm's law. Cells in series. The verification of Ohm's law is not a particularly simple matter; Ohm himself experienced difficulty because at that time there was no suitable voltmeter, nor were batteries as reliable as they are today. The circuit of Fig. 32.5*a* can be used to prove the law if a suitable voltmeter is used. Thus a voltmeter which has been converted from a milliammeter, as explained on page 359, has been so made on the assumption that Ohm's law is true for the resistors in it; it is therefore not suitable unless its scale has been re-checked against standard potentials. Ideally an electrostatic voltmeter (one which takes no current) should be used; and it should have been calibrated against standard potentials, e.g. a battery of identical cells.

The electromotive force of a cell is the p.d. between its terminals when it is on *open circuit*, i.e. supplying no current. Cells which are joined in series have an e.m.f. which is the sum of their separate e.m.f.s. This follows from the fact that electric potential follows the ordinary rules of algebraic addition. Thus if a point has a potential of +5 volts and the potential of the surroundings falls by 3 volts, the new potential of the point is +2 volts.

In electric cells there are potential differences where the poles touch the electrolyte, and the e.m.f. of the cell is the sum of these. Fig. 32.6 shows three cells in series, with the end negative terminal

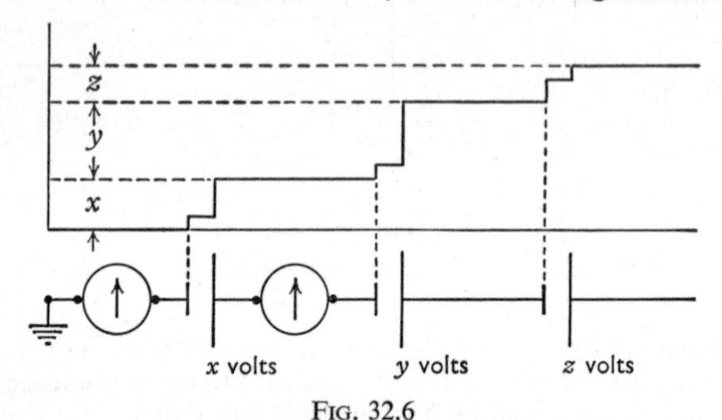

FIG. 32.6
Electromotive force of cells in series

connected to earth; anything connected to earth is reckoned to be at zero potential. There is no current in the system, as is shown by the centre-zero galvanometer—which can be put anywhere in the series. The corresponding graph shows how the potential varies along the line, there being no potential difference in conductors in which no current is flowing. The potential of the positive pole of the third cell is $(x+y+z)$ volts; if all three cells had been identical with the first one, then the potential would have been $3x$ volts. This fact is made use of in the following experiment for testing Ohm's law.

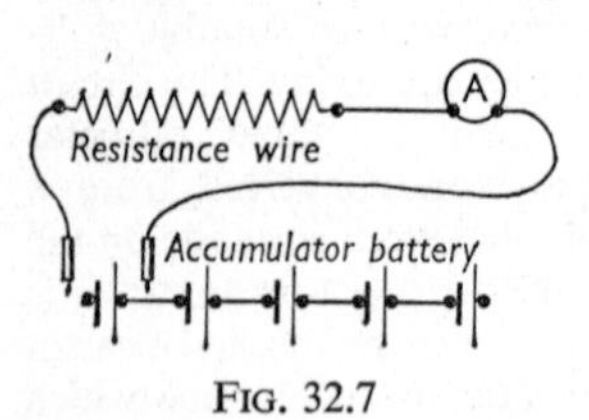

FIG. 32.7

Experiment 1. Connect five accumulators, of the same type, in series as shown in Fig. 32.7. Connect an ammeter, reading to 1 amp, in series with $2\frac{1}{2}$ metres of constantan (contra, eureka) wire s.w.g. 28 immersed in an oil bath, or cooled by a fan. By means of two wander-connectors or probes, connect this part of the circuit to each of the accumulators in turn, to check that the action of each on the circuit is identical. Then connect the probes across two, three, four and then all five of the cells, and observe the corresponding currents.

Specimen results

Number of cells	Current in amp.	$\frac{\text{No. of cells}}{\text{Current}}$
1	0·192	5·21
2	0·385	5·20
3	0·580	5·18
4	0·770	5·20
5	0·960	5·21

The figures in the last column are constant within the limits of experimental error, and therefore the current is proportional to the potential difference. Actually the circuit is not strictly constant throughout the experiment. Each extra cell meant the addition, to the circuit, of the internal resistance of a cell. Because the internal resistance of an accumulator is very low, the additions proved negligible. But the experiment would not have 'worked' with cells of higher resistances.

32.5. Resistance. The Ohm equation. The current (I) flowing in a metallic conductor is proportional to the potential difference (V) between its ends. For a given conductor

$$\frac{V}{I}=k \text{ where } k \text{ is a constant}$$

The value of the constant depends on the nature of the conducting material, its dimensions and its temperature. If the value of k is large for a particular conductor, it means that a large potential is needed to drive unit current in the conductor, i.e. the conductor offers much resistance to the flow. k is therefore a useful measure of resistance.

Resistance is defined, quantitatively, by the equation

$$\frac{V}{I}=R \text{ or } V=IR$$

If V is the number of volts and I the number of amps, the unit in which R is expressed is the **ohm.**

Definition. A resistance of **one ohm** passes a current of **one amp** when a potential difference of **one volt** exists between its ends.

Standard resistances are made of wire, usually constantan or manganin. Resistances made with these alloys change very little with rise of temperature.

The Ohm equation, $V=IR$, can be applied to a circuit as a whole, or to parts of a circuit. When applied to a whole series circuit the symbol V represents E, the total of the e.m.f.s in the circuit; and R represents the **total resistance,** including any internal resistance of the supply.

So that if R=total external resistance

r=internal resistance of the supply

$$E=I(R+r)$$

Thus a cell of e.m.f. 1·50 V and internal resistance 0·50 ohm, connected in series with resistors of 2·00 and 2·50 ohms, would set up a current I given by the equation

$$1{\cdot}50=I(0{\cdot}50+2{\cdot}00+2{\cdot}50)$$

whence $$I=0{\cdot}30\text{ A}$$

The p.d.s across the resistors would be $0{\cdot}30\times 2{\cdot}00=0{\cdot}6$ V and $0{\cdot}30\times 2{\cdot}50=0{\cdot}75$ V. The sum of these is 1·35 V; so that a voltmeter connected across the whole circuit would read 1·35 V, which is less than the e.m.f. of the cell. This effect, known as *lost volts*, always happens in a closed circuit and is due to the internal resistance of the supply.

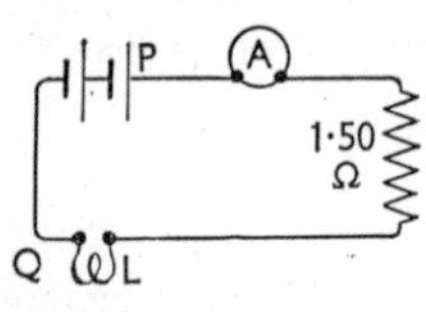

FIG. 32.8

EXAMPLE 5. *In Fig.* 32.8 *each cell has an e.m.f. of* 1·50 *V and an internal resistance of* 0·60 *ohm. The ammeter A has a resistance of* 0·10 *ohm and registers* 0·50 *A. The resistor is* 1·50 *ohms. Calculate* (a) *the resistance of the lamp L and* (b) *the p.d. across its terminals;* (c) *the p.d. between P and Q.*

Let x ohms=resistance of the lamp.

(*a*) For the whole circuit

$$1{\cdot}50+1{\cdot}50=0{\cdot}50\ (0{\cdot}60+0{\cdot}60+0{\cdot}10+1{\cdot}50+x)$$

$$\frac{3{\cdot}00}{0{\cdot}50}=2{\cdot}80+x$$

$$6{\cdot}00=2{\cdot}80+x$$

$$x=3{\cdot}20$$

∴ Resistance of the lamp=3·20 ohms

(*b*) p.d. across the lamp=$0{\cdot}50\times 3{\cdot}20=1{\cdot}60$ V.

(*c*) P and Q are the terminals of the battery. But the p.d. between P and Q is not equal to the e.m.f., 3 volts, because the battery is not on open circuit. Because the current flows from P to Q in the **external** circuit, of resistance $1{\cdot}60+3{\cdot}20=4{\cdot}80$ ohms, the required p.d. $=0{\cdot}5\times4{\cdot}8=2{\cdot}40$ V.

32.6. Resistors in series and in parallel. Resistors in series (Fig. 32.9*a*) give a combined resistance R which is the sum of their separate resistances (r_1; r_2; r_3 etc.).

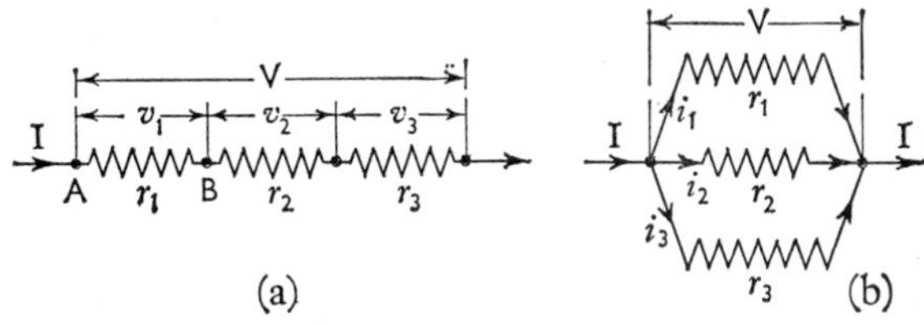

FIG. 32.9

(*a*) *Resistors in series* (*potential dividers*). (*b*) *Resistors in parallel* (*current dividers*)

The potential difference across the group is equal to the sum of the potential differences across the separate resistors.

$$V=v_1+v_2+v_3$$

But they all carry the same current I.

$$IR=Ir_1+Ir_2+Ir_3$$
$$R=r_1+r_2+r_3$$

Resistors connected in the manner shown in Fig. 32.9*b* are said to be connected in parallel. Their combined resistance is always less than the least single resistance in the group. Each one helps to carry current; each one helps to make the whole arrangement a better conductor (i.e. less resistance). The incoming current is the sum of the separate currents in the resistors.

$$I=i_1+i_2+i_3$$

But the p.d. across each conductor is the same, and is the same as the p.d. across the whole network. Let this be V.

Then $$\frac{V}{R}=\frac{V}{r_1}+\frac{V}{r_2}+\frac{V}{r_3}$$

whence $$\frac{1}{R}=\frac{1}{r_1}+\frac{1}{r_2}+\frac{1}{r_3}$$

For *two* resistors r_1 and r_2 in parallel, the combined resistance R is given by

$$\frac{1}{R}=\frac{1}{r_1}+\frac{1}{r_2} \quad \text{whence} \quad R=\frac{r_1 \times r_2}{r_1+r_2}=\frac{\text{product}}{\text{sum}}$$

This last formula is useful for quick calculation; but it cannot be used when there are more than two resistors in parallel.

Fig. 32.10 shows how current divides between 4 ohms and 6 ohms in parallel when there is a p.d. of 24 V across each. The same proportion of current still holds good whatever the p.d. across the combination may be; in any circuit this particular combination carries $\frac{6}{10}$ of the current in the 4 ohms and $\frac{4}{10}$ of the current in the 6 ohms.

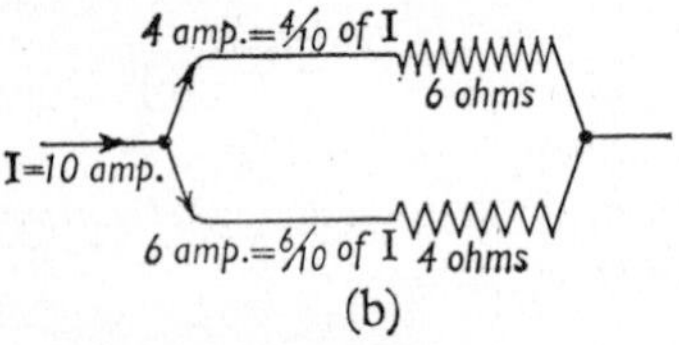

FIG. 32.10

Division of current in a branched circuit

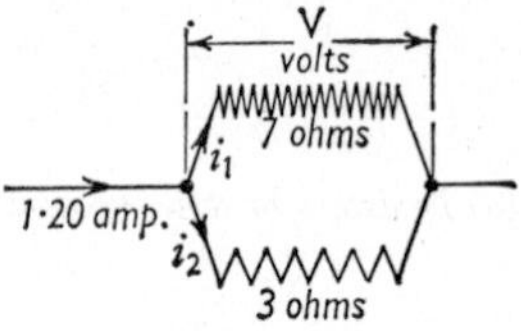

FIG. 32.11

EXAMPLE 6. *Deduce the unknown quantities, denoted by letters, in Fig.* 32.11.

The current in the 7-ohm resistance will be 3/(3 + 7) of the main current.

$$i_1=\tfrac{3}{10} \times 1{\cdot}20=0{\cdot}36 \text{ A}$$

Therefore, by difference

$$i_2=1{\cdot}20-0{\cdot}36=0{\cdot}84 \text{ A}$$

The value of V can be found by applying the Ohm equation to either the 7 ohms or to the 3 ohms separately. Thus V is equal to $7 \times 0{\cdot}36$ and to $3 \times 0{\cdot}84$, giving a value of 2·52 V. The value of V can also be found by considering the network as a whole.

Thus the combined resistance of the network is

$$7 \times 3/(7+3)=2{\cdot}1 \text{ ohms}$$

The total current carried by it = 1·20 A

$$\therefore \; V=1{\cdot}20 \times 2{\cdot}1=2{\cdot}52 \text{ V}$$

This affords an alternative method of finding i_1 and i_2.

$$i=2{\cdot}52/7=0{\cdot}36 \text{ A} \qquad I=2{\cdot}52/3=0{\cdot}84 \text{ A}$$

32.7. The lost volts effect. Terminal potential difference. Batteries, dynamos and power lines are commonly used to supply current from a particular voltage, the e.m.f. of the supply. When current is taken from the terminals of the supply, it is found that the p.d. between the terminals drops below the nominal e.m.f. It can be shown that this decrease (known as *lost volts*) is not due to any change in the e.m.f. of the supply, but is due to the potential required to keep the supply-current going in the internal resistance of the supply. The effect is most noticeable when the internal resistance is relatively large, or when the supply-current is large. Thus a medium-resistance voltmeter connected to a high-resistance cell would register only a fraction of the true e.m.f. When the self-starter motor of a car is set in action, headlights which are on at the same time go dim, showing a drop in the supply-potential—though there is no real drop in the supply's e.m.f. A similar effect is sometimes to be seen in a building lit by electricity, when a powerful electric motor in the same building is first switched on. The effect is due to the large current taken by electric motors at the moment of starting.

The effect can be studied by a consideration of Fig. 32.12

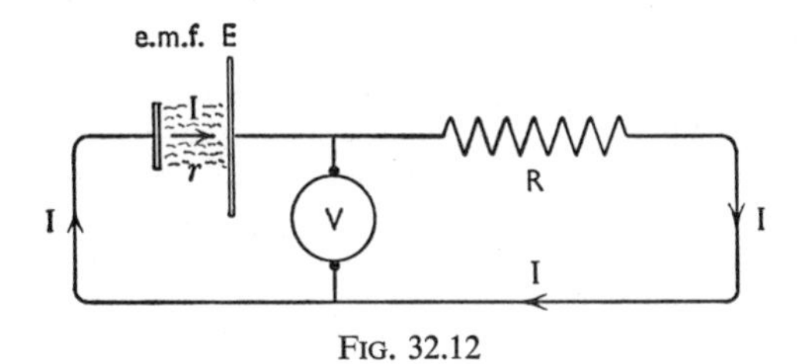

FIG. 32.12

which shows a cell, of e.m.f. E and internal resistance r, connected to an external resistance R and sending a current I round the whole circuit. So that

$$E = I(R + r) = IR + Ir \quad . \quad . \quad . \quad (1)$$

The voltmeter reads what is known as the **terminal potential difference (t.p.d.).** This can be regarded as the potential difference between the **terminals of the cell** or the potential difference between the **terminals of the circuit.** Both p.d.s are numerically the same; and the p.d. across the terminals of the circuit is given by the equation

$$V = IR \quad . \quad . \quad . \quad . \quad . \quad . \quad . \quad (2)$$

Subtraction of the equations (1) and (2) gives

$$(E-V)=Ir$$

or **Lost volts = current × internal resistance**

Division of the equations (1) and (2) gives

$$\frac{V}{E}=\frac{R}{R+r}$$

which shows that the circuit can be regarded as a potential divider, dividing the e.m.f. so that the voltmeter reads $R/(R+r)$ of E. This is made the basis of one method of finding the internal resistance of a cell. The cell is connected to a high-resistance voltmeter to find E, then connected to a known resistance R, and the same voltmeter is used to find the terminal potential difference V. The only unknown in the equation is then r, the internal resistance of the cell. An instrument for testing the internal resistance of car-accumulators makes use of the lost volts effect. Two spring-loaded prongs are connected to a fairly low resistance, across which is connected a voltmeter. The prongs are pushed against the terminals of the cell under test, thus causing a fairly large current to flow. If the voltmeter reads much below the normal e.m.f. of the cell it means that the cell has an unduly high internal resistance, and is either faulty or in need of a re-charge.

32.8. Resistivity. Because the resistance of conductors in series is the sum of their separate resistances, the resistance of a wire of uniform cross-section is **directly proportional to its length** (l)

$$R \propto l \text{ (area, material and temperature all being the same)}$$

Thick wires can be considered to be made up of thinner wires in parallel; so the resistance of equal lengths of wire of the same material, but of different cross-sections, are found to be **inversely proportional to the area of cross-section** (a).

$$R \propto \frac{1}{a} \text{ (length, material and temperature all being the same)}$$

These two relations can be expressed in the form

$$R \propto \frac{l}{a} \text{ (for a given material at a given temperature)}$$

or

$$R=\rho\frac{l}{a}$$

where R = resistance of a conductor, l = its length, a = its area of cross-section, and ρ is a constant depending on the nature of the material and on its temperature. This constant ρ is known as the **resistivity of the material.** A re-arrangement of the above equation gives

$$\rho=\frac{Ra}{l}$$

so that $\rho=R$ when l and a are both unity. The resistivity of a material can thus be defined as the resistance along the length of a prism of the material, 1 cm long and 1 sq. cm in cross-section (Fig. 32.13*a*). A unit in which resistivity is measured would thus be ohm-sq. cm/cm; it is never given in this form, but is abbreviated to *ohm cm.*

A particular case of the 1 cm length, 1 sq. cm cross-section, is the cube of side 1 cm. Resistivity is therefore sometimes defined as the resistance between opposite faces of a centimetre cube of the substance. (Note that this is not the same as the resistance of a cubic centimetre, since 1 c.c. can have any shape. One possible shape is shown in Fig. 32.13*b*.) Resistivities are sometimes quoted in *ohms per cm-cube.*

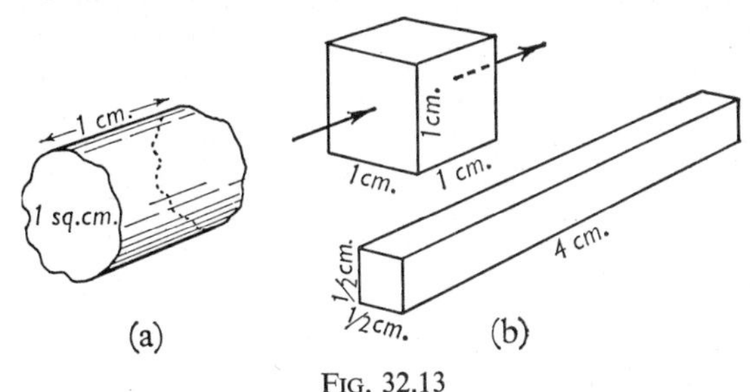

FIG. 32.13

The resistivity of the best conductors is of the order of a few millionths of an ohm (microhms) per cm-cube. Mercury, and the alloys used for resistance wires, have resistivities of the order of 50-100 microhms per cm-cube. Strong solutions of acids, alkalis and salts reach values of 1–10 ohms per cm-cube, insulators are of the order of many millions of ohms (megohms) per cm-cube.

EXAMPLE 7. *Calculate the resistance of* 1 *metre of aluminium tape,* 5 *mm. wide and* 0·04 *mm. thick. Resistivity*=2·9 *microhm cm.*

$$R=\rho\frac{l}{a}=\frac{(2{\cdot}9\times10^{-6})\times100}{0{\cdot}5\times0{\cdot}004}=0{\cdot}145$$

Resistance = 0·145 ohm

EXAMPLE 8. *A column of mercury at 0°C, 106·3 cm long and 1 sq. mm cross-section has a resistance of 1·000 ohm. Calculate the resistivity of mercury at 0°C.*

1 sq. mm = 0·01 sq. cm.

$$1{\cdot}000 = \frac{\rho \times 106{\cdot}3}{0{\cdot}01}$$

$$\therefore \rho = \frac{0{\cdot}01}{106{\cdot}3} \text{ ohm cm}$$

$$= \frac{0{\cdot}01 \times 10^6}{106{\cdot}3} \text{ microhm cm}$$

$$= 94{\cdot}6 \text{ microhm cm}$$

Resistivity of mercury at 0°C = 94·6 microhm cm.

32.9. Resistance and temperature. The resistance of pure metals increases with rise of temperature. For example, the resistance of the tungsten filament of an electric lamp increases about tenfold when it is lit up. Many pure metals have zero resistance at temperatures within a few degrees of Absolute zero. Thus a current in a ring of lead at 7°A will continue to flow for days with little decrease. The phenomenon is known as *supra-conductivity.*

The rate of increase of resistance with temperature is extremely small for most alloys. Because a rise in temperature has little effect on eureka (constantan) and manganin, wires of these substances are generally used for making standard resistances.

The resistance of carbon and of electrolytes (such as fused salts, glass, aqueous solutions of acids, alkalis and salts) decreases with rise of temperature.

Experiment 2. Coil about half a metre of iron wire to form a compact spiral and connect it in series with a 2-volt accumulator, a resistance of about 2 ohms and an ammeter reading to 1 amp. Note the current, and then make the iron spiral red-hot with a bunsen flame. The current will be found to decrease. This shows that there has been either an increase in the resistance of the iron or the development of an opposing e.m.f. in the hot iron. By repeating the experiment without the accumulator in the circuit, it can be shown that heating the iron wire does not produce any current in the circuit.

SUMMARY

Electrical power depends on both current and potential difference.

Power (in **watts**) = current (in **amps**) × p.d. (in **volts**).

Electrical energy is measured in **kilowatt hours** (kWh).

Ohm's law states: The current flowing between any two points in a metallic conductor is directly proportional to the p.d. between the two points, provided that the physical conditions of the conductor remain constant.

$$I \propto V$$

The Ohm equation,

$$V = IR$$

(p.d. between two points) = (current between the points) × (resistance between the points)

For a complete circuit

$$E = I \times \textbf{total} \text{ resistance of circuit}$$

A resistance of 1 ohm passes a current of 1 amp when a p.d. of 1 volt exists between its ends.

For resistors in **series,**

$$R = r_1 + r_2 + r_3 \ldots$$

For resistors in **parallel,**

$$\frac{1}{R} = \frac{1}{r_1} + \frac{1}{r_2} + \frac{1}{r_3}$$

For **two** resistances in parallel,

$$R = \frac{\text{product}}{\text{sum}}$$

The **resistivity** ρ of a material is equal to the resistance between opposite faces of a centimetre-cube of the material. It is expressed in units such as *ohm cm, ohms per cm-cube.*

$$R = \rho \frac{l}{a}$$

The e.m.f. E of a supply is the p.d. between its terminals when on *open circuit*, i.e. when it is not delivering any current. When on closed circuit, the p.d. between the terminals (t.p.d.) is less than E by the product *current × internal resistance.* The decrease in voltage is known as the *lost volts* of the supply.

Questions

1. Define the term *power*. Express the power of each of the following in *watts.* (*a*) 4800 joules of work done per min. (*b*) 43,200 joules of work done per hour. (*c*) A current of 15 A flowing under a p.d. of 12 V. (*d*) A battery of e.m.f. 13 V supplying a

current of 50 A. (*e*) A current of 5 mA flowing under a p.d. of 30 kV. (*f*) A power which uses 6 kWh in 24 hours.

2. Define the *kilowatt-hour*. Calculate the number of joules in one-tenth of a kWh. For how long can a 50-W lamp be used before consuming 1 kWh?

3. Give expressions for the energy involved in each of the following instances; state the units corresponding to each expression. (*a*) Energy supplied for x hours at the rate of J joules per min. (*b*) A power of W watts maintained for t seconds. (*c*) A power of X kilowatts maintained for y min. (*d*) A current of 100 A flowing under a p.d. of V volts for 15 min.

4. Draw circuit diagrams to show how you would connect the following groups of lamps to a 240-V supply so that all lamps were lit to their normal brightness. (*a*) Six lamps, each marked 40 V 20 W. (*b*) Four lamps, each marked 240 V 60 W. Calculate the current taken from the supply by each group, and the cost of running each group for 150 hours if the supply-cost is 2*d* per kWh.

Discuss the effects, in each case, of the breakage of one of the lamps in each group.

5. You are provided with six lamps, each labelled 2 V 0·4 W. Draw circuit diagrams to show how you would connect them so as to light all six to their normal brightness using (*a*) a 2-V supply, (*b*) a 4-V supply, (*c*) a 6-V supply, (*d*) a 12-V supply. Calculate the current taken from the supply in each case.

6. Describe how you would use an ammeter and a voltmeter, with any other apparatus needed, to find out whether the current in a given carbon rod is proportional to the p.d. across the rod.

7. The current in a certain semi-conductor is proportional to V^6, where V is the p.d. across the substance. If a specimen of the substance carries a current of 3·10 microamp when the p.d. is 12·0 V, what current will be carried when the p.d. is 120 V?

8. State *Ohm's law*. Define the *resistance* of a conductor. Calculate the p.d. required to send a current of (*a*) 4 A through 3 ohms, (*b*) 3 A through 5 ohms, (*c*) 15 mA through 200 ohms, (*d*) 1000 A through 50 microhms, (*e*) 55 microamp through 2 megohms.

9. A 6 V accumulator of negligible resistance is to be connected to a circuit of negligible resistance. Calculate the additional resistance needed to limit the current to (*a*) 12 A, (*b*) 1·5 A, (*c*) 60 mA, (*d*) 240 microamp.

10. Calculate the current in a 30-ohm resistor connected to (*a*) a cell of e.m.f. 1·08 V and internal resistance 6 ohms, (*b*) a cell of e.m.f. 2·15 V and internal resistance 0·10 ohm.

11. Calculate the current flowing when each of the cells of

Question 10 is short-circuited, i.e. the terminals are joined by a wire of negligible resistance.

12. A cell of e.m.f. 1·44 V sends a current of 0·120 A through a resistance of 8·5 ohms. Calculate (*a*) the internal resistance of the cell, (*b*) the p.d. across the external resistance.

13. Calculate the combined resistance of 7 ohms and 3 ohms in parallel. This combination is connected in series with a resistance of 7·5 ohms and a cell of e.m.f. 1·5 V and internal resistance 0·4 ohm. Calculate the current in each of the resistances.

14. Resistances of 4 ohms and 6 ohms are joined in series and connected to a 16-V battery of negligible internal resistance. Calculate the current. A 12-ohm resistance is then connected in parallel with the 6-ohm resistance. Calculate the current in each of the resistances.

15. A cell of e.m.f. 1·40 V and internal resistance 2 ohms is connected to a resistance of 3 ohms. Calculate the current in the resistance. A second cell, identical with the first, is then added to the circuit. Calculate the current in the resistance when the second cell is connected to the first (*a*) in series, (*b*) in parallel. Draw circuit diagrams to illustrate the connections.

16. Calculate the resistance which must be connected to a resistance of 11·0 ohms to give a combined resistance of 10·0 ohms. If the combination is put into an electric circuit and the current in the circuit is then 0·242 A, find (*a*) the p.d. across the combination, (*b*) the current in each component of the combination.

17. The following values give the results of a test on a metal filament lamp.

p.d. between the lamp terminals:

0·30 0·95 2·40 5·40 10·0 V

Current flowing in the lamp:

0·50 1·00 1·50 2·00 2·50 A

Calculate the corresponding values of the resistance. Plot a graph of the resistance of the filament against the current flowing through it. From your graph estimate the resistance of the lamp when the current in it is negligible.

18. A cell of e.m.f. 1·50 V and internal resistance 0·50 ohm is connected in series with a resistance of 6·20 ohms, an ammeter of resistance 0·05 ohm, and a combination resistance consisting of a 3-ohm coil and a 1-ohm coil in parallel. Give a circuit diagram and calculate (*a*) the reading on the ammeter, (*b*) the reading of a high-resistance voltmeter joined across the terminals of the cell.

19. Explain the fact that the p.d. between the terminals of a cell is less than the e.m.f. of the cell when the cell is supplying current to an external circuit.

A battery of internal resistance 1000 ohms is connected to a voltmeter of resistance 9000 ohms; the voltmeter registers 99·0 V. Calculate (*a*) the current in the circuit, (*b*) the e.m.f. of the battery.

20. Describe any one method of finding the internal resistance of a cell. Draw a diagram of the circuit and explain how the result is calculated from the observations.

A cell can supply a current of 0·40 A through a resistance of 4·50 ohms, and 0·25 A through a resistance of 7·50 ohms. Calculate the e.m.f. and the internal resistance of the cell.

21. Two resistors in parallel have a resistance of 4·000 ohms. If one has a resistance of 4·200 ohms, what is the resistance of the other?

If the combination is in an electric circuit carrying 1·05 A, find (*a*) the p.d. across the combination, (*b*) the current in each component of the combination.

22. When an accumulator, of e.m.f. 12·00 V, is connected to a resistance of 0·500 ohms the p.d. across the terminals of the accumulator is 11·00 V. Calculate the internal resistance of the accumulator.

23. A pencil line, 0·20 mm wide, ruled on an insulator, has a resistance of 2000 ohms per cm. Calculate the average thickness of the line. (Resistivity = 6000 microhm cm.)

24. A uniform strip of constantan, of resistivity 0·000050 ohm cm, has a length of 200 cm, a width of 1·50 mm and a resistance of 3·16 ohms. Calculate the thickness of the strip.

If the strip is bent into the form of a circle and its ends are soldered together, what will be the effective resistance between two points on the circle which are at opposite ends of a diameter?

25. A block of material 2 cm × 3 cm × 5 cm has a resistance of 4·50 megohms between its 2 × 3 faces. Calculate (*a*) the resistivity of the material, (*b*) the resistance between the 3 × 5 faces.

26. Calculate the length of nichrome wire, 0·560 mm in diameter, which has a resistance of 3·36 ohms. (Resistivity = 110 microhm cm.)

27. Calculate the length of constantan wire, diameter 0·710 mm, which has a resistance of 1·000 ohm. (Resistivity = 49 microhm cm.)

28. Two wires of the same material, each 120 cm long, and each having an area of cross-section of 0·550 sq. mm, have a combined resistance of 0·750 ohm when joined in parallel. Calculate (*a*) the resistance of each wire, (*b*) the resistivity of the material.

29. A resistance wire of resistivity 0·000044 ohm cm, has a length of 110 cm and a resistance of 1·00 ohm. Calculate the area of cross-section of the wire.

If the wire is drawn out to double its length, the volume remaining the same, what will be its resistance?

CHAPTER 33

Magnets and Magnetic Effects

33.1. Magnets. Whenever a direct current is flowing in a wire it tends to turn certain substances, called **magnetic substances,** into magnets when they are suitably placed near the wire. The effect is stronger if the wire is coiled round the material to be magnetised. The following substances are magnetic: iron, steel, nickel, cobalt, black oxide of iron (Fe_3O_4). Certain alloys of copper, aluminium and manganese, known as *Heusler alloys*, are magnetic though the separate metals of the alloys are not.

All steels are alloys containing iron; the names of some of them are given in the table on page 339. Much research has been done to discover steels which make strong permanent magnets or which make good electromagnets (powerful while the current is on, weak when the current is off). Ticonal and Alnico are the trade-names of steels useful for permanent magnets; they are used in the making of small powerful magnets in galvanometers, telephone ear-pieces and loud-speakers. Soft iron (which is nearly pure iron) is useful for electromagnets. A recent development has been the manufacture of magnetic powders; these have their uses in the magnetic tape of tape-recorders, where the powder is evenly spread through the plastic material of the tape.

A bar magnet or a horse-shoe magnet has patches at its two tips where the attractive force for iron and steel seems to be concentrated. These are known as the poles of the magnet; they are known as the **north-seeking pole** or N. pole (sometimes coloured *red* by the manufacturers) and the **south-seeking pole** or S. pole (sometimes coloured *blue*). These names are given to them because a pivoted or suspended magnet sets with its magnetic axis (the line joining the poles) in a north-south line. Pl. 29 illustrates this action for a magnetised razor-blade floating on water; the N. pole is so named because it seeks the north direction.

Simple experiments with powerful magnets, such as are illustrated in Fig. 33.1, show the fact that **like poles repel, unlike poles attract** each other. This suggests that the tendency of a N. pole (or 'red' pole) to move northwards may be due to the earth itself acting as a magnet, with south-seeking polarity (a 'blue' pole) somewhere in the northern regions. A region in which forces on magnets can be detected is called a **magnetic field;** exploration over the earth's surface shows that the earth has a magnetic field.

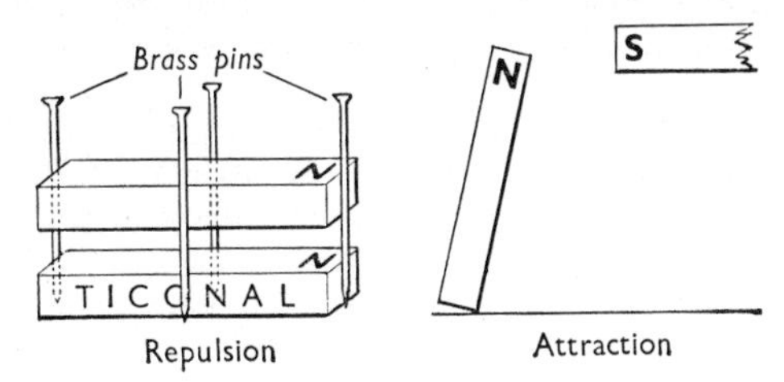

FIG. 33.1

Like poles repel, unlike poles attract

33.2. The earth's magnetic field. Variation. Dip. The vertical plane containing the poles of a freely pivoted magnet is known as the magnetic meridian. The angle between this and the geographical meridian is known as the angle of declination, or the **variation** of

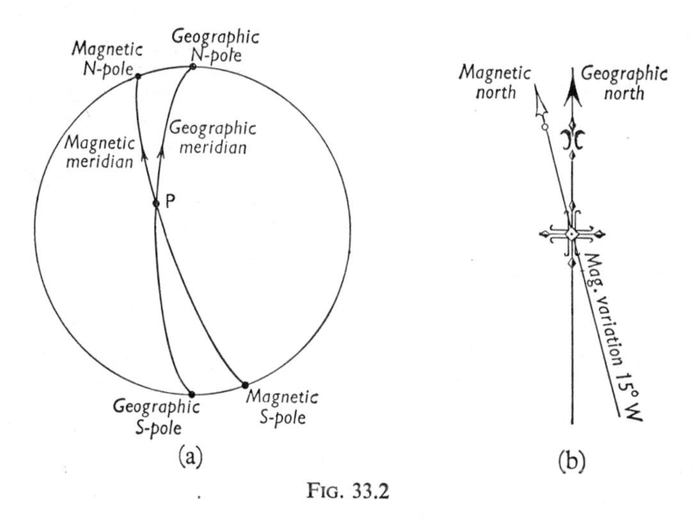

FIG. 33.2

the compass (Fig. 33.2*a*); this angle varies with position on the earth's surface.

A navigator, whether by sea or by air, needs to know the compass variation at all points on the journey. A record of the variation over the area is printed on the maps and charts he uses. If it is a map of a large area, then lines (called *isogonic lines*) are printed on the map showing all places which have the same variation; if it is a map of a small area the variation is indicated as shown in Fig. 33.2*b*.

A compass needle shows the direction of the earth's field in a horizontal plane only. But if a magnet is suspended at its *centre of gravity* and is also free to turn in any direction, it sets in the magnetic meridian and also tilts at an angle. In the northern hemisphere this tilt increases as one approaches the northern magnetic pole, and the N. pole of the magnet is the lower pole in the tilt; in the southern hemisphere the S. pole tilts downwards. The angle between the magnetic axis of the magnet and the horizontal direction in the magnetic meridian is known as the **angle of dip.**

A simple apparatus which will demonstrate the effect of the dip-angle is shown in Fig. 33.3. An unmagnetised steel rod is mounted in a piece of cork, cut to the shape shown in the diagram, and it is balanced on brass pins. The points of the pins are moved up or down until the balance is very nearly at the stage of being top-heavy. The arrangement is placed so that the plane of its swing is in the magnetic meridian. When the steel is magnetised it tilts at an appreciable angle (except at places near the Equator). The way in which the earth's magnetic field varies is very nearly that which would be expected if the earth had a magnet within it, the south-seeking pole being towards the N. magnetic pole (Fig. 33.4).

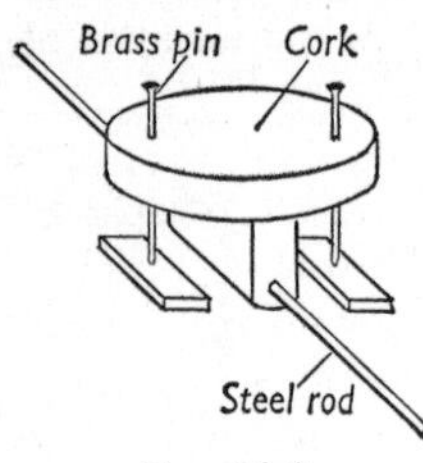

FIG. 33.3

33.3. Magnetic compasses. A simple pocket compass has a pointed strip of magnetised steel pivoted in a non-magnetic case, and the base or the side of the case is marked with the chief compass points. In a ship's compass the directions are marked on a light disc of mica or aluminium, to which a number of bar magnets are fixed, all parallel with the N.–S. line on the disc; the arrangement is pivoted on a hard jewelled bearing. Using several magnets instead of one makes the disc more easily balanced, increases the time of swing and makes the compass steadier in action. In this case the magnets move the disc, and a particular course is set by steering to bring that course opposite the lubber line. The *lubber* *line* is a line marked on the casing of the compass and it is set to mark the direction of the ship's keel. The compass case, which is

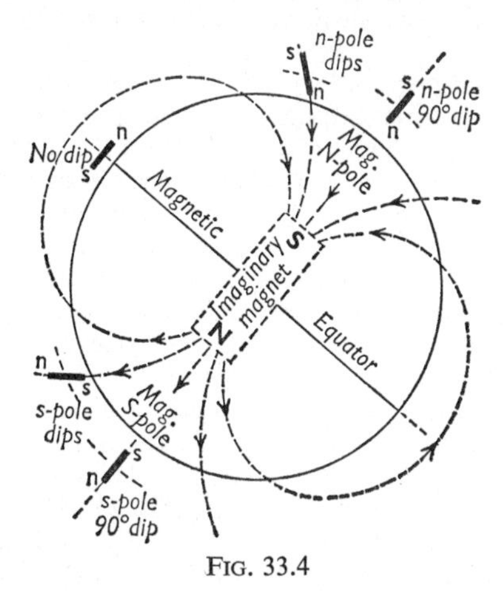

FIG. 33.4

bowl shaped and weighted at the base, is filled with liquid to slow down any swinging of the disc; the liquid is water, mixed with alcohol to prevent freezing in very cold weather. To keep the compass horizontal despite any rolling or pitching of the ship, the compass bowl is mounted in *gimbals*. The bowl is pivoted, along a

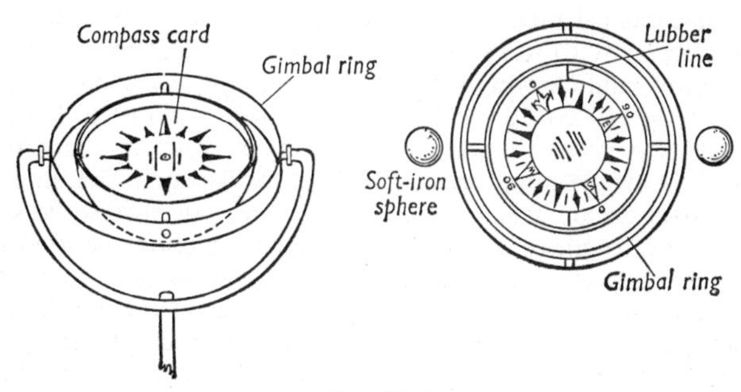

FIG. 33.5
A ship's compass

diameter, in a brass ring which is itself pivoted along a diameter perpendicular to the bearings which carry the bowl (Fig. 33.5). In large ships the compass and its mounting are housed in a non-magnetic pedestal called the *binnacle*; this also contains devices for correcting for the permanent magnetism in the ship.

33.4. Induced magnetism. A piece of unmagnetised iron, e.g. an iron nail, becomes magnetised when held near a magnet; its two ends will attract iron filings (Fig. 33.6). Steel shows a similar effect, but for bars of the same length and cross-section more filings can be held by iron than by steel, i.e. the iron becomes more intensely magnetised. On the other hand an iron bar shows little magnetism in comparison with steel when the inducing magnet is removed, i.e. a steel bar is more *retentive* than an iron bar, and is thus more suitable for making a permanent magnet. Magnetism caused in this way is called induced magnetism, and the effect is called **magnetic induction.** A N. pole induces S. polarity in the end of the material nearest to it. The induced magnetism is stronger if the magnetic material is stroked with the magnet. It is found that the inducing magnet does not lose any of its strength in the process.

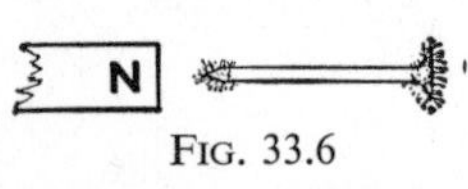

FIG. 33.6
Magnetic induction

A coil which is appreciably longer than its diameter is called a **solenoid.** A current in a solenoid gives very uniform magnetic conditions inside it and so it is useful for making bar magnets. Its magnetising force is measured by the product *current in amp* $\times$ *number of turns per unit length.* This is usually reckoned in **ampere-turns per metre.** Thus a solenoid wound with 4 layers of wire, spread at 10 turns per centimetre (equivalent to 1000 turns per metre), and carrying a current of 10 amps has a magnetising force of $4 \times 1000 \times 10 = 40{,}000$ ampere-turns per metre. This is sufficient to give full magnetisation to cobalt-steel; about four times this magnetising force is required for Ticonal. The induced magnetism occurs at once—the current does not have to be kept on for any length of time. A solenoid can therefore be used for making magnets by connecting it, via a press-switch, to an accumulator battery (Fig. 33.7*a*). The magnetising current is large because the resistance of the circuit is low; to prevent damage to the wiring the switch is closed for only a moment. The poles of the induced magnet are of the same kind as those of the solenoid; the right-hand grip rule, illustrated in Fig. 33.7*b*, shows which end is the N. pole.

The earth's magnetic field has an inductive effect. A bar of mild steel lying in the magnetic meridian becomes slightly magnetised if tapped several times with a hammer, the northerly end becoming a N. pole. The steel girders in buildings, the steel framework of ships, the iron parts of gas pipes, iron retort stands in a laboratory,

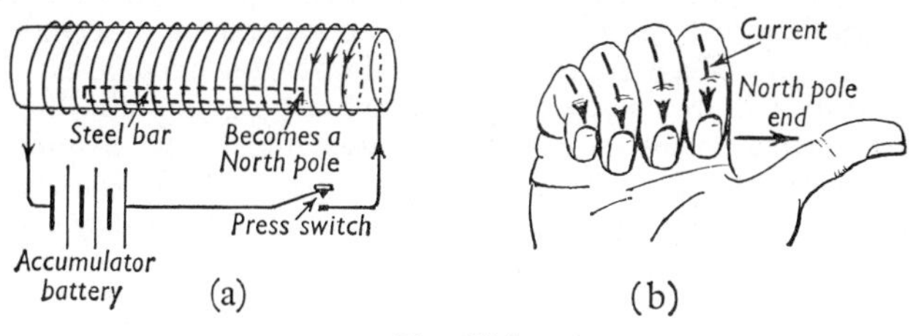

FIG. 33.7
A magnetising coil

all become slightly magnetised under the influence of the earth's field. In the case of retort stands it is the vertical component of the field which is effective; in the northern hemisphere it induces a N. pole at the bottom.

33.5. Lines of force. Magnetic flux. Magnetic fields can be mapped as a series of lines showing the directions of the forces on magnetic poles. These lines are known as **lines of force** or **magnetic field lines.** A tangent to the line at any point shows the direction of the force at that point; an arrow-head is usually marked on the line to show the direction of the force on a N. pole. The general *shape* of a magnetic field of force can be mapped very simply by the use of iron filings, and the *direction* of the field can be found with a compass. Pls. 30, 31 show magnetic maps, in a horizontal plane, obtained by sprinkling iron filings on to a sheet of thin cardboard put over the magnets under test; the paper was gently tapped to help the filings settle into the directions of the forces.The falling filings become magnetised by the field and in the stronger regions of the field they quickly turn to be in line with the forces acting on their poles; in the weaker regions the tapping of the cardboard reduces the friction on the filings and helps them to turn in line with the forces. In some magnetic fields the forces due to the different poles have no resultant. A place where this occurs is called a **neutral point;** neutral points can be seen in Pls. 30, 31.

Magnetic field lines are considered to be continuous lines; they do not cease at the S. pole of a magnet but continue through the magnet, emerging at the N. pole region. The lines of force are said to *flow*. There is no real movement of the lines of force, and the word flow is used in the same sense as is used by an artist in speaking of the flowing lines in a drawing. To distinguish this special meaning of the term flow the Latin word for it, **flux,** is used to describe the flowing lines of a magnetic field. Thus it is common observation that magnetic effects are very noticeable where the lines are closely bunched. Also that where lines from unlike poles link up (Pl. 30) there is attraction as though the lines were under tension, pulling at their sources of origin. Where lines of force approach and turn away (Pl. 31), seeming to repel each other, the places they come from suffer repulsion.

33.6. Magnetic flux in iron and steel. A rough idea of the magnetic flux in a magnet is given by weighing the amount of iron filings or small iron rivets it can support. Fig. 33.8*a* shows iron and steel

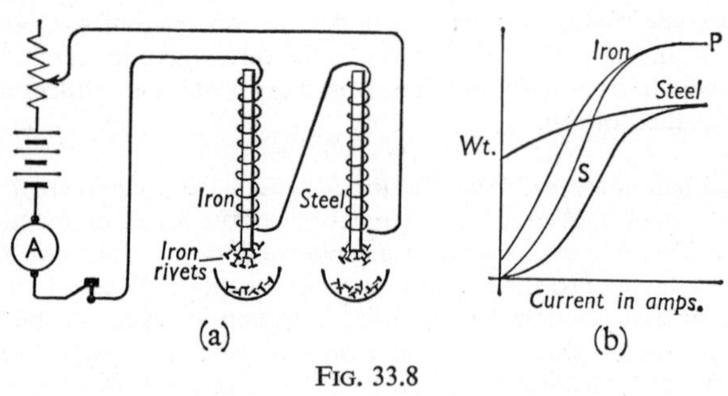

FIG. 33.8

The different magnetic properties of bars of iron and steel

bars, of the same dimensions, wound with identical solenoids and put in an electric circuit in which the current can be varied. By finding the changes in weight of the dishes of rivets, the weight held up, for a set of increasing and decreasing currents, can be found. The results are shown in the graphs of Fig. 33.8*b*. The initial slope S of the iron curve is greater than that for steel, showing that the iron is more **permeable** to the flux. The peak **P** of the iron curve is the higher of the two, which again shows the greater **permeability** of the iron. The peaks of both curves are flat, showing a state known as **magnetic saturation.** Reduction of the current to zero results in the iron losing nearly all its magnetic flux, but the steel retains most of its flux. The steel bar is said to be the more **retentive.**

Actually a *ring* of iron retains magnetism well. The reason why a *bar* of iron does not, is the strong poles made at its ends; these have a great demagnetising effect on iron, but not so great an effect on steel. Even so, it is advisable to use iron *keepers* on permanent magnets. These keep the flux in a magnetic circuit and so avoid free poles (see Fig. 33.9, Pl. 32).

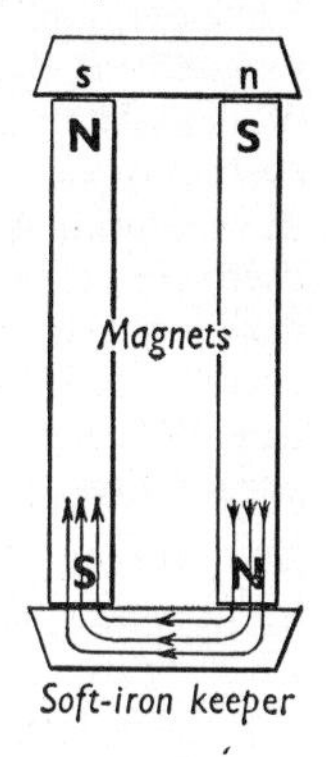

FIG. 33.9

The fact that iron is very permeable to magnetic flux makes it a suitable material for magnetic shielding. Rings, hollow cylinders, or hollow spheres of iron are often used when it is desired to shield a region from external magnetic fields. In a cathode ray tube, for example, the electron beam can be shielded from the action of the earth's magnetic field by surrounding part of the tube with a sheet of mu-metal, a very permeable iron alloy. Fig. 33.10 shows the way in which the flux from a magnet is affected by an iron ring, giving magnetic shielding in the region A.

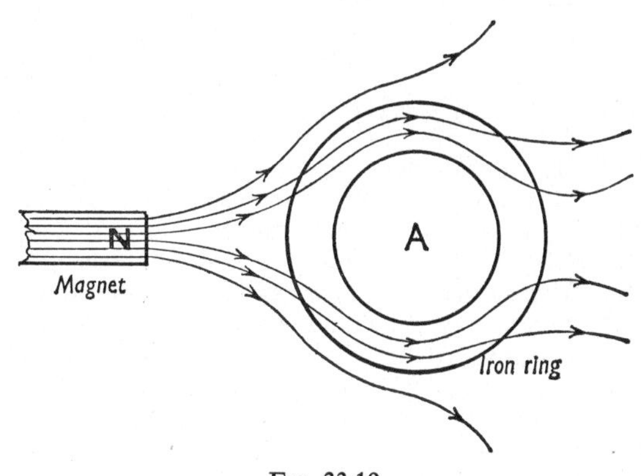

FIG. 33.10
Magnetic shielding

33.7. Demagnetisation. Magnets usually lose some of their magnetisation with time. Rough treatment, mechanical vibration and hammering can also cause some reduction in magnetisation. Complete demagnetisation can be effected by heating the magnet to red-heat. All magnetic substances lose their magnetic properties at some definite temperature, known as the *Curie Point*. Iron, for example, becomes non-magnetic above 750°C. But heat treatment sometimes alters other properties of a steel, such as springiness and hardness; and heat treatment would clearly be unsuitable for demagnetising the hair spring of a watch. The most satisfactory way of demagnetisation is to use a solenoid in which an alternating current is passing. The solenoid is set at right angles to the meridian, the material inserted, and one of the two following methods is used: (*a*) the current is steadily reduced to zero, (*b*) the material is drawn out slowly along the axis of the solenoid, while the maximum current is still flowing, to a position clear of the magnetic field. In either case the poles are reversed many times per second and are progressively weakened until there is no polarity left.

33.8. Theory of magnetism. If a magnetised strip of steel is broken into several pieces, each piece is a separate magnet (Fig. 33.11*a*).

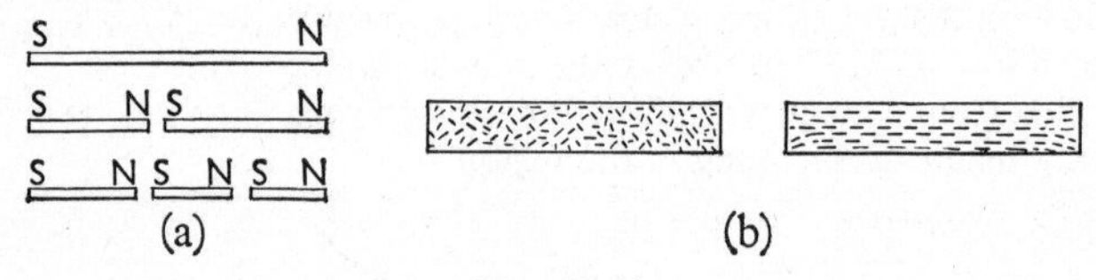

FIG. 33.11

(a) Effect of breaking a magnet. (b) Illustration of Weber's theory

If the breaking process could be continued down to the smallest particles of the substance—the molecules—then the individual molecules might act as miniature magnets. On this theory, suggested by Weber in 1852, an unmagnetised substance consists of miniature magnets arranged in a random manner and so producing no external magnetic flux; the application of a magnetising force swings the magnets into line (Fig. 33.11*b*). Throughout the bar the opposing poles neutralise each other, but at the ends there will be free poles. Mutual repulsion at the ends of the bar causes a spread of polarity over the end regions. Magnetic saturation is explained as occurring when all the miniature magnets are aligned. It may also be supposed that the vibration of the molecules, caused by rough treatment or by the action of heat, disturbs the orderly arrangement and results in a partial return to the random arrangement. The random arrangement may not be entirely disorderly, but is likely to consist of closed chains of miniature magnets with like poles adjacent (Fig. 33.12*a*). Such closed chains would require an appreciable magnetising force before being broken up sufficiently for the flux to increase greatly.

It has been suggested that the electron orbits of magnetic atoms could have the property of self-alignment, giving rise to groups of many atoms forming what are called **magnetic domains** (Fig. 33.12*b*)). There is some experimental evidence for this, and

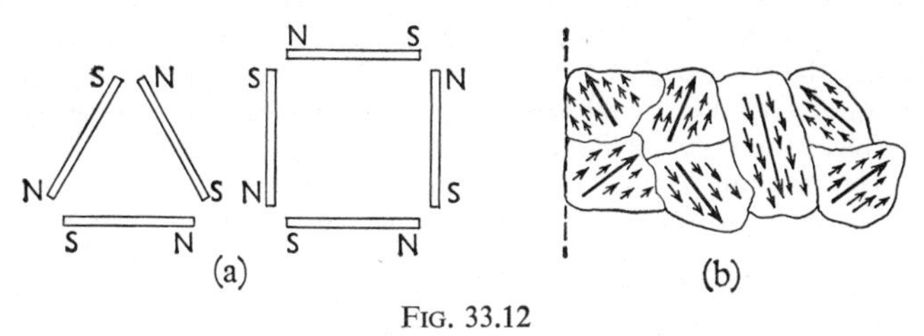

FIG. 33.12

(*a*) *Closed magnetic chains.* (*b*) *Magnetic domains*

measurement of the domains shows them to be about a thousandth of a centimetre across. It is unlikely that the whole domain turns under the influence of an applied magnetising force. The magnetic axis of a domain could change by the turning of the individual atoms which comprise it, much as a column of soldiers could 'about face' without making the whole column turn through 180°.

MAGNETIC PROPERTIES OF MATERIALS

Material	Composition	Magnetising force to give full magnetisation (amps-turns/m)
Mu-metal . .	Cu 5, Ni 76, Fe 19	
Permalloy . .	Ni 78, Fe 22	320
Ferrite . . .	($MnO.Fe_2O_3$)	400
Soft iron . . .	(0·02% C)	4,000
Stalloy . . .	(4% Si)	4,000
Tungsten steel . .	($5\frac{1}{2}$% W)	13,000
Cobalt steel . .	(35% Co)	40,000
Alnico steel . .	Al, Ni, Co, Cu, Fe	100,000
Ticonal . . .	Al, Ni, Co, Cu, Fe	160,000

SUMMARY

Permanent magnets are made of steel alloys, magnetised by an electric current in a solenoid. The magnetising force of the solenoid is measured by the number of **ampere-turns per metre.**

A pivoted magnet sets in an approximate north-south direction under the influence of the earth's magnetic field. The **N.** and **S.** poles of a magnet are **north-seeking** and **south-seeking** respectively.

Like poles repel, unlike poles attract.

The **variation** of the compass (angle of declination) at any place is the angle between the magnetic meridian and the geographical meridian.

The **angle of dip** is the angle between the magnetic axis of a magnet, freely suspended at its centre of gravity, and the horizontal direction of the magnetic meridian.

A **line of force** in a magnetic field shows the direction of the force on a N. pole situated on it; the **tangent** to the line at any point gives the direction of the force at that point. Groups of such lines are known as **magnetic flux.**

Magnetic flux tends to crowd into magnetic substances, inducing S. polarity where it enters and N. polarity where it leaves.

An electric current produces magnetic flux, even though there may be no magnetic materials near it.

Iron can be more strongly magnetised than steel but, unless it is in the form of a complete ring, it does not retain its magnetism well.

Questions

1. Describe how you would magnetise a bar of steel so that a given end, marked A, becomes a N. pole (*a*) by using a permanent magnet, (*b*) by using an electric current. Describe how you would test that your method had been successful.

2. What is meant by the term *magnetic induction*? Describe one simple experiment to illustrate magnetic induction.

3. Two steel needles, hanging from the bottom of a vertical bar magnet, do not hang vertically. Explain this fact. What changes in their position would you expect to occur if first the N. pole and then the S. pole of another magnet were brought towards them from below? Illustrate your answer with diagrams.

4. The N. pole of a weak magnet is found to repel the N. pole of a compass needle when the two are moderately close, but attraction is found to occur when they are very close. Explain this.

5. Name **two** substances, other than iron and steel, which are magnetic. What is the difference between the behaviour of a rod

of iron and a rod of steel (*a*) when introduced into a magnetic field, (*b*) when removed from a magnetic field? Describe **one** experiment in each case in support of your statements.

6. What is meant by *magnetic screening*? Give one example of a practical application of the effect.

7. What is meant by the *angle of dip*? Describe a simple experiment which shows the effect of dip in the earth's magnetic field. How, if at all, would your experiment be affected if carried out in the neighbourhood of the equator?

8. What is meant by a *neutral point* in a magnetic field? Draw a diagram to show some of the lines of force round two bar magnets so arranged that they give at least one netural point in the field. Show the positions where any neutral points might be expected if the magnets were of equal strength. Describe how you would find the position of any neutral points experimentally, using iron filings.

9. Draw a diagram to show the lines of force round two equal-sized parallel bars, one of the bars being a magnet and the other being made of iron. Label with the letter W the parts of the field which will become weaker, and label with the letter S the parts of the magnetic field which will become stronger when the iron bar is removed.

10. Describe any one simple experiment or observation which illustrates the effect of magnetic dip. State clearly the result of the experiment or observation when it is made in (i) the northern hemisphere, (ii) the southern hemisphere.

11. Describe the structure of a ship's compass. Give an explanation of the chief features of its design.

12. Describe simple magnetic tests which would enable you to distinguish between (i) a bar of iron and a bar of copper, (ii) a bar of iron and a bar of steel. Explain the fact that a keeper (a bar of iron) is put across the poles of a horse-shoe magnet when the magnet is not in use.

CHAPTER 34

Magnetic Effects of an Electric Current

34.1. Magnetic fields due to currents. Oersted's experiment, illustrated in Fig. 31.6, shows that there is a magnetic field round a straight flow of electricity. The field can also be shown by pushing a stiff straight wire vertically through a horizontal card, and sprinkling iron filings on the card while the wire is carrying an electric current (of the order of 10 A). When the card is tapped,

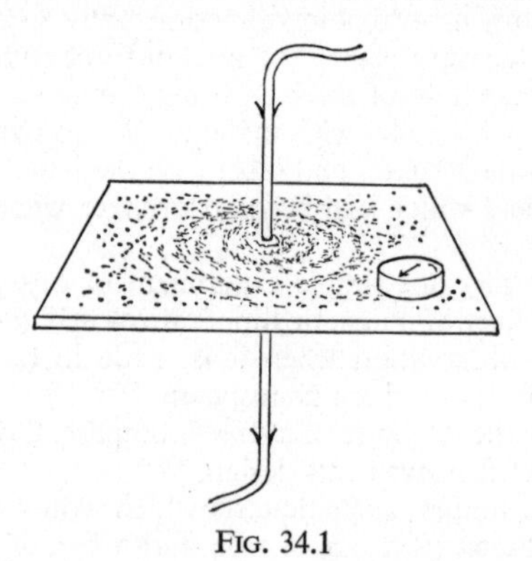

FIG. 34.1

the filings near the wire set in a circular pattern, showing the lines of force to be circles with the wire as their centre. The direction of the flux can be shown by placing a small compass near the wire (Fig. 34.1). A right-hand grip rule is useful for remembering the direction of the flux.

Right-hand grip rule. Imagine the wire gripped in the right hand, with the thumb along the wire and pointing in the direction of the current. Then the direction of the curl of the fingers gives the direction of the lines of force (Fig. 34.2).

The lines of force can also be plotted with a single compass, putting it down anywhere in the field, marking the position of the N. pole, moving the compass on to the mark and repeating the action to give a line of marks. In such circumstances the effect of

35. *Apparatus for illustrating Lenz's Law.* [p. 384]

36. *Armature and brushes of the self-starter motor of a car.* [p. 387]

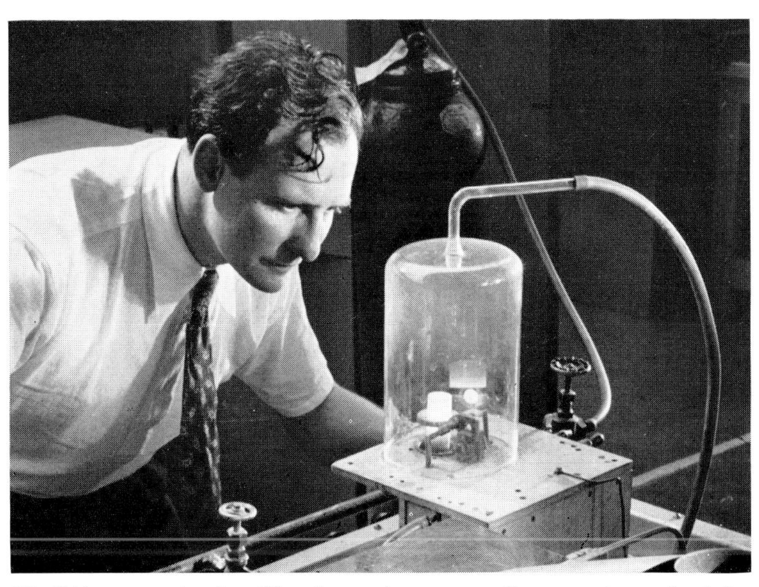

37. *Eddy-current heating. The picture shows parts of a magnetron valve being brazed together in an atmosphere of mixed hydrogen and nitrogen. The metal has become white-hot due to the large eddy currents induced in it by a high-frequency alternating magnetic flux; the frequency is of the order of 1 mega-cycle per second. The coil, which produces a vertical magnetic flux, lies in the box below the heated metal. The maximum power supply is about 10 kilowatts and the heating operation takes up to 3 minutes, depending on the size of the metal being heated.* [p. 388]

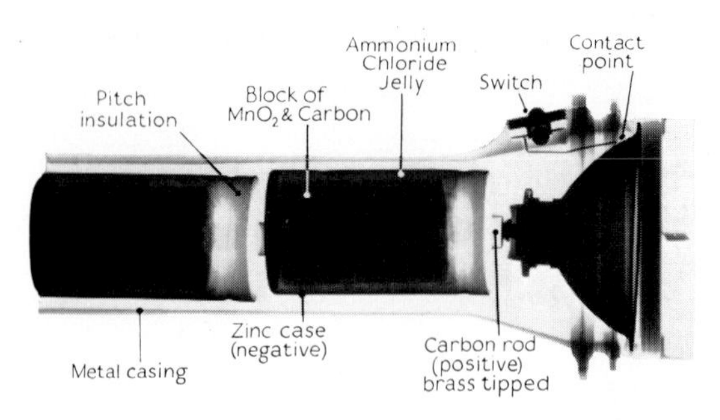

38. *A print made from an X-ray negative of an electric torch. It shows two dry cells joined in series. The zinc base of the second cell makes contact with the metal casing via a metal spring not shown in the picture.* [pp. 401, 430]

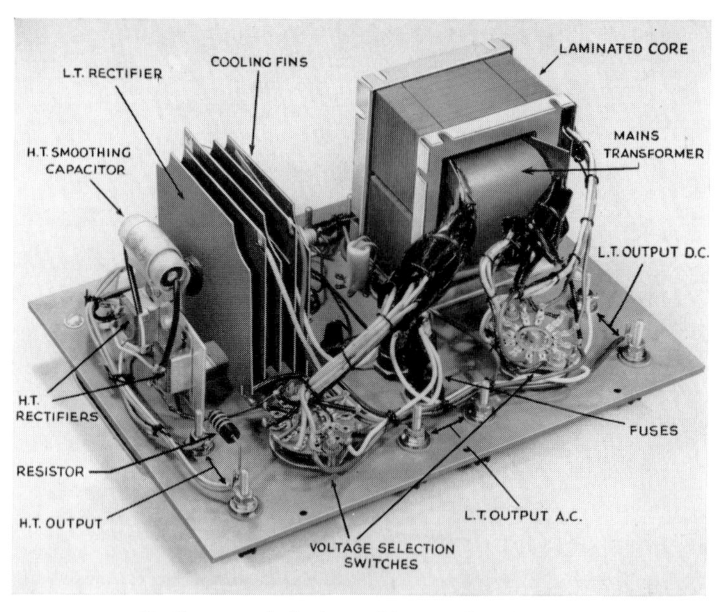

39. *Power pack for l.t. and h.t. supplies.* [p. 416]

the earth's horizontal component will also be seen, and the field will be the resultant of the earth's field and the current's field (Fig. 34.3). A *neutral point* occurs on the side of the wire where the

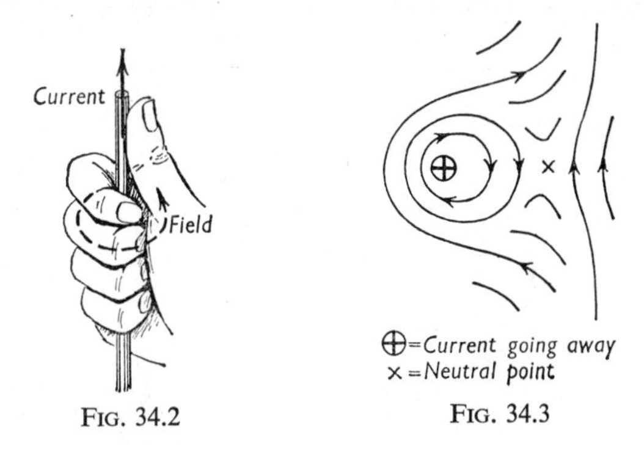

FIG. 34.2

FIG. 34.3

two separate fields are in opposition. By assuming that the flux behaves like stretched elastic threads which repel each other, we should deduce that the current experiences a force tending to drive it towards the neutral point. The force on a current due to the earth's field is usually a weak one, but it is detectable; a beam of electrons such as occurs in a cathode-ray tube, is noticeably deflected by the earth's field, and magnetic shielding (p. 337) has to be used to avoid this effect.

The magnetic flux of a coiled current is nearly straight inside the coil, and is similar to the flux of a bar magnet outside the coil (Fig. 34.4). Again making use of Faraday's idea of tension in lines of force we should expect the turns of the coil to be pulled together. This effect can be shown by the experiment known as Roget's spiral. A loosely wound spiral of copper or brass wire hanging vertically is weighted at one end and connected, through mercury, to a circuit as shown in Fig. 34.5. The current is increased until the weight is drawn out of the mercury. When this happens the circuit is broken, but the falling weight then sets up a make-and-break action and the spring continues to oscillate. Currents flowing in opposite directions repel one another as can be shown by sending a current through a strip of aluminium tape bent into a V shape; the two sides of the tape move away from each other (Fig. 34.6).

Fig. 34.7 shows the resultant magnetic field due to two currents flowing (*a*) in the same direction, (*b*) in opposite directions. In (*a*) there is attraction between the currents, in (*b*) there is repulsion.

Currents flowing in the same direction attract each other. Currents flowing in opposite directions repel each other.

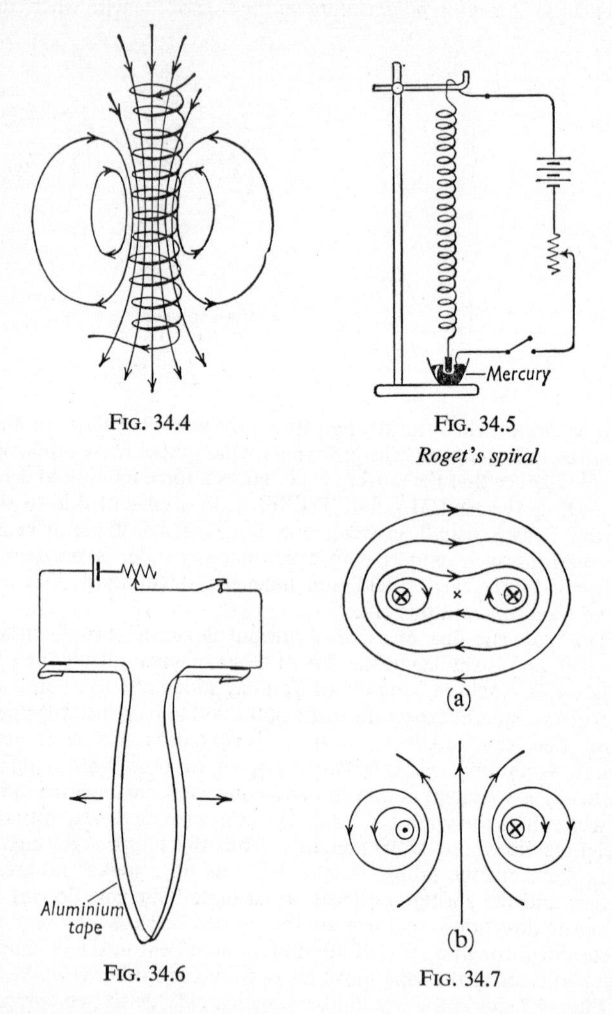

FIG. 34.4

FIG. 34.5
Roget's spiral

FIG. 34.6

FIG. 34.7

The force between electric currents has been made the basis of the definition of unit current. On the metre-kilogram-second or m.k.s. system, the unit is called the **ampere** and is defined as follows.

Definition. An **ampere** is the electric current which, flowing in each of two infinitely long straight wires, 1 metre apart *in vacuo*, results in a force of 2×10^{-7} newton on each metre length of the wires.

In practice, i.e. in the construction of current balances, the wires are coiled and the force between the coils is calculated.

34.2. Electromagnets and their uses. Electromagnets are designed to exert a pull only when current is passing through their coils. The core is made of soft iron, which can be strongly magnetised by the current and which loses its magnetism when the current is switched off. (When an iron drawbar is fitted across the poles the pull may still persist after the current is broken, the iron acting as a keeper. To avoid this the poles or the drawbar are faced with some non-magnetic material.) Fig. 34.8 shows two types of electromagnet

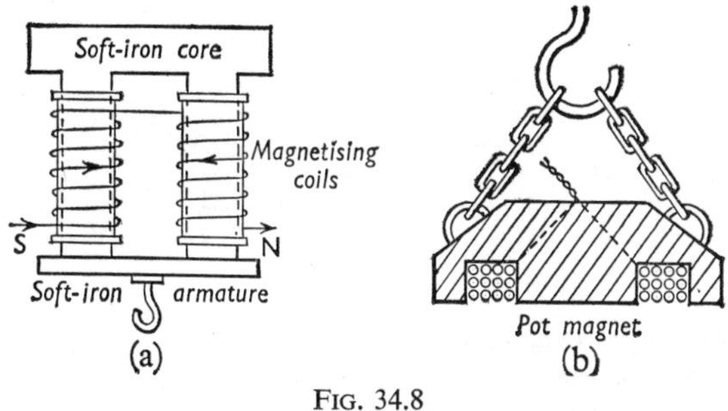

FIG. 34.8
Electromagnetics

used for lifting purposes. The pull depends on the product *number of turns × current*, a quantity known as the **ampere-turns** of the electromagnet. Electromagnets have extensive uses in electric relay systems, in electric bells and telephone systems, in electric motors and generators. Hospitals use them for the removal of steel splinters embedded in a patient's eye, and they are widely used in industry for sorting magnetic metals from other materials, for hauling and lifting iron and steel. For industrial purposes the current may be as high as 100 amp, the coils which carry the current being wound with insulated copper strap.

34.3. The electric bell. Relays. The electric bell has an electromagnetic make-and-break. When the switch S in the circuit shown in Fig. 34.9 is closed the electromagnet pulls the iron armature

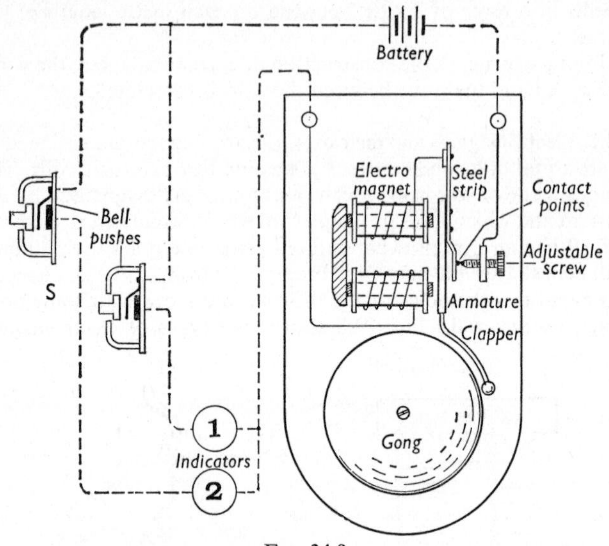

FIG. 34.9
Electric bell

towards it and at the same time breaks the circuit at the contact points. The electromagnet loses its pull and the springy piece of steel which holds the armature then pulls the armature back so that the points are in contact again. Thus the process is repeated, with continued hammering of the gong by the clapper. The break in the circuit causes sparks at the contact points. These points are therefore made of a metal which has a high melting point and which is not readily oxidised; silver is used in the smaller bells, platinum in more powerful alarm bells.

Indicators are sometimes put in the wiring when more than one bell-push is used to work the same bell. Fig. 34.10 shows two simple types of indicator. In (*a*) the current causes the hanging iron armature to be attracted to the electromagnet. When the bell-push is released the armature swings back, and continues swinging for a time; the moving indicator flag shows in which room the bell-push was used. In (*b*) the electromagnet attracts an iron armature which is part of a bell-crank lever; the horizontal part of the lever

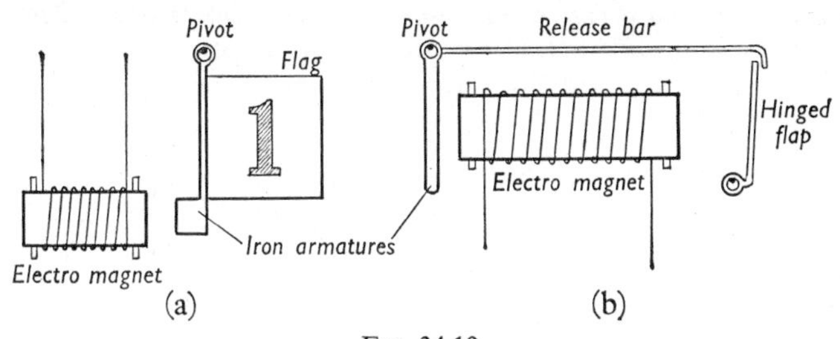

FIG. 34.10
Bell-circuit indicators

is raised and releases a hinged flap. This type has been used on telephone circuits to indicate an incoming call.

Electromagnets can be used to close the contacts of a switch in some other circuit. Such a device is called a **relay.** It is often used in the remote control of switchgear. The arrangement of Fig. 34.10*b* could be used to start a relay circuit. For example, the weight of the fallen flap could close two contact points and start a current in another circuit. In this case the current would flow until the flap was raised again. More usually the moving armature is itself fitted with contact points and is normally held in place by a spring, so

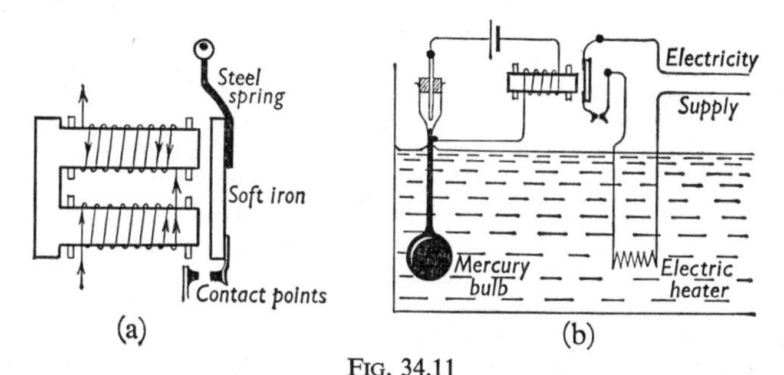

FIG. 34.11
(*a*) *A switch-closing relay.* (*b*) *A switch-opening relay used with a thermostat*

that it flies back when the electromagnet is not in operation (Fig. 34.11). The starter-motor switch on some motor-cars works a relay circuit; the switch controls an electromagnet which works a much bigger switch near the starter-motor.

34.4. Force on a current in a magnetic field. The 'motor' effect. When two magnetic fields are acting together the combined flux is the resultant of the two. This is illustrated in Fig. 34.12 which

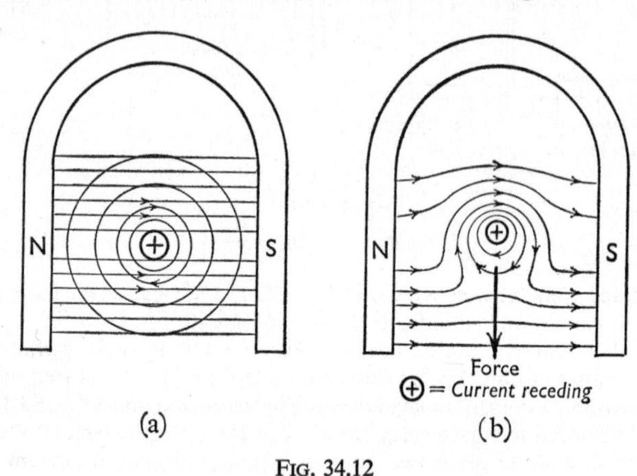

FIG. 34.12

Force on a current in a magnetic field

shows the separate and combined fields of a horse-shoe magnet and a wire carrying a current downwards into the plane of the diagram. The lines become more bunched on one side of the wire, less so on the other; and a neutral point occurs. Note that the combined field is similar to that of Fig. 34.3; for the reasons given on page 343 it is to be expected that there would be a force on the wire in the direction shown in the diagram. Experiment shows that there is a force on a current situated in a magnetic field, a force which is at right angles to the flux and to the current; the current is not pushed along the flux but across it.

Fig. 34.13 shows an experimental way of showing this effect, using a long strip of aluminium tape carrying a current of several amperes and set flat on a bench between magnet poles. It is found that the tape is not attracted to either pole of the magnet, but is either lifted upwards off the bench or is pressed flat against the bench. For the conditions shown in Fig. 34.13 the tape is lifted up.

This effect of a magnetic field on a current has been put to many uses, e.g. in galvanometers, in electric motors. Fleming found a rule which applies to it, a rule known as **Fleming's left-hand rule** (Fig. 34.14). Arrange the thumb, first finger and second finger of the *left* hand to be mutually at right angles. Let the *fore-*

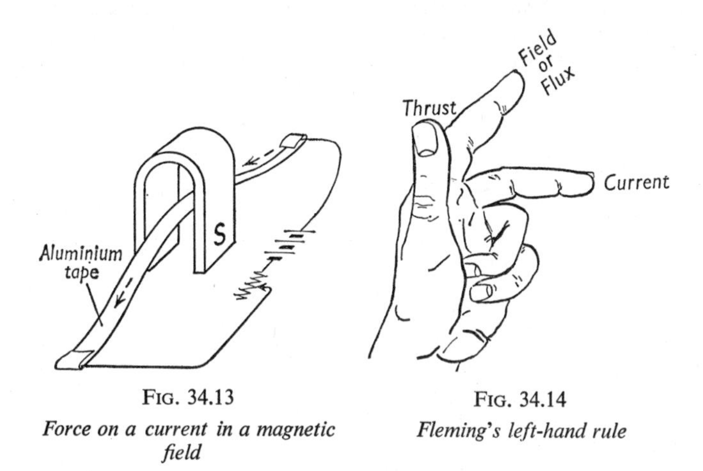

Fig. 34.13
Force on a current in a magnetic field

Fig. 34.14
Fleming's left-hand rule

finger point in the direction of the *field* or *flux*, the *second finger* in the direction of the *current*; then the *thumb* shows the direction of the *thrust* on the current. (Practise the use of the rule in Fig. 34.12*b* and Fig. 34.13.)

The direction of the current in this rule is the conventional direction, i.e. the assumed direction of flow of positive electricity. The rule can be applied to electron currents by assuming the electron current to be equivalent to a conventional current flowing in the opposite direction. Thus in Fig. 40.2*b* a stream of electrons (negative particles) is deflected by a magnet. You will find that Fleming's left-hand rule applies to this case if you point the second finger in the opposite direction to the flow of the rays.

The force on a current in a magnetic field can be explained by applying Newton's third law of motion, i.e. action and reaction are equal and opposite. Thus in Fig. 34.13 the aluminium tape has lines of force round it given by the right-hand grip rule. This causes a downward force on the N. pole of the magnet and also a downward force on the S. pole of the magnet. The fact that the current tries to push the magnet poles downwards results in the current itself being forced upwards. Just as a person can lift himself up by pressing downwards on parallel bars, so the tape is lifted up by pushing downwards on the magnetic poles at the side of it.

A coil carrying a current can be made either to turn on an axle (as in galvanometers and electric motors) or to move to and fro (as in the moving-coil loud-speaker) by putting it in a suitable magnetic field. In the coil-speaker (Fig. 34.15) a *radial* field is used

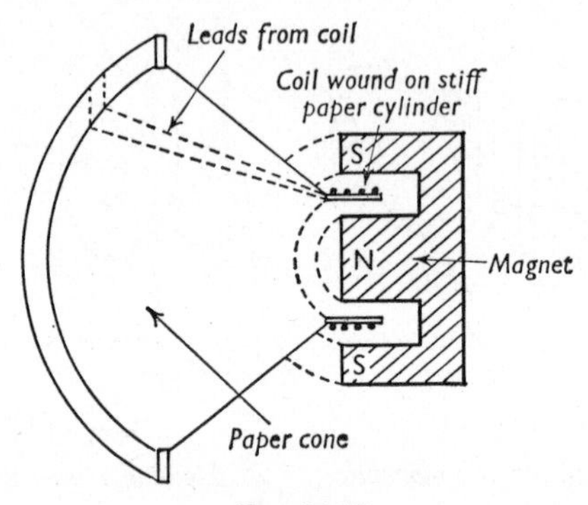

FIG. 34.15

A moving-coil speaker

with the plane of the coil in the plane of the field; a radial field is one in which the flux spreads out like the spokes of a wheel. When a current flows, the wiring of the coil is either pushed in the direction of the arrow or in the opposite direction; you can check this by applying Fleming's rule to the diagram. When alternating currents (originally produced by some source of sound) pass through the speaker, the coil moves to-and-fro and sets the stiff paper cone moving in such a way as to reproduce the sound. To make a coil turn on an axle either a uniform field (parallel flux) or a radial field (radiating flux) can be used; the latter gives a more uniform torque (twist) on the axle. Fig. 34.16 shows a simple model to illustrate the action of a moving-coil galvanometer. A coil of about 10 turns of insulated copper wire (s.w.g. 26-30) is wound on a circular slab cut from a cork; about 10 cm of wire is left at each end for supporting the coil and for making connection to a circuit. These ends are tied round brass pins so that the plane of the coil is horizontal, and a light pointer is stuck to the cork with sellotape or plasticine: plasticine can also be used to trim the balance of the pointer. A current is sent through the coil, e.g. by connecting the ends to a dry cell. When a bar magnet is brought up to the coil in the position shown in the diagram, the coil turns and the pointer is deflected. You can decide whether the pointer tips up or down by applying Fleming's rule to the current directions marked in Fig. 34.16. The detailed structure of a moving-coil galvanometer is shown in Fig. 35.3. It has a radial field (Fig. 35.4*b*).

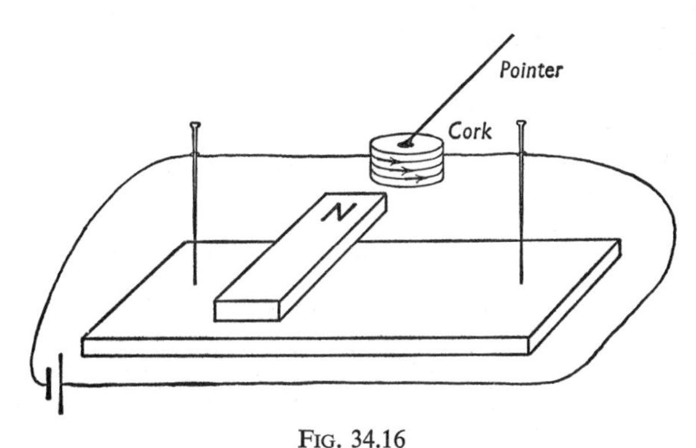

FIG. 34.16

Simple model of a moving-coil galvanometer

To get a coil to continue to rotate on an axle it is necessary, if the supply is direct current, to fit a **commutator** which alters the direction of the current as the coil turns (Fig. 37.8).

SUMMARY

The magnetic flux round a **straight current** consists of **circular lines** of force with the current as their centre. The direction of the flux is given by a right-hand grip rule (thumb = current).

The magnetic flux of a **coiled current** consists of nearly straight lines of force inside the coil. The direction is given by a right-hand grip rule (thumb = flux).

Currents flowing in the same direction attract each other.

Currents flowing in opposite directions repel each other.

There is a force on a current in any magnetic field which is not parallel to the current. The direction of the force is given by **Fleming's left-hand rule,** in which the direction of the **thumb** gives the direction of the **thrust** when the **forefinger** points in the direction of the **field** and the **second** finger in the direction of the (conventional) **current.**

A **radial field** is used to give a uniform turning effect on the axles of electric motors and of many types of moving-coil ammeters.

Questions

1. What is meant by a *line of force* in a magnetic field? Draw a diagram to show the lines of force due to a straight wire carrying a current of electricity, and describe how you would demonstrate these lines of force experimentally.

A vertical straight wire carries a current of electricity. Close to the wire, and west of it, a pivoted compass needle sets with its N. pole pointing south; further to the west of the wire the compass sets with its N. pole pointing north. Explain this, and deduce the direction of the current in the wire.

2. Describe how you would use a small compass to determine the direction of a direct current flowing in a cable when the cable is (*a*) vertical, (*b*) horizontal and lying north-south.

3. Describe the structure of a simple form of electromagnet. State three factors on which its lifting force depends.

4. Describe, with a diagram, the structure and the action of an electric bell. Show, in the circuit, an arrangement of two bell-pushes connected so that either can operate the bell.

5. Draw a circuit diagram to show how a bell-push, a battery and an electromagnetic relay could be used to set an alarm-bell ringing as a result of a single push on the switch. Explain how your circuit acts.

6. Explain the fact that two iron bars, placed side by side in a horizontal solenoid, spring apart when a direct current is passed through the solenoid. What will be the effect of reversing the current?

7. Describe a simple experiment which illustrates the fact that a force acts on a current situated in a magnetic field. State a rule for the direction of the force in relation to the directions of the magnetic field and the current.

Draw two small circles, A and B, about 5 cm apart, to represent a section through two parallel wires carrying currents in opposite directions. Draw one of the magnetic lines of force, due to the current in A, which would pass through B. Hence deduce the direction of the thrust on B. By considering the field which B sets up in the region of A, deduce the direction of the thrust on A.

8. A small square coil of wire lies flat on a table over which there is a powerful magnetic field, parallel with a side of the square. When a current is passed through the coil, the coil stands

up on one edge. Explain this, and deduce the further motion of the coil which will result if the current is reversed.

9. Describe, with the aid of a diagram, the structure of a moving-coil loud-speaker. Explain how it will act when an alternating current of frequency 50 cycles/s is passed through the coil.

10. A piece of copper wire is bent twice at right-angles to form three sides of a square. It is set vertically so that it rests with its ends dipping in two vertical test-tubes containing mercury. The test-tubes are put in series with a 2-volt accumulator and a switch, and the middle section of the copper wire is in a strong horizontal magnetic-field. When the switch is closed the wire jumps upwards to a considerable height. Draw a diagram of the arrangement, showing how you would produce the strong magnetic field, and give an explanation of the effect.

CHAPTER 35

Galvanometers. Ammeters. Voltmeters. Potential. Resistance

35.1. Moving-magnet galvanometers. A simple type of galvanometer, or current detector, can be made by wrapping a coil of insulated copper wire round a compass. This type was first made in 1820 by Schweigger; he called the arrangement a multiplier, since the number of turns in the coil increases or multiplies the magnetic field which the coil sets up when a current passes through it.

The coil is usually set in the magnetic meridian; the field due to the coil is then at right angles to the initial position of the magnet. With only ten turns of wire, wound close to a small compass, a current of a thousandth of an amp can readily be detected. The type shown in Fig. 35.1 is more sensitive because it has many turns

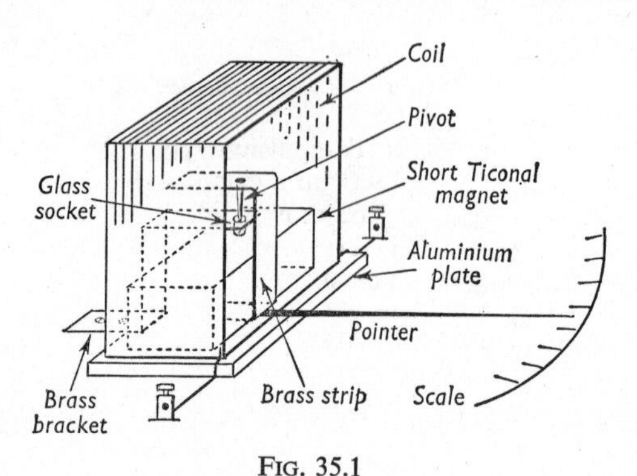

FIG. 35.1

Moving-magnet galvanometer

of wire and because the ends of the coil are arranged to be very close to the magnet poles. The base is made of aluminium, because it is found that when a magnet sweeps across a good electrical conductor the motion is retarded; the pointer of the galvanometer settles in its final position without much oscillation if the aluminium base-plate is used. The effect is due to *eddy currents* in the aluminium (see p. 388). A device such as this, for steadying the deflection of a galvanometer, is called a *damping* device. When the current in a moving-magnet galvanometer is switched off, the earth's magnetic field brings the magnet back to the magnetic meridian again.

35.2. Moving-iron instruments. Two simple types of moving-iron instruments are illustrated in Fig. 35.2. They show the main

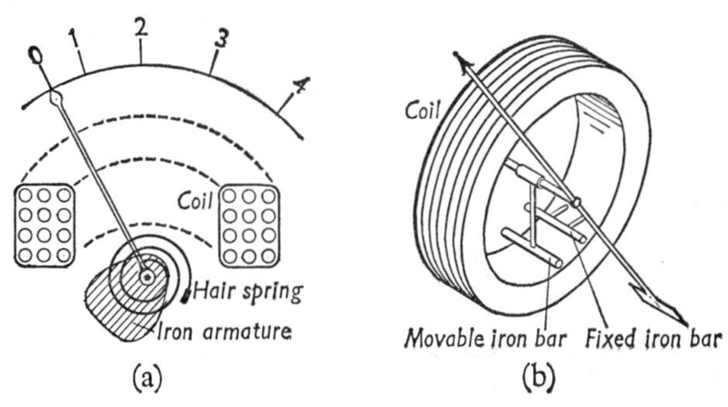

FIG. 35.2

Moving-iron galvanometer

features of the attraction and repulsion types. In (*a*), a current flowing in a short solenoid sets up a magnetic field which attracts the iron armature into it. The movement of the pointer is controlled either by a small weight (gravity control) or by a hair-spring (spring control). In (*b*), which shows a simple repulsion type, the short solenoid has two iron bars inside; one of the bars is fixed and the other movable. Both become magnetised, with like poles alongside, when a current flows in the coil; hence there is a force of repulsion between them. Gravity control or spring control is used to regulate the extent of the deflection for a given current.

Reversal of the current in the moving-iron instruments does not reverse the direction of the deflection; hence they are much used as meters for **alternating current.** As will be seen from Fig. 35.2*a* the scale of the simple type is not exactly uniform; the more modern ones have the iron armature specially shaped to give a fairly uniform scale.

When these instruments are made for use as **ammeters** the

solenoids have a few turns of thick copper wire and their resistance is therefore low. For voltmeters the solenoids have very many turns of thin copper wire. Their resistance is high and they take very little current when in action; the small current which they take has a large enough magnetising force by reason of the large number of turns.

35.3. Moving-coil instruments. The moving-coil galvanometer was first used by Sturgeon in 1836, and was later improved by Kelvin and d'Arsonval. In the most sensitive types the coil is suspended from a phosphor-bronze strip and the coil carries a mirror which reflects a beam of light on to a scale.

The more robust pointer-type instrument has the coil pivoted on jewelled bearings, and is spring controlled. Two hair springs are usually fitted, and they also act as leads for the current (Fig. 35.3, Pl. 32). The coil is wound on a copper or an aluminium frame

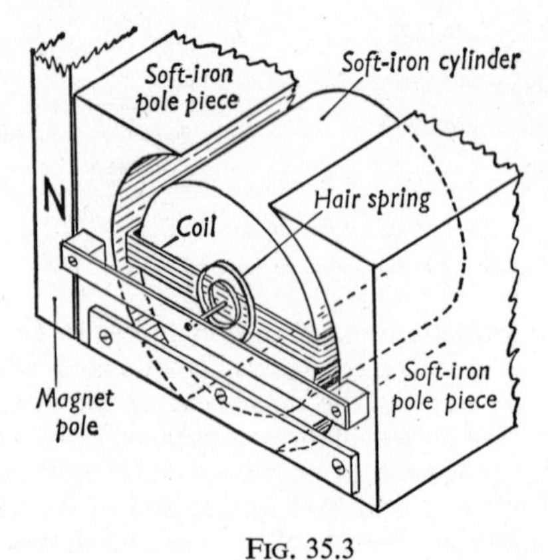

FIG. 35.3
Moving-coil galvanometer (pivoted type)

and this plays an important part in the damping of the instrument. As the frame moves across the magnetic flux a current becomes induced in it; this opposes the motion and makes the galvanometer dead-beat in its action. The coil rotates in the gap between curved iron pole-pieces and a soft-iron cylinder which is bolted to the framework of the instrument. The soft-iron cylinder concentrates the flux in the gap so that the lines seem to radiate from the centre of the cylinder, giving a *radial* field. Fig. 35.4 shows the directions of the forces on the wiring in a parallel field and in a

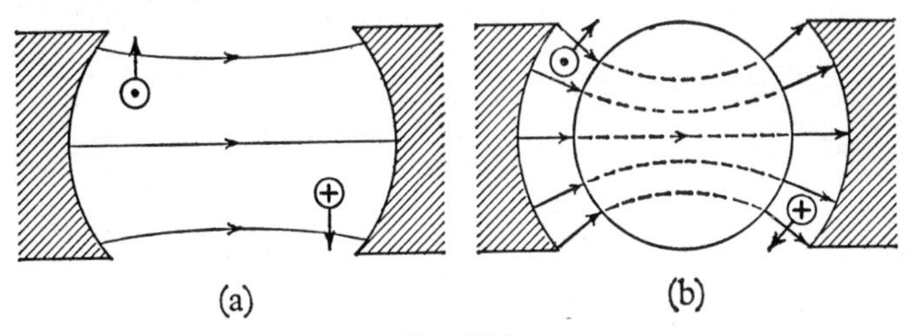

FIG. 35.4

(a) Forces on a coil in a uniform field. (b) Forces on a coil in a radial field

radial field. In a radial field the forces on the wiring are at right angles to the plane of the coil in all its positions. This gives the maximum turning effect wherever the coil is situated; as a result the scale of the instrument is a uniform one.

The pivoted moving-coil galvanometer has the following advantages. (i) It can be made very sensitive. (ii) It is not affected by stray magnetic fields, unless these fields are very strong. (iii) It has a uniform scale. (iv) When the coil is wound on a conducting frame, no separate damping device is needed. (v) It is robust, and can be constructed to be easily portable.

These galvanometers are usually constructed with a full-scale reading which is a matter of milliamps. Instruments with this sort of range can readily be converted to ammeters or to voltmeters. They are often fitted with switches connected to resistance attachments which then make them *multi-range* instruments. Examples of this are the Avo-meters and the Crompton All-Tests and Universal Indicators.

35.4. Ammeters and voltmeters. (a) Ammeters. An ammeter is designed to have a low resistance, generally a fraction of an ohm, and is connected in series with the line of current flow. It thus has little effect on the total resistance of the circuit.

Any sensitive galvanometer can be converted to an ammeter by the addition of a **shunt.** This acts as a by-pass, shunting some of the current away from the meter; and, because it is connected in parallel, it reduces the resistance of the meter. The Crompton All-Tests and Universal Indicators normally read up to 15 mA and have a coil-resistance of 5 ohms. By connecting 5 ohms in parallel, the incoming current is divided equally between the two. So that when the meter reads 15 mA there is a current of 30 mA in the main circuit. The range of the meter has been doubled and it now reads to 0·03 A (Fig. 35.5). By putting nine 5-ohm coils in parallel with each other and in parallel with the meter (making in all ten channels for the current), the current in the main circuit would be ten times that in the meter. But nine 5-ohm coils in parallel have a resistance of $\frac{5}{9}$ ohm; so $\frac{5}{9}$ ohm in parallel with this meter will increase its range ten times. In general the range of a meter can be increased n times by fitting it with a shunt which is $1/(n-1)$th of the resistance of the meter. The meter and its shunt are then equivalent to n meters in parallel.

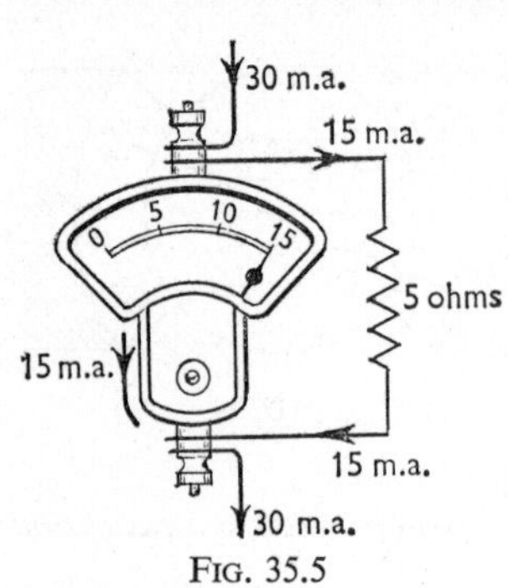

FIG. 35.5

Increasing the range of an ammeter by fitting a shunt resistance (a resistance in parallel)

EXAMPLE 1. *A milliammeter of resistance* 5 *ohms has a full-scale reading of* 15 *mA. Calculate* (a) *the shunt required to convert it to an ammeter reading to* 1·5 *A*, (b) *the resistance of the ammeter so formed.*

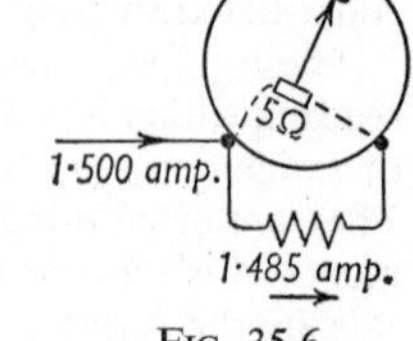

FIG. 35.6

As shown in Fig. 35.6, an input current of 1·500 A makes the pointer move to the 15 mark, showing 15 mA or 0·015 A in the milliammeter. Therefore, by difference, the current in the shunt is 1·500 − 0·015 = 1·485 A.

Let S ohms be the resistance of the shunt. Then since the potential drop is the same for the coil as for the shunt,

$$1{\cdot}485\ S = 0{\cdot}015 \times 5$$

$$\therefore\ S = \frac{15}{1485} \times 5 = \frac{1}{99} \text{ of } 5 = 0{\cdot}0505$$

Shunt resistance = 0·0505 ohm

The resistance of the ammeter can be found by applying the formula for resistances in parallel, or by applying the Ohm equation to the meter as a whole.

Let R ohms = resistance of the ammeter.

Then $\quad 1{\cdot}500 \times R = 0{\cdot}015 \times 5$

whence $\quad R = 0{\cdot}0500$

Resistance of the ammeter = 0·0500 ohm

(Note that the range of the meter has been increased 100-fold by using a shunt which has $\frac{1}{99}$th of the resistance of the meter.)

EXAMPLE 2. *Fig. 35.7 shows a galvanometer of resistance* 6 *ohms fitted with a* 2-*ohm shunt. The current in the galvanometer is* 0·13 *A. Calculate* (a) *the current* I *in the main circuit,* (b) *the combined resistance of the meter and shunt.*

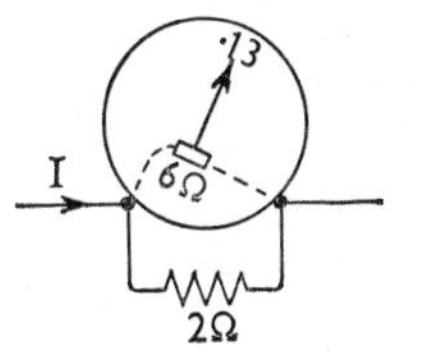

FIG. 35.7

Let V volts be the p.d. across the terminals and i amp the current in the shunt.

Then $\quad V = 6 \times 0{\cdot}13 = 2 \times i$

$\therefore\ i = 0{\cdot}39$

$\therefore\ I = 0{\cdot}39 + 0{\cdot}13 = 0{\cdot}52$

Current in the main circuit = 0·52 A.

The combined resistance = $2 \times 6/(2+6) = 1{\cdot}5$ ohms

(b) Voltmeters. Any meter which is used to measure potential is connected with its terminals joined to the two points whose p.d. is required. If the two points are part of an electric circuit, the meter is thus connected in parallel with the circuit.

The ideal voltmeter would take no current from the circuit. There are *electrostatic voltmeters* which meet this ideal condition, e.g. the gold-leaf electroscope. The ideal condition also occurs in the *potentiometer* (p. 361), which can be made both sensitive and accurate.

All other types of voltmeter are designed to have a high resistance. Moving-iron voltmeters, commonly used for alternating potentials, have many turns of thin wire for the coil. Direct current voltmeters are usually sensitive moving-coil galvanometers fitted with a suitable series resistance. This resistance may be fitted inside the case of the meter, or fitted as an external attachment.

A meter reading up to 15 milliamp and having a coil-resistance of 5 ohms will read up to 15 volts if a resistance of 995 ohms is connected in series. This brings the total resistance to 1000 ohms, and to send 15 milliamp through this needs

$$\frac{15}{1000} \times 1000 = 15 \text{ volts}$$

This illustrates a typical medium-resistance voltmeter. Its total resistance is not particularly high, the current it takes at full-scale deflection is not in all circumstances negligible. It is used mainly for low-resistance circuits; it is not suitable for testing the e.m.f.s of cells whose resistance is more than a few ohms.

EXAMPLE 3. *A sensitive galvanometer, scaled* 0-10 *and of resistance* 80 *ohms, gives a full-scale deflection for a current of* $\frac{1}{2}$ *mA. Calculate the additional resistance needed to convert it to a voltmeter reading to* 10 *volts.*

Let the additional series resistance $= R$ ohms.

A p.d. of 10 V brings the pointer to the 10 mark, showing a current of $\frac{1}{2} \times 10^{-3}$ A

$$10 = \tfrac{1}{2} \times 10^{-3}(R + 80)$$
$$20{,}000 = R + 80$$
$$R = 19{,}920$$

Hence a series resistance of 19,920 ohms is required. (The total resistance of the meter will then be 20,000 ohms.)

This meter has a resistance of 2000 ohms per volt at full-scale deflection, and at full-scale deflection it takes only $\frac{1}{2}$ mA from the circuit to which it is attached.

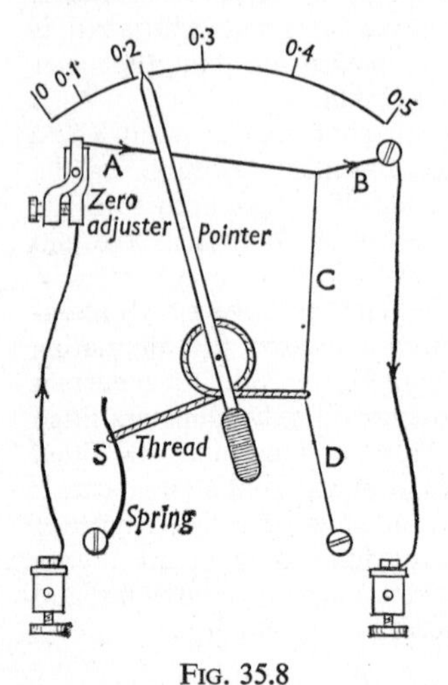

FIG. 35.8

Hot-wire ammeter

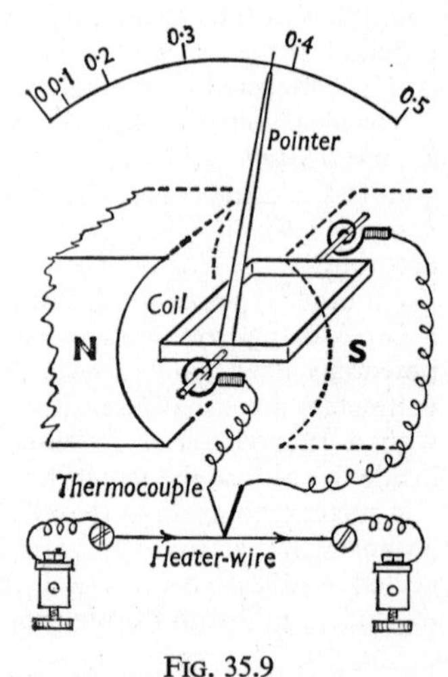

FIG. 35.9

Thermo-couple ammeter

35.5. Hot-wire instruments. These depend on the expansion of a wire which is heated by the current. They are used chiefly as ammeters, and since the heating effect does not depend on the direction of the current they can be used for a.c. as well as d.c. The current is passed through a length of fine platinum or nichrome wire AB (Fig. 35.8). As a result of expansion the wire sags, and so makes the phosphor-bronze wire CD become slack. The slack is taken up by a spring S acting on a thread attached to CD and passing round the drum of a small pulley, which turns as the slack is taken up. The pointer is mounted on the pulley and turns with it.

In the **thermo-couple ammeter** (Fig. 35.9) the heater-wire is used to warm one junction of a thermo-couple which is connected to a sensitive moving-coil galvanometer. The e.m.f. of the heated thermo-junction gives a small current and so causes the pointer to move to an extent depending on the current in the heater-wire. The meter will detect currents of the order of a few milliamp, and is particularly useful for measuring high-frequency alternating currents such as occur in radio circuits.

35.6. Measurement of potential. The potentiometer. The potential difference between two points is usually found by joining each terminal of a voltmeter to each of the two points. If necessary the pointer should be adjusted to zero by means of the zero adjustment.

A voltmeter can be checked against a standard voltmeter by connecting the two in parallel.

Although voltmeters are commonly used to measure p.d.s, a **potentiometer** is always used when great accuracy is needed. The simplest form of potentiometer consists of a uniform resistance wire (usually 50, 100, or 200 cm long) stretched over a scale and carrying a constant current. For such a wire the **p.d.** between any two points in it is **directly proportional to the length of wire** between the two points.

The scale under the wire is a potential scale, each centimetre representing some fraction of a volt. Because the scale is so much longer than a normal voltmeter scale the instrument is more accurate than an ordinary voltmeter. To make use of this long scale we apply the principle of potential balance; **if two points are at the same potential no current flows between them.** Fig. 35.10 shows a simple potentiometer circuit for the comparison of the e.m.f.s of two cells, e.g. a dry cell and a Daniell cell. An accumulator is used to supply a steady current through the potentiometer wire; the dry cell (e.m.f. about $1\frac{1}{2}$ volts) is connected to a sensitive centre-zero galvanometer, a protective resistor R (about

1000 ohms) and a movable contact P, known as a probe or a jockey. The cell and the accumulator have like poles connected to the zero end of the wire. The diagram shows this as a common negative connection, but a common positive one will do equally well. For the connection shown in the diagram, the potentiometer wire is at high potential on the right, low potential on the left. If P is touched against the 90 mark the high potential of the wire will overcome that of P and will send current into the test circuit; if P is touched against the 10 mark, the potential of the wire will be so low that the test circuit will send current into the supply circuit, and the galvanometer will then be deflected in the opposite direction. Between these two points you will be able to find a contact position for P such that the galvanometer deflection is neither to the right nor to the left, i.e. no current flows. This point is known as the **balance point,** P_1, the corresponding length from the zero end is known as the **balance length,** l_1 cm.

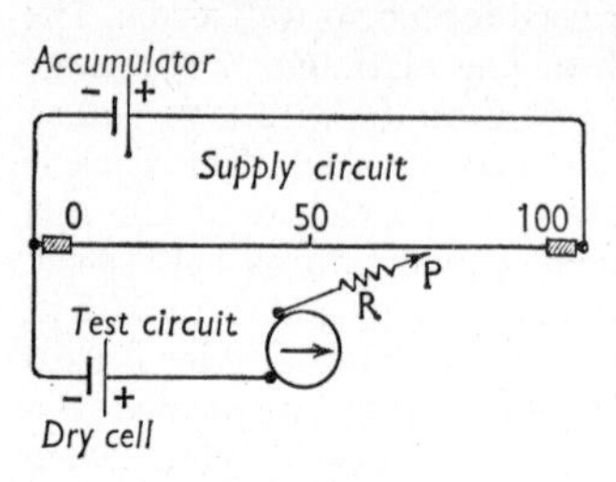

FIG. 35.10

Potentiometer circuit

If the resistor R is removed or short-circuited it will be found that the balance point is still at P_1 but that the slightest movement of the probe away from P_1 causes a marked deflection, i.e. the potentiometer-balance is now **more sensitive.** By repeating the experiment with a Daniell cell (e.m.f. about 1 volt) in place of the dry cell, the balance point P_2 will be nearer the zero, the balance length l_2 will be less than l_1. The lengths l_1 and l_2 give a comparison of the e.m.f.s of the two cells, i.e. if the e.m.f.s of the dry and Daniell cells are E_1 and E_2 respectively, then $E_1/E_2 = l_1/l_2$.

A potentiometer thus acts like a voltmeter with the following properties:

(i) The scale is uniform and is a long one.

(ii) The 'pointer' (the probe or jockey) is hand-operated, the right position on the scale being found by a null method (no current in the galvanometer).

(iii) At the balance point, no current is taken from the circuit under test. The connection to the test circuit is, in effect, electrostatic.

35.7. Measurement of resistance

(i) **The ammeter-voltmeter method.** The resistance under test is put in series with a rheostat, an accumulator battery of suitable e.m.f. and an ammeter of suitable range. A voltmeter is connected in parallel with the unknown resistance X. Readings are taken of the current I in the ammeter and of the potential difference V of the voltmeter, for different settings of the rheostat. The mean value of V/I is then calculated.

Fig. 35.11 shows two possible circuits. Circuit (i) is suitable

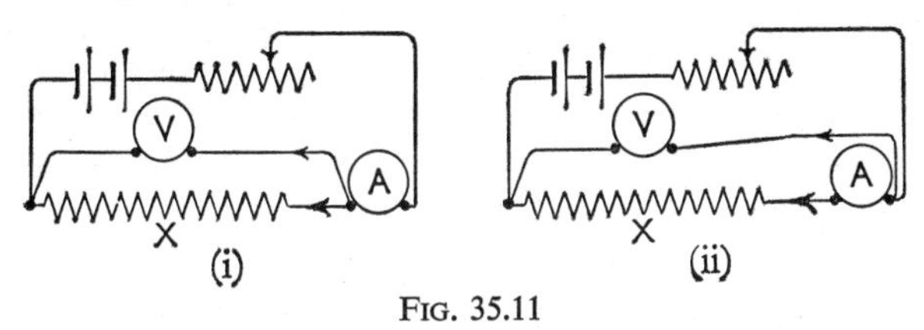

FIG. 35.11

Resistance determination (ammeter-voltmeter methods)

when the resistance of the voltmeter is very much bigger than X. (The circuit really gives the resistance of X and the voltmeter in parallel.) Circuit (ii) gives the combined resistance of X and the ammeter in series. Subtraction of the resistance of the ammeter then gives the true value of X.

(ii) **The substitution method.** This needs a set of standard resistances or else a standard resistance box. The structure of a section of a resistance box is shown in Fig. 35.12. The separate coils are

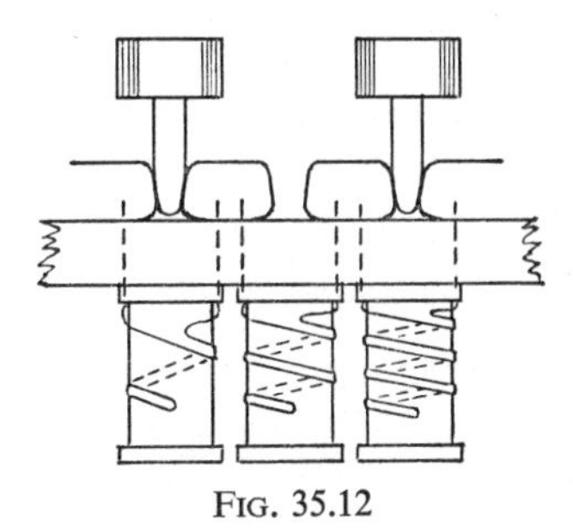

FIG. 35.12

Part of a resistance box

wound on bobbins and are connected to sections of thick brass on the top of the box. The various sections can be bridged or shorted by plugs keys. With all the keys in place the resistance is zero;

removal of a key puts the corresponding resistance in circuit. Such boxes usually have resistances of 1, 2, 2, 5, 10, 20, 20, 50 ohms, etc., in series so that any chosen number of ohms can be obtained by removal of plugs.

The unknown resistance X is put in series with a milliammeter and a source of e.m.f. sufficient to give nearly a full-scale deflection (Fig. 35.13); the meter is shunted if it is too sensitive. X is removed, a resistance box is substituted for it, and the resistance is adjusted until the meter reading is the same as before; this gives the value of X. The method is usually accurate only to the nearest ohm; it is better to plot a graph of meter-reading against standard resistance and find the unknown resistance from the graph.

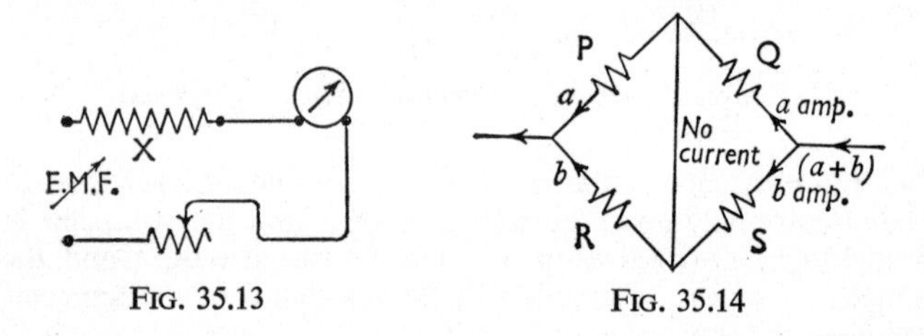

FIG. 35.13 FIG. 35.14

(iii) **Wheatstone bridge methods.** In these methods a sensitive centre-zero galvanometer is used to act as a bridge across two parallel circuits and to detect a state of no-current in the bridge. Fig. 35.14 shows the arrangement in this no-current or balanced condition. Since there is no current in the bridge-over, the p.d.s across P and R must be the same and the p.d.s across Q and S must be the same, i.e.

$$aP = bR \text{ and } aQ = bS$$

Dividing the two equations gives

$$P/Q = R/S$$

So that if three of the resistances of a balanced network are known the fourth can be calculated.

The number of standard resistances required is reduced from three to only one in the **wire pattern** instruments. Illustrations of these can be seen in instrument-makers' catalogues. Fig. 35.15 shows the structure of one type of **metre bridge,** and a diagram of the circuit connections. The copper strip, on an insulating baseboard, has two gaps with terminals to which the known and unknown resistances are connected. When the switch is closed the current flows along the two parallel circuits. A probe or jockey J, connected to the galvanometer, is touched down at opposite ends of

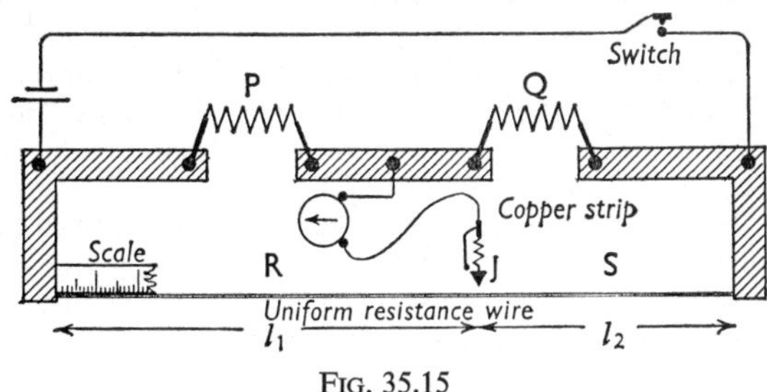

FIG. 35.15

Wheatstone's bridge apparatus (wire pattern)

the wire, when deflections in opposite directions should result. J is then moved along the wire to find the balance point (no deflection in the galvanometer). The protective resistance in series with J is then switched out of action; this makes the arrangement more sensitive, and the balance point can be re-checked with more certainty. When the bridge is balanced $P/Q = R/S$. But, because the resistance wire is of uniform cross-section, the resistances of R and S are proportional to their lengths;

$R/S = l_1/l_2$.

$$\frac{P}{Q} = \frac{l_1}{l_2} \text{ or } \frac{\text{unknown resistance}}{\text{known resistance}} = \frac{l_1}{l_2}$$

$$\text{unknown resistance} = \text{known resistance} \times \frac{l_1}{l_2}$$

Experimental details

(i) Connection of the standard resistance should be made with short lengths of thick copper wire or copper strip.

(ii) Whenever possible, the standard should be chosen so as to give a balance point within the middle third of the wire. Accuracy is greatest when the balance point is at the centre; l_1 and l_2 are then *both* as long as possible.

(iii) The positions of the known and unknown resistances should be interchanged to re-determine the unknown, and the mean result taken.

SUMMARY

Types of galvanometer. Moving magnet and moving-coil types for d.c.; moving-iron and hot-wire types for a.c. and d.c. Damping devices are fitted to make the instrument dead-beat.

The pivoted moving-coil meter has springs to act as controls, and to carry the current in and out. The coil is wound on a non-magnetic conducting frame to render it dead-beat. A fixed soft-iron cylinder concentrates the flux of the magnet and makes it radial, thus giving a uniform scale.

A sensitive meter can have its range increased by fitting a shunt: the range is increased n times by a shunt which is $1/(n-1)$th of the resistance of the meter. A sensitive meter can be converted to a voltmeter by the addition of a series resistance.

Potential differences and e.m.f.s are measured by voltmeters or by potentiometers. The potentiometer uses a null method and is sensitive; its scale is long, so it is accurate; at the point of balance it takes no current from the cell or circuit being tested.

Resistances are measured by ammeter-voltmeter methods, or by a substitution method, or by Wheatstone's bridge.

Questions

1. Draw a diagram to show the structure of any **one** type of moving-magnet galvanometer. Explain how the galvanometer acts, and name any one disadvantage which this type of galvanometer has in comparison with a moving-coil galvanometer of equal sensitiveness.

2. Draw diagrams to show the structure of any *two* of the following types of ammeter; (*a*) moving iron, (*b*) moving coil, (*c*) hot wire. Write notes on their mode of action. State, for each instrument, whether it is suitable for direct current, alternating current or for both; give reasons for your answers.

3. What is meant by a *radial* magnetic field? Describe, with the aid of diagrams, how you could get an approximately radial magnetic field using (*a*) a U-shaped magnet and a short cylinder of iron, (*b*) a bar magnet and a ring of iron large enough to slip over the magnet.

4. A short powerful pivoted bar magnet has a rectangular coil of wire, slightly larger than the magnet, surrounding the magnet so that both are in the same plane. The coil is suspended by a fine wire. When a current is passed through the coil, both coil and magnet are deflected but in opposite directions. Explain this.

5. Explain how a milliammeter of a few ohms resistance can be converted for use as (*a*) a voltmeter, (*b*) an ammeter. In each case give a numerical example to illustrate your answer.

6. Three ammeters A, B, and C are connected in series in a circuit and register 1·30, 1·10 and 1·00 amp respectively. How would you use a standard 1-ohm coil and a standard high-resistance voltmeter to find which of the ammeters is registering correctly? Draw a circuit diagram of the arrangement. If B is correct, explain the fact that A can be made to register correctly by connecting a suitable length of resistance wire across the terminals of A.

7. Two voltmeters A and B are connected in a circuit in series with each other and with a milliammeter of negligible resistance. A reads 3·0 V, B reads 5·4 V and the milliammeter reads 3·0 mA. Calculate the p.d. across the arrangement and the resistance of each voltmeter.

8. How would you adapt a voltmeter, of resistance 2000 ohms and reading up to 3 volts, so that it shall read up to 12 volts?

9. Describe how you would use an ammeter and a voltmeter to determine the resistance of a wire. Point out possible sources of error and suggest a suitable range for the voltmeter if the ammeter has a range up to 2·0 A and the wire a resistance of approximately 5 ohms.

10. An ammeter gives its full scale reading for a current of 0·010 A and its resistance is 5·00 ohms. Explain how you would adapt it (*a*) to give a full-scale reading of 2·00 A, (*b*) for use as a voltmeter to read up to 20 V.

11. A galvanometer reads up to 0·0150 A, and has a resistance of 24·0 ohms. Show, by a sketch, how it may be adapted to read up to 5·00 A, and calculate the value of the necessary resistance.

12. A meter of resistance 40 ohms, shunted by a resistance of 10 ohms, is in an electric circuit. The meter registers 12·0 mA. Calculate (*a*) the current in the circuit, (*b*) the p.d. across the meter-terminals, (*c*) the resistance of the shunted meter.

13. Two ammeters X and Y, connected in parallel, are in an electric circuit. X registers 3·0 A, Y registers 2·0 A. If the resistance of Y is 0·060 ohm calculate (*a*) the current in the circuit, (*b*) the resistance of X, (*c*) the p.d. across the ammeters.

14. Explain the principle of the potentiometer. Describe how you would use a potentiometer to compare the e.m.f.s of two cells.

15. The supply battery for a potentiometer should have a constant e.m.f. The supply battery for a Wheatstone bridge circuit need not have a constant e.m.f.

Explain these statements.

16. Describe a method of comparing the resistance of two wires, giving a diagram of the circuit used.

17. Resistances of 3 ohms, 4 ohms, 9 ohms and 12 ohms are connected to form a balanced Wheatstone bridge circuit. Draw a diagram to show any one correct way of connecting them; include the supply cell in your diagram. Given that the supply cell has an e.m.f. of 3·36 V and is of negligible internal resistance calculate (*a*) the current in each resistance, (*b*) the p.d. across each resistance, (*c*) the current in the cell.

CHAPTER 36

Energy and Power. Electrical Heating

36.1. Electrical energy. Energy is needed to keep an electric current flowing. In a dynamo the energy of the supply comes from the energy put into turning the dynamo when it is supplying the current; in electric cells the energy comes from the chemical changes inside the cell. In a lead accumulator, for example, lead dioxide PbO_2 is reduced to lead sulphate $PbSO_4$ and lead is oxidised to lead sulphate. Both these changes evolve heat. For instance, if sulphur dioxide is passed over lead dioxide in a test-tube, lead sulphate is formed and the tube becomes very hot.

$$PbO_2 + SO_2 \rightarrow PbSO_4 + \text{heat}$$

Yet when PbO_2 is reduced to $PbSO_4$ in an accumulator, by setting electricity in motion, hardly any heat is produced in the accumulator. Similarly the energy for the current supplied by a dry cell comes from the oxidation of the zinc. Conversion of zinc to zinc chloride normally evolves heat; in a dry cell the chemical action results in a flow of electricity instead.

The energy which sets electric charges in motion is later transformed to **other forms of energy.** Often it is entirely converted to **heat** in the circuit. But in electric motors most of the electrical energy is used in doing **mechanical work.** In radio and television transmitters some of the energy of the supply is radiated out into space as an **electromagnetic wave.** In a television tube the power pack of the set drives electrons across the vacuum of the tube. The electrons reach speeds of thousands of kilometres per second. In this case the electrical energy is used in giving the electrons kinetic energy, energy which is transformed to heat and light when the electrons hit the fluorescent screen.

36.2. Electrical power. Whatever may be the medium through which a current flows, the power used in sending a current of I amp under a p.d. of V volts is VI watts (p. 313).

$$\text{Power} = VI \quad . \quad . \quad . \quad . \quad . \quad (1)$$

For a metallic conductor $V=IR$ or $I=V/R$.

Substituting these expressions in equation (1), we can deduce two more equations for the **power in a metallic conductor.**

$$\text{Power} = I \times IR = I^2R \quad . \quad . \quad . \quad (2)$$
$$\text{Power} = V \times V/R = V^2/R \quad . \quad . \quad (3)$$

Equation (2) shows that the heating power of different currents in the same resistance is proportional to the square of the current. This was first discovered experimentally by Joule who, with a calorimeter and electric heating-coils, showed that the heat produced by an electric current in a metallic conductor is proportional to the **square of the current,** proportional to the **resistance** of the conductor, and proportional to the **time** of flow. These are known as **Joule's laws** and can be summarised in the following manner.

The rate of production of heat due to the flow of a current I in a resistance R is proportional to the product I^2R.

Equation (3) is useful when making calculations on electric heaters connected to a constant-voltage supply: the formula shows that for a given voltage of supply the power is inversely proportional to the resistance.

EXAMPLE 1. *Calculate the resistance of each of the following appliances intended for use on a* 240-*V supply.* (a) *A* 100-*W lamp.* (b) *A* 10-*kW immersion heater.*

Let R ohms be the required resistance.

(*a*) $100 = 240 \times 240/R$
$R = 576$
Lamp resistance = 576 ohms.

(*b*) $10{,}000 = 240 \times 240/R$
$R = 5{\cdot}76$
Heater resistance = 5·76 ohms.

EXAMPLE 2. *A current of* 10 *A is passed through resistances of* 7 *ohms and* 5 *ohms in series. Calculate* (a) *the p.d. across the combination,* (b) *the power used in each resistance.*

(*a*) Total resistance $= 7 + 5 = 12$ ohms.
p.d. $= 12 \times 10 = 120$ V

(*b*) For the 7-ohm resistance,
power $= 10 \times 10 \times 7 = 700$ watts
For the 5-ohm resistance,
power $= 10 \times 10 \times 5 = 500$ watts

EXAMPLE 3. *The heater of an electric kettle uses* 3000 *W on a* 250-*V supply. Calculate* (a) *the current it takes,* (b) *the time taken to heat*

1500 *g of ice-cold water to boiling point.* (*Assume that* 1 *joule gives* 4 *calories of heat.*)

(*a*) $3000 = 250 \times \text{current}$ $\quad\therefore$ Current $= 12$ A.

(*b*) $3000\ \text{W} = 3000\ \text{joules/s}$

$= 750\ \text{cal/s}$

Let the heater be switched on for t seconds.

Then $\quad 750t = 1500 \times 100$

$t = 200$

The time required is 200 s or 3 min 20 s.

36.3. Joule's equivalent (J). When electrical energy is completely converted to heat in an electric circuit there is a definite proportion between the energy in joules and the heat in calories. The constant of proportionality, which has been found experimentally to be 4·185 joules per calorie, is known as **Joule's equivalent,** or the **mechanical equivalent of heat (J).**

The experimental determination of J from electrical standards can be done using the apparatus and circuit of Fig. 36.1. The heat

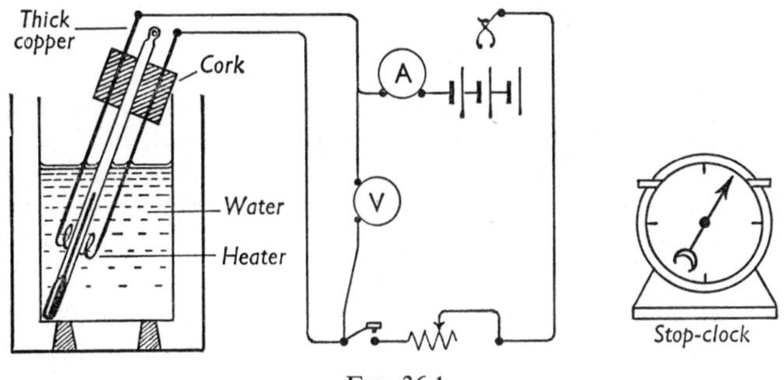

FIG. 36.1

is developed in a coil of resistance wire, about 1 ohm, soldered to thick copper leads. A 6-volt accumulator, capable of giving a current of 6 A, is a suitable supply for the current. The calorimeter is weighed empty and then with about 70 ml of cold water in it. After taking the initial temperature the current is switched on, and readings of the current I and the p.d. V observed at regular intervals until a suitable rise in temperature is obtained. The current is switched off after a definite time, the water is stirred and the final steady temperature observed. (Heat losses are reduced by using Rumford's method, i.e. arranging for the final temperature to be as much above room temperature as the initial temperature was below.)

If M = mass of water
m = mass of calorimeter of sp.ht. s
c = thermal capacity of heater
θ = rise in temperature
t = time in seconds
W = average wattage (i.e. the average of VI)

$$Wt = J(M + ms + c)\theta$$

from which J can be calculated.

EXAMPLE 4. *Calculate the cost of heating* 120 *kg of water at* 15°*C to* 45°*C using an immersion heater. Assume that heat losses are equivalent to the loss of* 0·3 *joule from the heater for every calorie retained by the water.* (*Energy cost* = 1d *per kWh.* J = 4·2 *joules/cal.*)

Number of calories supplied $= 120{,}000 \times 30 = 36 \times 10^5$
Number of joules required $= 36 \times 10^5 \times (4{\cdot}2 + 0{\cdot}3)$
But 1 kWh $= 1000 \times 60 \times 60 = 36 \times 10^5$ joules
Number of kWh $= (4{\cdot}2 + 0{\cdot}3) = 4{\cdot}5$
Cost $= 4\frac{1}{2}d.$

EXAMPLE 5. *A copper calorimeter weighs* 150 *g when empty and* 655 *g when partly filled with water. A lamp connected to a* 100-*V supply is immersed in the water and raises its temperature from* 10·0°*C to* 30·4°*C in* 10 *minutes. Calculate the current in the lamp.* (*Sp.ht. of copper* = 0·1. J = 4·19 *joules/cal.*)

Assuming there are no heat losses,
Heat supplied by current = Heat gained by water and copper

$$100 \times I \times 600/4{\cdot}19 = (505 + 150 \times 0{\cdot}1)20{\cdot}4$$

whence $I = 0{\cdot}74$

Current in the lamp = 0·74 A

In the last example, use is made of the fact that a current of I amp flowing under a p.d. of V volts for t seconds takes VIt joules from the supply and gives VIt/J cal of heat. It follows from equations (2) and (3) on page 370 that heat supplied electrically in metallic conductors can also be calculated from the formulae I^2Rt/J and V^2t/RJ.

36.4. Distribution of electrical power. Wiring of buildings. The transmission of electrical power, whether from a large power station, or from a battery of accumulators as in a telephone exchange, requires cables to conduct the supply. These cables need to be insulated. A rubber or a plastic covering is used for underground cables. The high-voltage cables of an overhead system are bare, insulated from the pylons by porcelain insulators and from each other by the insulating properties of air. The resistance of the cables must be as low as possible. A cable of resistance R ohms carrying a current of I amp requires a p.d. of IR volts. Hence the voltage at the consumer's end is IR volts less than the supply voltage of the generator. R must be kept small to reduce this effect, known as the **volt drop** along the cables. Underground cables are usually made of strands of copper, overhead cables of strands of aluminium (which has a low density and high conductivity) interwoven with strands of steel to give the necessary strength (steel has a much greater breaking stress than aluminium). There is also a *power loss* in the cables. This is given by I^2R, where I is the current taken. If I is large the effect of the I^2 term can be serious. A tenfold increase in current causes the power loss to be 10^2 or 100 times as great. To keep down power losses the power is transmitted at very high voltages, since the supply current is then relatively small. **Large power demands can be transmitted economically only by using a high-voltage supply.**

When alternators are used for the supply, a.c. transformers (p. 390) can be used for transforming the voltage as required. In the grid system the a.c. generators give an output of 11,000 volts which is transformed to 132,000 volts and the supply fed into the main grid network. Sub-stations have transformers which reduce the voltage to 33,000 volts for the secondary transmission lines, and these are linked by 11,000-volt and 6600-volt lines to local transformers giving voltages of 440 for cinemas and industrial power plants, 230 for houses.

The supply cables to buildings are connected in parallel with the main 230-volt output cables, since only in this way can the supply be delivered at the same potential to each. The parallel connection is also used for the different lighting and power points in the building (Fig. 36.2). One of the supply cables is earthed, the other changes alternately positive and negative—usually with a frequency of 50 cycles/s. Where the parallel branches end in wall-sockets there are 3 holes to the socket, to take 3-pin plugs. One of the sockets is connected by bare wire to earth. The appliance to be used is connected to the 3-pin plug by 3-core cable, the leads being usually coloured red (live wire), black (neutral wire) and green (earth wire). The green lead, which is joined to the casing of the appliance, becomes earthed when the corresponding pin of the plug goes into the earthed socket. In this way any short-circuit to the casing is automatically earthed, and no danger can arise from handling the casing (Fig. 36.2). Another of the dangers of internal

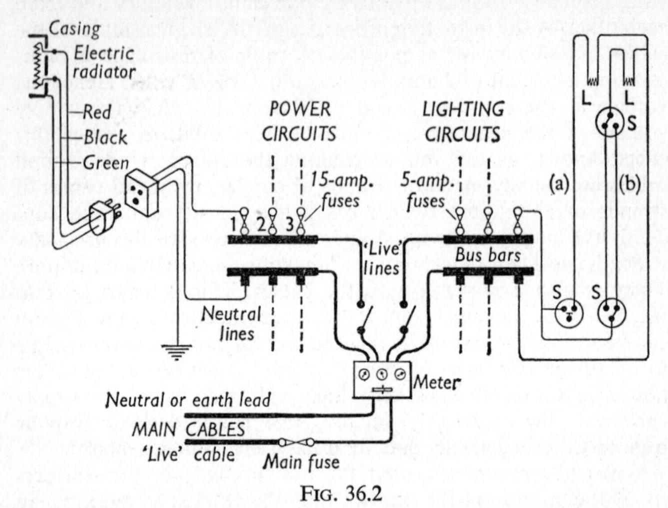

FIG. 36.2

House wiring system. L=lamp. S=switch. (a) Single lighting point and switch. (b) Single lighting point controlled by either of two switches

shorts is safeguarded by putting a *fuse* in each supply line; the fuses are often grouped in a box known as the *fuse-box*, but power-points are often safeguarded by havng the fuse inside the plug which goes into the socket of the power point. Without fuses, the large current resulting from short circuit might make the whole wiring red-hot, burning off the insulation and possibly setting fire to the building. Fuses are thin pieces of tinned copper held in a fire-proof frame (Fig. 36.3) which usually fits by spring clips into the wiring circuit. The main supply fuses are generally inserted in the main switch-box. This consists of a 2-pole switch which completely isolates the wiring from the supply and is so constructed that it cannot be opened until the supply has been

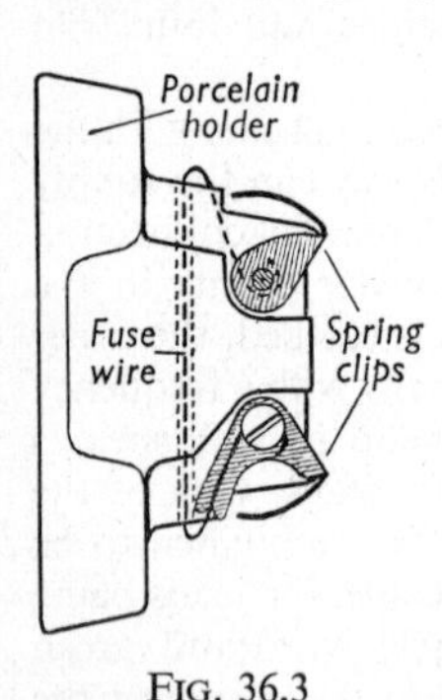

FIG. 36.3

Fuse and fuse-holder

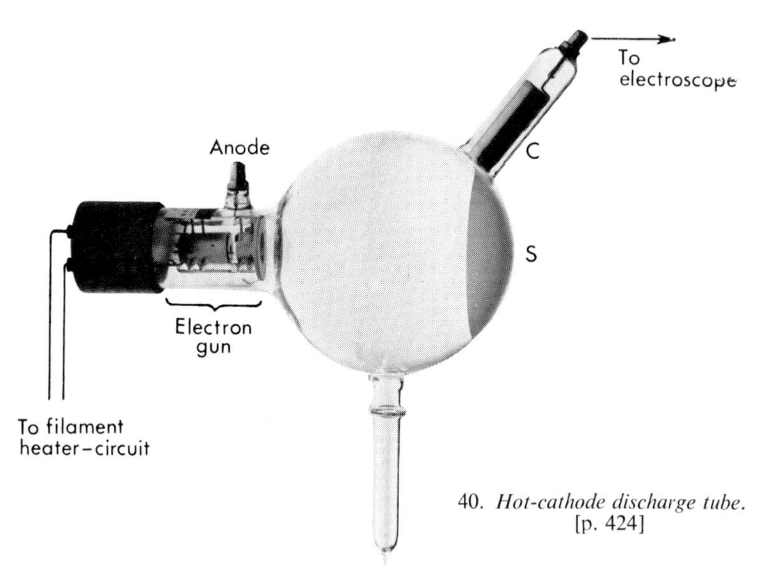

40. *Hot-cathode discharge tube.* [p. 424]

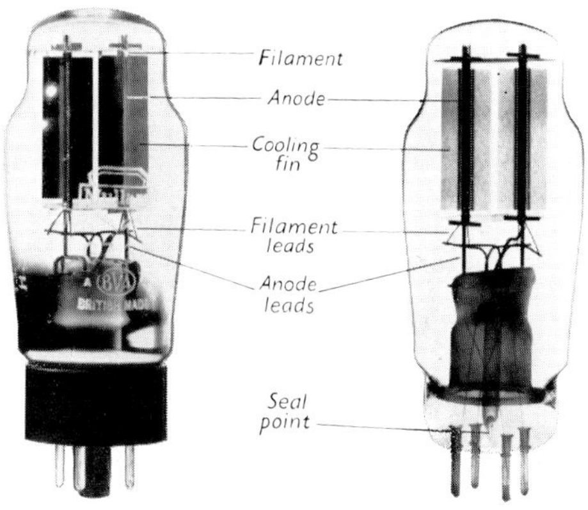

41. *A photograph and an X-ray print of a double-diode valve. The filaments are an inverted V shape and are viewed edgeways in the picture; they are connected in parallel. The anodes are flattened cylinders fitted with cooling fins.* [pp. 425, 430]

42. *The structure of a lead accumulator.* [p. 403]

43. *Tracks of alpha-particles in a cloud chamber. The emission is from thorium* (c+c[1]); *the tracks show two distinct ranges.* [pp. 43[illegible], 442]

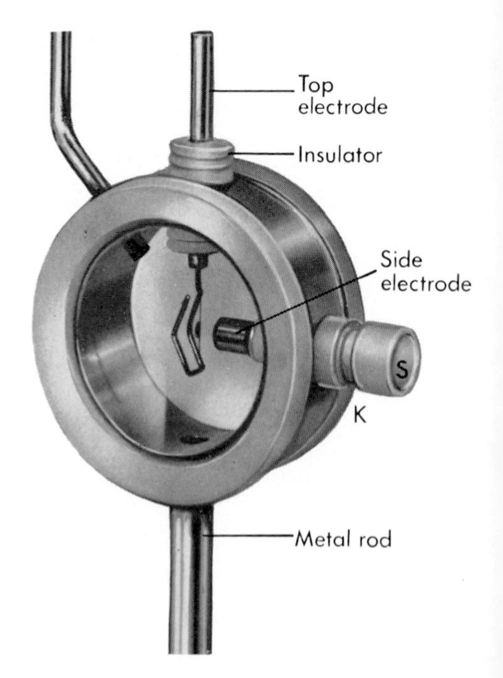

44. *Pulse electroscope.* [pp. 428, 442]

switched off. Any excessive current in the circuit causes the fuse-wire to become so hot that the metal is melted and the circuit broken. The thin fuse-wire has more resistance per unit length than the main wiring, so the heat developed per unit length is greater. It also has less surface area per unit length, and because the heat cannot escape so quickly from its surface the temperature of the metal rises rapidly. The fusing current of a wire depends on the nature of the metal and on the diameter of the wire; the larger the diameter the greater is the fusing current.

36.5. Heating and lighting appliances

(i) **Heaters.** The heating element of heaters is made of *nichrome* (Ni 60, Fe 25, Cr 15) which has a high resistivity and which does not oxidise when red-hot. The actual form of the design depends on the purpose of the heater. In electric fires the wire is coiled on fire-proof insulating material and the gauge of wire is chosen so that the wiring becomes red-hot; much of the heat is then given out as thermal radiation. In electric irons the heating element is a zig-zag of nichrome strip held between insulating plates of mica. Immersion heaters are similarly insulated with mica or asbestos and are metal-covered to prevent the liquid from reaching the wiring. A number of heating appliances, such as electric irons, electric kettles and immersion heaters, are fitted with thermostats to avoid waste of power or to avoid over-heating; for example, immersion heaters become over-heated inside if they are not covered with liquid.

(ii) **Electric lamps.** Early electric lamps, invented by Edison and Swan in 1878–79, had a carbon filament connected to platinum wires in a sealed glass bulb, exhausted of air to prevent oxidation. The filament could not be heated to brighter than yellow-hot (about 1300°C) or carbon particles were driven off the filament, blackening the sides of the bulb. Metal filament lamps were introduced at the beginning of the present century, the metal used nowadays being tungsten. This has a very high melting point (about 3400°C) and can be used *in vacuo* at a temperature of 2000°C without any bulb-blackening. In the *gas-filled lamp* (1913) the bulb contains an inert gas, such as nitrogen or argon, at a pressure of 70 cm Hg. The gas molecules reduce the evaporation of particles from the filament, which can thus be run at a higher temperature, giving a whiter light and a greater percentage of heat energy converted to light. The filament is a **coiled wire** to make the filament more compact and so reduce the convection losses due to the presence of the gas. Better efficiency and an even whiter light is obtained by coiling the coiled filament; **coiled-coil filaments** (Pl. 33) are the most efficient of the filament lamps.

The filament lamp is still much used for domestic lighting, car lighting, electric torches, projection lanterns; but the vapour discharge lamps (Figs. 36.4, 40.1) are becoming increasingly used because of their higher efficiencies. These lamps contain no filament; the light energy is given out by the charged ions of gas or vapour in the discharge tube, or from fluorescent powders on the walls of the tube. Fig. 36.4 gives a review of the progress of electric lighting.

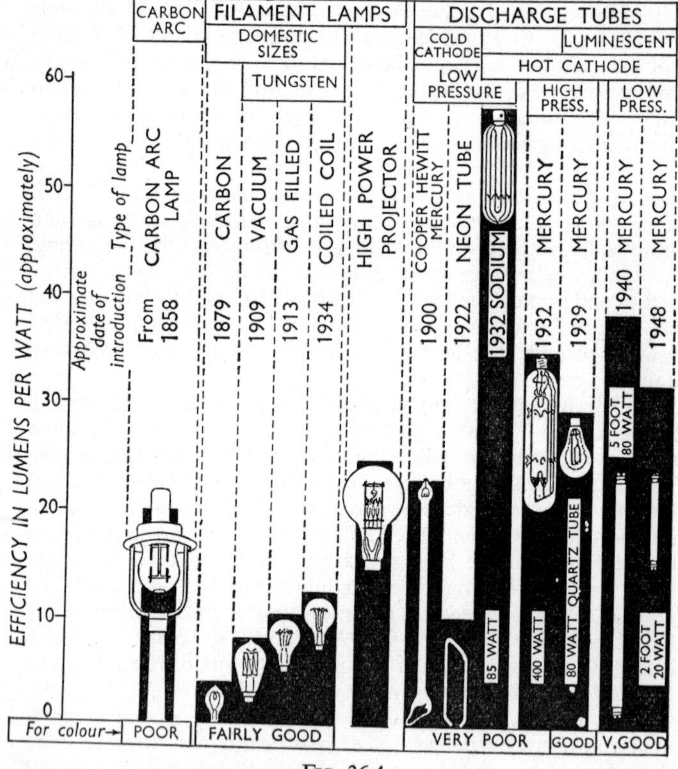

Fig. 36.4

Types of electric lamp. Based on the diagram on page 15 of 'Darkness into Daylight' published by H.M.S.O.

(iii) **Electric arc.** When two carbon rods, connected to a supply of over 40 V, are allowed to touch they become white-hot at the points of contact. When separated they continue to give a dazzling white light, the space between them being a bright region of glowing gas (which contains charged ions in motion). The chief applications of this **carbon arc** are in commercial cinema projectors and in searchlights, where it is an advantage to have a small very bright source. The carbons slowly burn away during use and have to be moved to keep them at the right distance apart. A d.c. arc is more silent in use than is an a.c. arc. On d.c., most of the light comes from a crater in the positive carbon, which is made thicker than the negative one because it burns away more rapidly (Fig. 36.5).

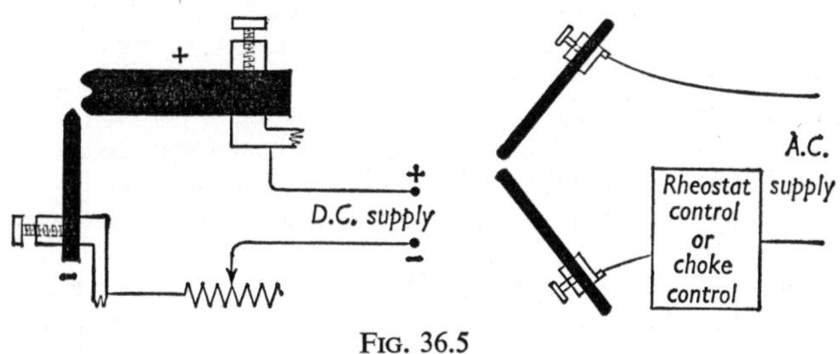

FIG. 36.5

Carbon arc lamps

The carbon arc is also used in electric furnaces, e.g. melting steel, manufacture of calcium carbide from lime and coke, production of nitrates from atmospheric nitrogen.

SUMMARY

Formulae for electrical power. In all circuits, Power $= VI$. In resistors, Power $= I^2R = V^2/R$.

Joule's laws of heating. The rate of production of heat due to the flow of a current I in a resistance R is proportional to the produce I^2R.

Energy and heat. Energy $= VIt$ joules
Heat $= VIt/J$ cal.

For metallic conductors, Heat $= I^2Rt/J = V^2t/RJ$ cal.

Efficient distribution of power on a large scale can only be done at high voltages. The high voltage, if a.c., can be transformed down for local use by means of a.c. transformers.

Safety devices in wiring systems are (i) good insulation, (ii) the use of fuses or cut-outs, (iii) earthing the casing of electrical appliances, (iv) automatic switch-off when fuses and other bare wiring are inspected.

Questions

1. Distinguish between energy and power. Classify the following units as applying to either energy or power. Foot-pound, joule, watt, kilowatt-hour, horse-power, calorie, megawatt.

2. Calculate the power in each of the following instances. (*a*) A 12-V accumulator supplying 40 A. (*b*) A heater of resistance 40 ohms on a 240-V supply. (*c*) A current of 5 A flowing in 12 ohms. (*d*) A motor which does 12,000 joules of work per minute.

3. A lamp is marked 250 V 1000 W. Calculate (*a*) its resistance when in use, (*b*) the heat available from it per minute if all the energy it emits is absorbed. (Assume $J=4$ joules per cal.)

4. Calculate the resistance of a 72-watt heater intended for use on a 12-volt accumulator of negligible internal resistance.

Calculate the power supplied by this heater if the circuit wiring has a resistance of 0·4 ohm, assuming the resistance of the heater to remain constant. Account for the loss of power in this case.

5. Define the *watt* and the *kilowatt-hour*. Express 50 watt-hours (*a*) in kilowatt-hours, (*b*) in joules.

6. Describe the structure of *two* of the following domestic appliances. (*a*) An electric filament lamp. (*b*) An electric kettle. (*c*) An electric fire. Explain two precautions, other than good insulation, which are applied in an electric wiring system.

7. Explain the purpose and the action of a fuse in an electric circuit. How would you test the fusing-current of a given specimen of fuse-wire?

Two lengths of 5-amp fuse-wire fuse at 10 amp if they are in parallel, with a space between them. If twisted together they fuse at less than 10 amp. Explain these facts.

8. An electric appliance is designed to use 1000 watts when there is a voltage of 200 volts between one pair of its terminals marked AA or when there is a voltage of 100 volts between another pair of its terminals marked BB. Calculate, for each of these cases (*a*) the current in the appliance, (*b*) the supply voltage required if connection is made through cables having a total resistance of 0·10 ohm, (*c*) the power loss which occurs in the cables.

9. Explain the fact that the main cables of the grid system carry

the supply at very high voltage, and explain why this voltage is transformed down for domestic use.

10. Give an account of a method you would use to determine Joule's equivalent by a method of electrical heating.

An aluminium kettle weighing 2 kg holds 2000 c.c. of water and consumes electric power at the rate of 2000 watts. If 10% of the heat supply is wasted, find the time taken to bring the kettle of water to boiling point from an initial temperature of 20°C. (Specific heat of aluminium = 0·20. Joule's equivalent = 4·2 joules per cal.)

11. 300 grams of water are heated from 15·0°C to 47·0°C in 240 seconds by passing a current through a wire, of resistance 15·0 ohms, immersed in the water. Assuming no heat losses, find the value of the current. ($J = 4{\cdot}2$ joules/cal.)

12. An electric lamp is marked 8 V 24 W. State what is meant by this marking, and calculate (*a*) the resistance of the lamp when in normal use, (*b*) the time taken for the lamp to use 1 kWh of energy.

Describe, with the aid of a circuit diagram, how you would check the accuracy of the lamp marking, using a 12-volt battery as a source of current.

CHAPTER 37

Dynamos. Motors. Electromagnetic Induction

37.1. Electric generators. Alternators. If a permanent magnet or an electromagnet is caused to rotate, it will induce a voltage in coils which are suitably placed near by. The effect, which is known as **electromagnetic induction,** has been applied to all large-scale production of electrical power. It is also used in the dynamos such as are fitted to motor-cars for the lighting system, and in the dyno-hub which can be fitted to bicycle wheels to work the lighting kit. In the very large generators which supply power to houses and factories the output voltage is nearly always an alternating one, and the machine is then known as an **alternator.** Fig. 37.1 shows the arrangement in diagram form. The iron armature or rotor, wound with coils on its pole pieces, is rotated inside an iron framework which has stationary coils wound on it. This stationary part is called the stator. Pl. 34 shows the details of an alternator.

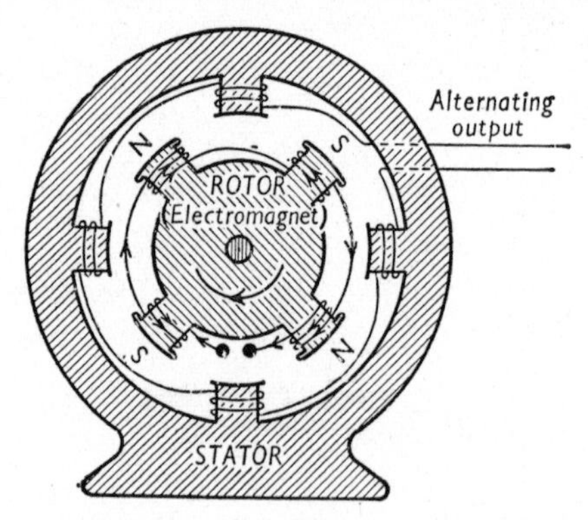

FIG. 37.1

Stationary and moving parts of an alternator

The electromagnets of the rotor are supplied with current from a d.c. generator mounted on the same shaft, driven by a water-turbine or by a steam-turbine. As each pole of the rotor approaches each coil of the **stator** it produces a voltage which rises to a peak and then dies away; as the pole moves away from the coil it produces a voltage acting in the opposite direction. A graph of the effect is shown in Fig. 37.2. The dyno-hub of a bicycle works in a

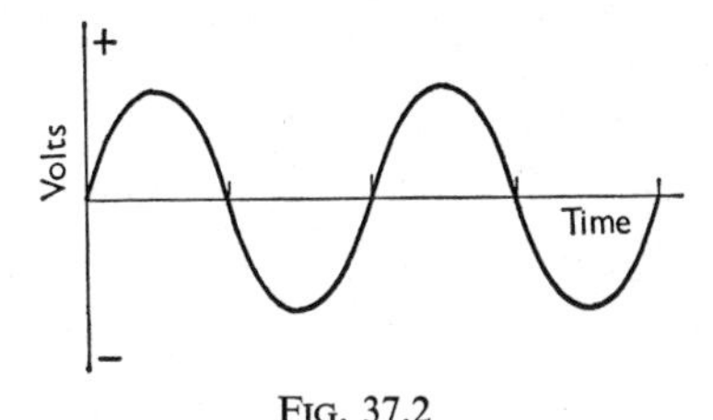

FIG. 37.2
Voltage output of an alternator

similar way. But here the magnet is a permanent magnet and it is fitted as part of the wheel; so it rotates around and outside the coils, which lie in the hub of the wheel.

37.2. Electromagnetic induction. The production of an electromotive force by the action of a magnet on a coil is one of the most remarkable of electrical effects. The magnet does not become any weaker in the process, nor is the moving magnet ever in contact with the electrons which it sets in motion. The effect was first discovered by Faraday in 1831, and he showed that it was caused by the magnetic flux put into the coil; only when the magnetic flux is *changing* is there an induced e.m.f. Thus the voltage of an alternator occurs while the magnetic flux from the rotor-poles enters the soft-iron core of the stator-coils, and also as the magnetic flux is removed from them. To put a magnet inside a coil and leave it there does not give a permanent e.m.f. **Electromagnetic induction is the development of an e.m.f. in a conductor as the result of a change of magnetic flux.** The conditions which affect the induced e.m.f. can be studied experimentally with the apparatus shown in Fig. 37.3 which shows a magnet being put into a coil, of about 50 turns, connected to a sensitive centre-zero galvanometer which acts as a sensitive voltmeter for detecting the e.m.f.

When the magnet is put inside the coil a deflection of the voltmeter occurs. It occurs only while the magnet is moving, and when the magnet is at rest in the coil the voltmeter reads zero. When the magnet is pulled back out of the coil there is another *momentary* deflection, but in the *opposite direction.* If it is pulled out more slowly the voltmeter reading is less; *the more rapid the movement, the greater is the deflection.*

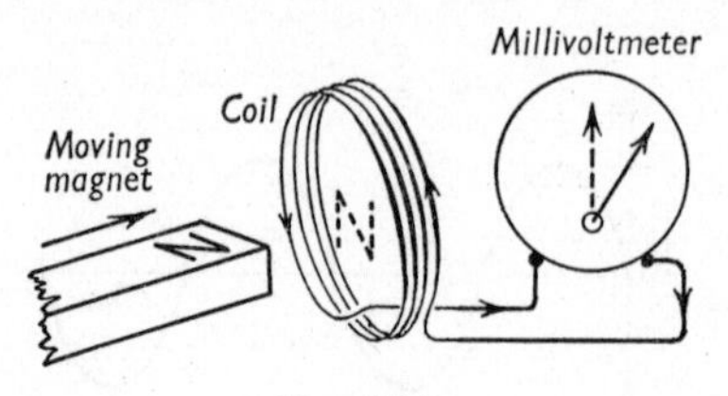

FIG. 37.3

The following table gives the results of an experiment in which different coils were used with a powerful Ticonal magnet, the magnet being pulled out of the coil in one second on each occasion.

No. of turns	e.m.f. in millivolts	$\frac{\text{e.m.f.}}{\text{No. of turns}}$
40	15	0·37
50	18	0·36
60	22½	0·37
80	29	0·36

The results show that the induced e.m.f. is proportional to the number of turns in the coil, being between 0·36 and 0·37 millivolts per turn for this particular experiment. The same results are obtained if the magnet is at rest and the coil is moved over it. These and other experiments led Faraday to think of the effect as being caused by magnetic lines of force being linked up with the circuit; the word *linked* is used to convey the idea of the flux being linked up or coupled with the circuit in a manner similar to that in which parts of a chain are linked together. Thus in Fig. 37.4*a* the lines c and d are linked with the coil, the others are not. But when the arrangement is altered to the position shown in Fig. 37.4*b* all of the six lines of force are linked up with the coil; and the change of linkage seems to be the cause of the e.m.f. The effects were summarised by Faraday in his laws of electromagnetic induction.

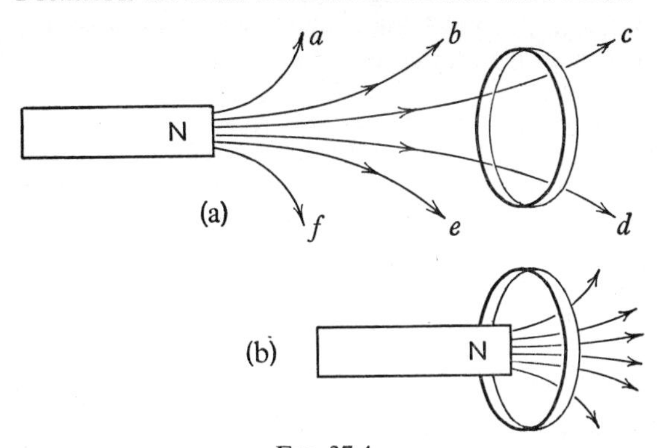

FIG. 37.4
Linkage of flux with a circuit

37.3. Faraday's laws of electromagnetic induction

(1) **Whenever a conductor moves across the direction of a magnetic flux, or whenever there is a change in the magnetic flux linked with a circuit, an electromotive force is developed.**

(2) **The magnitude of the induced e.m.f. is proportional to the rate of change of the magnetic flux.**

By a suitable choice of units, the induced e.m.f. is equal to the rate of change of flux. A change of flux at the rate of 1 *weber per second induces* 1 *volt,* the weber being defined in the following manner.

Definition. If a magnetic flux, which is taken from or added to a circuit of **one turn,** causes an e.m.f. of **one volt** for the duration of **one second** then the magnitude of the flux is known as **one weber.**

$$1 \text{ weber} = 1 \text{ volt-second}$$

A weber is quite a large unit of magnetic flux. Weak magnets have a flux of about a micro-weber, strong ones of large cross-section may reach a value of several milli-webers. The specimen results given on page 382 show that the Ticonal magnet had a magnetic flux of 0·365 milli-webers since it could induce an e.m.f. of 0·365 milli-volts for 1 second in each turn of the coil.

The horizontal magnetic flux of the earth's field is so small that a vertical square coil of side 1 metre, with its axis in the magnetic meridian, would contain a flux of only about 20 micro-webers.

Note that Faraday's laws refer to *electromotive force*, not to current. An e.m.f. is obtained even if the conductor is not part of a closed circuit. If the circuit is closed, the magnitude of the current will depend on the resistance of the circuit.

EXAMPLE. *A magnetic flux of* 4 *milli-weber is removed, in one-tenth of a second, from within an aluminium ring of resistance* 0·001 *ohm. Calculate the induced e.m.f. and the current in the ring.*

Rate of change of flux = 0·004 weber per tenth-second
= 0·04 weber/s
Induced e.m.f. = 0·04 V
Current = 0·04/0·001 = 40 A.

37.4. Lenz's law. The Russian scientist Lenz stated a law for the direction of the induced e.m.f.

The induced e.m.f. acts in such a direction that any current which flows opposes the change in flux, and any motion, which caused it.

One example of Lenz's law can be seen illustrated in Fig. 37.3. A N. pole is approaching the coil, putting magnetic flux into it. The induced current flows in an anti-clockwise direction, making that end of the coil act as a N. pole. So this induced current produces a flux in the opposite direction to the flux coming into the coil. Removal of the magnet causes a current in the opposite direction, tending to keep the flux in the coil. In one case the repulsion of the two N. poles opposes the entry of the N. pole; in the other, attraction between the N. and S. poles opposes withdrawal of the N. pole. The **work done in moving the magnet** against the opposing force **supplies the energy** of the induced current.

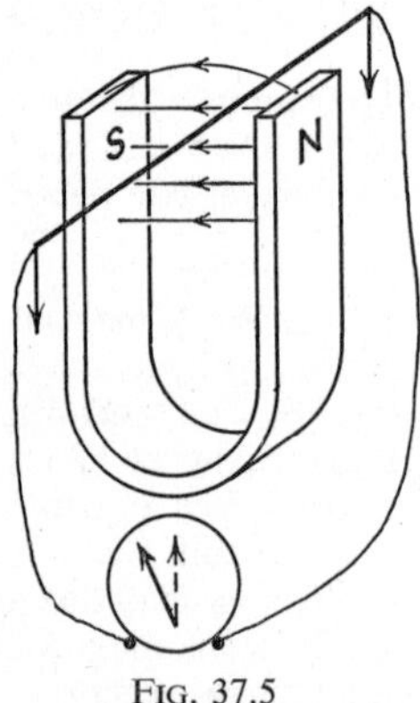

FIG. 37.5

Another experiment which illustrates Lenz's law can be done with the apparatus of Pl. 35. This is a low-resistance coil of thick copper wire, which is balanced so that it can swing like a see-saw. In the ordinary way it will continue to swing for some time; but if a strong bar magnet is placed in the position shown in the picture, any swinging of the coil quickly dies out. The motion of the coil through the magnetic flux of the magnet induces currents in the coil; and, whichever way the coil is moving, the currents oppose the motion of the coil.

If a wire is moved across a magnetic flux, as shown in Fig. 37.5, an e.m.f. is induced; the number of lines of force linked up with the circuit has been changed. Although the direction of the current can be deduced from Lenz's law, Fleming stated another rule which is useful for this particular effect. It is known as **Fleming's right-hand rule.** The forefinger and second finger are used in the same way as in the left-hand rule (p. 349), but the **thumb represents the motion** which causes the induced current. In the left-hand rule the thumb represents the **thrust on the current** in the conductor.

37.5. Simple types of generator. Fig. 37.6*a* shows a simple type of **a.c. generator** in which the magnetic flux is provided by a permanent magnet. A coil rotated in the magnetic flux gives an alternating e.m.f. Consider the side AB (shown end-on as A in Fig. 37.6*b*). It is moving upwards and at right angles to the magnetic

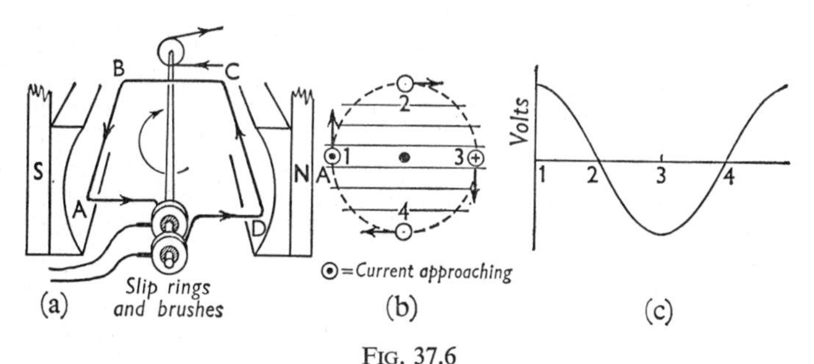

FIG. 37.6

Simple a.c. generator

flux, thus developing an e.m.f. Fleming's right-hand **rule** shows that the internal current is flowing towards A, making A the positive side of the output. After a quarter of a turn AB is moving parallel to the flux and no e.m.f. is induced. During the next half-turn the wiring moves downwards across the flux, giving an opposite e.m.f. which has its maximum value when the wiring moves perpendicularly across the flux. The graph of Fig. 37.6*c* illustrates these changes.

The output is increased by winding the coil on an iron cylinder and by using an electromagnet as the source of flux. The output is connected to the external circuit by means of **brushes** which make contact with **slip rings** (insulated from the shaft) connected to the ends of the coil. The brushes are blocks of carbon.

Some cycle dynamos have a coil which spins in the flux of a U-shaped magnet; others have a permanent magnet which spins inside coils which are fixed in the outer casing; both these types give an alternating supply.

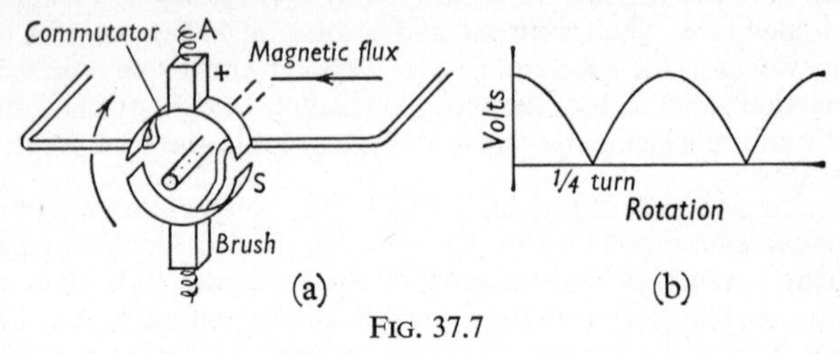

FIG. 37.7

Split-ring commutator of a simple d.c. generator

A **d.c. generator** has a structure similar to the a.c. one but is fitted with a **split-ring commutator** (current reverser) instead of slip rings. For the position shown in Fig. 37.7*a*, A acts as the positive pole for a quarter of a turn. The brush then makes contact with the other segment S which has swung round to meet it. A is therefore again in contact with a wire which is moving up through the flux, and this continues for a further half-turn, giving an output such as is shown in Fig. 37.7*b*.

37.6. Simple d.c. motors. A d.c. generator will act as a motor if connected to a d.c. supply. Thus the arrangement shown in Fig. 37.8

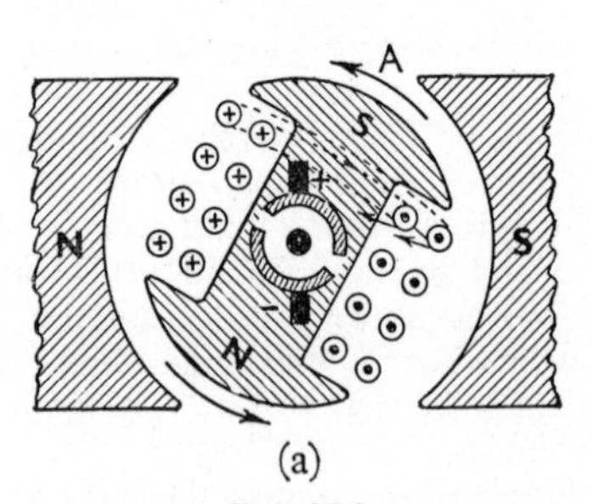

FIG. 37.8

Permanent-magnet motor with a bi-polar armature

can act either as a generator or as a motor. It consists of an iron-cored armature (*bi-polar*, having two poles) mounted on a shaft which carries a split-ring commutator connected to carbon brushes; it can rotate between the pole-pieces of a magnet. In the diagram it is shown acting as a motor, the current supplied to the coil flowing clockwise seen from A. This end thus becomes a S. pole, the other a N. pole. So the pole pieces of the magnet force the armature to turn anti-clockwise as shown in the diagram. After nearly half a turn, the commutator will have been carried round to a position which reverses the current in the coil, changing the S. pole to a N. pole just as it passes the fixed N. pole of the pole-piece. In this way the armature is kept spinning.

If no current is supplied to the machine and the shaft is forcibly turned anti-clockwise, an e.m.f. will be produced in the coils and the brushes will be + and − as shown in the diagram. And if the generated e.m.f. is used to supply current, then the current will be in the opposite direction to that shown in the diagram, for it will be coming out from the + terminal instead of being sent in there.

To get smoother running in a d.c. motor, or to get a steadier output from a d.c. generator, the wiring is set in a number of uniformly spaced slots in the cylindrical iron armature; the commutator then has a corresponding number of segments. The arrangement is illustrated in Pl. 36.

37.7. Back e.m.f. in motors. The current in a motor is proportional to the voltage only if the armature is held at rest. Once the armature begins to move, its wiring cuts across the magnetic flux and this causes a **back e.m.f.** which opposes the voltage of the supply. The current is then very much less than the current which would flow with the armature at rest. In powerful and efficient motors the current is comparatively small when the motor is running free and unloaded. The current becomes bigger when the motor is set to do some work; the load reduces the speed of the motor, there is less back e.m.f. and therefore more current. The armature of a powerful motor has very little resistance, and precautions have to be taken that the full voltage of the supply is not connected when the armature is at rest; otherwise the armature might be burnt out by the excessive current. One precaution is to put a rheostat in the supply circuit to control the current.

37.8. Eddy currents. Putting a block of metal into a magnetic flux causes a swirl or eddy of current in the metal. The flux change induces an e.m.f., and the metal as a whole acts as a short-circuit to the e.m.f. Though the induced e.m.f. may be small (often only a fraction of a volt) the resistance of the circuit is so very small that large currents flow.

Fig. 37.9 illustrates a way of showing the effect of eddy currents which, like all induced currents, oppose the motion which causes them. The diagram shows a pivoted aluminium plate which has been set swinging between the poles of a powerful magnet. The part of the plate which is moving across the magnetic flux acts as a generator; the rest of the plate acts as a short-circuit, giving currents flowing as shown in the diagram. With a very powerful magnet the aluminium plate rarely does more than half a swing; it behaves as though it were moving in a very viscous liquid. If vertical slots are cut in the metal plate it swings more freely in the field. The slots increase the resistance and the eddy currents are almost negligible.

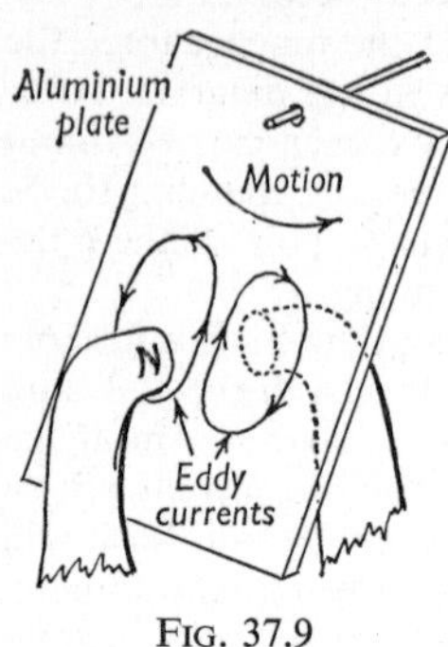

FIG. 37.9
Eddy currents

The counterpoise to the coil in Pl. 35 is made of sheet copper. If a magnet is brought near it while it is swinging, the swing soon dies away owing to eddy currents in the copper.

Alternating currents produce an alternating magnetic flux which can cause alternating eddy currents in blocks of metal near by. This effect has been put to useful purpose in the **induction furnace.** Induction furnaces are used to make small quantities of metal red-hot, or even molten, by heat from eddy currents in the metal. The outside of the furnace consists of a low-resistance coil carrying high-frequency a.c.; the coil itself is relatively cool. Pl. 37 shows an application of eddy-current heating.

The heating effect of eddy currents is not always an advantage; it could cause serious power losses in a.c. circuits (e.g. in the iron cores of transformers) or in the spinning armatures of dynamos and motors. Such iron cores are **laminated** (made of thin sheets bolted together, instead of in a solid piece) so that eddy currents are prevented by the high resistance in their path.

37.9. Self-induction. Self-induction is the production of an induced e.m.f. in a circuit due to the flux made by the current in the circuit itself. It occurs when the circuit is made or broken.

The effect can be shown with the apparatus of Fig. 37.10, which shows a coil of about 1000 turns of wire fitted with an iron core. The terminals of the coil are connected to a 6-V battery and a press-switch. Also connected across the terminals is a neon lamp—

which will not light unless it receives a voltage of well over 100 V. When the switch is closed the neon shows no glow. But when the switch is released there is a flash in the neon, showing the occurrence of a large voltage. It is due to the sudden disappearance, when the circuit is broken, of the flux in the iron bar.

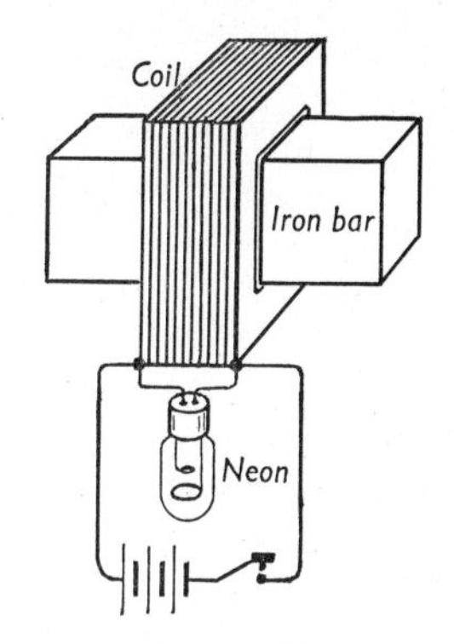

FIG. 37.10
Self induction

This circuit is said to be **inductive**; the coil is called an **inductor** and is said to have **inductance.** Inductors in a.c. circuits are sometimes referred to as **chokes** because they reduce the current; their apparent resistance in an a.c. circuit is greater than their resistance in a d.c. circuit.

An electric bell circuit is inductive, owing to its electro-magnets. When in action, the self-induced e.m.f. is the cause of the noticeable sparking which occurs at the contact points. The switching of highly inductive circuits (electro-magnets, transformers, motors) is usually done with switches fitted with springs, to give them a quick snap-action; otherwise self-induction might cause an arc at the switch.

The wiring of standard resistance coils (Fig. 35.12) is made *non-inductive* to avoid unwanted induced e.m.f.s; the wire is bent double before being coiled, so that the current flowing out and back produces no magnetic flux.

Self-induction occurs when a circuit is made as well as when it is broken. But the induced e.m.f., which opposes that of the supply, is never greater than the supply; all that the induced e.m.f. does is to increase the time taken for the current to reach its maximum steady value.

37.10. Mutual induction. Transformers. Mutual induction is the name given to the induction of an e.m.f. in one circuit owing to a change of current in another. The effect can be shown by coupling two separate coils as shown in Fig. 37.11. A short solenoid is wound with about 100 turns, and another of several hundred turns is made to fit over it. These coils are connected to what are called *primary* and *secondary* circuits (Fig. 37.11). When the primary circuit is made by closing the switch, there is a momentary deflection in the galvanometer; and when the primary circuit is broken there is a momentary deflection, in the opposite direction. Similar effects, but on a smaller scale, occur if the current in the primary is increased or decreased by the use of the rheostat.

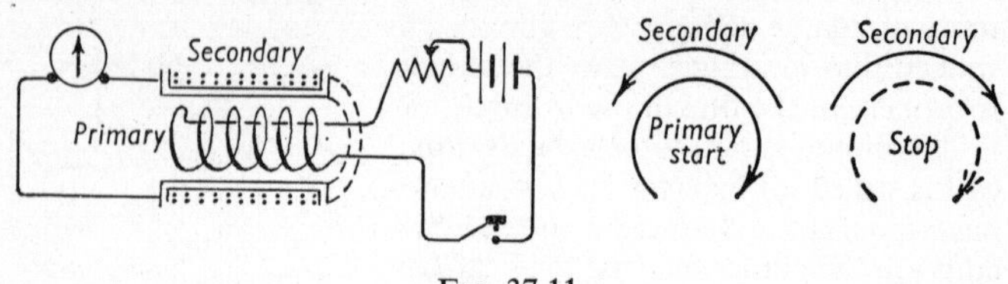

FIG. 37.11
Mutual induction

The effects are due to the increase or decrease of the magnetic flux from the primary which is linked with the turns of the secondary. Fig. 37.11 shows the direction of the induced currents. Bigger deflections are obtained if a bar of iron is put inside the primary. The magnetisation of the iron by the primary current produces a greater flux linked with the secondary.

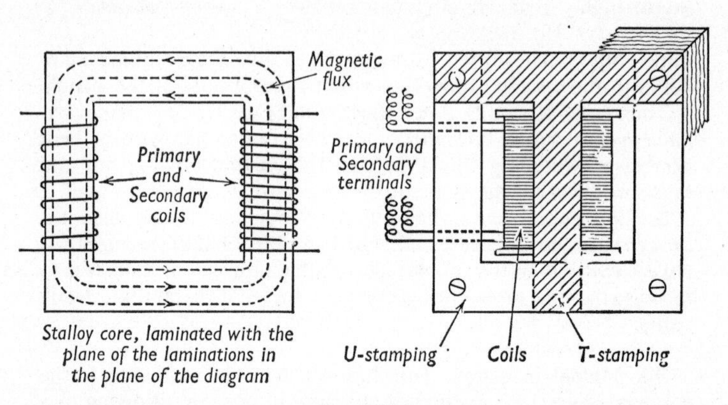

FIG. 37.12
A transformer. The left-hand diagram shows a simple type. The right-hand diagram shows the more usual structure with both primary and secondary coils wound on a central limb

The phenomenon of mutual induction has many practical applications, e.g. in transformers, spark coils, magnetos, car ignition coils. The a.c. transformer is used to transform an alternating voltage either to a higher value (*step-up* transformer) or to a lower one (*step-down* transformer). The step-up transformer has a greater number of turns on the secondary coil than on the primary; the reverse is the case in the step-down transformer. In addition to its use on a.c. transmission lines, the a.c. transformer has many laboratory and workshop uses; it is also used in telephone, radio and television circuits. The general principles of its structure are shown in Fig. 37.12. The core is made of *stalloy*, an alloy of iron and silicon. It is laminated to reduce eddy currents, and is shaped to form a complete circuit of magnetic material with no air gaps. On the core are wound the primary and secondary coils.

An alternating voltage applied to the primary sets up a small alternating current in the primary and a large alternating flux in the core. As long as there is no leakage of magnetic flux from the magnetic circuit, both coils experience the same rate of change of flux; and so they therefore have the same e.m.f. per turn.

$$\frac{\text{Voltage in primary}}{\text{Number of turns in primary}} = \frac{\text{Voltage in secondary}}{\text{Number of turns in secondary}}$$

37.11. Spark coils. The induction coil or spark coil (also known as the Ruhmkorff coil) applies the principle of mutual induction to get a high voltage from a low-voltage d.c. supply. The primary and secondary coils are wound on an iron core which is usually made up of a bundle of iron wires to reduce eddy currents. The primary is a solenoid of fairly thick copper wire with sufficient number of turns to magnetise the core fully when connected to the supply. The primary circuit gives interrupted d.c., a make-and-break being fitted in series with the primary coil (Fig. 37.13). The secondary consists of thousands of turns of very fine insulated wire. Its ends are connected to terminals on insulating pillars; the terminals usually carry metal rods, ending in discharge knobs.

An important feature is a condenser, of capacitance about a microfarad, connected in parallel with the contacts of the make-and-break. Without this the coil gives only very small sparks. When the primary supply is switched on, sparking occurs at the contacts owing to self-induction in the primary coil. The sparking is reduced by making the contacts of platinum. The condenser causes the break to be very sudden. The large e.m.f. due to self-induction charges the condenser instead of prolonging the break by sparking at the contacts.

The inductance of the primary delays the growth of current at the make, and the induced voltage in the secondary is not nearly as great as at the break. The induced voltages at the make and at

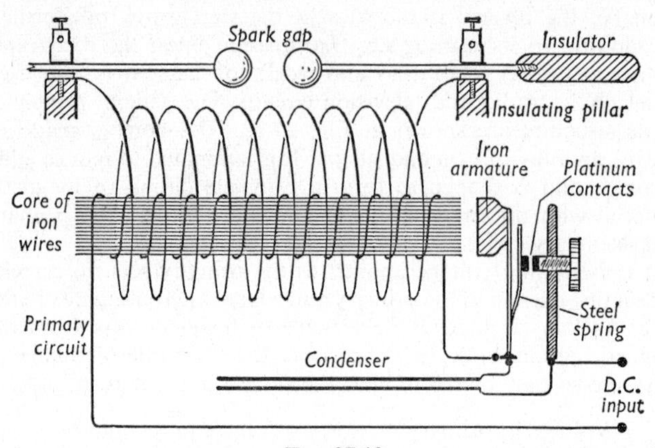

FIG. 37.13
Spark coil

the break are in opposite directions, but the much higher voltage at the break causes the discharge to be nearly one-way only.

The spark coil has been used for studying the discharge of electricity through gases and for supplying high voltage to X-ray tubes; but nowadays X-ray tubes are often worked from high-voltage transformers. A modification of the spark coil is used in car ignition systems. In these the make-and-break is worked mechanically by a cam driven by the engine, and a rotating distributor-switch is connected in the secondary circuit which leads to the spark plugs.

37.12. Telephones. A simple telephone circuit consists of a microphone or transmitter, in series with a receiver or earpiece. The **carbon microphone** (Fig. 37.14*a*) makes use of the fact that the resistance of a column of carbon granules varies with the pressure put upon it. Sound vibrations falling on a diaphragm cause changes in the resistance; with a battery in the circuit, there are corresponding changes of current. In the receiver (Fig. 37.14*b*) these changes of current make another diaphragm vibrate with the same frequency and so reproduce the original sound. The current passes through coils of many turns wound on soft-iron extensions of the poles of a permanent magnet. These soft-iron pole-pieces become magnetised more strongly or less strongly as the current in the

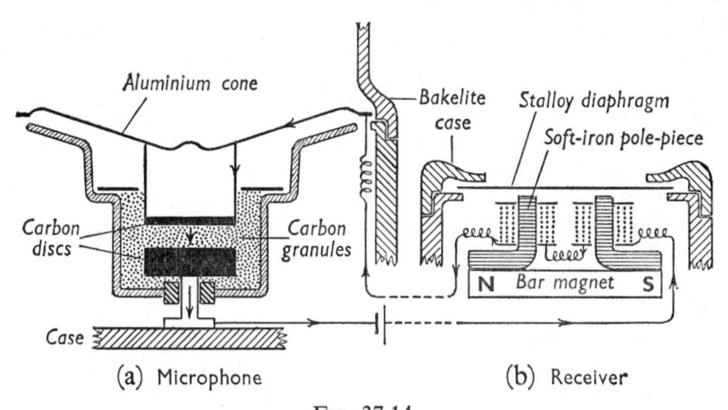

FIG. 37.14

A telephone transmitter and receiver

coils increases or decreases. Their attraction for the iron diaphragm changes in the same way and so they cause it to vibrate.

When a telephone is used for long-distance work the resistance of the long connecting wires weakens the changes in current. To allow for this, a transformer circuit is used to step-up the voltage output of the microphone circuit.

There are several different kinds of microphone which are used in the reproduction of sound. The moving-coil microphone has the same general structure as the moving-coil speaker (Fig. 34.15); the sound makes the coil vibrate across the magnetic flux; variations of voltage are induced in the coil and these cause variations of current in the receiver. The crystal microphone, which is much used in broadcasting and in public-address systems, contains a crystal of quartz or of Rochelle salt which has the property of producing variations of voltage under the varying pressures of the sound waves. These variations of voltage are very small and need to be amplified by means of radio-valves or by means of transistors.

SUMMARY

Faraday's laws of electromagnetic induction. (i) An e.m.f. is generated in a conductor which moves across the lines of a magnetic flux, or when the magnetic flux linked with the conductor changes. (ii) The magnitude of the induced e.m.f. is proportional to the rate of change of flux.

Lenz's law. The induced e.m.f. acts in such a direction that any current which flows opposes the change in flux and any motion which caused it.

Induced e.m.f. in volts = Flux change in webers/Time in seconds

Self-induction is the production of an induced e.m.f. in a circuit due to the flux made by the current in the circuit itself.

Mutual induction is the induction of an e.m.f. in one circuit owing to a change of current in another. The effect is applied in transformers, induction furnaces, spark coils.

Questions

1. What is meant by the term *electromagnetic induction*? Describe any one simple experiment in which a magnet is used so as to generate an electric current. Illustrate your answer with a diagram, and show clearly the direction of the current in the experiment you describe. Upon what factors does the magnitude of the current depend?

2. What is meant by the term *mutual induction*? Describe an experiment which illustrates mutual induction.

3. State the laws of Faraday and Lenz with reference to electromagnetic induction. Describe an experiment to illustrate Lenz's law.

4. A long bar magnet hangs, with its axis vertical, from a spiral spring; just below the magnet is the centre of a coil of wire of low resistance, with its plane horizontal. When the magnet is set oscillating vertically there is (*a*) an alternating voltage in the coil, (*b*) a rapid decrease in the swing of the oscillations when the coil is short-circuited. Explain both (*a*) and (*b*).

5. Describe, with the aid of a diagram, any one simple type of electromagnetic generator. Explain how it acts, and state whether its output is alternating or direct.

6. Describe, with the aid of a diagram, any one type of d.c. motor. Explain the action of the motor.

7. A d.c. motor has a voltmeter connected across its terminals and an ammeter in the supply line. When the supply is switched on the ammeter registers a large current which decreases as the motor gains speed. When the supply is switched off, the voltmeter gives a reading which steadily decreases as the motor slows down. Explain these observations.

8. Draw a labelled diagram to show the structure of an a.c.

transformer suitable for running a 12-V lamp from a 240-V a.c. supply. Explain the action of the transformer.

9. Draw a labelled diagram to show the structures of a telephone microphone (transmitter) and receiver (ear-piece). Show, on the diagrams, the circuit in which they are connected. Explain how sounds falling on the microphone cause changes in the current in the circuit.

10. A low-resistance telephone earpiece, an electric bell, a battery and a switch are connected in series so that the bell rings when the switch is closed. Describe the type of sound which is heard in the earpiece and give an explanation of how it is caused.

11. A solid aluminium flywheel is set spinning. Describe and explain an electromagnetic method of stopping the spin. Illustrate your answer with a diagram.

12. A simple transformer consists of two coils X and Y wound on an iron bar; coil X carries an alternating current. Explain the fact that the terminals of Y have a potential difference which is alternating and that the iron bar becomes hot.

Explain the cause of the humming sound to be heard when the transformer is placed on a sheet of iron.

13. A permanent-magnet d.c. electric motor has an armature resistance of 0·50 ohm. When running freely on a 24-V supply it takes a current of 1·0 A. Calculate (*a*) the power supplied to the motor, (*b*) the power wasted in the armature, (*c*) the power used in overcoming friction.

Explain the following facts. (i) The motor takes more than 1·0 A when it is used for working a machine. (ii) A starting-rheostat is needed in the circuit if the armature cannot safely take a current of more than 20 A.

14. What is meant by the term *eddy currents*, and in what circumstances are such currents produced? Give one example of a practical use of eddy currents, and one example where their formation has to be prevented.

15. If the apparatus of Pl. 35 is at rest and the magnet is moved upwards, the coil moves upwards too. Explain this, and suggest how you could prove that the motion is not due to a draught of air. What effect would you expect if the magnet were put back to its original position? Give a reason for your answer.

16. A short-circuited square coil rests on a horizontal table in a vertical magnetic field. The coil is turned over, using one of its sides as a hinge. Describe and explain the induced current which flows as a result of this action. What is the source of the energy of the current and what ultimately becomes of this energy?

17. Draw a labelled diagram to show the structure of a simple type of alternating current generator. Describe and explain the variation of its e.m.f. during one revolution of the shaft.

A simple a.c. generator, rotating at 25 revolutions per second, gives an output of frequency 50 cycles/s and a maximum e.m.f. of 30 V. State any **one** way in which a maximum output of 15 V could be obtained from the generator, and state whether the output frequency would be altered; if you consider that additional apparatus is needed, show how it should be connected to the generator.

18. Draw a labelled diagram to show the structure of any one type of spark coil. State the functions of the various parts and explain how the high voltage is caused.

CHAPTER 38

Electrolysis. Cells

38.1. Electrolysis. Many substances, in solution or in the molten state, conduct electricity and undergo a chemical change as a result (see pp. 303-305). Such substances are called **electrolytes;** the decomposition of an electrolyte by the action of an electric current is called **electrolysis.** Acids, alkalis and salts are electrolytes; alcohols, oils, sugars and the chemical elements are examples of non-electrolytes. When an electric current is sent through an electrolyte, the electrical leads are known as **electrodes;** the entry terminal (the one connected to the positive of the supply) is the **anode,** the exit terminal (connected to the negative of the supply) is the **cathode.**

Some of the effects of electrolysis were discovered soon after the discovery of electric cells. In 1802 Nicholson and Carlisle decomposed water by the action of a current; in 1807 Davy used an electric battery to decompose the caustic alkalis, isolating the metals sodium and potassium. Faraday, who at one time was Davy's assistant, made many important discoveries in electrochemistry. Since that time electrolysis has been widely applied in chemical industry. It is used in the isolation of metals such as sodium, calcium, copper, aluminium, gold; for the manufacture of caustic soda and persulphates; for electroplating and electrotyping.

The actual results of electrolysis depend on the nature of the electrolyte. But the following generalisations can be made.

(i) Decomposition does not occur throughout the electrolyte as a whole; the products occur only at or near the electrodes.

(ii) At the cathode, the terminal to which the current is flowing, liberation of either hydrogen or a metal occurs.

Some of the chemical changes which occur in electrolysis are difficult to do by chemical action alone; this puzzled the early experimenters. We now know that electrolytes are composed of molecules, some or all of which exist in an ionised condition, i.e. they contain atoms or groups of atoms which are positively or negatively charged. These charged particles are called **ions.** When electrodes are put into an electrolyte, the positive ions move to the negative electrode and the negative ions move to the positive electrode. Ions which make contact with the electrodes can give up their charges to the circuit and become ordinary chemicals, free and un-ionised. Electrolysis is not really a matter of chemical decomposition; it is a giving of charges to ionised chemicals. Because hydrogen and metals are liberated at the cathode (negative) it follows that **hydrogen ions and metallic ions are positively charged.**

Water contains a small proportion of its molecules in an ionised state. These have split up into hydrogen ions H^+ and hydroxyl ions OH^- as expressed by the equation

$$H_2O \rightleftharpoons H^+ + OH^-$$

Copper sulphate crystals contain the substance in a completely ionised state. The crystals are made up of an orderly arrangement of copper ions Cu^{++} and sulphate ions SO_4^{--}. By passing an electric current through a jelly containing copper sulphate, which touches a jelly containing sulphuric acid, the movement of the ions in the electric field can be seen; as a result of such experiments it is found that the copper ion is blue in colour, the sulphate ion colourless.

Fig. 38.1 shows the circuit diagram of an apparatus which can be used to study electrolysis; the electrodes are carbon plates or carbon rods. If distilled water is used as the electrolyte and the switch is closed, the voltmeter will record the applied p.d.; but the current will be barely detectable even though the rheostat is set to zero. *Pure water has a high resistivity* (low conductivity). If the voltmeter is removed and the supply battery increased to 50-100 V, a few milliamp may now flow; and, if you wait long enough, you will see bubbles of gas on the electrodes showing that water is an electrolyte. It is considered as a **weak electrolyte** because of its low conductivity. But if, using the low-voltage source, a little sulphuric acid is added to the water, a much higher current will be obtained. An ammeter with a higher range will be needed as more acid is added. The evolution of gas at the electrodes will be much more rapid. If the current is stopped it will be found that the voltmeter registers a small voltage. This is an example of **polarisation,** the formation of new poles owing to electrolysis; the hydrogen and oxygen on the plates act as an electric cell.

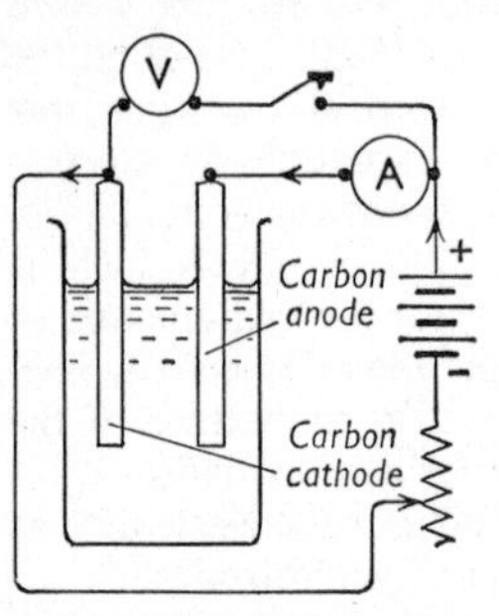

FIG. 38.1

Chemical analysis shows that the mass of sulphuric acid does not change during the electrolysis; only the water is decomposed.

In the electrolysis of water the hydrogen ions move to the cathode, give up their charge and become hydrogen atoms H which link together to form hydrogen molecules H_2. In similar fashion the hydroxyl ions give rise to uncharged hydroxyl groups OH, and the following action then takes place.

$$4OH = 2H_2O + O_2$$

Addition of sulphuric acid to the water increases the total number of ions present and so makes the liquid more conducting, but it does not affect the final products of the electrolysis because the hydroxyl ions are more readily discharged than the sulphate ions. Nitric acid, sodium sulphate, sodium hydroxide also increase the conductivity of water without affecting its electrolysis.

The electrolysis of copper sulphate (p. 304) is not so simple. The solution contains ions from the water as well as the copper and sulphate ions. It is a **mixed electrolyte.** The hydrogen ions and the copper ions move towards the cathode, but it is only the copper ions which are discharged, giving a copper plating. The hydroxyl ions and the sulphate ions move to the anode. If the anode is carbon or platinum, only the hydroxyl ions are discharged and so oxygen is evolved. If the anode is copper, **neither of the negative ions is discharged** at all; instead, copper atoms in the anode give two electrons to the circuit and so become copper ions which mix with the solution.

$$Cu - 2e = Cu^{++}$$

In this way the strength of the copper sulphate solution remains unchanged. Whenever objects are electroplated, the anode of the plating vat is made of the same metal as the metal which is being deposited.

38.2. Faraday's laws of electrolysis. (i) **The mass, m, of any substance liberated as a result of electrolysis is directly proportional to the quantity of electricity, q, passed through the electrolyte.**

$$m \propto q \text{ or } m \propto It$$

where I = current, t = time of flow.

(ii) **The masses of different substances liberated from different electrolytes by passing the same quantity of electricity through each are directly proportional to their chemical equivalents.**

This law can be tested by passing a current through different voltameters (electrolytic cells) in series. Fig. 38.2 shows the type of circuit. The ammeter A is introduced only to check that a suitable current is passing. It does not matter if the readings of the ammeter

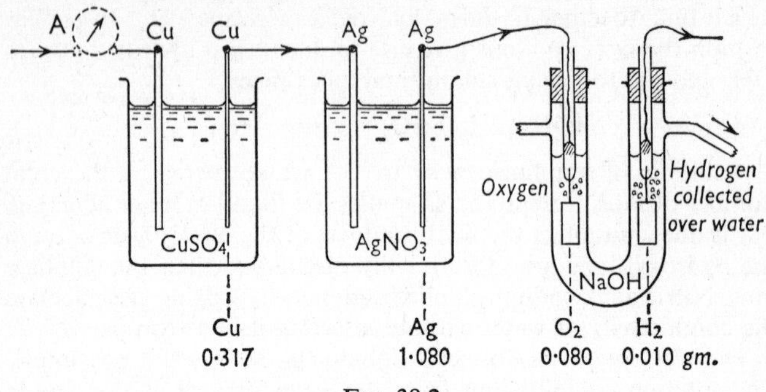

FIG. 38.2

Different weights of material set free by the same quantity of electricity

change during the experiment, for in a series circuit the same quantity passes through each section, i.e. there is no loss of electric charge. The diagram shows a typical set of results in which the current was stopped after a calculated volume of oxygen had been evolved. This was the volume, under the conditions of the experiment, which would weigh 0·080 g—a matter of some 50 ml. That the weights are in the same proportion as the chemical equivalents can be seen by multiplying each of them by 100.

EXAMPLE 1. *A current is passed through a gold-plating vat and a silver-plating vat connected in series. Calculate the mass of silver deposited in one when* 3·50 g *of gold has been deposited in the other. (Equivalents of gold and silver are* 66·0 *and* 108 *respectively.)*

Let s g = mass of silver deposited.

$$\frac{s}{3{\cdot}50}=\frac{108}{66}$$

$$\therefore\ s=\frac{3{\cdot}50\times108}{66}=5{\cdot}90$$

Mass of silver = 5·90 g.

38.3. Electro-chemical equivalents. The electro-chemical equivalent, z, of a substance is defined as the mass of it liberated in electrolysis

by the passage of one coulomb. Its value is usually expressed in grams per coulomb or in milligrams per coulomb. The mass m of a substance, liberated by the passage of a current of I amp flowing for t seconds is given by the formula

$$m = zIt$$

It follows from Faraday's second law of electrolysis that the electro-chemical equivalents are in the same proportion as the corresponding chemical equivalents.

Table of Electro-chemical Equivalents
in mg/coulomb

Element	e.c.e.	Element	e.c.e.
Hydrogen	0·01044	Chlorine	0·367
Oxygen	0·0829	Copper (cupric) .	0·3294
Aluminium	0·0932	Mercury (mercuric).	1·044
Sodium	0·238	Silver	1·1180

EXAMPLE 2. *Calculate the time taken to produce* 5 *litres of hydrogen at s.t.p., using a current of* 100 *A.* (*Density of hydrogen at s.t.p.* $= 0{\cdot}089$ *g/litre. e.c.e. of hydrogen* $= 0{\cdot}00001044$ *g/coulomb.*)

The mass of hydrogen required $= 5 \times 0{\cdot}089 = 0{\cdot}445$ g
Let t seconds = time required.

Then $\quad 0{\cdot}445 = 0{\cdot}00001044 \times 100 \times t$
$\qquad\quad 0{\cdot}445 = 0{\cdot}001044\ t$

whence $\qquad t = 426$

Time required = 426 s or 7 min 6 s.

38.4. Leclanché cells. The Leclanché cell (Fig. 38.3*a*) was devised in 1868; the dry cell and the torch-battery (Fig. 38.3*a*, Pl. 38) are modifications of it. The poles are carbon and manganese dioxide (positive) and zinc (negative); the electrolyte is sal-ammoniac (ammonium chloride NH_4Cl). The electrolyte contains ammonium ions NH_4^+ and chloride ions Cl^-, together with hydrogen ions H^+ and hydroxyl ions OH^- from the water. When the poles are connected to a circuit, the current flows from the carbon to the zinc and back through the electrolyte. The current here consists of a drift of ions, the positive ones moving with the current, the negative ones against it, so that electrolysis occurs at the poles. The hydrogen ions are discharged in the carbon and manganese dioxide mixture, and the hydrogen set free would cause **polarisa-**

tion (p. 398) and give a back e.m.f. if allowed to accumulate. The carbon of the mixture acts as a conductor; the manganese dioxide of the mixture oxidises the hydrogen to water and so acts as a

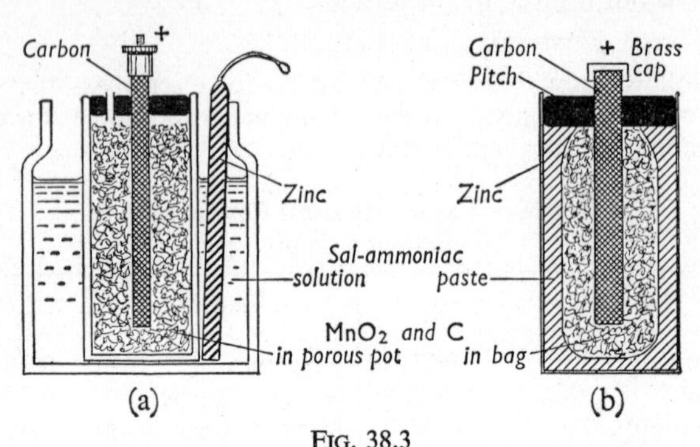

FIG. 38.3

Types of Leclanché cell. (a) 'Wet' pattern; (b) dry cell

depolariser. At the zinc, neither of the negative ions is discharged; instead the zinc ionises, the atoms losing two electrons each and becoming zinc ions in the electrolyte. When the cell is in use the zinc is steadily eaten away because of this steady ionisation of the metal.

The wet type of Leclanché cell is well suited to occasional use, e.g. electric bell circuits. The manganese dioxide in the porous pot is loosely packed, so the depolarisation is not rapid. The cell usually shows some signs of polarisation after use, but it recovers its e.m.f. in a few minutes. In the dry cell the carbon and manganese dioxide mixture is very tightly packed. This gives a low internal resistance and a rapid depolarisation. Theoretically these cells should remain active until all of the zinc container has been used up. In practice, one part becomes eaten away first, so that the paste becomes exposed and dries up; this increases the internal resistance of the cell so much that it becomes useless for its normal purpose.

38.5. Secondary cells. Accumulators. In secondary cells the active chemicals can be formed by passing an electric current through the cell. The **lead** and **nickel-iron** accumulators are good examples of this. The action of the lead accumulator was discovered by Planté in 1879; Fig. 38.4 shows a circuit which is a modification of Planté's original experiment. Two lead plates are put in a vessel containing fairly strong sulphuric acid. The plates are connected in series with a circuit which is capable of sending 0·1–0·2 A through the cell. A pea-lamp is connected to the lead plates through the switch S_2. If the switch S_1 is closed and the switch S_2 left open, the first thing that happens is the electrolysis of water with the evolution of hydrogen and oxygen at the plates. After a while a dark chocolate colour is to be seen on the positive lead plate. This is due to **lead dioxide,** PbO_2. It forms a new pole in the electrolytic cell and causes an e.m.f. of about 2 V, as can be shown by testing with a voltmeter. If S_1 is now opened and S_2 is closed, the lamp lights and may remain alight for as long as a minute before the newly-made cell is discharged. If the experiment is repeated several times, the length of time for which the lamp remains alight becomes longer. This is due to the formation of a greater thickness of active material.

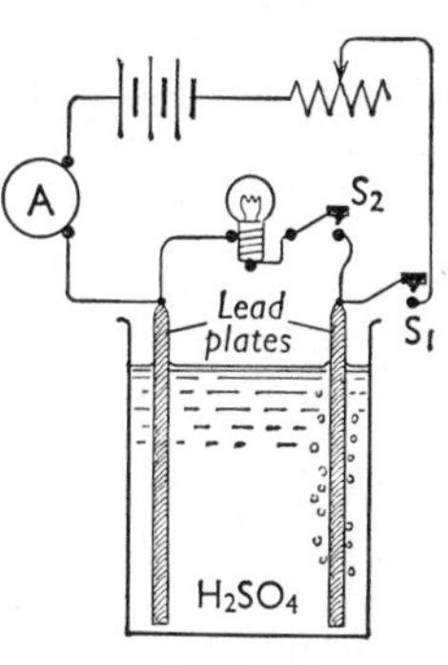

FIG. 38.4

This simple accumulator has **lead dioxide** PbO_2 for its **positive** pole, **lead** Pb for its **negative** pole. When discharged, both plates have a coating of grey **lead sulphate** $PbSO_4$, and the acid density is less because of a loss of sulphate ions during the formation of the lead sulphate. When put into a charging circuit the chemical changes are reversed, the acid becoming denser and the plates coated with lead dioxide (+) and spongy lead (−).

The forming of the plates of a Planté accumulator is a long process. Modern accumulators are made by a method devised by Faure. The plates are lead grids into which pastes of lead oxides and sulphuric acid have been compressed. The negative plate is made from a paste containing PbO, the positive plate from a paste containing red lead Pb_3O_4, a substance which reacts with sulphuric acid to give lead dioxide and lead sulphate. The plates are thus already partly formed, and a first-charge completes the process. The capacity of the accumulator in ampere-hours is greatly increased by reason of the larger mass of active material. There is often one more positive plate than negative, to make sure that full use is made of both sides of the positive plate. The closer the plates, the less is the internal resistance of the cell; accumulators which have their plates close together are fitted with thin perforated insulators between the plates (Pl. 42).

When the accumulator is first put into service the sp.gr. of the acid is about 1·25. Near the end of its discharge the sp.gr. may drop to 1·1., and the e.m.f. to 1·8 V. The low sp.gr. of the acid, which can be tested with a hydrometer, is an indication of the need of a re-charge. If the accumulator has a glass container the positive plates can be inspected; if they are not a dark chocolate colour but have a 'milk-chocolate' look they are in need of a re-charge. The cell should not be left standing uncharged, or the fine particles of grey lead sulphate become white and lumpy. The accumulator is then said to be *sulphated*; its capacity is less because the lumpy white sulphate is less reactive.

Charging is done by connection in a d.c. circuit with an ammeter to record the current and a rheostat to control it. The direct current is generally obtained from the a.c. mains. A transformer is used to step down the voltage of the supply and the output is connected in series with a rectifier, which allows the current to flow one way only (Fig. 38.5). The positive of the output is led to the

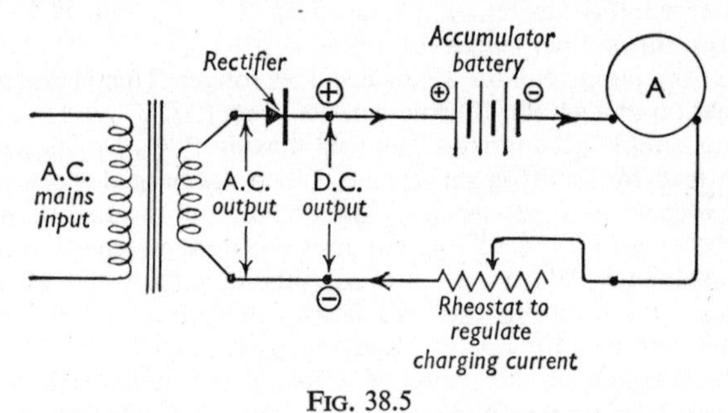

FIG. 38.5

Re-charging an accumulator battery from an a.c. supply

positive of the accumulator and the current is not allowed to exceed the normal charging rate recommended by the manufacturers. Charging is completed when the original sp.gr. of the acid is restored. After that, electrolysis of the water occurs and the accumulator is said to be *gassing*. This gassing is a useful sign that the charging has been completed. Loss of liquid through evaporation or through continued gassing should be made good from time to time by adding distilled water; more acid should be added only if some acid has been spilt.

EXAMPLE 3. *A 12-V 72-amp-hour accumulator, of negligible internal resistance and normal charging rate 2 A, is to be charged from a dynamo of e.m.f. 20 V. Calculate the least resistance to be added to the circuit; estimate the charging time.*

The dynamo and accumulator must be connected so that their e.m.f.s are opposed.

$$\text{Effective e.m.f.} = 20 - 12 = 8 \text{ V}$$

If R ohms = resistance in the circuit,

$$8 = 2 \times R \quad \therefore R = 4$$

A resistance of at least 4 ohms is needed.

A current of 2 A must flow for 36 hours to supply a charge of 72 amp-hours. If the cell is fully discharged, and if all the input charge is fully used, a charging time of at least 36 hours is required.

The various makes of **nickel-iron** or **alkali cell** are the result of researches by Edison in America and Jungner in Sweden. The electrolyte is potassium hydroxide, and the plates are in the form of thin steel boxes with many perforations. The active materials in the boxes are nickelic hydroxide in the positive plate and powdered iron (sometimes mixed with cadmium) in the negative. During discharge the nickelic hydroxide is reduced to nickelous hydroxide, the iron oxidised to ferrous hydroxide; the electrolyte remains unchanged. The e.m.f. of each cell, about 1·2 V, is not quite constant during discharge, and in this respect the lead accumulator is better. But for the same capacity the alkali cell is lighter than the lead one, is undamaged by excessive currents or by being left uncharged, and is much used for driving the motors of small traction vehicles and for emergency lighting supplies.

SUMMARY

Electrolytes, substances which conduct electricity and give decomposition-products at the electrodes, are **ionised.**

Metallic ions (+) and **hydrogen ions** (+) travel in the **same direction as the current.** One or other of these ions is discharged **at the electrode to which the ions are travelling.**

Negative ions travel in the **opposite direction** to the current. When they arrive at the anode, an action takes place in one of the following ways:

(i) A **negative ion** is discharged.
(ii) An atom of the electrode ionises to give a **positive** ion which then travels away from the anode.

The electro-chemical equivalent, z, of a substance is the mass m of it liberated in electrolysis by the passage of 1 coulomb.

$$m = zIt$$

Leclanché cell	C, MnO_2	NH_4Cl	Zn
Lead accumulator	PbO_2	H_2SO_4	Pb

Questions

1. Describe a simple experiment to show that the conductivity of dilute sulphuric acid is greater than that of distilled water. State the products of electrolysis which would occur during the use of the apparatus described.

2. 1·584 g of copper is deposited in 160 min 0 s by a current of 0·500 A. Calculate the electro-chemical equivalent of copper.

3. Define *electro-chemical equivalent.* Calculate the e.c.e. of calcium from the following information. Equivalent weights: Ag 108, Ca 20·0, e.c.e. Ag = 1·118 mg/coulomb.

4. Draw a labelled diagram to show the structure of any one type of Leclanché cell. Give an account of the chemical changes which occur when the cell is in use.

For how long can a Leclanché cell, the mass of whose zinc pole is 4·00 g, supply a current of 1·50 A if only 80% of the zinc is usable? (e.c.e. of Zn = 0·000340 g/coulomb).

What becomes of the metal used up? What factors, other than the mass of the zinc, can limit the useful life of the cell?

5. Describe the structure of any one type of lead accumulator and name the active chemicals when the cell is in a fully charged condition. What changes in its condition enable a person to tell when the cell is discharged?

6. Draw labelled circuit diagrams to show how a 2-V accumulator can be re-charged from (*a*) a 12-V car battery, (*b*) a 240-V a.c. supply. How could you tell when the charging process was complete?

7. Describe and explain the electrolysis which occurs when a current is passed through copper sulphate solution using (*a*) carbon electrodes, (*b*) copper electrodes.

8. Draw a labelled circuit diagram to show how you could copper-plate a carbon rod with a uniform deposit of copper. Assuming that copper does not adhere well if the current exceeds 10 mA per sq. cm, what is the maximum current which can be used for plating a rod 25 cm long and 2·10 cm diameter? Neglect the area of the ends of the rod, and take π as 22/7.

9. Two pieces of tinned copper wire are connected to an ac-

cumulator, one piece to each pole. When the free ends of the wires are dipped into a solution of sodium chloride, bubbles of gas appear round one wire only. When the wires are removed, one wire is unchanged and the other has lost its tin coating from the part which was in the solution. State, giving your reasons, which wire was connected to the positive pole and which to the negative pole of the accumulator.

10. A steady current is passed through a copper voltameter and an ammeter connected in series. If 0·251 g of copper is deposited in 600 s when the ammeter reads 1·20 A, find the error in the ammeter. (e.c.e. of copper = 0·000329 g/coulomb.)

11. State Faraday's laws of electrolysis. If a factory can produce 60·0 kg of calcium per hour by electrolysis, how much aluminium could it produce per hour using the same current? (Equivalent weights: Ca 20, Al 7.)

12. Calculate the time taken to isolate 1 kg of sodium by the electrolysis of molten sodium chloride using a current of 500 A. What weight of chlorine will be evolved at the same time? (e.c.e. Na = 0·000240 g/coulomb. Equivalents of Na and Cl are 23 and 35·5 respectively.)

13. Draw a circuit diagram to show the re-charging of a 6-V 60-amp-hour accumulator, at a charging rate of 3 A, from a 15-V d.c. supply. Calculate the total resistance which must be in the circuit, and estimate the charging time.

What weight of silver-plating could be done with the charged accumulator? (e.c.e. of silver = 0·001118 g/coulomb.)

14. Calculate the time taken to deposit 2·08 g of nickel using a current of 3·12 A in a nickel-plating process. (1·19 g of nickel is deposited per ampere-hour.)

15. Two identical accumulators, each of capacity 30 amp-hours, are connected to voltameters having the same resistance, one accumulator being connected to a copper voltameter and the other to a silver voltameter. Calculate the masses of copper and silver deposited by the discharge of the accumulators. How, if at all, would the masses have been affected if only one accumulator had been used and the two voltameters joined to it (*a*) in series, (*b*) in parallel? (e.c.e. of copper = 0·00033 g/coulomb. e.c.e. of silver = 0·001118 g/coulomb.)

CHAPTER 39

Alternating Current

39.1. An alternating current flows as the result of applying an alternating voltage to a circuit. The voltage of the a.c. mains supply can be expressed as a **sine curve** (Fig. 39.1*a*). It sets up an alter-

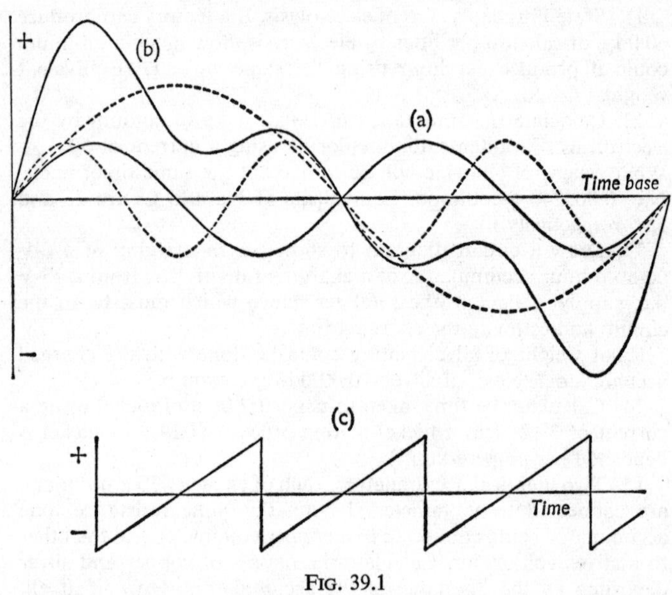

FIG. 39.1

(*a*) *Sinusoidal a.c.* (*b*) *A complex a.c.* (*c*) *Saw-tooth wave-form*

nating current which can also be expressed as a sine curve; such voltages and currents are said to be **sinusoidal.**

The speech currents of a telephone circuit are more complex. They can be shown to be made up of many sine-variations of different frequency and amplitude. They have a **wave-form** which is not a sine curve; Fig. 39.1*b* shows a wave-form which is a combination of the three sine-curves in the diagram. Fig. 39.1*c* shows another type of wave-form which is known as **saw-tooth** wave-form; this sort of voltage is put on the X-plates of a cathode ray tube to make the spot of light travel uniformly across the screen repeatedly.

In the following sections of this chapter, only the simple sine wave-form will be considered. The chief effects of a direct current are chemical, shock-producing, magnetic and thermal; all of these effects are shown by an alternating current.

39.2. Chemical effects. When alternating current is passed through an electrolyte the electrodes become alternately anode and cathode, so that mixed products are sometimes formed, e.g. mixed hydrogen and oxygen in the electrolysis of water. Sometimes the reverse current reverses the chemical change caused by the forward current, and no chemical change at all occurs; this happens when a.c. is sent through a copper voltameter. In the following experiment a moving electrode is used to show a chemical effect of a.c.

Experiment. A piece of white blotting paper is soaked in a solution of potassium iodide and starch. This is laid on a flat metal plate connected to the negative of a d.c. supply of about 4 V. A metal rod connected to the positive of the supply is drawn across the surface of the paper, and a continuous black line shows the formation of iodine at the positive pole. If the experiment is repeated with a low-voltage a.c. supply, a line of black dashes is obtained, showing that the metal rod is positive for only part of the time (Fig. 39.2). A rough idea of the frequency can be obtained by

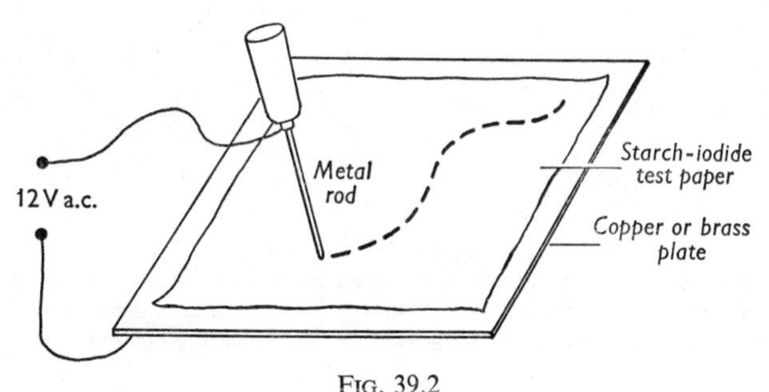

FIG. 39.2

A chemical effect of alternating current

drawing the line for an estimated second and counting the number of dashes obtained.

A more accurate value of the frequency of the supply can be

obtained from this experiment by putting the metal plate on a gramophone turn-table rotating at a known speed and letting the metal rod trace out a spiral pattern. The average number of dashes in a complete turn can then be found.

39.3. Shock effect. The human body is very sensitive to the shock of a *change* of current. If you put your fingers across the poles of a 50-V high-tension battery there may be a shock at first contact, but hardly any if you keep up the contact. It is possible to send a current of 20 mA through a person's arms without giving a shock, provided that the current is brought very slowly up to that value and then reduced slowly. But a sudden change of 20 mA gives a dangerous shock, and an alternating 20 mA could kill a person. An exception to this occurs with extremely high-frequency a.c.; this flows over the surface of the skin and hardly affects the nerves at all.

39.4. Magnetic effects. The magnetising force of a.c. at any given instant is exactly the same as that given by a d.c. of the same value. So the *magnetising force* of a.c. keeps in step with the current. But the *magnetic flux* developed in iron or steel is not always in step with the current. Fig. 39.3*a* shows how the flux alters in an electro-

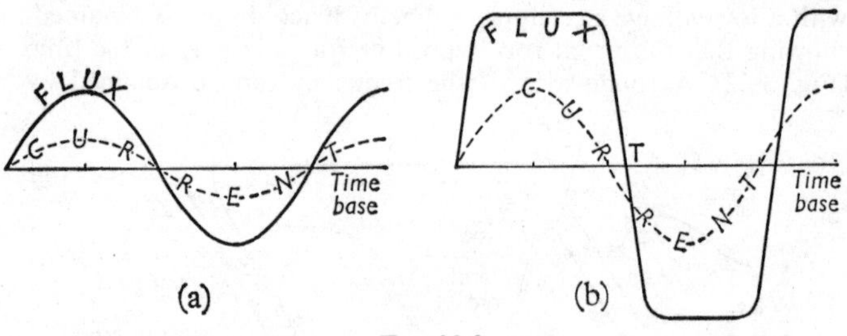

FIG. 39.3

(a) An alternating magnetic flux caused by an alternating current. The two are in step in this example. (b) Alternating magnetic flux in steel which has been magnetised to saturation by an alternating current

magnet when the current is not large enough to cause magnetic saturation in the iron; here the flux is in step with the current. If a steel bar is put in a solenoid carrying enough current to magnetise the steel fully, the flux variations in the steel will be as shown in Fig. 39.3*b*. Flux and current are not quite in step, and the reversal of the flux is very sudden. This explains why the steel bar is always fully magnetised, in one direction or the other, when the current is switched off. The chances of switching off at the moment marked T, when the flux is zero, are negligible.

39.5. Heating effect. The heating effect is the same whichever way the current flows, so a.c. produces heat in a resistor. The heating rate varies as shown in Fig. 39.4. In bulky heaters such as electric

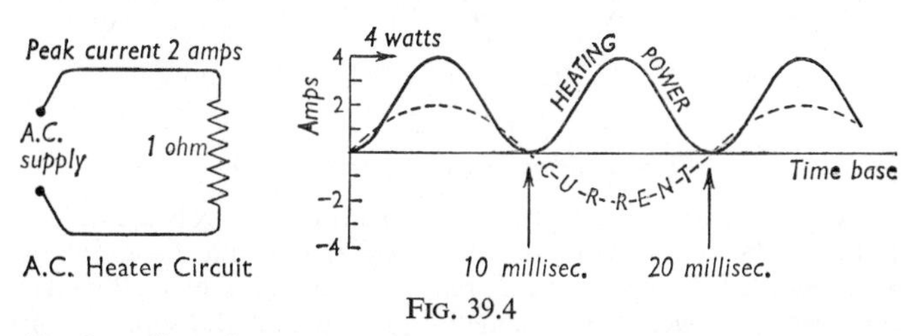

FIG. 39.4

Heating effect of a.c. in a resistor. In this example the peak power is 4 watts. The average power is only 2 watts

fires, which have a large thermal capacity, there is little variation of temperature, despite the fact that the heat is not being supplied uniformly. Filament lamps, however, show a slight temperature variation, and the light from them varies slightly. If you waggle anything shiny in the light from an a.c. filament lamp you will see a band of light which is not uniformly bright.

39.6. Resistor circuits. In the remaining parts of the chapter the following symbols will be used with reference to a.c.

v, i. Values of voltage and current **at a particular instant.**
V_p, I_p. **Maximum** or **peak** values of voltage and current.
$\bar{V}$, $\bar{I}$. Values recorded by **a.c. meters (effective values).**

In **resistor** circuits v and i vary with time, but the equation $v=iR$ applies at any instant. The current is therefore in step with the voltage as shown in Fig. 39.5 which illustrates what happens when $R=2$ ohms.

Alternating current meters are constructed to give steady pointer-readings with alternating supplies. When a voltmeter and an ammeter are connected as shown in Fig. 39.6 they show the effective values of the voltage and current, $\bar{V}$ and $\bar{I}$. **These are equal to the steady d.c. values which would give the same heating rate in a resistor.**

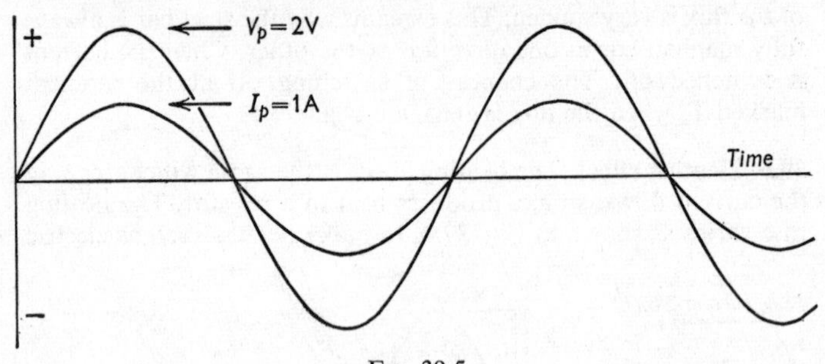

FIG. 39.5
Current and voltage curves for a resistor

Now the heating rate of a current i in a resistance R is equivalent to i^2R watts. The variation of this power is shown in the graph of Fig. 39.6. It is a *sine*² curve. It reaches peak value of $I^2{}_pR$ watts; the average power is less than this. Because of the symmetrical shape of the curve it is in fact exactly half of $I^2{}_pR$ (for a whole number of cycles).

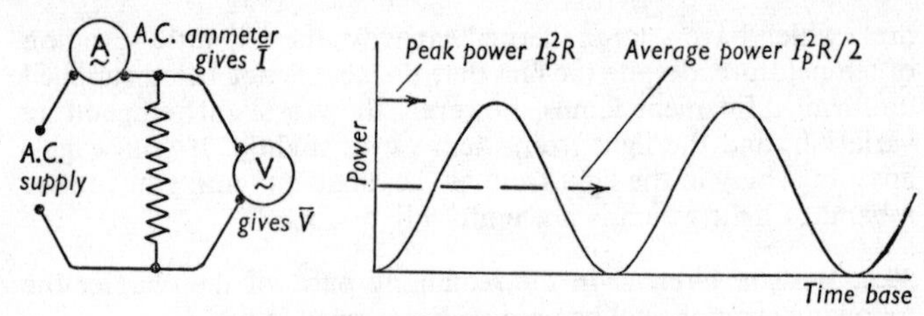

FIG. 39.6
Power taken by a resistor in an a.c. circuit

The average power of a.c. in a resistor is half that which would be given by the peak current flowing all the time.

Now the meter value, $\bar{I}$, is defined as the steady current which would develop the same power as the a.c. does.

$$\bar{I}^2R = \tfrac{1}{2}I^2{}_pR$$
$$\bar{I} = I_p/\sqrt{2} = 0{\cdot}707\ I_p$$

The meter-reading value of a.c., the effective current, is 0·707 of the peak current. This is known as the **r.m.s.** current or **root-mean-square** current, since it is the square-root of the average of (current)².

Similarly it can be proved that the r.m.s. voltage is 0·707 of the peak voltage.

R is given by the equation $v=iR$. Because v and i are in step, $V_p=I_pR$.

$$\therefore\ R=\frac{V_p}{I_p}=\frac{\bar{V}\sqrt{2}}{\bar{I}\sqrt{2}}=\frac{\bar{V}}{\bar{I}}$$

Division of the meter readings gives the value of the resistance.

39.7. Capacitor (condenser) circuit. A condenser switched into a d.c. circuit becomes charged to the voltage of the supply. There is a sudden flow of current, which stops when the charging is complete; if the resistance of the connecting wires is negligible the charging is almost instantaneous.

A similar process occurs in an a.c. circuit, but it produces different effects. The condenser becomes alternately charged, discharged, and reverse-charged; the corresponding flow of charge causes an alternating current in the leads. Because it allows a.c. to flow the condenser *seems* to act as a *resistance*; the name **reactance** is given to this property. The reactance of a capacitor is not a constant, for it depends on the **frequency** of the supply. At higher frequencies more current is passed; the reactance has become less.

Condensers play an important part in the circuits of radio and television sets. They are used as *tuning condensers* in the aerial circuit, as *blocking condensers* to prevent the flow of unwanted d.c., and as *by-pass* condensers to permit the passage of a.c.

39.8. Inductor or choke circuit. A large solenoid, wound with fairly thick copper wire, is likely to have only a few ohms of resistance. Yet when connected to an a.c. supply it passes comparatively little current, and very little indeed if the solenoid has an iron core. The self-inductance of the solenoid has a *choking effect*, and the coil behaves as though it had appreciable resistance; this property is called **inductive reactance.** The reactance of an inductor or choke is not a constant, for it depends on the frequency of the supply. At higher frequencies less current is passed; the reactance has become greater.

Chokes are used in some kinds of a.c. lighting circuits; they have the effect of a resistance but do not become heated by the current. They also play an important part in the circuits of radio and television sets. Air-cored coils are used in the *tuning circuits*, other air-cored coils are used as *high-frequency chokes* to block the path of unwanted high-frequency currents, iron-cored *low-frequency chokes* are used to smooth out the d.c. supplies from the power-pack to the valves.

39.9. Inductance of a transformer. The reactance of the primary of a transformer is usually very high because it has a large inductance. So that a transformer connected to an a.c. supply takes very little current. And very little power is lost in the copper windings. Thus a transformer can be left connected to the a.c. supply for which it was designed without using any power. Some types of electric bell are supplied from the a.c. mains through a bell transformer; no power is taken by the transformer unless the bell switch is closed.

When the secondary of a transformer is used to supply current, the magnetic flux in the core is reduced (Lenz's law), there is less back e.m.f. in the primary and so the current in the primary increases; more power is then taken from the supply.

39.10. Rectifiers. When d.c. is wanted from an a.c. supply a rectifier is generally used. A rectifier allows the current to flow one way only. The contact between copper and cuprous oxide, between iron and selenium, between a metal and silicon, acts in this way; rectifiers of this type are known as **metal rectifiers** (Fig. 39.7*a*).

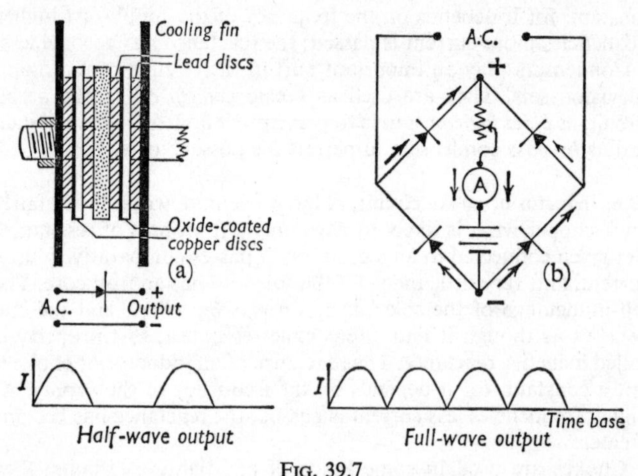

FIG. 39.7

Rectifiers. (a) Copper and cuprous oxide rectifier. (b) Four rectifiers in bridge-connection giving full-wave rectification. The thick arrows show the current flow when the left-hand terminal of the supply is positive; the thin arrows show the flow when the right-hand terminal is positive

Metal rectifiers are used in accumulator-charging circuits, and in power packs for supplying d.c. voltages of the order of 100-3000 V.

Used singly they give **half-wave** rectification (Fig. 39.7*a*). Using four in bridge-connection (Fig. 39.7*b*) they work on both the positive and negative halves of the cycle and give **full-wave** rectification. Diode valves (p. 425) are also used as rectifiers.

It will be seen that the output, though direct, is not steady. This may not matter for accumulator charging, but where a steady output is required a *smoothing circuit* is connected. The simplest smoothing circuit consists of a condenser, of the order of several microfarads, connected across the output and linked by a resistor to another condenser which becomes charged and acts as a nearly constant voltage supply. Better smoothing is obtained by using a choke in place of the resistance.

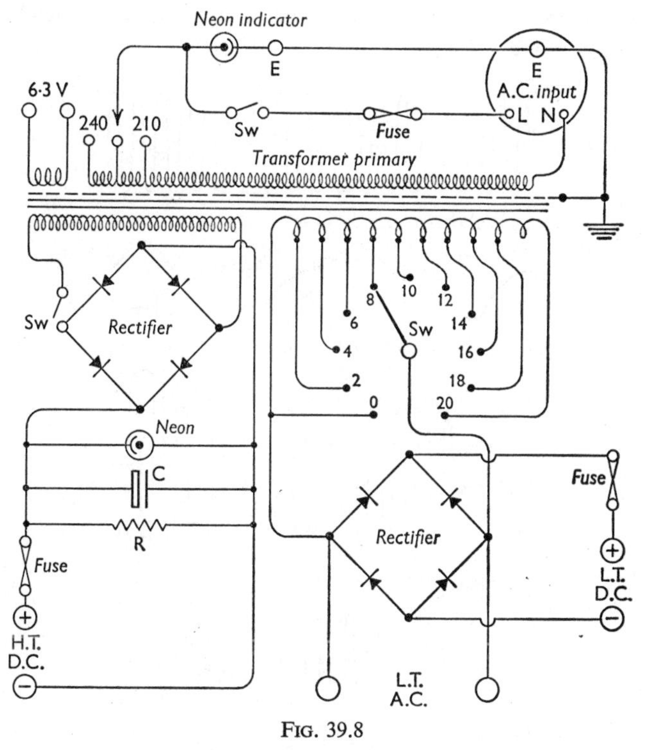

FIG. 39.8

Power pack for a.c., low tension and high tension, from an a.c. supply

Pl. 39 shows the lay-out of one type of power pack such as is used in laboratories for the supply of both l.t. and h.t. from the mains; it uses metal rectifiers. Fig. 39.8 shows the corresponding circuit diagram.

39.11. Radio waves. An important feature of alternating currents in wires is that some of the energy input is radiated from the wire in the form of electromagnetic radiation. For low-frequency a.c., such as is supplied to a house or factory, the energy which is emitted as radiation is extremely small, but for high-frequency a.c. such as occurs in the oscillator circuits of radio transmitters (millions of cycles/s), most of the input energy escapes from the circuit as electromagnetic waves. These waves travel with the same speed as light (3×10^8 metres/s) and their wave-length is given by the equation $3 \times 10^8 = f\lambda$, where λ is the wave-length in metres and f the frequency in cycles/s.

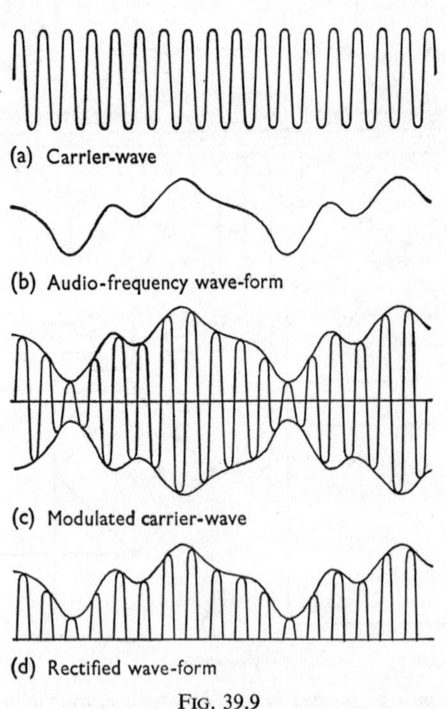

FIG. 39.9

The wave sent out from a transmitting aerial is known as the **carrier wave.** To get a signal carried this wave has to be varied or **modulated** by putting a microphone in the transmitting circuit. Thus a carrier wave such as is shown in Fig. 39.9*a* is affected by a microphone giving an audio-frequency, such as that of Fig. 39.9*b*, to give a modulated wave, Fig. 39.9*c*. This type of modulation is called *amplitude modulation* because the amplitude of the carrier-wave has been altered. At the receiving aerial the effect of the incoming wave is made greater by electrical resonance. The aerial is coupled to a tuned circuit, containing an inductor and a capacitor, which responds to the frequency of the incoming waves. When you adjust the tuning control of a radio set you are moving the plates of a capacitor, such as is shown in Fig. 30.10*a*, to make the circuit respond to the incoming frequency. In order to make the loud speaker reproduce the audio-frequency, the alternating current in the aerial and tuned circuit has to be **de-modulated** as shown in Fig. 39.9*d*. This is done by a detector device, or rectifier, which allows only the top halves of the wave-forms to be effective. Usually the current in the detector is not strong enough to work a loud speaker directly and its effects have to be amplified.

Questions

1. What is meant by (*a*) a *sinusoidal* alternating current, (*b*) a current which has a *saw-tooth wave-form*. Illustrate your answer by diagrams and comment on the effects of passing each of these currents through (i) a resistor, (ii) copper sulphate solution.

2. An alternating supply of peak value 1 V is connected to a resistor of value 1 ohm. Draw graphs, on the same time-base, to show the variations of current and power in the resistor. Plot the current graph by plotting the following values at equally spaced intervals:

0 0·50 0·866 1·00 0·866 0·50 0 −0·50 −0·866 etc.

Plot the power graph by plotting the squares of these numbers. Mark on the graphs (i) the value of the average power per cycle, (ii) the value of the steady d.c. current which, flowing in the resistor, would give the same power as the average per cycle.

3. What is meant by the *r.m.s. value* and the *peak value* of an alternating supply? Illustrate your answer by reference to a supply of r.m.s. value 10 V sending a current of r.m.s. value 2 A through a resistor. What is the resistance of the resistor?

4. Describe simple experiments, one in each case, to show a magnetic effect and a chemical effect caused by an alternating current. How, if at all, would the result of each experiment differ if a d.c. supply were used?

5. What is meant by the term *frequency* with reference to a.c.? If the time interval corresponding to the numbers given in Question 2 is 0·08 second between each, what is the frequency of the supply? A moving-coil centre-zero ammeter is put in an a.c. circuit, the frequency of which gradually increases from 2 cycles/s to 200 cycles/s. Describe and explain how the movement of the pointer is likely to vary over this range of frequency.

6. Explain the following facts. (*a*) The leads to a capacitor joined to an a.c. supply have an alternating current in them. (*b*) An electromagnet joined to an a.c. supply takes much less current than it does when connected to a d.c. supply of the same r.m.s. value.

How would you expect the frequency of the supply to affect each of these circuits?

7. Define instantaneous current i, peak current I_p, and r.m.s. current $\tilde{I}$ in relation to an a.c. circuit. Give an equation relating I_p and $\tilde{I}$. Calculate the peak current for r.m.s. values of (i) 2 A, (ii) 0·707 A; and the r.m.s. currents for peak values of (iii) 10 A, (iv) 1·414 A.

8. A d.c. supply of e.m.f. 10 V and an a.c. supply of peak value 10 V are each separately connected to a resistor of value 2·5 ohms. Calculate for each case (*a*) the current in the resistor, (*b*) the heat produced in the resistor per minute. (J=4·2 joules/cal.)

9. Each plate of a 10-microfarad condenser is connected to each of two centre-zero galvanometers, the other terminals of which are connected to wires. The ends of the two wires are brought into contact with the poles of a 50-V battery, removed and then connected together. Describe and explain the deflections which occur in the galvanometers. Calculate the maximum charge on the condenser during the process.

10. Draw a labelled diagram to show the structure of any one type of metal rectifier. Explain what is meant by *half-wave* rectification.

A 6-V accumulator of negligible resistance is to be charged from an a.c. supply of r.m.s. value 30 V, using a single rectifier of resistance 10 ohms. If the current in the rectifier must never exceed 1 A, what is the least value of the additional series resistance required? Draw a circuit diagram of the arrangement, and estimate the average current in the accumulator.

11. A 10-microfarad condenser is connected, via a switch, to an

alternating supply of peak value 400 V. The switch is closed and then re-opened, several times. On each occasion the condenser is found to be charged, but a given plate of the condenser is sometimes positive, sometimes negative. Explain this. Describe how you would discharge the condenser without risk of shock.

CHAPTER 40

Electronics

40.1. Discharge of electricity through gases. Cathode rays. A potential difference of about 30,000 V is required to give a spark between spherical electrodes 1 cm apart in air at atmospheric pressure. At lower pressures less voltage is required. Fig. 40.1

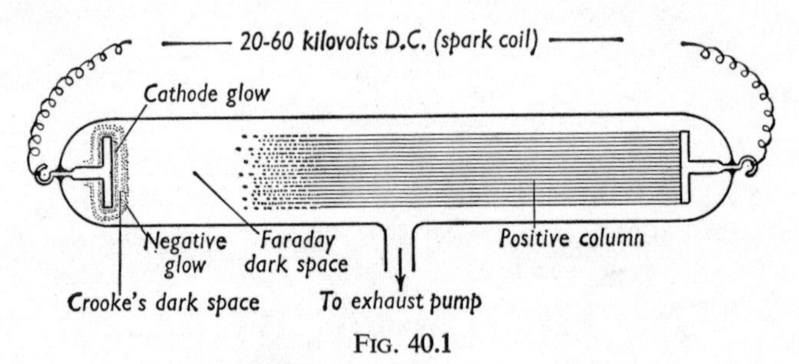

FIG. 40.1

Electrical discharge through a gas at low pressure

shows an experimental tube for the study of the discharge at different pressures. A silent steady coloured discharge takes place when the pressure is of the order of 10 mm Hg; the width of the glowing column increases as the pressure is reduced. Fig. 40.1 shows the appearance when the pressure is about 1 mm Hg. Most of the tube is filled with a bright column reaching to the positive electrode and is known as the **positive column.** The colour is characteristic of the gas in the tube—pink for air, pale blue for coal gas, red for neon, purple for argon, blue-white for mercury vapour. In the discharge tubes of advertising signs, and in the mercury-vapour and sodium-vapour lamps it is the positive column which gives out the light. Between the positive column and the glow round the cathode are two darker spaces. It is thought that charged particles or ions are accelerated in these spaces and that they cause light by collision with and ionisation of other gas molecules in the positive column.

At lower pressures the positive column breaks up into patches and decreases in length. The Faraday dark space and the Crookes dark space increase in length until finally the Crookes dark space fills the whole tube. At this stage the walls of the tube fluoresce (green in the case of soda glass, blue in the case of lead glass). The shape and the position of the fluorescence suggest that rays are leaving the cathode in straight lines perpendicular to its surface (Fig. 40.2). The rays are known as **cathode rays.** The nature of these

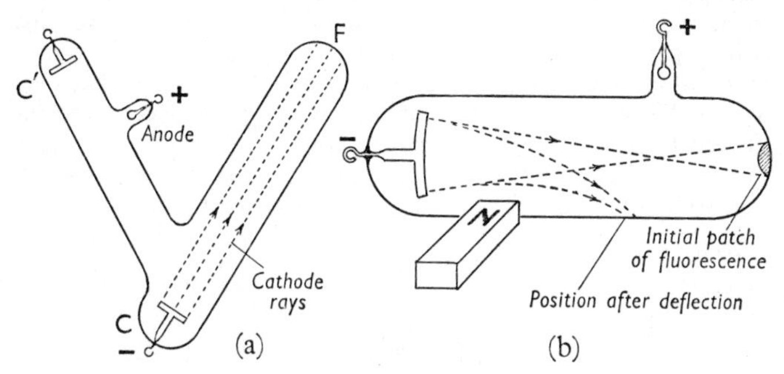

FIG. 40.2

Cathode rays. (a) Rays emitted at right angles to the cathode surface. F represents the fluorescent patch; the rays themselves are invisible. If C′ is made the cathode the fluorescent patch appears near the letter (a) and a shadow of C appears within the patch. (b) Focusing effect of a concave cathode. Deflection of the rays by a magnet

rays was established largely as the result of the work of J. J. Thomson. The rays can turn small paddle wheels; an obstacle placed in their path casts a sharp shadow in the fluorescence on the wall of the tube. A magnetic field deflects the rays in the opposite direction to that expected if the course of the rays were a conventional current (Fig. 40.2*b*); if the rays hit an isolated conductor they charge it negatively. These and other experiments showed the rays to be a beam of **negatively charged particles.** Later experiments showed that their speed was very great—about a tenth that of light, that their charge is equal to the charge on a hydrogen ion, that their mass is only $\frac{1}{1840}$ of the mass of a hydrogen atom. The particles are known as **electrons.**

40.2. Positive rays. In any discharge tube in which there is still some gas remaining, positively charged atoms of the gas are produced; under the action of the high voltage applied to the tube they move in the opposite direction to the cathode rays. They are known as **positive rays** and were discovered as a result of using a perforated cathode in a discharge tube; luminous streaks appeared behind the holes in the cathode. Magnetic fields deflect these rays in a direction which suggests that they are positively charged; and very much stronger fields are needed to deflect them to the same extent as cathode rays. This could be due to the particles having greater mass or greater speed, or to both these effects. Thomson put the matter to experimental test by making the cathode a narrow tube (which gave a narrow beam of rays), detecting the positive rays by photographing their impact on a photographic plate. The rays were deflected by an electromagnet whose pole-pieces were insulated from the main magnet and connected to a high voltage supply. A sketch of the receiving end of the system is shown in Fig. 40.3, where O represents the point reached by the rays when

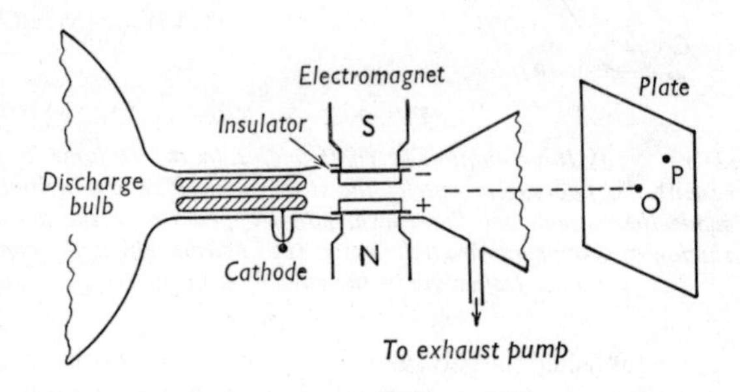

FIG. 40.3

Thomson's mass-spectrograph

they are not deflected. When the electric and magnetic fields are switched on, positive particles would be deflected upwards by the electric field and sideways by the magnetic field, to a point such as P if the particles all had the same mass, charge and speed. In actual fact a group of parabolic curves was obtained; any one of these parabolic curves shows the impact points of particles of the same mass and charge but of different speeds—the less speedy ones being further from the origin. The various different curves are due to the different masses of the different atoms used, or to some of the atoms carrying two or even three times as much charge as the others. The rays were in fact differently charged ions of the gases in the discharge tube.

From measurements on the different curves it was possible to compare the masses of the different particles. Taking the mass of the hydrogen atom as unity, the masses of the others were found to be almost exactly whole numbers, which implies that the atoms of matter are made up of particles of the same mass as the hydrogen atom. (See also p. 434, Qu. 16.)

When neon, of atomic weight 20·2, was used in the tube two parabolas appeared, corresponding to atomic weights of 20 and 22. Neon would thus appear to be a mixture of two gases having the same properties but different atomic weight. Aston later showed this to be so by separating the two components of neon by a diffusion process. Many instances are now known of elements having the same chemical properties but different atomic weight; these differing atoms of the same element are called **isotopes** of the element.

An apparatus, such as Thomson's, which enables us to find the relative mass of the isotopes of an element is known as a **mass-spectrograph.** Since Thomson's time mass-spectrographs have been designed giving a much greater accuracy, and it is found that the relative masses of the isotopes of the elements are not quite exactly whole numbers. Thus when the mass of an atom of the common isotope of oxygen is taken as exactly 16, the atomic masses of the commonest isotopes of hydrogen and helium are respectively 1·00814 and 4·00388. The difference between the mass of four hydrogen atoms and one helium atom is only 0·02868 atomic mass units (a.m.u.); but it sets free a large amount of energy when four hydrogen atoms are made to fuse together to form one helium atom. (1 a.m.u. = $\frac{1}{16}$ of the mass of an atom of the isotope ^{16}O.)

40.3. Cathode-ray tubes. The cathode-ray tubes used by J. J. Thomson were *cold cathode* tubes and required voltages of the order of 30,000 V. Most cathode-ray tubes nowadays are of the *hot cathode* type and require less than a tenth of the voltage to work them. The electrode system which gives the electron beam is known as the **electron gun.** Modern tubes are fitted with voltage controls for focusing the beam and varying its intensity. Fig. 40.4 shows a very simple type of electron gun. It consists of an electrically heated filament which emits electrons, and an anode with a hole in it to attract the electrons and to allow some of them to pass through the hole. The high potential of the anode attracts and accelerates the electrons; to concentrate the electron beam a cylinder at a negative potential surrounds the filament (cathode); this cylinder is known as the **Wehnelt cylinder** or **grid.**

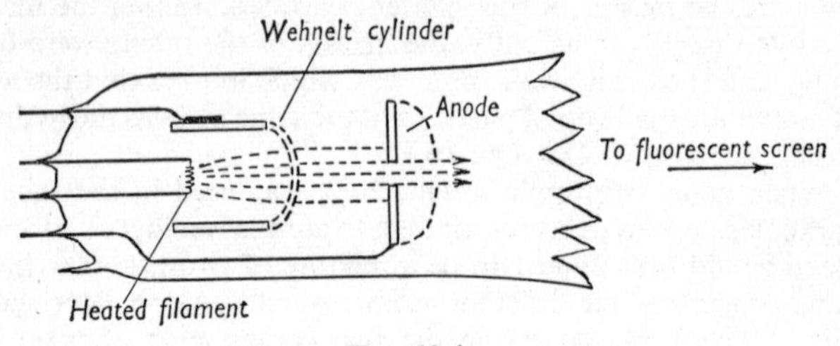

FIG. 40.4

A simple form of electron gun

The electron beam passes through the vacuum of the tube and hits the glass wall which is coated inside with a fluorescent material; from there the electrons flow back through a graphite coating to the anode connection. The electrons have such a small mass that they can follow instantly the variations of any force which deflects them. The deflection of the beam can be done by *magnetic deflection* (generally by coils carrying a current outside the tube) or by *electrostatic deflection* (by electrodes at different potentials inside the tube).

Pl. 40 shows a simple form of hot cathode tube for investigating some of the properties of cathode rays. For instance, the effect of magnetic deflection can be observed on the fluorescent screen S, and by arranging for the deflected beam to enter the metal cup C the negative charge on the rays can be shown. An electroscope connected to the cup becomes charged; when a rubbed polythene rod (negative) is brought near the electroscope the deflection is further increased showing that the electroscope has become negatively charged by the rays.

In cathode-ray oscilloscopes the electron beam is made to move from left to right at a uniform speed and then return very suddenly to its starting point. The line of light so traced on the screen is known as a **time-base.** Such tubes are used in the study of a.c. circuits and the wave-forms of sound, in radar, and in television where the time-base is rapidly repeated up and down the screen to give a square pattern of light. The incoming signals in the aerial of the set modify the brightness of the moving spot of light, and so form a picture.

40.4. Thermionic emission. Valves. Metals and certain metallic oxides give off electrons when heated. The effect is known as thermionic emission; the rise in temperature gives the electrons, which form part of the structure of matter, enough energy to escape from the material, in a way similar to the evaporation of molecules of vapour from a liquid. The emitted electrons form a cloud of negative charge, known as the **space charge** around the emitter; and for any particular temperature there is equilibrium between the electrons leaving the emitter per second and those returning to it per second from the space charge.

If an electrode is put near such an emitter *in vacuo* the arrangement is called a **diode valve.** If the electrode is given a positive potential, electrons from the space charge are attracted across the space and a current flows; if the electrode is given a sufficiently negative potential no current flows. Such diode valves are commonly used as rectifiers. The filament or cathode is made of tungsten, or thoriated tungsten (tungsten containing some thorium oxide or thoria), or else a filament coated with oxides of barium and strontium. The oxide-coated filament is the more emissive and requires a lower temperature for the electron emission, but its surface structure is likely to break up if large currents are taken

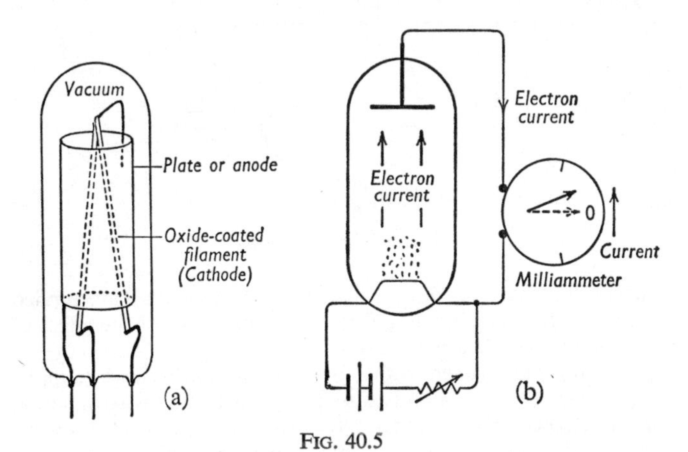

FIG. 40.5
(a) A diode valve. (b) Thermionic emission

from it. Fig. 40.5*a* shows the structure of a typical diode; Pl. 41 shows a double diode—two diodes in the same envelope.

Experiment 1. Examine a diode or a double diode such as is used for the rectifier valve in the power-pack of a radio set. If the envelope is of clear glass you should be able to see the tubular anode and the strap-shaped filament with its grey-white coating of oxides.

Fit the valve into the circuit shown in Fig. 40.5*a*. Switch on the heater current and increase it with the rheostat until the milliammeter just begins to show a current. This shows that electrons from the space charge have enough energy to reach the anode. Note that the direction of the electron flow is opposite to the direction of the conventional current indicated by the meter. Increasing the temperature of the filament gives an increased current, showing greater emission at higher temperatures.

By putting dry cells in series with the meter you can estimate the negative potential which must be applied to the plate to prevent electrons from the space charge reaching it.

Experiment 2. Use the circuit of Fig. 40.6 to measure the different

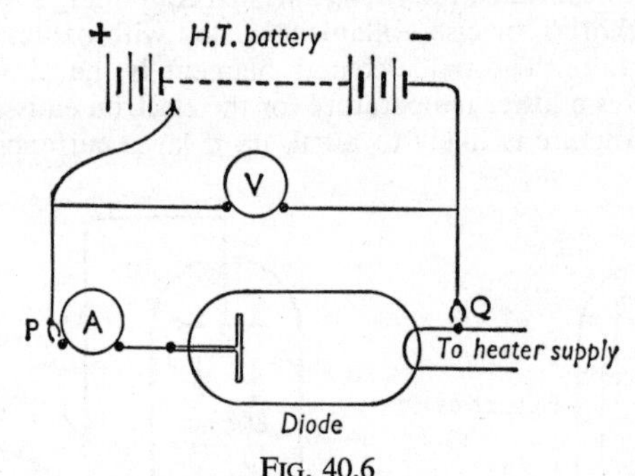

FIG. 40.6

Test-circuit for a diode

currents flowing in the diode when different + potentials are applied to the anode. The clips P and Q can be used to test the effect of reversing the applied potential.

Repeat the experiment with a lower voltage for the heater supply.

The circuit of Fig. 40.6 is similar to that for the determination of a resistance by the ammeter-voltmeter method. Typical results for a diode are shown in Fig. 40.7, and it is clear that the diode does not act as a fixed resistor would do. The current is not proportional to the voltage, and it finally reaches a limiting value, known as the **saturation current,** where a further increase in voltage gives no further increase in current. This suggests that a given filament at a given temperature can emit a definite number of electrons per second. If a particular voltage is high enough to remove all this emission, a higher one can do no more, i.e. the

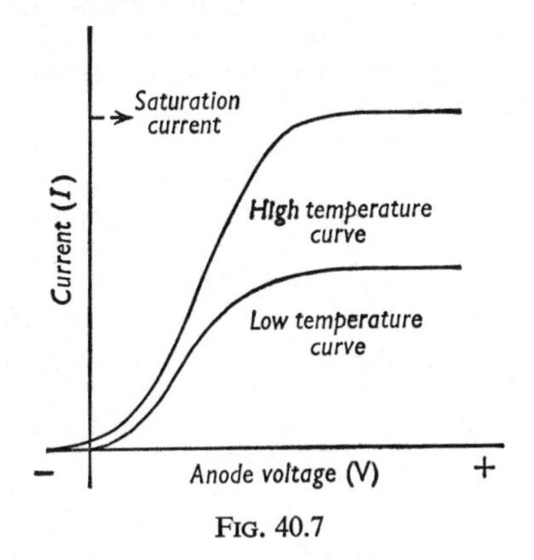

FIG. 40.7

voltage of the anode does not affect the maximum emission of the filament. This is borne out by the fact that the saturation current is less when the filament is less hot.

The diode valve is commonly used as a rectifier. Its chief use in

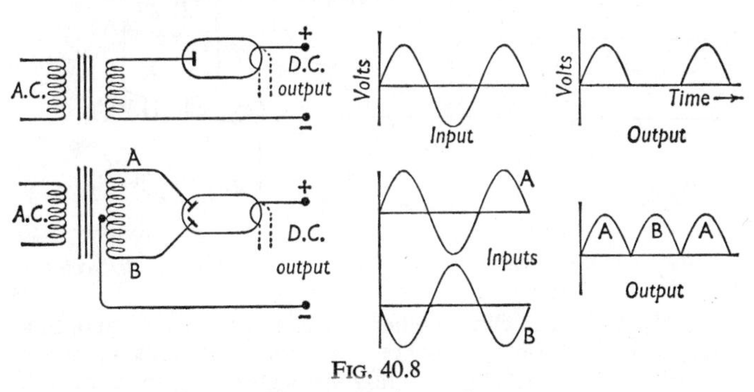

FIG. 40.8

Diode and double-diode rectifier circuits

an a.c. mains radio set is to supply high-voltage d.c. to the anodes of other valves in the set. A single diode gives half-wave rectification, a double diode and a centre-tapped transformer (Fig. 40.8) gives full-wave rectification, the two sections of the diode rectifying alternate half-cycles of the two sides of the transformer output.

For accumulator charging, where lower voltages are sufficient, a **gas-filled diode** is used, the gas being an inert gas such as argon or mercury vapour. Collision of electrons with the gas molecules causes ionisation; as a result the saturation current is obtained with the use of a lower anode voltage.

The **triode valve** was invented by Lee de Forest in 1907. It is a diode in which a wire mesh or a wire spiral is inserted between the filament and the anode; this extra electrode is called the grid. The current in the valve is very sensitive to small changes of voltage on the grid. A triode can therefore be used as amplifier of small fluctuating voltages such as come from gramophone pick-ups, microphones, photo-electric cells. Applied to the grid of a triode, these voltages set up alternating currents of appreciable magnitude in the valve, and the p.d. across a resistor in the anode circuit is used as the amplified output (Fig. 40.9).

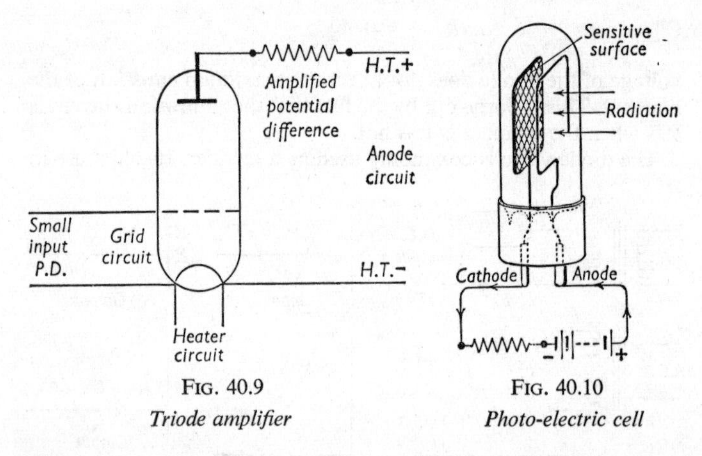

FIG. 40.9

Triode amplifier

FIG. 40.10

Photo-electric cell

40.5. Photo-electric cells. Another type of electron emission occurs when 'light' (infra-red, visible or ultra-violet) hits a metal. It was first observed with zinc in ultra-violet light; a clean zinc plate connected to a negatively charged electroscope loses its charge in ultra-violet light. The effect, known as the **photo-electric effect**, has been proved to be due to the emission of electrons from the metal. If such an illuminated zinc plate (earthed) is near the top electrode of a pulse electroscope (Pl. 44), which has been charged by connecting a high positive potential to the side electrode, a regular flicking of the electroscope fibre shows the attraction of negative ions to the top electrode; if the applied potential is negative, no ionisation current flows.

The photo-electric effect is more marked with the alkali metals—sodium, potassium, rubidium and caesium. The number of electrons emitted per second is proportional to the intensity of the light, and this effect is applied in the photo-electric cell to convert variations of light intensity to variations of electric current. The *photo-electric cell* is an evacuated glass tube containing a coating of alkali metal, and a metal wire or mesh which is in the centre of the tube. The alkali metal is made the cathode of a circuit, the wire or mesh being the anode (Fig. 40.10). When light or other radiation falls on the sensitive surface, electrons are emitted and attracted towards the anode, causing a small current to flow in the circuit. For practical purposes an amplifier is used to magnify the effect of the small photo-electric current.

Photo-electric cells are used to reproduce sound from the variable-density or the variable-area sound tracks of cine-films (Pl. 9). Light from a small lamp, the *exciter-lamp*, passes through the sound track on to the cathode of the cell, which is coupled via an amplifier to a loud-speaker.

The photo-electric effect is also used in television cameras. The sensitive surface is enclosed in a cathode-ray tube. It consists of many small particles of a caesium-silver alloy, known as the *mosaic*. Each particle of the mosaic is separately affected by the picture formed on it; and to detect the electrical changes which occur, a cathode-ray beam moves across or *scans* each part of the picture in turn.

The quantum nature of the photo-electric effect is referred to on p. 223.

40.6. X-rays. When high-speed electrons in a cathode-ray tube or in a diode hit the screen or plate their kinetic energy is lost and they then travel relatively slowly along the conducting parts of the circuit. Most of their energy is converted into heat at the point of impact; a small fraction of the energy is converted into a penetrating radiation known as X-rays or Röntgen rays. The rays were first discovered by Röntgen who found that sealed packets of photographic plates became fogged if left near a cathode-ray tube in action. The source of the rays was traced to the place where the cathode rays hit the walls of the tube. More intense rays were obtained by putting a platinum or tungsten target into the tube and using a concave cathode to focus the cathode rays on it. Modern X-ray tubes (Fig. 40.11) have a heated filament to act as

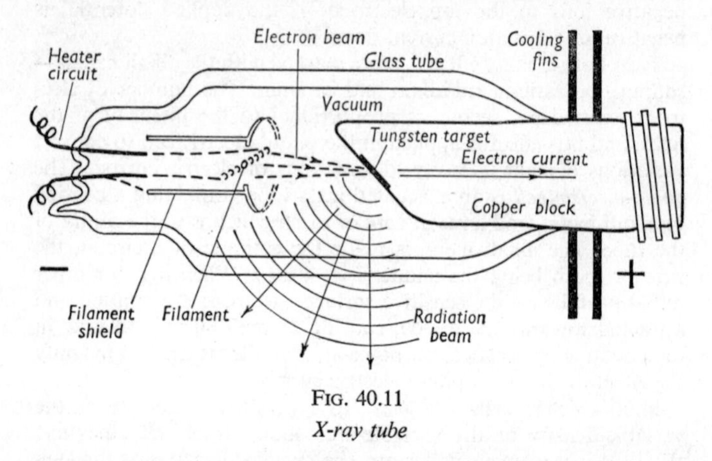

FIG. 40.11
X-ray tube

the electron source, and voltages of the degree of hundreds of kilovolts are applied to the tube to give a high-speed electron beam and an intense X-radiation. Much of the input is converted into heat, and the target-block has to be fitted with a cooling system in the more powerful tubes.

X-rays travel in straight lines and are not deflected by magnetic or electric fields. They are not charged particles but are an electromagnetic radiation similar to light waves and radio waves. Their wave-length is very much shorter even than ultra-violet radiation; this has been discovered by reflecting them from the space-lattice of crystals, where the layers of atoms act like a diffraction grating. They produce fluorescence in certain chemicals, e.g. barium platinocyanide, and a screen coated with such chemicals can be used as a viewing screen. If an X-ray screen is fluorescing under the action of the rays and an obstacle is put in the path of the rays, a shadowgraph showing its internal structure appears on the screen —the penetration of the rays is inversely proportional to the density of the substance. X-ray photographs are obtained either by using a photographic plate in place of the screen or by taking a photograph of the screen with a camera—the latter method is used in mass-radiography. Examples of X-ray shadows are to be seen in Pls. 38, 41.

Continued exposure to X-rays is harmful to the tissues of the body. X-ray tubes are therefore encased with high-density material, generally lead sheet, a small window being left to allow a restricted beam to emerge.

When X-rays pass through matter they cause the ejection of electrons from some of the atoms, the atoms becoming positively charged as a result; the matter is said to have become **ionised.** X-rays passing through air cause **ionisation** of the air and so render the air conducting. The effect can readily be seen when a charged electroscope stands in the path of the rays; the deflection of the leaf falls off to zero. If the electroscope is positively charged then the charged metal parts and the leaf itself will repel positively charged molecules of the gas to the case and attract electrons (and any molecules which have become negatively charged by the emitted electrons); in this way the charged metal parts of the electroscope will have their charge neutralised. The resulting current through the air is known as an **ionisation current.**

In making a quantitative study of the ionisation produced by X-rays (or by any other source of ionisation) it is usual to pass the rays through an ionisation chamber rather than into the case of the electroscope. A simple ionisation chamber consists of two parallel metal plates. Fig. 40.12 shows two ways of connecting them to an

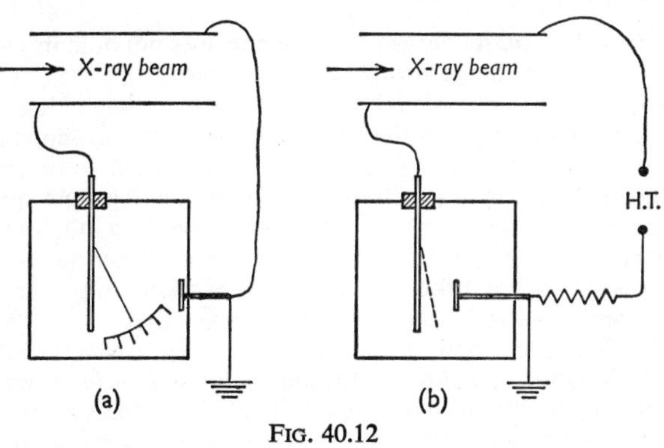

FIG. 40.12
Ionisation of air by X-rays

electroscope for studying an ionisation current. In (*a*) one of the plates is earthed and the other, connected to the electroscope, is given a charge. When a beam of X-rays is passed between the plates the time is taken for the leaf to fall between two chosen fixed marks on its scale. To compare the intensity of the rays at some further distance from the source, or after passing through a sheet of some material, the experiment is repeated under the new conditions. The relative intensities of the X-rays is in the inverse ratio of the two times; the experiments should be repeated and an average value of the ratio found.

In (*b*) one of the plates is connected to a high voltage d.c. supply, in the range 1-5 kV, and the other to the electroscope. The electroscope in this case is a modified one, being fitted with an adjustable electrode—known as the **counter electrode**—which enables the leaf to be discharged when it touches the electrode. When a beam of X-rays is passed between the plates, the leaf rises, touches the counter electrode, falls and repeats the process. The number of flicks of the leaf in a definite time is counted, the position of the counter electrode and the voltage of the supply being adjusted to give a suitable rate of flicking. The experiment is repeated under the new conditions. The relative intensities of the rays in the two circumstances is then in direct proportion to the number of flicks, which should be re-determined and an average value of their ratio found.

Either of these methods can be used to study other ionising radiations, e.g. those from radioactive substances.

40.7. Cosmic rays. A charged electroscope does not hold its charge indefinitely. The charge slowly leaks away even when the insulator is kept at the same potential as the leaf-system. Something other than conduction through the solid parts of the electroscope must be the cause of this. Experiments show that it is due to ionisation of the air caused by a penetrating radiation coming from outside the earth and hence known as **cosmic radiation.** The radiation can penetrate considerable thicknesses of lead. Experiments with balloons showed that the intensity of the radiation increases with height, and its variation with latitude suggested that it was deflected by the earth's magnetic field. There are several components of cosmic radiation, but at high altitudes it consists chiefly of very fast protons (hydrogen nuclei). The effects of the radiation are to be seen in the random tracks in cloud-chamber experiments (p. 443) and in the random clicks heard in the loud-speaker of a counter attached to a Geiger-Müller tube (p. 444).

Questions

1. A glass globe is fitted with four equally spaced electrodes lying in the same plane. The electrodes are (i) a small sphere, (ii) a

plane disc, (iii) a convex disc, (iv) a concave disc having twice the radius of curvature of the globe. The pressure in the globe is 0·01 mm Hg. Describe and explain the appearance on the walls of the globe if electrode (i) is made the anode and each of the others in turn is made the cathode of a high-voltage d.c. circuit.

2. State, in the form of a list, the nature and properties of cathode rays. Describe two experiments which show that they are negatively charged.

3. Explain how you would use a cathode-ray tube, working so as to give a central spot on the screen, to determine (*a*) the N. pole of a magnet, (*b*) the direction of the current in a large coil of wire. Illustrate your answer with diagrams.

4. What is meant by the terms *thermionic emission, space charge*? Draw a diagram to illustrate a simple form of electron gun and explain how it acts.

5. Explain why a snapshot of a television tube in action, taken with a very short exposure, would not show the whole picture.

6. A cathode-ray tube is set up to give a diverging beam from the electron gun. An obstacle in the tube casts a sharp shadow on the screen except when the obstacle is a magnet or a copper plate kept at a negative potential. Explain these facts.

7. Draw a diagram to show the structure of an X-ray tube of the hot-cathode type. Explain the fact that such a tube is usually fitted with (i) a cooling system, (ii) a lead shield.

A bar magnet is embedded in a block of wood. How could its position be detected by X-rays? Would the position be sharply defined? Give a reason for your answer.

8. Give a list of the properties of X-rays. Describe a simple experiment which shows that X-rays cause ionisation in air. How would you determine experimentally the percentage absorption which occurs when an X-ray beam passes through a thickness of 1 mm of lead?

9. Draw a diagram to show the structure of any one type of thermionic diode valve. Describe and explain the effects of connecting to the two electrodes of the valve, when its filament is hot, (*a*) a milliammeter, (*b*) an alternating voltage of peak value 20 V, (*c*) an alternating voltage of peak value 150 V, (*d*) a d.c. supply of e.m.f. 20 V. (It may be assumed that the saturation current of the valve occurs at 100 V.)

10. One terminal of an alternator is connected in series with a copper voltameter to the anode of a diode valve; the other terminal is connected to the filament of the valve, which is independently heated. Draw a diagram of the circuit. Describe the flow of charge

in the different parts of the circuit in terms of the electron and ionic theories.

11. You are provided with two diodes, the filaments of which are identical in shape and size, but one is made of tungsten and the other is coated with barium oxide. How would you determine which filament gave the greater emission when connected to a 2-V supply? Draw a circuit diagram of the arrangement you would use.

12. Draw a circuit diagram to show the charging of a 24-V accumulator battery from 200 V (r.m.s.) a.c. mains using a transformer and a diode valve. Estimate a suitable value for the turns-ratio of the transformer.

13. What are *positive rays* and in what circumstances are they formed. What is meant by the *isotope* of an element?

14. Describe the process of conduction in (*a*) an electrolyte, (*b*) an ionised gas.

15. State the possible causes of a slow leak of charge from a charged electroscope. Explain the fact that the rate of fall of the leaf is much reduced if there is a capacitor connected to the terminals of the electroscope.

16. Assuming the apparatus of Fig. 40.3 to give upward deflections y which are related to the sideways deflections x by the equation $y=0{\cdot}05Mx^2$ for single-charged ions, plot the graphs of y against x for mercury, neon and oxygen, the values of M being 200, 22, 20 and 16. Make the y scale range from 0 to 9, the x scale from -8 to $+8$ (negative values representing a reverse magnetic field); the graphs are such that the least value for y is $1{\cdot}0$.

Sketch the shape and the range of the curves you would expect to get for mercury if each of the following changes were made to the apparatus; (*a*) the magnetic field is made weaker, (*b*) the voltage applied to the deflector plates is made less.

CHAPTER 41

Radioactivity. Atomic Structure

41.1. Radioactivity. The discovery of X-rays in 1895 was followed about a year later by the discovery of the phenomenon of radioactivity by Becquerel. He found that salts of the element **uranium** affected a nearby photographic plate even when the plate was wrapped in light-proof paper or thin metal foil. The uranium salt was giving out some sort of penetrating radiation. It was found that it could also produce fluorescence on zinc sulphide and barium platinocyanide screens, and could cause ionisation in air so that a nearby charged electroscope gradually loses its charge.

Measuring the activity, by the ionising effect, showed that the natural ore *pitchblende* was more radioactive than the uranium obtained from it. Pierre and Marie Curie investigated the cause of this and by a laborious process of chemical separation succeeded in isolating small quantities of salts of two other radioactive elements. One, divalent and chemically similar to barium, was named **radium;** the other, trivalent and chemically similar to bismuth, was named **polonium.** Radium is about a million times more radioactive than uranium. The Curies also showed that the element **thorium** is radioactive.

41.2. Alpha particles. Beta particles. Gamma rays. Much of the pioneer work on radioactivity was done by Rutherford and his co-workers. They discovered that the rays given out are of three different types, which are known by the names α-particle, β-particle and γ-ray. Becquerel himself discovered that β-rays can be deflected by a magnetic field, the direction of the deflection being the same as it would be for electrons. Using the apparatus shown in Fig. 41.1*a* he found that after a time the photographic plate became affected over the region AB showing that the rays had been deflected by the magnetic field; the fact that they were not deflected to one spot on the plate suggested that the rays had different speeds. Later experiments, such as the collection of negative charge from these rays, showed them to be a stream of electrons. Alpha particles are deflected in the opposite direction by a magnetic field and are very much less deflected than the beta particles; gamma rays are unaffected by the field. Fig. 41.1*b* shows this, in diagram form, for a magnetic field directed perpendicularly towards the plane of the diagram. The diagram is not to scale—it exaggerates the relative

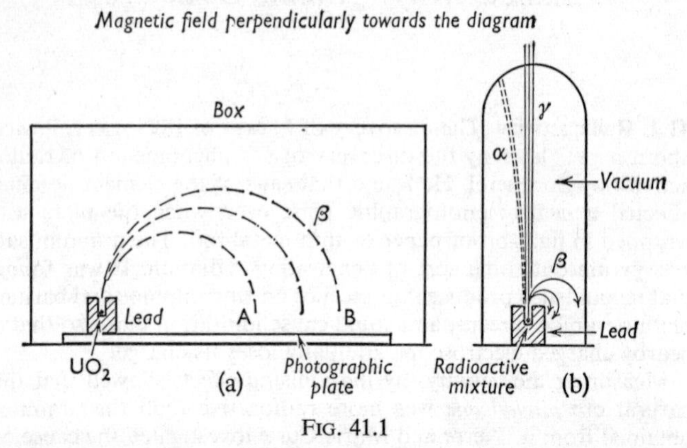

FIG. 41.1
Effect of a magnetic field on radiations from radioactive substances

deflection of the α-particles; if you apply Fleming's left-hand rule to this diagram you will see that the α-particles behave as a positive current, the β-particles as a negative current.

(i) **Alpha particles.** These are positively charged particles emitted with speeds of the order of 10^9 cm/s, the speed depending on the particular element which emits them. The charge is twice the magnitude of the electronic charge, and the mass of each particle is equal to that of a helium atom. α-particles are ionised helium and can be given the symbol He^{++}, representing a helium atom which has lost two electrons. Rutherford confirmed this by enclosing the radioactive gas radon (radium emanation) in a glass tube with a thin-walled end, so that the α-particles could penetrate the glass there. This tube was sealed into an evacuated discharge tube (Fig. 41.2) and the spectrum of the discharge observed. After a time the spectrum of helium began to be emitted from the discharge tube. α-particles travel through gases for a distance which is inversely proportional to the pressure. They cause intense ionisation along their paths; the ionisation can be detected in an ionisation chamber (p. 441) and the effects of it are to be seen in the vapour trails made by the particles in a cloud chamber (Pl. 44). The range of the particles in air at atmospheric pressure varies between 3 and

10 cm and is characteristic of the element emitting the rays. In solid materials the range is very much shorter, about 0·3 mm in aluminium.

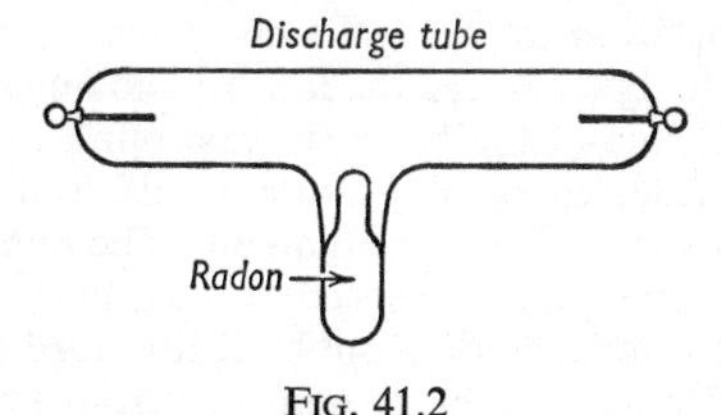

FIG. 41.2

Detection of helium from radium emanation (radon)

When α-particles strike a screen coated with zinc sulphide, each particle produces a flash of light. The effect has been applied in an instrument called the **spinthariscope** (Fig. 41.3), which can be used for counting the number of impacts in a given time and also for finding the range of the particles. The screen and magnifying lens are mounted in a tube which can be adjusted in relation to the radioactive source. The apparatus has to be used in the dark, and

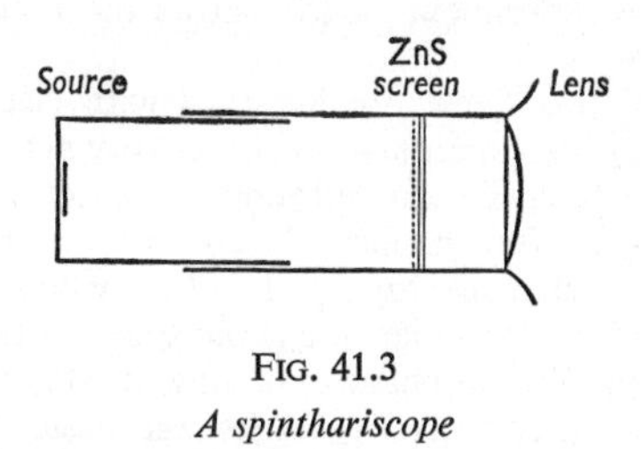

FIG. 41.3

A spinthariscope

the observer has to rest his eyes for some minutes before taking observations. To study the number of flashes over a small area of the screen, the lens is replaced by a microscope. α-particles do not travel far in solids, so there is no risk of their reaching the observer's eye. But if the source emits strong beta or gamma radiations as well, it is necessary to protect the observer from them. This involves the use of lead screens round the apparatus and a reflecting prism in the microscope; the light from the flashes is reflected to the eyepiece but the other radiations are not.

The scintillation method has been used in many experiments on the behaviour of α-particles. Thus Geiger and Marsden used it in 1913 to investigate the deflection of the particles by thin metal foil. A narrow beam of α-particles was directed, in a vacuum, on to the foil, beyond which was a zinc sulphide screen attached to a microscope. Flashes in the field of view showed the arrival of the particles which had penetrated the foil. By moving the microscope out of the direct line of the beam, it was found that some of the particles were deflected by the atoms in the foil through quite large angles—in some cases more than 90°. The number of flashes, the angle of deflection, and the speed of the α-particles were found to agree with a formula, worked out by Rutherford on the assumption that the deflection was due to repulsion from a positive electric charge in the core or nucleus of an atom of the metal. Comparatively few of the particles were deflected in this way, showing that the nuclei of the atoms must be relatively widely spaced.

An effect of the ionisation caused by α-particles can be shown by arranging two parallel conductors about a millimetre apart, connecting the conductors to a variable d.c. supply of about 3 kV and adjusting the potential until it is just on the point of sparking. When an α-source is brought near, sparking occurs in a random fashion at different points along the conductors. The sparking is due to ionisation of the air as a particle passes between the conductors, and the experiment clearly shows the random nature of the emission.

(ii) **Beta particles.** These are identical with electrons and are emitted with very high speeds—sometimes very nearly the speed of light. The mass and speed can be found by deflection methods and it is then discovered that the mass depends on the speed in accordance with the formula $m = m_0 \div \sqrt{(1 - v^2/c^2)}$ where m_0 is the rest mass (the mass when stationary), v is the speed of the particle, c is the speed of light. Thus a particle moving at 90% of the speed of light has a mass which is over twice its rest mass.

β-particles produce ionisation in materials, but to a smaller extent than α-particles; they have smaller mass and kinetic energy, although they move faster. They are more penetrating than the α-particles, the more energetic ones being able to penetrate about a millimetre of lead.

(iii) **Gamma rays.** These rays, undeflected by magnetic fields and of great penetrating power, are found to have the same nature as X-rays. They are electromagnetic waves; the wave-length is characteristic of the substance emitting them, ranging from 10^{-8} cm to 10^{-11} cm. The penetration from some radioactive sources is so great that the source can be used in place of the more cumbersome X-ray

equipment for some purposes; the source needs to be well shielded to prevent the rays from reaching the people who are using it. For example the γ-rays from ^{60}Co can easily penetrate 15 cm of steel. Despite the great penetration, the intensity of the rays is less than can be got with X-ray equipment, so the exposure time is longer. In general the ionising effects of γ-rays is less than is given by an X-ray tube.

41.3. Radioactive change. The emission of an α-particle or a β-particle from a radioactive atom causes a complete change in the properties of the atom. The loss of an α-particle carries away 4 units of atomic mass, so the atomic mass changes. And the loss of two electronic units of charge alters the chemical properties—the new element is in a Group which is two levels lower down the Periodic Table of the elements. Emission of a β-particle has negligible effect on the atomic mass, but the loss of an electron puts the new element in a Group which is one level higher up in the Periodic Table. These effects are illustrated in the diagram on p. 450.

Thus during a radioactive change other elements are continually being formed. Uranium salts, for example, contain Uranium X, an isotope of thorium; this element has different chemical properties and can be separated from the uranium by chemical methods. Radium contains several other elements mixed with it as a result of a series of radioactive changes.

This change is known as **radioactive disintegration** or **radioactive decay.** The rate of the change is characteristic of the element concerned and cannot be hastened or reduced; for example, it is quite unaffected by change of temperature.

The rate of decay is found to be an *exponential* decay, which means that a graph of the decay is similar in shape to the graph of $y=A^{-bx}$ where A and b are constants; this is a curve, but a plot of $\log y$ against x gives a straight line. Such a curve is shown in Fig. 41.4a with time on the x-axis and number N of radioactive atoms (or *parent atoms*) on the y-axis. It is one of the properties of this graph that equal intervals of time give the same percentage change in N, e.g. 90% after 1 second, 90% of 90% after 2 seconds and so on. In the diagram, time intervals have been marked in which the percentage change is 50%, i.e. N falls to half its value after each T seconds. For a radioactive element this is known as the **half-value period** or **half-life**. Half-value periods vary greatly, as is shown on p. 450.

The half-life of a radioactive element can usually be found experimentally by studying its activity with an ionisation chamber, a

cloud chamber or by some form of radiation counter. By plotting a graph showing its variation with time it is possible to find the times at which the activity is $\frac{1}{2}$, $\frac{1}{4}$ or $\frac{1}{8}$ of any chosen initial value.

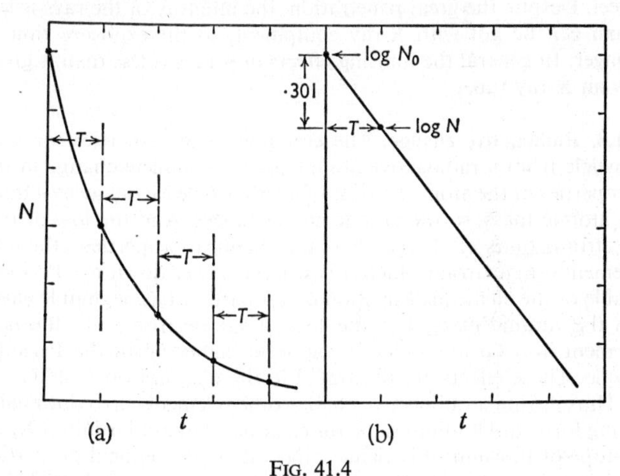

FIG. 41.4

Graphs of radioactive decay

A more accurate value is found by plotting the logarithm of the activity against time. This gives a straight line of negative slope $\log 2/T$ or $0{\cdot}301/T$, as is shown in Fig. 41.4*b*.

This follows from the fact that the equation relating N, the number of atoms remaining, and N_0, the number at first, is given by

$$N = N_0\left(\frac{1}{2}\right)^{\frac{t}{T}}$$

You can check this by substituting $t=T$, $t=2T$, $t=3T$ in the equation, a rearrangement of which is

$$N = N_0 2^{\frac{-t}{T}}$$

Taking logarithms of both sides of this equation

$$\log N = \log N_0 - t\,\frac{\log 2}{T}$$

$$\frac{\log N_0 - \log N}{t} = \frac{\log 2}{T}$$

There are other examples in science of exponential decreases. They occur whenever the loss of a quantity is proportional to the quantity that is already there; as in the loss of charge from a capacitor discharging through a resistor, the loss of heat from a surface cooling in a draught, the fall in level of a liquid issuing from a burette. The rate of radioactive decay is proportional to the number of atoms present, and it seems to be affected solely by the laws of chance. Thus in radium one atom in about 10^{11} decays every second; at this rate half the original number of atoms in a given quantity of radium will have been transformed in about 1600 years, the half-value period for radium.

The determination of half-life becomes complicated when the daughter-element is radioactive and has a relatively short half-life itself. The activity is then a combination of growth and decay curves, and the combined curve can in fact rise before falling off with time.

41.4. Experimental determination of ionisation

(i) **Ionisation chambers.** A closed ionisation chamber, connected to a pulse electroscope, or Wulf electroscope (Fig. 41.5) is some-

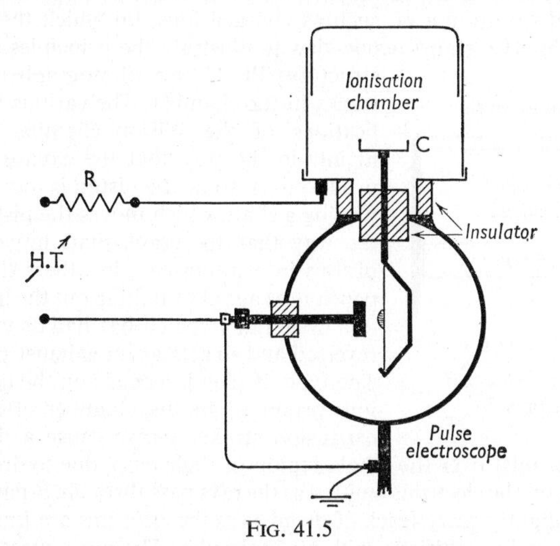

FIG. 41.5

Pulse electroscope with ionisation chamber

times used for the study of radioactivity. The electroscope has an adjustable counter-electrode, as in the moving-leaf electroscope, but the moving system is a fibre or leaf under tension so that it quickly returns after touching the counter-electrode (Pl. 44). A high voltage is applied to the ionisation chamber, the other electrode being the side electrode. The voltage is adjusted to be high enough to discharge the ions as fast as they are formed, i.e. to produce saturation current in the chamber. If an α-source is put at the bottom of the chamber the ionisation current (as measured by the number of flicks of the fibre per minute) is found to increase with the height of the chamber, since the further the particles go the more ions they produce. The limited range of α-particles sets a limit to this increase, and by having a telescopic wall for the chamber the position at which there is no further increase in ionisation current can be found. The distance between the source and the top of the chamber then gives the range.

(ii) **Cloud chambers.** The first cloud chamber was designed by C. R. T. Wilson in connection with the early researches on electrons, but it can be used for the detection of ionising agents generally. Wilson showed that if water-saturated air is suddenly expanded by about one-third of its volume, the air becomes supersaturated owing to cooling but drops of water do not condense unless there are nuclei, such as charged ions, on which they can form. Fig 41.6 shows a side-view to illustrate the principles of the structure; Pl. 43 is a photograph of ion tracks in the chamber. The various modifications of the Wilson chamber differ mainly in the way that the expansion is produced. In some the piston is moved by turning a shaft, which moves the piston in the way that the crank-shaft moves the pistons in a motor-car; in others the expansion is caused by pulling out the handle of a cycle pump which has had its washer reversed and so acts as an exhaust pump. The type of cloud depends on the type of ions produced in the chamber after the expansion stroke. γ-rays cause a diffuse cloud or mist over the whole region of their path, due to droplets formed on the electrons emitted as the rays pass through. β-particles give a slightly wavy track of droplets as the electrons are knocked off course by collisions with air molecules. The more massive α-particles produce straight tracks which end abruptly, showing the end of their range of ionisation.

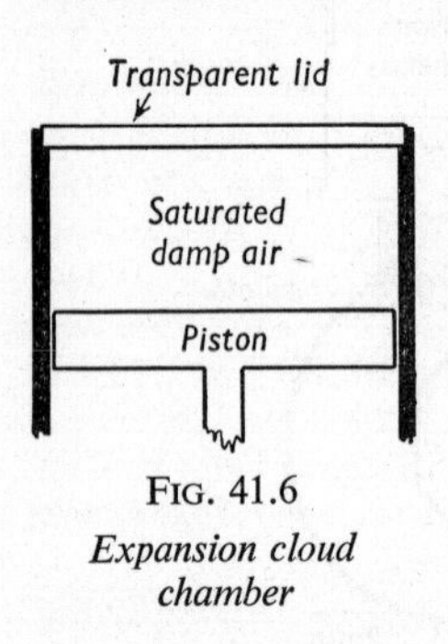

FIG. 41.6
Expansion cloud chamber

The expansion type of cloud chamber gives a view of an ionising event only at the moment when it occurred; to see another event another expansion stroke must be made. **Diffusion cloud chambers** are almost continuously sensitive to ion tracks and there are no moving parts. Supersaturation is obtained by diffusion of a vapour from a warm to a very cold end of the chamber. Fig. 41.7 shows

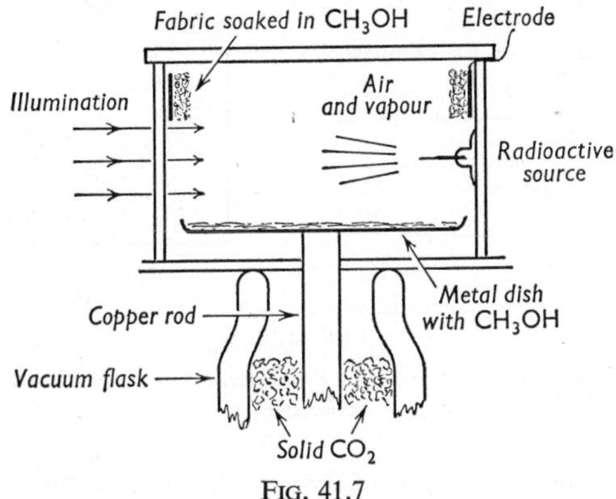

FIG. 41.7
Diffusion cloud chamber

one in which methyl alcohol is used to provide the vapour, with solid carbon-dioxide as the coolant. The background is painted black and the chamber illuminated from the side. Ion tracks are visible a centimetre or so above the level of the liquid; an electrode at the top, connected to a supply of about 200 V, is useful for clearing the tracks after they have been formed. Occasional random tracks are to be seen even when no laboratory source is being used; they are due to ionisation by cosmic rays. If a point carrying a weak α-source is put in the chamber the straight ion-tracks can be seen, and because the chamber works continuously the sudden and random appearance of the tracks can also be seen.

(iii) **Geiger-Müller tube and counter.** This is illustrated in Fig. 41.8*a* and consists of a straight wire anode surrounded by a cylindrical cathode in a gas-filled glass envelope and connected to a d.c. supply whose potential is not sufficient to cause discharge through the gas. Radiation can be permitted to enter the side of the tube or through the end window; specially thin end windows are made for dealing with α-particles. When an ionising radiation enters the tube there is a sudden discharge across the electrodes and the small voltage pulse across the resistor R can be amplified to give a click in a loud-speaker or operate an electronic counter. The operating voltage has to be set to a suitable value. A source is put near the tube and the voltage control is increased to the point where the initial clicks per minute have risen to a maximum. The variation of count-rate with voltage is shown in Fig. 41.8*b*; the suitable working voltage is on the flat part of the curve.

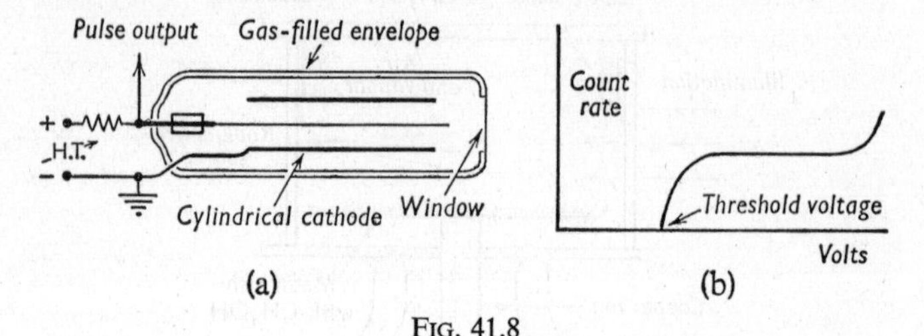

FIG. 41.8

(a) A Geiger-Müller tube. (b) Effect of potential on a G-M tube receiving radiation

When using a G-M tube and counter for quantitative work it is important to take the mean of several observations of the background count and deduct it from the actual test count. The final figures are more accurate if the total count is made as large as possible—for the ionisations are random events, not coming at regularly-spaced intervals; the greater the total count the less is the likelihood of error due to the random emission.

41.5. Atomic structure. The structure of the atom has been a constant source of speculation and theory; even today we are not sure of all the details of its structure, though we have a better understanding than in the days when it was considered as a tiny hard ball.

The mass of an atom, though very small, varies greatly among the different atoms. The relative mass, taking the mass of the common isotope of oxygen as 16, is known as the **atomic mass.** The actual mass is related to the atomic mass by the *Avogadro number* $6{\cdot}025 \times 10^{23}$, the number of atoms in the gram-atom or the atomic mass expressed in grams. There is less variation in size, which for all atoms is a matter of a few Ångström units (10^{-8} cm). The **nucleus** of the atom, in which most of its mass is concentrated, is very much smaller. This was shown by Rutherford, who bombarded metal foil with α-particles. For the most part they just went straight through the foil, not dodging about among the atoms; some were deflected through small angles, and a few recoiled backwards, presumably through hitting the nucleus. Assuming an inverse square law for the force between the charges on the nucleus and on an α-particle, Rutherford was able to calculate the size of the nucleus (about 10^{-12} cm) and its electric charge.

The chemistry of the elements suggested that their properties could be related if they were put in the sequence of their atomic weights, as shown in the Periodic Table of the elements, each atom being associated with an **atomic number,** e.g. H 1, He 2, Li 3, B 4 and so on. This number is now given the symbol Z.

The discovery of isotopes with atomic weights very nearly exact whole numbers suggested that the different elements might be composed of the same elementary particle, e.g. the nucleus of the lightest atom, hydrogen. The presence of electrons in matter indicates that the atom is electrical in character, and the neutral condition of the atoms of ordinary matter means that the atomic nucleus must carry a positive charge. It was therefore probable that the nucleus of the atom contains **protons,** positively charged hydrogen nuclei, the number of them being sufficient to neutralise the number of electrons.

Some difficulties in imagining that an atom is made up solely of protons and electrons were overcome in 1932 by the discovery of the **neutron,** an uncharged particle having almost the same mass as the proton. Neutrons are ejected from beryllium and boron when these elements are bombarded with α-particles. Having no charge they are more penetrating than other particles and they do not cause ionisation directly. Neutrons can eject fast-moving protons from a substance containing hydrogen, e.g. paraffin wax, and because the ejected protons can cause ionisation this is one of the ways of detecting neutrons.

A theory of atomic structure, which explains many of the properties of atoms, assumes the nucleus to be made up of Z protons (where Z is the atomic number) and sufficient neutrons to bring the nuclear mass up to the required value A, the **mass number** (which is very nearly the same as the atomic mass of the isotope concerned). To neutralise the positive charge on the nucleus, the atom would have Z electrons in its structure. The number of neutrons would be $A-Z$.

This atomic composition can be represented by the chemical symbol of the element together with its mass number and atomic number. Thus ${}^{1}_{1}H$ ${}^{2}_{1}H$ ${}^{4}_{2}He$ ${}^{7}_{3}Li$ ${}^{9}_{4}Be$ ${}^{235}_{92}U$ and ${}^{238}_{92}U$ represent the atomic structure of hydrogen, heavy hydrogen, helium, lithium, beryllium and two of the isotopes of uranium. Thus ${}^{235}_{92}U$ has 92 protons, 92 electrons and 143 neutrons in its structure; the heavier isotope has 146 neutrons. In writing the symbol for an isotope the atomic number is sometimes omitted because it is implied in the symbol itself. Thus the two uranium isotopes referred to are commonly expressed as U 235 and U 238.

Using this atomic structure notation the decay of radium into radon and an α-particle, and the decay of actinium into an isotope of thorium and a β-particle can be expressed by the following equations.

$$^{226}_{88}\text{Ra} = {}^{222}_{86}\text{Rn} + {}^{4}_{2}\text{He}$$

$$^{227}_{89}\text{Ac} = {}^{227}_{90}\text{Th} + {}^{0}_{-1}\text{e}$$

Note that the top lines of numbers and the bottom lines of numbers add up to the same on both sides of the equation. Note too that the emission of an α-particle has caused a decrease of two in the atomic number of the daughter atom, whilst the emission of a β-particle causes an increase of one. This means that in the latter case the number of protons in the nucleus has increased by one, and can be explained by assuming that a neutron has given off the electron and become changed to a proton.

The same total for the mass numbers on both sides of the equation simply means that the total *number* of heavy particles in the nuclei has not changed. It does not mean that there has been no mass change. Thus Ra=226·05, Rn=222·0 and He=4·003, atomic mass units. The total mass on the right-hand side of the equation is 0·047 of an atomic mass unit less than on the left-hand side. The difference accounts for the energy which appears in the decay process and which is obtained at the expense of the mass lost. It is given by Einstein's equation $E=mc^2$ where m is the change of mass, E the energy evolved and c the speed of light. In the decay of radium, energy appears in the kinetic energy of the α-particles and as heat in the surroundings; radium salts are always slightly warmer than the surroundings.

41.6. Transmutation. Artificial radioactivity. Chemists have always dreamed of the possibility of converting one element into another artificially. Such a transformation was first achieved, using α-particles, by Rutherford in 1919; but the first truly artificial disintegrations were done by Cockroft and Walton in 1932 using protons accelerated by a potential of 500 kV. Since then neutrons have been used in atomic transformations to produce radioactive isotopes of the commoner elements and also, in atomic piles, to produce elements such as plutonium which do not occur naturally.

In Rutherford's experiment α-particles from radium C were passed through nitrogen; rays were occasionally produced having a range greater than the α-particles. Cloud chamber photographs showed that this was due to a collision between an α-particle and a nitrogen nucleus with the emission of a proton. The action can be represented by the equation

$$^{14}_{7}N + ^{4}_{2}He = ^{17}_{8}O + ^{1}_{1}H$$

In Cockroft and Walton's experiment α-particles were formed from the bombardment of lithium, the equation being

$$^{7}_{3}Li + ^{1}_{1}H = 2^{4}_{2}He$$

The bombardment of nuclei by particles has led to the discovery of many radioactive isotopes which do not occur in nature. Thus a radioactive isotope of nitrogen is formed when boron is bombarded with α-particles and when carbon is bombarded with high-speed deuterons (nuclei of heavy hydrogen). The equations are

$$^{10}_{5}B + ^{4}_{2}He = ^{13}_{7}N + ^{1}_{0}n$$
$$^{12}_{6}C + ^{2}_{1}H = ^{13}_{7}N + ^{1}_{0}n$$

The isotope $^{13}_{7}N$ has all the chemical properties of nitrogen but is radioactive with a half-value period of 10·2 min. The particle it emits is a **positron,** a particle with the same mass as an electron but having a positive charge. It would seem that 6 neutrons is too few to form a stable nucleus with 7 protons, so one of the protons tends to change to a neutron by the emission of a positron and the atomic number of the atom becomes 1 less

$$^{13}_{7}N = ^{13}_{6}C + ^{0}_{+1}e$$

Many radioactive isotopes are made by neutron bombardment. Thus radioactive sodium is formed in this way and it decays by electron emission to the stable isotope of magnesium; the half-value period is 15 hours

$$^{23}_{11}Na + ^{1}_{0}n = ^{24}_{11}Na = ^{24}_{12}Mg + ^{0}_{-1}e$$

Under neutron bombardment the more abundant isotope of uranium U 238 absorbs a neutron to become U 239; this successively decays, by β-particle emission, first to neptunium of atomic number 93 and then to plutonium of atomic number 94.

$$^{238}_{92}U + ^{1}_{0}n = ^{239}_{92}U = ^{239}_{93}Np + ^{0}_{-1}e$$
$$^{239}_{93}Np = ^{239}_{94}Pu + ^{0}_{-1}e$$

The artificial production of radioactive isotopes of the commoner elements such as carbon, sodium, phosphorus, iron, iodine, has had many applications in biology and in medicine. Compounds which take part in biological processes such as photosynthesis or bone-formation can have their course in the plant or in the animal body traced by using a small quantity of the radioactive compound of the element concerned, carbon in the one case, calcium or phosphorus in the other. The situation and concentration of the resulting products can be detected with the aid of a Geiger counter apparatus. The effect, on the surrounding tissues, of such **tracer elements** is avoided by the use of only very small quantities of the tracer.

41.7. Nuclear fission. Release of nuclear energy. A remarkable effect of neutron bombardment was discovered by Hahn and Strassmann in 1939. It was found that when the U 235 isotope of uranium was bombarded with slow neutrons the nucleus broke up into approximately equal parts with the emission of more neutrons. The process is known as **fission;** at each fission about three neutrons are emitted.

It thus follows that a chain process is possible in a mass of pure U 235, with the release of a great deal of energy because the mass of the fragments is less than the original mass. The chain process cannot take place in a small mass of the substance for the neutrons travel an appreciable distance before making a direct hit on another nucleus to cause another fission. In a small lump of the material the neutrons produced by a fission would escape before producing more. For the fission process to be cumulative the material must be bigger than a certain *critical size*. Two pieces of U 235, each somewhat less than this critical size, can produce a violent explosion when they are suddenly driven together as was done in the first atomic bomb. U 235 is present to the extent of only **0·7%** in natural uranium; to make the bomb a laborious and costly process of chemical separation of the U 235 from U 238 had to be done.

The chain reaction which acts so destructively in an atomic bomb can be made to proceed more slowly in an **atomic pile.** The pile, which contains the fissile material, also contains materials known as **moderators.** They reduce the speed of the fast neutrons emitted by fission and they do so by elastic collisions between their nuclei and the neutrons. The lighter atoms, provided that they do not absorb the neutrons, are most effective; the most practicable substances are graphite and heavy water. To control the rate of action of the pile, cadmium rods are introduced. Cadmium absorbs neutrons readily, and when the rods are fully inserted in the pile they stop the chain reaction; the reaction can be started by gradual withdrawal of the rods.

41.8. Nuclear fusion. The energy from an atomic bomb or an atomic pile comes from the loss of mass which occurs during fission. Loss of mass also occurs when nuclei of the lighter elements are made to link together or fuse to make another element; this is because the total mass of the protons which fuse is greater than the atomic weight of the element formed by the fusion. Very high temperatures are needed to achieve this, such as the temperatures in an atomic bomb reaction; and such a reaction has been used in the hydrogen bomb to release suddenly the energy available when atoms of hydrogen are fused to form helium. Attempts are now being made to control the action so that the energy can be released more steadily and so put to more practical use.

Because of the very high temperatures which exist in the interior of the sun and the stars, which are composed mainly of hydrogen, it is thought that a continuous fusion of hydrogen nuclei occurs in them. This would account for the vast amounts of energy which they give out without becoming cooler.

SUMMARY

Radioactive decay is the spontaneous change of one element to another element with the emission of a charged particle. The change is unaffected by physical conditions; γ radiation may also be emitted in the change.

The **half-value period** or **half-life** of a radioactive element is the time taken for half its mass to have changed to another element by radioactive decay.

α-particles are positively charged helium nuclei.

β-particles are electrons.

Positrons are positively charged and have the same mass as an electron.

Protons are positively charged; they are hydrogen nuclei.

Neutrons are uncharged particles having a mass very nearly the same as a proton.

γ-rays are electromagnetic radiation of very short wave length; they have properties similar to those of X-rays.

An element whose **mass number** is A and whose **atomic number** is Z has Z **protons** and $(A-Z)$ **neutrons** in a nucleus which is surrounded by Z **electrons.** The symbol for such an element is ^{A}E. Such an element may have several **isotopes,** with the same chemical properties, the same value for X, but different values for A.

The **atomic mass** of an isotope is the *relative mass* of its atom, that of the common isotope of oxygen being taken as 16; its value is nearly the same as the mass number A, e.g. $^{9}Be = 9{\cdot}02$.

At. wt. (see p. vi) is approximately an average value of the atomic masses of the isotopes in the natural element.

Matter is a form of energy, and energy itself has mass. They are related by the equation $E=mc^2$.

CONSTANTS

The faraday $F=Ne$	$=9{\cdot}650\times10^4$ coulomb/g-eqt.
Avogadro's number N	$=6{\cdot}023\times10^{23}$/gram-mole
1 a.m.u. $1/N$	$=1{\cdot}660\times10^{-24}$g
Electron charge e	$=1{\cdot}602\times10^{-19}$ coulomb
Electron mass m	$=0{\cdot}000549$ a.m.u. $=9{\cdot}108\times10^{-28}$g
Proton mass	$=1{\cdot}0076$ a.m.u.

Symbol	Pb	Bi	Po	At	Rn	Fr	Ra	Ac	Th	Pa	U	
Atomic No.	82	83	84	85	86	87	88	89	90	91	92	
Group in Periodic Table	IV	V	VI	VII	O	I	II	III	IV	V	VI	Half-life
Uranium, U238											238	$4{\cdot}5\times10^9$ yr.
Uranium X$_1$, Th234									234 → β		α	24 days
Uranium X$_2$, Pa234										234 → β		1 min.
Uranium II, U234											234	10^6 yr.
Ionium, Th230									230		α	8×10^4 yr.
Radium, Ra226							226		α			1700 yr.
Radon, Rn222					222		α					4 days
Radium A, Po218			218		α							3 min.
Radium B, Pb214	214 → β		α									27 min.
Radium C, Bi214		214 → β										20 min.
Radium C', Po214			214									10^{-6} s.
Radium D, Pb210	210 → β		α									25 yr.
Radium E, Bi210		210 → β										5 days
Radium F, Po210			210									137 days
Lead, Pb206	206		α									Stable

FIG. 41.9

Disintegration of U238. The numbers in the circles are atomic mass numbers

Questions

1. Show, in tabular form, the electric charges and the relative masses of a hydrogen atom, a proton, a neutron, an electron, a positron, and an α-particle. Give the relative masses in atomic mass units and express the charges in the form *positron*$=+e$.

2. Illustrate, by means of labelled diagrams, the action of a uniform magnetic field and of a uniform electrostatic field on the course of α-particles, β-particles and γ rays travelling *in vacuo*. (Show clearly the direction of the magnetic field in your diagram.)

3. Calculate the energy of the radiation produced by the annihilation of a positron and an electron. (Mass of electron$=$ 0·00055 a.m.u. 1 a.m.u.$=1{\cdot}66\times10^{-24}$ g. $c=3\times10^{8}$ metres/s.)

4. What is meant by (*a*) a radioactive element, (*b*) radioactive decay, (*c*) the half-life, or half-value period, of a radioactive element?

Thoron is a radioactive gas with a half-life of 54 s. What fraction of the mass of a sample of this gas remains, as thoron, after (i) 108 s, (ii) 216 s, (iii) 540 s?

How would you determine experimentally the half-life of thoron, given a supply of thoron mixed with air?

5. A radioactive source, emitting alpha, beta and gamma radiations, is at the centre of a hollow glass sphere, about half a metre in diameter and with walls about a centimetre thick. Compare the actions of the radiations after they have left the source when the sphere contains (*a*) a vacuum, (*b*) air.

6. What is meant by the terms *atomic fission*, *atomic fusion*? How is it that energy is available from both these processes?

A nuclear reactor, using natural uranium, costing £10 per gram, is used to work a power station. Calculate the material-cost per kWh. (Einstein's equivalent$=9\times10^{13}$ joules/g. Change in mass of 1 g of natural uranium$=10^{-3}$ g. Overall efficiency$=20\%$.)

7. Draw a labelled diagram to show the structure of a pulse electroscope. Describe, with the aid of circuit diagrams, how you would use a pulse electroscope (*a*) to compare the resistance of two resistors of the order of thousands of megohms, (*b*) to investigate how the ionisation current, in an ionisation chamber containing a radioactive source, varies with time.

8. Describe any one experiment for finding the range in air of α-particles from a given source. How would the results of the experiments differ if the source emitted α-particles having two distinct ranges?

9. Draw a labelled diagram to show the structure of a Geiger-Müller tube. Explain how the tube can act as a detector of ionising radiation.

What is meant by *background radiation* and *background count*? Explain how background radiation can cause the gradual loss of charge from a gold-leaf electroscope.

10. What is meant by the *random* nature of radioactive decay? Describe an experiment which shows the random nature of the emission of α-particles. When counting methods are used for the study of radioactivity, how are errors due to random emission reduced?

11. The following is a summary of observations taken with a G-M tube and counter with the tube at different distances from a gamma source, after allowing for background count.

Counts per min (N)	6,200	3,090	1,190	595	370
Distance in cm (d)	20·0	30·0	50·0	70·0	90·0

Assuming that the intensity of the gamma rays is inversely proportional to the distance from the source and that there has been no zero error in the distance measurements, then a graph of the reciprocal of $\sqrt{N}$ against d gives a straight line through the origin. Plot a graph to check whether the above results conform with this idea.

12. The rate of emission of β-particles from a radioactive source decreases with time in the following manner.

Time in min (t)	0	1	2	3	4	5	6	7
Count-rate (N)	260	195	140	100	73	52	37	27

Plot graphs of N against t and log N against t. Use each graph to find the half-life of the source; show your working and state which, of the answers obtained, you consider to be the more reliable. Estimate the count-rate (*a*) when $t=4$ half-value periods, (*b*) when $t=10$ min. What fraction of the radioactive material disintegrates (*c*) in the first 5 min, (*d*) in the second 5 min?

13. An atom of an element of atomic number Z and mass number A has Z protons in its nucleus. How many electrons and how many neutrons are present in this atom? Name the atoms for which (*a*) $Z=1$, $A=1$; (*b*) $Z=1$, $A=2$; (*c*) $Z=3$, $A=7$; (*d*) $Z=92$, $A=235$; (*e*) $Z=92$, $A=238$.

An atomic nucleus consists of Z protons and N neutrons. What will be the composition of the residual nucleus (*a*) after the emission of an α-particle, (*b*) after emission of a β-particle, (*c*) after capture of a neutron and subsequent emission of a β-particle?

14. Given a radioactive source emitting β-particles with different speeds how would you show (*a*) deflection of the particles by a magnetic field, (*b*) the fact that the particles have different speeds?

An element of atomic number 7 and mass number 13 disintegrates by positron emission. State the atomic number and the mass number of the new element formed. Is the new element an isotope of the original element? Give a reason.

15. What is meant by an *isotope* of an element? Explain the fact that the separation of the isotopes of an element from a mixture of them is not an easy matter. Mention, giving only the physical principles of the process, an instance where such a separation has been achieved.

An element A disintegrates by α-particle emission and the new element suffers two further disintegrations, both by β-particle emission, to form an element B. Explain the fact that A and B are isotopes.

Answers

CHAPTER 1 (p. 12)

1. (*a*) 240 cm/s; (*b*) 156 cm; (*c*) 240 cm/s upwards
2. 39·2 m/s, 78·4 m **4.** 5 m/s^2, 40 m
6. 3·6 ft/s in a direction which makes an angle of 56·3° with the bank; 41·8° (upstream) from his intended direction
7. $2{\cdot}45+1{\cdot}00+3{\cdot}61=7{\cdot}06$ s **8.** 5 s **9.** 168 m

CHAPTER 2 (p. 22)

6. (*a*) 700 dynes; (*b*) 150 newtons; (*c*) 800 newtons; (*d*) 600 newtons; (*e*) 12 poundals
7. (*b*) 5·88 m/s^2 **8.** 27 *g* or 264·6 m/s^2

CHAPTER 3 (p. 36)

7. (*a*) Oxygen, $4{\cdot}84\times10^2$, Bromine $2{\cdot}16\times10^2$; (*b*) Oxygen, $7{\cdot}18\times10^2$, Bromine, $3{\cdot}06\times10^2$ m/s

CHAPTER 4 (p. 45)

1. (*a*) 8·3 g/c.c.; (*b*) 40·6 c.c.; (*c*) 132 g; (*d*) 73·5 c.c.
2. 8·9 g/c.c. **3.** 880 and 0·09 kg/cu.m **4.** 8 lbf **5.** 1625 g
6. 1·123 g/c.c. **8.** 4 c.c. **9.** 1·100 g/c.c. **10.** 0·0484 sq. cm

CHAPTER 5 (p. 54)

1. (*a*) 120; (*b*) 1440; (*c*) 84·8 lbf ft units **7.** 70-cm mark, 260 gf
8. 0·7 m **9.** 25 kgf **10.** 1 gf upwards
11. Rear man 120 lbf; front man 60 lbf

CHAPTER 6 (p. 61)

1. 13 kgf, 22·6° with 12 kgf **2.** 2·9 lbf, 58° with 4 lbf
3. 4·47 units, 26·6°W. of N. **4.** 7·81 kgf, 34° E. of N.
5. 21·7 kgf, 12·5 kgf **8.** 3·05 kgf **9.** 116 lbf, 31 lbf

CHAPTER 7 (p. 71)

1. 7 m-kgf or 68·6 joules
2. (*a*) 28 ft lbf; (*b*) 8 ft lbf; (*c*) 14 ft lbf
3. 250 m-kgf or 2450 joules; (*a*) 1470 joules; (*b*) 14 m/s; (*c*) 980 joules

5. 0·8 or 80% **6.** 200 m-kgf **7.** (*a*) 0·2hp; (*b*) 9 hp
8. (*a*) 0·083; (*b*) 0·030; (*c*) 1·6; (*d*) 1·02
9. (*a*) 2080 joules; (*b*) 360,000 joules; (*c*) 250 joules; (*d*) 1440 joules
11. 9×10^5 kW **12.** (*a*) 125 kgf; (*b*) 62·5 m-kgf

CHAPTER 8 (p. 77)

3. 0·64 or 64% **4.** (*a*) 6·72 m-kgf; (*b*) 9·60 m-kgf
5. (*a*) 40 lbf; (*b*) 80 ft; (*c*) 3200 ft lbf; (*d*) 0·75 or 75%
6. (*a*) 1000 m-kgf; (*b*) 2 m **7.** 5 kgf
8. 3000 ft lbf **9.** 0·80 or 80%

CHAPTER 9 (p. 89)

1. (*a*) 189 gf; (*b*) 21 gf/sq. cm
2. (*a*) 0·044 sq. in.; (*b*) 0·25 sq. cm; (*c*) 200 sq. cm
3. (*a*) 450 kgf/sq. cm; (*b*) 0·50 kgf/sq. cm
6. 0·18 kgf/cm, 0·05 kgf/sq. cm. **7.** 15 sq. in.
10. (*a*) 12·5 gf/sq. cm; (*b*) 10·4(2) cm
1. (*a*) 122·4; (*b*) 1224. 75·4 kgf
16. (*a*) 80 gf/sq. cm; (*b*) 66·7 cm

CHAPTER 10 (p. 97)

2. 12,960 lbf **9.** 272 gf **10.** 992·8 cm

CHAPTER 11 (p. 105)

2. (*a*) 4 atm more; (*b*) 3 atm less **3.** 30 litres less
4. 89·6 cu. in. **5.** (*a*) 13·6 g/l; (*b*) 136 g/l. 1088g
6. 3·8 mm **7.** 0·95 kgf/sq. cm
8. (*a*) 6 lbf/sq. in.; (*b*) 0·844 lbf/sq. in. **9.** 51·5 cu. ft
11. (*a*) 80 cmHg; (*b*) 4 cm **12.** (*a*) 16·0 cm; (*b*) 26·7 cm

CHAPTER 12 (p. 112)

1. 108,390, 11·2 gf **3.** 19·5 lbf **4.** 12 cm **6.** 96 gf
8. 88 kgf **12.** 20·5 gf; 4·1 gf/sq. cm

CHAPTER 13 (p. 122)

2. (*a*) −15°C; (*b*) 5°F
4. 290°A; (*a*) 727°C; (*b*) 1340·6°F **5.** 10·6 mm
6. (*a*) 1·44 mm; (*b*) 0·80 mm. 37·5°C, 99·5°F
7. 60 units, 10 units **10.** (*a*) 20 cm, 18 cm; (*b*) 4·7 cm
11. (*a*) 50·75; (*b*) 10·75

CHAPTER 15 (p. 139)

2. (*a*) 0·000132 in.; (*b*) 0·058 ft; (*c*) 1·1 cm; (*d*) 0·055 cm
3. (*a*) 0·146 cm; (*b*) 3·73 cm; (*c*) 3·96 c.c.; (*d*) 90,000 c.c.; (*e*) 2936 c.c.; (*f*) 19·4 gal **4.** 0·0000160 per degC
5. (*a*) 0·00025 per degC ; (*b*) 0·000276 per degC
6. 65·98 ft, 1·0 ft **7.** 800°C, 40·4 cm
8. (i) 34·5°C; (ii) 60·0°C; (iii) 114°C
9. (i) 77 cm; (ii) 91 cm; (iii) 11 metres
10. 54·12 cm **11.** (*a*) 40·5 ml; (*b*) 0·0037(0) per degC
12. 31·7 ml **13.** 8 atm **14.** 0·000364 per degC
15. 5·68 g **16.** (*a*) 0·629 g/l; (*b*) 0·629 kg

CHAPTER 16 (p. 146)

1. (*a*) 37·2 cal/degC; (*b*) 0·55 kcal/degC; (*c*) 99 cal/degC; (*d*) 0·385 kcal/degC **2.** (*a*) 1200 kcal; (*b*) 110 cal; (*c*) 3·3 kcal; (*d*) 55 kcal
3. (*a*) 10°C; (*b*) 45·5°C; (*c*) 108°C; (*d*) 32°C
4. 0·35 **5.** 4·0 kcal **6.** 93 cal/degC, 0·093
7. 2·17 kcal/min **9.** 10, 40, 100°C
10. (*a*) 3·0 cal/s; (*b*) 0·11 **11.** Approximately 710°C
12. (*a*) 16·9 kcal/min; (*b*) 22·5 min

CHAPTER 17 (p. 158)

3. (*a*) 2·3 min; (*b*) 5·0 min **4.** (*b*) 103 cal **6.** 0·122
7. 1·25 g **9.** 1·6 g **10.** 12·5 min **11.** 79(·5) cal/g

CHAPTER 18 (p. 166)

12. (*a*) 50 cal/min; (*b*) 0·67 degC/s

CHAPTER 19 (p. 173)

5. 1·3(2) $\times 10^3$ cm, approx. 13 metres **6.** 420 cal
7. 7·0 min **8.** 4·5 degC **9.** 2·9%

CHAPTER 21 (p. 194)

1. (*a*) 18·0 cm/s; (*b*) 9·0 cm
3. (*a*) 3·4 m, 13·6 m; (*b*) 0·5 m, 2·0 m; (*c*) 10 cm, 40 cm
4. (*a*) 5 megacycles/s; (*b*) 1 megacycle/s
6. (*a*) 6×10^{14} c/s; (*b*) 2×10^3 **7.** 18·6 m/s

CHAPTER 22 (p. 205)

1. (*a*) 6·04 s; (*b*) 5·82 s **2.** (*a*) 0·93(2) s; (*b*) 1·08 s
5. 5·2 km/s **8.** (*a*) 1·60 s; (*b*) 2·00 − 1·20 = 0·80 s
15. 240 c/s **16.** 250 c/s **17.** 288 c/s
19. (*a*) 2·2 ft; (*b*) 8·8 ft **20.** $6{\cdot}8 \times 10^3$ c/s

CHAPTER 23 (p. 216)

4. 500 c/s

CHAPTER 24 (p. 227)

9. 500 s **10.** (*a*) $4{\cdot}2 \times 10^{-5}$ cm or 0·42 micron; (*b*) 0·28 micron
11. 0·5 μs, 150 m **15.** 15 cm, 30 cm
19. 1·3 million km, 17·4 mm

CHAPTER 25 (p. 240)

3. 46 cm **5.** 1·95 m, 0·95 m **10.** 50 cm
16. 30 cm behind the pole of the mirror, 6 cm high, virtual

CHAPTER 26 (p. 252)

3. 1·33, 1·50, 2·42; 49°, 41·6°, 24·4°
12. 1·48 **13.** 160 cm

CHAPTER 27 (p. 263)

2. (*a*) 5, image real and inverted; (*b*) 5, image virtual and erect
6. 4 times as long **7.** 8·3 cm
8. Values obtained by calculation are (i) height 0·9 units, 30 cm from the lens; (ii) height 1·5 units, 30 cm from the lens on the object side; (iii) height 1·2 units, 22·5 cm from the lens
9. (*a*) 36 cm from the object; (*b*) 12·9 cm. **10.** 60 cm
11. 6 cm further away from the lens
12. (*a*) +0·5, +4·0, +5·0, +12·5; (*b*) −2·0, −6·25
13. +20 cm, −100 cm, +25 cm
14. Width of bright circle = 1·5 cm. Width of dark ring = 1·5 cm. $f = 14$ cm

CHAPTER 28 (p. 274)

8. (*a*) A and B, or A and C; (*b*) A and E; (*c*) C and B
11. 4·8 in **12.** (*a*) 2·0; (*b*) 50 cm

CHAPTER 30 (p. 297)

1. 20 mA **11.** (*a*) 6×10^{-3} coulomb; (*b*) 50 V; (*c*) 0·6 μF
12. 0·1 A

CHAPTER 31 (p. 309)

4. 161 g **6.** +0·19A **7.** (*a*) 12 coulombs; (*b*) 24 joules
8. (*a*) 30 coulombs; (*b*) 30 coulombs; (*c*) 60 joules; (*d*) 120 joules
9. (*a*) Y; (*b*) X; (*c*) Y

CHAPTER 32 (p. 325)

1. (*a*) 80 W; (*b*) 12 W; (*c*) 180 W; (*d*) 650 W; (*e*) 250 W
2. $3{\cdot}6 \times 10^5$, 20 h **4.** (*a*) 18 *d*; (*b*) 36 *d*
5. (*a*) 1·2 A; (*b*) 0·6 A; (*c*) 0·4 A; (*d*) 0·2 A **7.** 3·1 A
8. (*a*) 12 V; (*b*) 15 V; (*c*) 3 V; (*d*) 50 mV; (*e*) 110 V
9. (*a*) 0·5 Ω; (*b*) 4 Ω; (*c*) 100 Ω; (*d*) 25 kΩ
10. (*a*) 0·03 A; (*b*) 0·071(4) A **11.** (*a*) 0·18 A; (*b*) 21·5 A
12. (*a*) 3·5 Ω; (*b*) 1·02 V
13. 2·1 Ω, 0·03 A in 7 Ω, 0·07 A in 3 Ω, 0·10 A in the others
14. 1·6 A. 2 A in 4 Ω; 1·33 A in 6 Ω; 0·67 A in 12 Ω
15. 0·28 A. (*a*) 0·40 A; (*b*) 0·35 A
16. 110 Ω. (*a*) 2·42 V; (*b*) 0·022 A in 110 Ω, 0·220 A in 11 Ω
18. (*a*) 0·20 A; (*b*) 1·40 V
19. (*a*) 11 mA; (*b*) 110 V
20. 2·0 V, 0·5 Ω
21. (*a*) 84 Ω; (*b*) 0·25 A in 4·2 Ω, 0·0125 A in 84 Ω
23. $1{\cdot}5 \times 10^{-4}$ cm
24. 0·021 cm, 0·79 Ω
25. (*a*) 5·4 meg Ω cm; (*b*) 0·72 meg Ω
26. 75·2 cm **27.** 80·8 cm
28. (*a*) 1·50 Ω ; (*b*) 68·8 microhm cm
29. $4{\cdot}84 \times 10^{-3}$ sq. cm, 0·25 Ω

CHAPTER 35 (p. 367)

7. 8·4 V, A=1000 Ω, B=1800 Ω
8. Add series resistor of 6000 Ω
10. (*a*) Shunt 0·0251 Ω; (*b*) Series resistor 1995 Ω
11. 0·722 Ω
12. (*a*) 60 mA; (*b*) 0·48 V; (*c*) 8 Ω
13. (*a*) 5 A; (*b*) 0·04 Ω; (*c*) 0·12 V

CHAPTER 36 (p. 378)

2. (*a*) 480 W; (*b*) 1440 W; (*c*) 300 W; (*d*) 100 W
3. (*a*) 65·5 Ω; (*b*) 15 kcal/min **4.** 2 Ω, 50 W
5. (*a*) 0·05 kWh; (*b*) 180,000 joules
8. (*a*) 5 A, 10 A; (*b*) 200·5 V, 101 V; (*c*) 2·5 W, 10 W
10. 8 min 24 s **11.** 3·35 A **12.** (*a*) 2·67 Ω; (*b*) 41·7 h

CHAPTER 37 (p. 395)

13. (*a*) 24 W; (*b*) 0·5 W; (*c*) 23·5 W

CHAPTER 38 (p. 406)

2. 0·000330 g/coulomb **3.** 0·207 mg/coulomb
4. 104(·5) min **8.** 0·87 A **10.** −0·07 A **11.** 21·0 kg/h
13. 3 Ω, 20 h, 241(·5) g **14.** 0·575 h (34·5 min)
15. Copper 35·6 g, silver 120(·7) g

CHAPTER 39 (p. 417)

3. 5 Ω **7.** (i) 2·828 A; (ii) 1 A; (iii) 7·07 A; (iv) 1 A
8. (*a*) 4 A, 2·83 A r.m.s.; (*b*) 57·1 cal/min, 28·6 cal/min
10. 14 Ω

CHAPTER 41 (p. 451)

3. $1{\cdot}64 \times 10^{-13}$ joule or $1{\cdot}64 \times 10^{-6}$ erg.
4. (i) 1/4; (ii) 1/16; (iii) 1/1024 **6.** 0·48 *d*

Formulae

Equations of motion $v=u+at \quad s=ut+\frac{1}{2}at^2 \quad v^2=u^2+2as$

Simple pendulum $T=2\pi\sqrt{\frac{l}{g}}$

Force and motion $F=\frac{m(v-u)}{t} \qquad Ft=mv-mu$

$F=ma \qquad Fs=\frac{1}{2}mv^2-\frac{1}{2}mu^2$

Kinetic energy $=\frac{1}{2}mv^2$

Mass and Energy Energy (of mass). . . . . m_0c^2

Mass (of energy) . . . . E/c^2

Mass and speed $m=m_0\Big/\sqrt{\left(1-\frac{v^2}{c^2}\right)}$ (m_0=rest-mass)

Vector resultant $R^2=A^2+B^2+2AB\cos\theta$

Efficiency $\epsilon=\frac{output}{input} \qquad \epsilon=\frac{m.a.}{v.r.}$

Density $d=\frac{m}{v}$

Molecular speeds (gases) $p=\frac{d\bar{c}^2}{3}$ ($\bar{c}^2$=average of *speed*^{2})

Pressure $p=\frac{thrust}{A}$

Fluid Pressure $p=hd$ gravitational units

$p=hdg$ absolute units

Temperature conversion $\frac{f-32}{c}=\frac{9}{5} \qquad \frac{f+40}{c+40}=\frac{9}{5}$

Expansion length . . . $l_0\alpha\theta \simeq l\alpha\theta$ volume . . . $V_0\alpha\theta$

Heat change $ms\theta$ mL

Work and heat $W=JH$

Gas equation $\frac{pv}{T}=k$

Speed of sound (gases)	$\frac{V}{V_0}=\sqrt{\frac{T}{273}}$	Increase per deg C $\simeq\frac{V_0}{546}$	
Waves	$V=f\lambda$ $f=\frac{1}{T}$	*Ventral segment* $=\frac{\lambda}{2}$	
Interference fringes	$\lambda=\frac{ws}{D}$	Grating (1st order) $\lambda=d\sin\theta$	
Reflection	$i=r$		
Refraction	$\sin i=n\sin r$	$n=\operatorname{cosec} C$	$n=\frac{c_0}{c}$
	$n=\frac{\sin\frac{1}{2}(A+d)}{\sin\frac{1}{2}A}$	(minimum deviation)	
Lenses & mirrors (real-positive)	$m=\frac{v}{u}$	$\frac{1}{u}+\frac{1}{v}=\frac{1}{f}$	$f^2=(u-f)(v-f)$
Charge	$Q=It$		$Q=CV$
Energy	VQ		VIt
Power		VI	
in resistors	I^2R		V^2/R
Circuits	$V=IR$		$E=I(R+r)$
lost volts		$E-V=Ir$	
Series resistors		$R=r_1+r_2+r_3$	
Parallel resistors		$\frac{1}{R}=\frac{1}{r_1}+\frac{1}{r_2}+\frac{1}{r_3}$	
Resistivity		$\rho=\frac{Ra}{l}$	
Alternating current		$v=V_p\sin 2\pi ft$	
		$i=I_p\sin 2\pi ft$	
	$v=iR$		$\bar{V}=IR$
	$\bar{V}=0{\cdot}707\,V_p$		$\bar{I}=0{\cdot}707\,I_p$
Reactance	$X_c=1/2\pi fC$		$X_L=2\pi fL$
Radioactive decay		$N=N_0 2^{-\frac{t}{T}}$	

$$\frac{\log N_0-\log N}{t}=\frac{\log 2}{T}$$

Index